COUNTRY WISDOM:
THE ART OF SUCCESSFUL HOMESTEADING

Dozens of how-to-do-it tips
for self-sufficient living in city or country!

BY THE EDITORS OF
COUNTRYSIDE MAGAZINE

TAB BOOKS Inc.
BLUE RIDGE SUMMIT, PA. 17214

FIRST EDITION

SECOND PRINTING

Printed in the United States of America

Reproduction or publication of the content in any manner, without express permission of the publisher, is prohibited. No liability is assumed with respect to the use of the information herein.

Copyright © 1982 by TAB BOOKS Inc.

Library of Congress Cataloging in Publication Data

Main entry under title:

Country wisdom.

    Includes index.
     1. Agriculture—Addresses, essays, lectures.
2. Home economics, Rural—Addresses, essays, lectures.
3. Gardening—Addresses, essays, lectures. 4. Country
life—Addresses, essays, lectures. I. Countryside.
S496.C68   630   81-18276
ISBN 0-8306-0076-0   AACR2
ISBN 0-8306-1356-0 (pbk.)

Contents

Introduction   vi

1 Planning the Homestead   1
The Ideal Homestead—Planning the Urban Homestead—
Clearing Land—Small-Scale Farming

2 Homestead Business Management   33
Managing the Homestead for Success—Homestead
Accounting—Setting and Reaching Goals—Farm Book-
keeping—The Computer—Homesteaders and Taxes—
Depreciation and Investment Credit for Homesteaders—
Loopholes for Homesteaders—Life Insurance

3 Zoning and the Homestead   59
Euclid Case—Definition of Farming—Types of Agriculture—The
Meaning of Animal Husbandry—The Piggery and the Law—
Chickens—Goats—Horses—Bees—Dogs

4 Building Projects   86
Mini-Barn—Compact Barn—Small Cabin—Geodesic Dome—A-
Frame—Backyard Bioshelter—Buildings with Sawmill Slabs—
Chick Brooder—Chick Waterer—A-Frame House for the Home-
stead Hog—Low-Cost Rabbit Shelter—Building the Homestead
Hog Hut—Salvaging Old Buildings—Building a Woodshed—Fruit
and Vegetable Bin—Compost Privy

5 Ways with Water   129
Digging Wells—Cisterns—Rain Traps—Driven Wells—Filtering
Water—Balancing the Small Farm Pond—Winterizing a Spring—
Irrigation by Flood and Furrow—Garden Sprinkler—Drip
Irrigation—Sunflowers for Irrigation

6 Septic System Installation   151
How It Works—Cost—Government Regulation—Getting
Started—The Tank—The Header—The Bed—The Last Detail—
Variations—Care and Feeding

7 Heating 161

Operating a Woodstove—More Help with Woodstoves—Safety Tips for Wood and Coal Stoves—Safe Heating with Wood—Finding and Repairing the Junkyard Stove—Rejuvenating the Junkyard Woodstove—Constructing the Heat Reflecting Stove Board—Pipe Cleaner Helps Reduce Creosote Problem—Gravity Water Heater—Let the Sun Warm the Animals

8 Alternative Energy 194

Homemade Solar Collector Combines Three Features—Solar-Wind System—Water Pumping Windmill—Power From the Wind—Wind-Powered Heat Pump—Energy Cost Answers Written in the Wind—Farmers' Alcohol—Checklist of Energy Savers

9 Tools, Machines, and Vehicles 231

Hammers—Hanging an Axe—A Jig for Kindling—Sharpening Handsaws—Choosing a Chain Saw—Tractor-Powered Log Splitter—Bumper Jack Baler—Homemade Hay Chopper—Seed Planter—Harvesting Equipment—Pea Sheller—Cream Separator—Foot-Powered Sewing Machine—Sewing Machine Turns into a Spinning Wheel—Washing without Wattage or Washboard—Make a Hand-Operated Washing Machine—Useful Wagon—New Low Profile 18 hp Power King Tractor—"Siamese" Farmall Is not a Hoax—Care of the Homestead Tractor—Spring Tractor Tuneup—Factors That Determine Used Equipment Prices

10 Wood 300

Making Lumber—Making Use of Waste Driftwood—Curing Green Wood—Using Cull Trees—Managing Your Woodlot—Cutting Wood—Firewood

11 Workshop Projects 325

Mechanical Drawing Short Course—"Scoop" from Recycled Cans—Homemade Soil Sifter—Planting Straight Rows—Glass Jugs Have Many Uses—Tires Can Feed and Water Livestock—Floodlight—Lawn and Garden Roller—Handi-Cart—Homemade Garden Cart—Sawhorse—Sawbuck

12 Crafts 342

Washcloths—Uses for Old Socks—A Three-Cut Jacket—Infants' Footwear—Sock Dolls—Denim Satchel—Pillows from Raw Wool—Rag Rugs—Crocheted Rugs—Hooked Rugs—Braided Rugs—Quilting—Spinning Wheel—Recycling Baling Twine into Rope—Weaving a Log Carrier out of Baling Twine—Recycling Baler Twine to Decorate the Home—Recyling Cans into Art

13 Fencing 369

All-Electric Fence—Types of Fences—Preserving Fence Posts—Making a Stile—Hedges Are Living Fences—Fence and Gate—Gate and Door Latches—Stump Fence and Hedgerow

14 Animals   **383**
The Homestead Horse—Pleasure Horses—The Norwegian Fjord
Pony—Six Breeds of Goats—Sheep—Working Stock Dogs

15 Livestock Feed   **411**
A Garden for Goats—A Garden for Rabbits—Food for
Chickens—Root Crops for Homestead Livestock—Feed for
Cows, Pigs, and Chickens

16 Butchering   **423**
The Basics—Butchering a Goat—Slaughtering Your Own
Beef—Cutting and Packaging the Meat—Cutting Beef—Cutting
Pork

17 Gardening Techniques   **442**
Gardening Organically—Organic Material Acts as a Buffer—
Organic Gardening Mistakes—Summertime Gardening—Winter
Garden in Your Kitchen—Gift Plants—Dealing with Spring
Frosts—Saving Seeds—Mushroom Gardening—Growing
Nuts—Green Mulch System—Mulch Guards—Sun Box
Lengthens Gardening Season

18 Vegetables and Herbs   **488**
Second Planting Will Fill the Cellar—Hybrid Vegetables—Indoor
Vegetable Growing—Cucumbers for the Small Garden—
Squash—Milkweed—Chinese Cabbage—Cabbage—Cauli-
flower—Lettuce—Onions—Beets—Potatoes—Beans—Toma-
toes—Okra—Greens—Sweet Peppers—Garlic: the Wonder
Herb—Chamomile—Sassafras—Persimmon

Index   **531**

Introduction

Many people are escaping the pressures of urban living by moving into the country and setting up a homestead. It's not easy to live off the land, though. Plenty of arduous work is involved.

This book has information on homestead planning and management, zoning, building and workshop projects, water requirements, heating, tools, machines, crafts, fencing, animals, and butchering. The final two chapters look at gardening, vegetables, and herbs.

All of the material in this book has been made available by the editors of *Countryside* magazine. Without their efforts and cooperation, this book would have been impossible.

Chapter 1

Planning the Homestead

This chapter has sections on the ideal homestead and planning the urban homestead. You learn how to clear land for your homestead. The economics of small-scale farming is discussed.

THE IDEAL HOMESTEAD

If home is where your heart is, then *that's where your homestead is, too.*

Too many prospective homesteaders think they have to move, or worse, have to move to some relatively wild and unsettled location. For some, this is because they don't have a very realistic picture of what modern homesteading is really all about. Others simply fail to see the opportunities that lie untapped in their own backyards, while still others have a rather immature "grass is greener" notion that a change of scenery will change their lives.

Location

In practice, there are homesteaders in just about any location you could think of: not only in deep forests and on mountain slopes, along sea coasts and on windswept prairies, but on surburban lots, small town tracts, and even in the tiny yards of large cities (Fig. 1-1). In theory, at least, even an apartment dweller can be a homesteader of sorts. Some people grow sprouts in a closet and mushrooms under the kitchen sink. They bake their own bread from home-ground wheat and sew at least some of their own clothes. They are at least partially self-sufficient without so much as a square inch of land.

While some people obviously prefer that type of homesteading, the "ideal" for most usually entails being a bit more removed from the cities which are the very symbol of the antithesis of homesteading. For those most attracted to this lifestyle, the city represents smog and pollution, crowding and pressures, dependence, and impersonalization, and the country side is just the opposite. So while we can assume that our ideal is in the countryside, the geographic location really isn't of much concern except on an individual basis.

As for specifics, the only rigid requirements would be that the site have a good water supply, and soil that, even if not wonderfully fertile now, can be made so. Most of the rest probably falls into the realm of aesthetics rather than necessities, and will vary among individuals.

For some, the ideal will be a view . . . of the mountains, the shore, a broad expanse or prairie or even the desert. Open water of some form seems to be part of the universal ideal, according to real estate agents. River frontage, a babbling brook, or at least a farm pond are a part of just about everyone's dream country place, homestead or not.

Site

One of the most common questions we hear is, "How much land does it take to homestead?" This, too, is filled with variables.

We have little doubt that an average family, with relatively good soil in a reasonably favorable climate, could produce at least the lion's share of its food on an acre or less. Surely there are many 1-acre plots in this country today that are sinfully under-utilized, and perhaps we could even say wasted.

For a variety of reasons (and again, largely aesthetic ones), the ideal of most people encompasses somewhat larger tracts of land. The practical considerations might include acreage for growing feed and for larger livestock, room for a pond, and a woodlot, as well as distance from neighbors and problems that can arise from the proximity of nonlivestock raising neighbors. Again, we doubt that under normal circumstances any family would require more than 5 acres even with larger livestock, with perhaps an additional five in woodlot. Anything more might make life more pleasant, it might bring satisfaction in one form or another, but it really isn't necessary.

Functions

There are thousands of country homes like those just described, but few of them are homesteads. The reason is *function*. The homestead is designed and maintained to produce more or less of the family's sustenance, which is different from the country place that features only a swimming pool, tennis court, spacious lawn, and carefully tended flower beds.

The chief function of a homestead is to produce food, primarily vegetables. Therefore, the garden is the heart of the homestead (Table 1-1).

Size will vary, naturally, with the size of the family, crops grown, and the proportion of vegetables the family desires to produce for itself. The ideal homestead will strive for variety, and with special emphasis on year-round food supply. Lettuce and radishes may be the mainstay of the average American garden, but the homestead will place greater emphasis on crops that will feed the family when the garden is buried under snow and

2

Fig. 1-1. View of a homestead.

Table 1-1. Standard Bulk Units of Food.

fruit	approximate weight/volume
Apples	45 to 50 lbs./bu.
Apricots	48 lbs./bu.
Berries (not strawberries)	64 lbs./bu. or 24 qts./crate
Cherries	60 lbs./32 qts. (or crate)
Cranberries	55 lbs./bu.
Grapes	sold in quart baskets
Peaches	40 to 50 lbs./bu.
Pears	50 to 55 lbs./bu.
Plums	50 to 55 lbs./bu.
Strawberries	50 lbs./32 qts.
Tomatoes	50 to 60 lbs./bu.

vegetables		grains	
Asparagus	40 lbs./bu.	Alfalfa seed	60 lbs./bu.
Beans, lima	32 lbs./bu.	Barley, hull-less	60 lbs./bu.
Beans, snap	30 lbs./bu.	Buckwheat	50 lbs./bu.
Beets	52 lbs./bu.	Flax	56 lbs./bu.
Beet greens	15 lbs./bu.	Millet	48 lbs./bu.
Broccoli	25 lbs./crate	Oats	32 lbs./bu.
Carrots	50 lbs./bu.	Rice	45 lbs./bu.
Chard, Collards	12 lbs./bu.	Rye	56 lbs./bu.
Corn	36 lbs./bu.	Wheat	60 lbs./bu.
Kale	18 lbs./bu.		
Okra	40 lbs./bu.		
Onions	52 lbs./bu.		
Peas, in pod	30 lbs./bu.		
Potatoes	60 lbs./bu.		
Soybeans	60 lbs./bu.		
Spinach	18 lbs./bu.		
Summer squash	40 lbs./bu.		
Winter squash, pumpkin	40 lbs./bu.		

ice or otherwise out of production. Tomatoes are one of the main crops on most homesteads because of the ease of growing them, the ease of preserving them, their nutritive value, and the variety of ways they can be utilized. Dry beans are also popular, again because of their prolificacy and nutritive value, but also because of the ease of storage.

Homestead gardens also vary from the more common variety in that they are taken much more seriously and are therefore planned more carefully. Even as far north as the Great Lakes states, the homestead garden is producing food as soon as the ground thaws in spring. Jerusalem artichokes and parsnips that wintered over under a mulch of straw and snow are dug, crisp and fresh, before other gardeners have even purchased any seeds. Radishes and lettuce are grown in cold frames that might have to have the snow brushed off them on occasion. Bedding plants are started indoors in early spring, partly because the quantities used in the homestead garden make this an economical endeavor; partly because the homestead gardener is adamant about specific varieties that might be available only as seed, not plants; and because doing it yourself is just part of the independence and self-sufficiency homesteaders strive for. In the extreme, even the seed sown in the homestead garden is home-produced.

The ideal of any homestead gardener just has to include a *greenhouse*.

Plain or fancy, large or small, extending the growing season on both ends is one of the most profitable, and satisfying, accomplishments of the dedicated homesteader.

In the fall, when most gardeners have left their plots to run to weeds or have plowed them under, the homesteader is still harvesting. Late plantings of kale, Chinese cabbage, turnips, and other cold weather crops survive the first frosts, flourish again in the Indian summer days that usually follow, and yield right up to the real onset of winter. Many a homesteader has harvested these and similar hardy vegetables from under a blanket of snow and some, such as carrots that are well mulched, even when the surrounding unprotected ground is frozen solid.

The ideal homestead garden features a compact but handy and attractive tool shed, for good tools, properly cared for, are the pride of any craftsman. The homestead gardener is a craftsman.

The *compost bins*, a feature of many gardens of all kinds today, are especially noticeable on the ideal homestead if only because such a place has animals that contribute manure and bedding to the garden. The garden also is noticeable by its layout. It's like a miniature farm in that it makes use of crop rotation and test plots and green manure (Table 1-2). All of these are

Table 1-2. Green Manure—What to Use, Where, and When.

soil preference	green manure	lime requirement	when to sow
Sandy loam	Blue lupine	Light	Spring/fall
	Cow pea	Light	Late spring/early summer
	White lupine	Light	Spring/fall
	Yellow lupine	Light	Spring/fall
	Millet	Light	Late spring/summer
	Mustard		Spring
Medium loam	Barley	Light	Spring/fall
	Field pea	Medium	Early spring/fall
	Lespedeza	Light	Early spring
	Mustard		Spring
	Purple vetch	Light	Spring/fall
	Rape	Light	Spring/summer
	Red clover	Medium	Fall/spring
	Winter wheat	Light	Fall
Heavy loam	Alsike clover	Medium	Spring/fall
	Bur clover	Medium	Fall
	Field pea	Medium	Early spring/fall
	Hungarian vetch	Light	Spring/fall
	White clover	Heavy	
Widely adaptable	Brome grass	Light	Fall/spring
	Buckwheat	Light	Late spring/summer
	Common vetch	Light	Spring/fall
	Hairy vetch	Light	Spring/fall
	Kale	Heavy	Summer/fall
	Mung beans	Light	Spring/summer
	Oats	Light	Spring/fall
	Rye (spring, winter, Italian)	Light	Spring/fall
	Sudan grass	Light	Late spring/summer
	Sunflowers	Light	Spring/summer
	White clover	Heavy	
	Woolly pod vetch	Light	Spring/fall

part of the long range and serious nature of the homestead garden, and the dedication and intelligence of the homestead gardener.

Permanent Plantings

Permanent plantings also play a large role on the ideal homestead. An orchard is taken for granted, and over much of the country might contain apples, pears, cherries, plums, peaches, and other fruits. Instead of only shade trees, the well-planned homestead might use nut trees: hickory, black walnut, butternut, pecan and others, depending on location.

Bramble fruits are important on the ideal homestead, as are grapes, rugosa roses (rose hips), and strawberries. Other permanent crops requiring little tilling or care might include rhubarb, asparagus, winter onions, comfrey, and various herbs as well as others.

Another form of "permanent plantings" is the wild fare found growing along fencerows, in woodlots, and similar locations. These might range from dandelion greens to morels, and include any number of wild fruits, berries, nuts, roots, and herbage.

Livestock

The purpose of homestead livestock is to feed the family, which puts certain restraints on this aspect. Other considerations might include space, feed available, experience, personal preferences, and similar factors. Livestock is an important part of the ideal homestead not only for the food value of meat and the variety it provides, but because animals are an important part of the ecological cycle of the closed system which the ideal homestead is. Not only does livestock provide manure for the garden, but the inevitable waste and surplus of a garden can go a long way toward maintaining some livestock.

Because of the initial investment, space, and time required, and rapid "harvest," *poultry* are usually the most important element of subsistence livestock farming. Theoretically, at least, a half dozen hens should keep a family in eggs with very little labor or expense. Fifty broilers, butchered at about 12 weeks of age (and grown during the season when supplemental heat will be required only for brooding and free-range will allow them to pick up as much as 20 percent of their dietary needs) will put a chicken in the pot almost once a week with a minimum of cost.

Rabbits are commonly second in popularity, again because of the rapid turnover, the small amount of space and investment and skill required to perform an adequate job, and their lengendary reproductive capabilities. Additional benefits of rabbit raising include the complete self-containment of the operation (although chicks can, of course, be hatched on the homestead and often are) and the fact that rabbits lend themselves more easily to year-around production. Fresh meat can be available regularly, without freezing or other preservation methods, which may be desirable from the standpoint of energy consumption and complete self-sufficiency.

6

Dairy products come next in importance from the standpoint of nutrition, supermarket cost, and home labor . . . the last being considerably more for dairy items than for vegetables or even meat. A dairy animal requires twice a day, 365 days a year care, and it's much more difficult to find a substitute milker than it is to find someone who will feed and water the poultry and rabbits.

Goats are the primary homestead dairy animal, again because of cost considerations, but also because they are easier for most homesteaders to house and handle. They will provide a more reasonable and steadier supply of milk for home use than a cow. They do, however, require more elaborate fencing, and their "naturally homogenized" milk presents problems in obtaining cream for butter making and other uses.

A homestead *cow* fits into many situations, but largely because of preference or in the case of very large families or because some other use is made of the surplus milk. If milk is sold, or bartered, we're overstepping the strict boundaries of "homesteading" as outlined here, however.

Both cows and goats will provide meat, from unwanted bucks and bulls, surplus or cull doelings and heifers, and cull milkers. Beyond this, many homestead families will enjoy the further variety and diversity provided by still other meat animals, primarily hogs and sheep. Both are highly adaptable to small -scale agriculture—which is what homesteading has become at this point.

Even further variety is provided (and certain esoteric pleasures realized) by an even wider array of animals: primarily other forms of poultry such as ducks, geese, guineas, and turkeys, but also horses, dogs, and cats.

One other important part of any ideal homestead is the *bee yard*, both for pollination and honey.

The Fields

While a farmer may or may not be a homesteader, just as a jeweler or a factory worker may or may not be a homesteader, a homesteader is not a farmer, that is, one who produces goods for sale. The fact that many people are a little of both doesn't alter the fact that by definition a homestead produces only for the family which operates it. Field crops therefore present a special problem (Table 1-3). While many homesteaders buy livestock feed, and grains for the kitchen, this obviously doesn't meet the ideal of self-sufficiency; but self-sufficiency in grains and fodder is usually attained only by the expenditure of a lot of hard labor or by gross mechanical inefficiency. In brief, the quantities required for subsistence entail plots that are too large to handle effectively by hand or garden methods, and too small for mechanization (or more accurately, the mechanization available today when most people are either farmers or nonfarmers).

Using traditional thinking and methods, the homesteader would plant such feed crops as corn, oats, and hay by hand and harvest them by hand. While this can be done quite easily on a small scale, and it can be accomplished on a larger scale if the time and ambition and physical endurance is available, there are other ways.

Hay is one of the lesser problems, which is fortunate because of its importance to many classes of livestock. A mature goat will require anywhere from three to 10 pounds of hay per day, depending on quality, waste, the type of hay, and other factors. One acre of alfalfa in the northern dairy regions can be expected to yield about three tons of hay per year or more. Therefore, a homestead with four goats can be expected to use anywhere from two to six tons of hay per year, which could be produced on anywhere from one-half acre to two acres. (The need for excellence can readily be seen here: if we have poor animals and poor hay, we do much more work than if we have good animals and good hay . . . and we need more land and more money!) One-half acre of hay would certainly be a reasonable goal to work towards, and an area that size can be cut, raked, and hauled by hand with little more effort or time than some folks spend on tennis or racquetball courts.

Comfrey should be mentioned here. Not only is it excellent feed for animals such as goats, easily harvested with nothing more than a good knife, and planted with ordinary garden tools, but perhaps of even more importance to the homesteader, it is much more permanent and yields much heavier than most types of hays. Curing comfrey for winter use is difficult, however, so it might be reasonable to suggest that the ideal homestead has both comfrey and hay.

Corn another mainstay in much of the country, is also easily cultivated using hand methods: in fact, sweet corn appears in most gardens in any size. The national average yield for corn is about 75 bushels per acre, which at 56 pounds per bushel is 4200 pounds. Yields of 300 bushels per acre are not unheard of, and the small, intensively fertilized and cared for plot should certainly yield more than the average for a given area.

Tilling an acre with a good *rotary tiller* is quite possible, although plots of that size can efficiently be worked with equipment often used by custom operators, or it may even justify the purchase of small equipment by the homesteader. Planting with the one-row seeders available today (Esmay or Golden Harvest) is no big deal. Ordinary farm corn planters are suppose to operate at "walking speed," and it isn't very difficult to plant 15 or 20 acres a day with a two-row planter. Planting an acre with a hand model shouldn't strain most people any more than a round of golf would. Cultivation is again a matter for the all-important tiller. It's difficult to see how the ideal modern homesteader could operate without one of those. A horse could do the job, of course, but we are assuming a homesteader has a job elsewhere. It's obvious that we have reached the point where some tradeoffs and concessions are necessary. If we're going to make use of a little technology, a tiller is indispensable.

Picking even an acre of corn by hand is not arduous, and on a crisp, fall day it can be both invigorating and pleasant. Since there is none of the rush involved in machine-picking large fields, it can be spread out over a long period . . . even until spring if need be, if deer and pheasants and other scroungers are no problem. Corn, then, can definitely be a homestead grain.

Table 1-3. Bushel Weight of Field Seeds and Sowing Rate Per Acre.

	pounds to bushels	pounds to acre
Alfalfa	60	15 to 18
Barley	48	96 to 110
Beans, field	60	60 to 90
Blue Grass, Ky., for lawns	14	75 to 100
Blue Grass, Ky., for pasture	14	20 to 30
Brome grass	14	15 to 20
Buckwheat	50	50 to 60
Cane seed, for sorghum	50	8 to 10
Cane seed, for fodder	50	25 to 30
Clover, med. & mammoth	60	10 to 12
Clover, Alsike	60	5 to 6
Clover, sweet	60	10 to 15
Clover, Ladino	60	2 to 4
Clover, Ladino in mixtures	60	1 to 2
Corn, field	56	7 to 12
Cow peas	60	60 to 90
Fescue, chewings & red	14	30
Feterita	50	10 to 25
Flax	56	50 to 60
Kaffir corn	50	10 to 25
Lawn grass		100 to 125
Lespedeza	25	15 to 25
Meadow mixture		30 to 40
Millet, golden & common	50	40 to 50
Millet, Hungarian	48	40 to 48
Millet, Japanese	40	25 to 40
Milo maize	50	10 to 25
Oats	32	64 to 96
Orchard grass	14	20 to 28
Pasture mixture		30 to 40
Peas, field	60	90 to 120
Potatoes	60	480 to 720
Rape	50	5 to 10
Red Top, solid seed		6 to 8
Red Top, unhulled	14	20 to 25
Reed Canary	44	6 to 8
Rye	56	85 to 112
Rye grass	24	24 to 30
Soybeans, broadcast	60	90 to 120
Soybeans, in drills	60	15 to 60
Spelt	40	60 to 80
Sudan grass, broadcast	40	30 to 40
Sudan grass, in drills	40	15 to 25
Sunflower	24	6 to 8
Timothy	45	10 to 15
Vetch	60	20 to 30
Wheat	60	90 to 120

(Don't forget that this field corn is what you use in the kitchen for muffins, cornmeal pancakes, mush, and other foods. Hand shellers and grinders of various types and prices are widely available.)

The small grains—oats, wheat, barley, triticale, buckwheat, rye, spelt, and others—are more of a problem, especially in plots large enough to feed any number of animals. The land can be worked with a tiller or by a custom operator with a plow. The grains can be planted by scattering by hand (which is usually haphazard and somewhat wasteful) or with a broadcast seeder such as a Cyclone or Horn.

In garden-size plots, which many people do plant for kitchen grain, the stalks can be gathered together in one hand and the bunch cut with a knife or other tool. Larger plots obviously make this extremely time consuming and inefficient. While scythes are available today, we know of only one place (Cumberland General Store, Crossville, Tenn.) to buy a scythe with a snath, which is necessary to keep the grain heads from shattering and falling to the ground. Even if you should happen to have one or run across one, it's an arduous and time-consuming task.

There are alternatives, more ideally suited to the very small farmer. They are used in many other parts of the world even today, where farms are too small or other considerations such as terrain make it difficult or impossible to use machinery. There is some evidence that livestock benefits. Those alternatives are *root crops*.

These might include mangel beets, carrots, turnips, parsnips, potatoes, Jerusalem artichokes, and rutabagas. Most small grains will yield less than a ton per acre, but the roots do far better. The reason they are so little used in this country, of course, is mechanization: the grains are easier and cheaper to produce, store, and transport on a large scale. The opposite might be true for the homestead.

Other "garden type" crops that can be grown for livestock might include kale, cabbage, sunflowers, and certainly the vitamin A rich pumpkin.

A combination of grains, roots and the other vegetables seems to be ideal both from the standpoint of the homesteader and the health and well-being of the stock. Individual capabilities, preferences, and experiences will dictate the ratio of the mix in any given situation. It should also be pointed out that soil and climate also play a large role in this particular aspect of homesteading.

Buildings

Given the function and activities of the ideal homestead, the house and outbuildings are naturally designed to work with them. The two-car garage, the sauna, and the bath house poolside are not as important as the barn and the smokehouse. A carpeted, all-electric kitchen may not be as desirable as one that is large enough and properly designed to can or otherwise process huge quantities of fruits and vegetables, cut up a beef, or make cheese and sausage.

Although lifestyles, means, and preferences vary so widely even within the context of homesteading, perhaps the "ideal" home and buildings can be given here.

☐ **House.** Ecologically sound, with protection from north and west winds, plenty of insulation, southern exposure but shaded in summer. Solar heat and water heating is the super-ideal, but provision for wood heating also rates high. The house is built in whatever manner it takes to avoid a gargantuan mortgage, the bane of homesteading.

☐ **Kitchen.** The heart of the house, just as the garden is the heart of the homestead. This is the room that comes alive first in the morning and darkens and quiets last at light. An ideal homestead kitchen is akin to the old-fashioned "keeping room." It's not just a place to thaw out frozen tv dinners or to open cans, but the epicenter of an entire way of life. The time and effort expended hoeing beans, making compost, mowing hay, cleaning pens, milking, egg-gathering, tomato picking and hog butchering all converge on that one small point on the face of the earth you call your kitchen.

While really fancy homesteads might have summer kitchens for the messy, steamy jobs of putting up the harvest by the ton, the average ideal homestead will find that function being fulfilled in the kitchen. A wood stove is ideal for many of these jobs: canning, boiling down maple syrup or sorghum, rendering lard, and even making soap (although many people will prefer doing that outside). A major feature is room. You want all the help you can round up when you start shelling peas, canning beans, or freezing strawberries, and help takes up room.

A kitchen can also be the logical place to cut and wrap meat, and that takes room to maneuver. It takes counter or table space, and a fancy kitchen carpet is definitely not an asset.

Actually, on the ideal homestead some sort of outbuilding is in order for such activities. You don't want to gut chickens or rabbits in your kitchen anyway, and a place that is free of flies in the summer and out of the chill wind in winter is a must. "Summer kitchen" is a classy-sounding name for it, but it could be one of the best building investments on the place.

We have seen pre-Civil War houses that had such facilities in the basement. A wood stove, butchering tools, even a hoist for large carcasses, and plenty of running water make this seem like an ideal, and that's what we're talking about. One such setup we saw incorporated a smokehouse into the house chimney. The freezer and preserves shelves were only a few steps away, and a dumb waiter connected with the kitchen above.

Kitchens are probably the most individualistic rooms in any house, and we wouldn't presume to suggest the details of an ideal homestead kitchen. If you think of it as the focal point of homesteading—the place where warmth, love, good food, laughter, satisfaction and work all come together—you can't to wrong. Ideally, the kitchen has easy access to the root cellar and is convenient to the garden, the barn, and other work centers.

The Barn

Homestead "barns" can be anything from sheds to full-blown barns (Fig. 1-2). Since the ideal takes into consideration not only types and numbers of livestock, but also existing buildings and other financial factors, plus a lot more, every one will be different. There are, however, a few items that could be considered standard.

For example, automatic watering is the ideal for every class of livestock, both from the standpoint of the animals' health and well-being, but also from the homesteaders' point of view. Hauling water in buckets and providing it in containers that get tipped, soiled, and which run dry, can only be considered grunt labor and dumb work.

There are dewdrop waterers for rabbits and similar systems for goats, sheep, and pigs. There are float valves for stock tanks, automatic fountains of various types for poultry, special heated and automatic fountains for hogs, sheep, cattle and horses, and others besides. Many can be homemade and any of them, even if not perfect, will be preferable to lugging water buckets. Gates and doorways should be wide enough to guide carts, wheelbarrows, or manure spreaders through.

While concrete floors are easiest to clean, they usually aren't best for the animals. Where compromises are necessary, it's difficult to point to an ideal. Wooden floors are a definite handicap, as are low ceilings.

The barn or livestock sheds should be located out of the wind as much as possible, with a southern exposure, and ample ventilation.

Details such as feeders, hayracks or mangers, arrangements of pens, etc., are all extremely important when we speak of the efficiency and attractiveness associated with an ideal. While ideas for these can be gleaned from books and magazine articles and neighbors, experience is the best teacher.

Other Outbuildings

The well-equipped homestead will have a need for many types of tools, and therefore a workshop in which to store and use them. Here again the specifics will be highly personal. While the homestead workshop will be somewhat better equipped than the average suburban home shop, and

Fig. 1-2. A homestead barn.

probably not as well-equipped as a good farm shop, there is plenty of room between. The basics are a hammer, saw, screwdrivers, wrenches, pliers, etc. A power shop would get into such items as a table saw, bench grinder, sander, and more. With any amount of machinery on the place, there may be socket wrenches, gear pullers, perhaps a welder, and much more.

Other outbuildings (some already mentioned) might include the smokehouse, greenhouse, garden tool shed, summer kitchen, granary, and corn crib.

Miscellaneous

The ideal homestead has livestock, and good animal husbandry demands good fencing. This is a troublesome and expensive enough item to warrant mention.

A woodlot is almost certain to be on everyone's list of factors that make a homestead ideal, not only for firewood but for the aesthetics such a piece of land provides. The wildlife it shelters, the native plants it harbors, the wild foods it produces, and the solitude and beauty it can provide can be more important than firewood, in some cases. While the amount of wood needed varies with climate, location, type and size of house, etc., and the amount of wood produced varies with the species, age and condition of the stand, and other factors, a minimum of 5 to 10 acres of the ideal homestead should be in woodlot. Nor should fencerows and windbreaks be neglected, for they have many of the same attributes as woodlots.

Then too, unlike most commercial farmers, the homesteader is not averse to having a little "waste" land—perhaps a marsh or bog that's too wet to till, but just right for pheasants or muskrats or deer. The homesteader may like a stony hill that's too steep and barren even for grazing sheep, but is a wonderful place to sit occasionally to watch a summer sunset.

On such a homestead a family could produce all of its own vegetables, fruits, nuts, berries, herbs, and honey. It could provide its own milk, butter, cheese, ice cream, and yogurt. The family's meat would come from its own labor: hams and bacons tinged golden with the aroma of apple or hickory smoke; steaks and lamb chops and plump chickens; delectable rabbit, tasty goose, and a wide array of sausages made (after some experimentation) just the way the family likes them.

The root cellar, the pantry, and the granary would never be completely empty from one season to another. The well-managed woodlot would provide a renewable source of energy. The orchard would increase in value as it matured, and the garden would grow more fertile with each passing year. Through experience, upgrading, and culling, the livestock would increase in health, productivity, and value.

Through all of these, the ideal homesteader has what is lacking in so many others today: security, a sense of personal value, and the inner peace that accompanies both. Such a complete homesteader could say what few others can: I left the world just a little better than it was when I entered it.

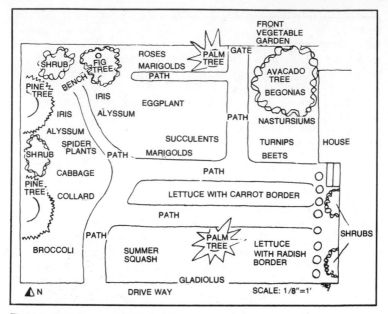

Fig. 1-4. Plan for a vegetable garden.

PLANNING THE URBAN HOMESTEAD

It is possible to homestead on a 50′ × 150′ residential lot, 20 minutes from downtown Los Angeles. Until that ideal can be fulfilled, it isn't necessary to succumb to the fast-food/television syndrome so often a part of suburban and urban life.

Following is a plan which includes dairy goats, meat rabbits, poultry, and an extensive vegetable garden. The 50′ × 150′ residential lot, 20 minutes from downtown Los Angeles, is not mythological. It is real and it works. There are shortcomings in the environment (such as the smog), in the availability of space, and in the plan itself. It is a starting point, however. It is proof that it isn't necessary to wait for that place of dreams "beyond the sidewalks" and, when the dream comes true, how nice to take some experience along.

True, there are special problems: city and country ordinances, proximate neighbors, neighborhood children, prowling dogs (not necessarily stray), and landlords. These matters will affect how far one can go toward the dream. Each individual must be the judge of the limits imposed by his/her own neighborhood and the restraints necessary. Where restrictions are very limiting, such as on rented property, the landlord might permit a trio of "pet rabbits" (two does, one buck) and a vegetable garden in an otherwise unused patch of backyard. Discuss your plans with neighbors, the landlord, if you have one, and city or county officials before you proceed. Then you know what to expect.

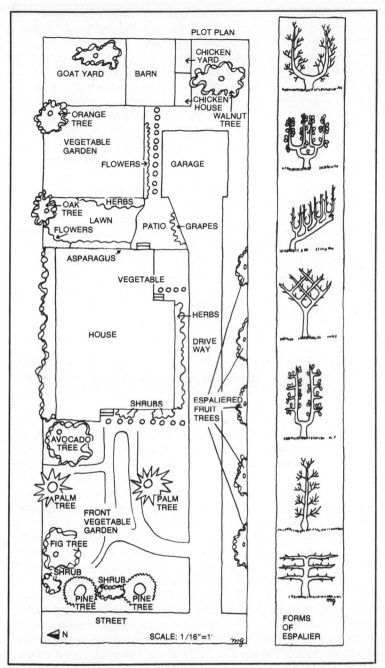

Fig. 1-3. Plot plan of a Los Angeles suburb lot.

The rules have reasons behind them. For example, you buy a goat. Although you take very strict care of your livestock and property, Jones, your neighbor, whose ideas of cleanliness might not be as stringent as your own, sees your goat and decides to purchase the hog he's always wanted to raise. If you complain about his hog, he'll complain about your goat. The rest of the neighborhood complains about you both and the law says both animals must go. The law hasn't time for special cases and after living next door to the Jones hog, you can appreciate the reason for the law.

If you are your own landlord, the neighbors don't object and you decide to get that dairy goat even though the city ordinance prohibits it, you must be prepared to take the consequences if the animal control officer comes knocking on your door. Sometimes it is possible to obtain a special permit for livestock with neighborhood backing, however, as did a family in Burbank, California. Their goat was allowed to stay when the neighbors signed a petition stating that the goat was not a nuisance in any way.

Figure 1-3 is a plot plan of the Los Angeles suburb lot, showing placement of buildings, gardens and so on. It is a good place to begin your own planning. The example here clearly will not suit everyone's lot, but shows how it has been done in one instance.

The garage and house were already situated on the lot, as were a number of large trees. These are things to work around. Keep in mind the importance of southern exposure to healthy plants.

In a neighborhood of well-kept lawns, it may take some courage to dig one up to make room for a vegetable garden, but when space is at a premium, it may be necessary. (See Fig. 1-4). Neighbors become highly skeptical. Offer to give them some of your lawn as you remove it, perhaps to fill in some bare spots or increase the size of their own. Neighborliness is rewarded! Later they will gladly share lawn clippings to mulch your crop.

Plan the front garden with eye appeal as well as palate appeal in mind. Allow some space for flowers and choose vegetables for this area that are attractive. Carrots, lettuce, and parsely make lovely borders. Eggplant has pretty lavender flowers, and the fruit is impressive. Yellow crookneck squash or sweet peppers might be suitable. Marigolds help repel some insects and lend color to any vegetable garden. Beets have striking foliage. The list is almost endless and imagination is an asset here. Also, there are many books available to help you make your selections. Browse the bookstores and the library for ideas before choosing seeds.

Rather than dedicating a whole area to a single plot, row upon row, break it up with some winding paths, perhaps a resting spot with a bench under a tree. Remember to make paths wide enough to accommodate your garden cart for transporting compost, etc., to the garden. If the front yard is shady, it may be the ideal spot for lettuce and other crops that require relief from a hot summer sun. As vegetables are harvested, plant the spaces left with follow-up crops, after working in an abundance of compost. Thus, your garden will be lush and green.

To remain on good terms with the neighbors whom you may be asking to accept a goat as well as a garden, it is important to keep this front garden especially well-weeded and neat. Grass clippings make a neater and more attractive mulch than straw. Keep paths raked and remove dying plants, faded blooms from flowers, and keep trees pruned. Bribes of fresh vegetables are acceptable, too.

As this front yard is the introduction to your homestead, for visitors as well as neighbors, particular attention is warranted.

Espaliered fruit trees are not new, though they are just beginning to come into their own in this country. In Europe, where agricultural land has long been at a premium, it is an age-old art. There are differences of opinion as to how the term originated, but basically, to espalier a tree is to train it so that its branches grow on a flat vertical plane, usually against a wall, though sometimes wires between posts are used to support and train the tree.

Most books which treat the subject recommend the use of dwarf trees, though some people feel that dwarf fruit trees do not produce as much fruit as their full-sized relatives and, in fact, make a poor showing. Apparently with severe pruning, a normal-sized tree may be espaliered as successfully as a dwarf and will produce more fruit.

If this idea appeals to you, locate a source a good instructions on the method and expect to put some effort into the project. Espaliered trees require attention for a number of years in the way of pruning, but the reward will be an abundance of tree-ripened, unsprayed fruit. The trees will be a visual asset to your property as well. In some communities it is possible to obtain already started espaliered trees from nurseries, though they are quite expensive. Your nurseryman may be a good source of information to help you train your own trees.

As long as there is no livestock to attract dogs, a low fence should be adequate to discourage them from entering the yard-garden. In neighborhoods where dogs tend to run loose, some precaution is necessary, if only to prevent them from walking through the middle of that newly planted lettuce bed on the way to investigate the trash cans next door. Even a fence only 2 feet high will do, especially if there are plants with some mass and height growing just inside it. This fence must enclose the entire yard, however. Put in gates where there are paths into the garden and remember again to allow enough width to accommodate gardening equipment, particularly the cart or wheelbarrow. If the fence is only 2' feet high, most people will step over the gates, but try lifting a wheelbarrow full of compost over! A high fence is acceptable, maybe even better, but also more costly. A wire fencing, called "flowerguard", is available 2' high. It requires no posts and is very easy to set in place. While more expensive than chicken wire, it is also more attractive and less expensive than wood fencing.

Wherever there is space going to waste because it is so small, plant herbs. The space between the driveway and the house might be ideal, as it is in the example. Herbs do well in small plantings which can be very decorative. Many also thrive in pots. The major requirement of most herbs is sunshine, so make sure that any site chosen has plenty of exposure. As with vegetables, many herbs are quite beautiful and can be used perfectly in an ornamental fashion. When planning the herb garden, choose to plant those varieties that are used regularly and perhaps try an experimental herb or two such as comfrey, which can be fed to the animals as well as the humans, or lemon balm for its delicious scent.

The back yard must be planned as carefully as would any full-sized homestead. Not only is space limited, making it necessary to fit a lot of parts into a small whole, but the parts must fit together and work smoothly. It wouldn't make sense to have the animals at one end of the yard, the compost heap at the other, and the garden in between. That would mean carting the animal waste across the garden to the compost heap, and then back again to the garden. Take the time to plan. Stand in the yard and imagine what it would be like in different arrangements. How close is the back door to the proposed vegetable garden? Where are the outdoor faucets located? Can the animals be seen from the house to check on them without going outdoors? Will you be able to get bales of hay to the goats or 100-pound sacks of grain?

If you have children, be sure to allow some space for a play area. Homesteading the children right out of their yard takes the pleasure out of the idea for them. A large tree might hold a treehouse and swings, utilizing space that probably would not be used for planting. The walnut tree in the southeast corner of the back yard has been used for that purpose in the example. What child wouldn't love a tree house? The driveway can be used to play catch, ride bikes or trikes, and for roller skating.

The barn, its attached chicken house and the pen for goats, will be a sizable project. The one here described was built at a cost of nearly $600 in 1977, using a combination of salvaged materials and new. The barn itself is 12′ × 16′ and was built in less than a month with only hand tools. The woman of the family did the majority of the construction, with her husband handling the roofing.

If was carefully planned (see Fig. 1-5) to accommodate two milking goats, their kids to three months of age, a trio of rabbits and their bunnies to butcher weight, three bales of alfalfa, 100 pounds of grain for the goats, 100 pounds of rabbit pellets, and tools for gardening, grooming animals, and care of the animals pens. Hay, grain and rabbit pellets are purchased in quantities larger than the barn can accommodate, and the remainder is stored in the garage. In the barn there is room for the milking equipment and milk stand that folds against the wall when not in use.

Basically the construction is pole-type, through 4″ × 4″ posts were used rather than poles. The posts are set 2′ deep in concrete at the four corners and on each side of the two doors. There is no foundation and the floors are dirt. The back, sides and roof are ½″ exterior plywood. This is an expensive material, but sturdy enough to be climbed on and banged against by goats and also to withstand weather.

It might be wise to note here that building codes must be taken into account and a pole-construction shed can sometimes pass as a temporary

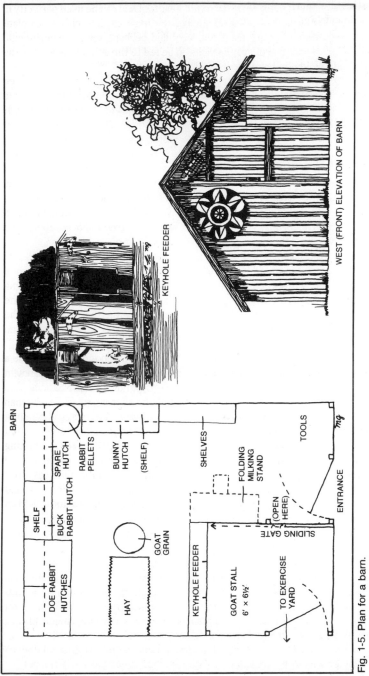

Fig. 1-5. Plan for a barn.

West (front) elevation of barn — KEYHOLE FEEDER

Plan view:

BARN

DOE RABBIT HUTCHES — SHELF — BUCK RABBIT HUTCH — SPARE HUTCH — RABBIT PELLETS — BUNNY HUTCH — (SHELF) — SHELVES

HAY — GOAT GRAIN

KEYHOLE FEEDER

FOLDING MILKING STAND

TOOLS

GOAT STALL 6' × 6½'

(OPEN HERE)

SLIDING GATE

ENTRANCE

TO EXERCISE YARD

19

structure, much as the metal tool sheds now widely available, due to its lack of foundation.

The plan takes into account the standard size of a sheet of plywood (4' × 8') and was developed to make use of it without waste. Thus, the sides of the barn are 4' high and 16' long, each side requiring two sheets of plywood to cover.

The 12' wide barn allows for a roof high enough for humans to stand comfortably inside, still using full 4' by 8' sheets of plywood. This time, four sheets to each side of the roof, placed lengthwise from the center beam to the edge, allow plenty of roof over-hang.

Passive Solar Heating

On the south slope of the roof one plywood panel was left out and corregated fiber glass was used in its place. During the summer the walnut tree to the south shades the barn, still allowing plenty of light to enter through the fiber glass. In the winter, when the tree is bare, the sunlight actually warms the barn interior. If such an arrangement is possible, take advantage of it.

Salvaged redwood boards 6" wide were used as siding for the front of the barn. These were laid on vertically with redwood grape-stakes, also salvaged, laid over the spaces between the boards. This type of siding is called *board 'n' batten* and is most attractive, lending a country look to the barn that plywood would not accomplish. With a coat of redwood stain you have the traditional red barn on a small scale.

The inside of the barn is planned for convenience in a limited space. Just inside the main door a sliding door opens from the goat stall into what becomes the milking room when the milking stand is let down. When the sliding door is opened, a goat enters the milk room and hops up on the stand. On the opposite wall shelves are placed within easy reach of the person sitting on the milking stand seat. The grain fed to the goats at milking time is located at the head of the milk stand and kept in a galvanized metal trash can with a secure lid to discourage rodents. If a cat is kept, it might do well to feed the cat in the barn which will also help to keep rats, mice, and other rodents away.

The hay is stacked three bales high near the keyhole feeder, leaving passage between the two. Rabbit pellets are also kept in a metal trash can located near the hutches. Shelves above the hutches are a convenient storage place for such things as rabbit nest boxes, gardening hand tools, grooming supplies, and first aid equipment.

Proper ventilation is an important consideration in planning for animal housing. In this case a screen stapled above the main door and to its right allows air to enter. The area in the rear wall of the barn formed by the peaked roof should also be screened, but here it is wise to provide a folded or rolled plastic shade which can be let down and secured in winter when cross-ventilation could result in drafts. Wind direction in both winter and summer should be considered.

A door opens from the side of the barn onto an exercise yard from the goat's stall. The entire backyard was already chain-link fenced in this case, as they often are in the suburbs. Consequently only one side of the fencing was required to make a complete pen, with the barn forming the fourth side. The same salvaged grapestake was used on this fence as on the barn front, tying the two parts together. When narrow boards are used for fencing, they must be closely spaced to prevent kids from escaping into the vegetable garden or the neighbor's roses. Four-foot grapestakes, placed vertically, no more than 3″ apart and nailed to the inside of 2″ × 6″ horizontal boards, work well. Redwood 4″ × 4″ posts should be set in concrete after treating with preservative. Whatever type of fencing is used, it should be strong and high, at least 4′, especially when there are neighboring properties to be demolished close at hand.

Foiling Killer Dogs

An adequate goat fence will also be one that will keep those stray dogs out. Dogs dig under fences and it is advisable to dig a 12″ trench along the fence line all the way around and also around the perimeter of the barn. Into this trench lay chicken wire which is stapled to the bottom of the fence or barn. Then place large, heavy rocks or concrete blocks onto the wire in the trench and fill the trench with dirt. This method is very effective. A large dog can make short work of digging under a barn wall and breaking open rabbit hutches. The rabbits he doesn't actually kill, he will maim through the wire bottoms of the cages. It is most unpleasant to enter the barn of a morning to find the buck rabbit torn to pieces at your feet, a hutch of butcher-ready bunnies with their toes eaten off, and large patches of skin ripped off through the wire. If this occurs once, you can be certain the dog will be back.

Don't wait to take the measures outlined. Even a grown goat is no match for a German Shepard, and those kids you waited for with such expectancy are easy prey unless you protect them.

A wide gate that opens from the goat pen onto the back vegetable garden functions for removal of waste from the pen. The compost pile would be best located near the gate for this reason. A daily raking of the goat's stall and pen will help keep flies from breeding and will keep neighbors more kindly disposed toward the livestock. This is a job that only takes five minutes per day and is well worth the effort. A homemade or purchased fly trap is effective as a means of fly control, as is fly paper hung in the barn out of reach of goats and where people working will not bump into it. Diatomaceous earth fed to the goats, rabbits, and chickens and applied to manure may also be of some help.

Flies are a very real nuisance and cannot be ignored in an urban situation. Do not let them get out of control. If necessary, it is better to resort to a dairy fly spray, used according to directions, than to have neighbors complain to the health authorities about the unchecked problem.

Make Use of Manure

The gardens rely on the waste products of the chickens, rabbits, and goats for fertility. Do not fail to make use of this valuable resource. All manure should be thoroughly composted and worked well into the garden soils on a regular basis. If the goat pen is raked daily, a pile can be built up within the pen, near the gate. This pile will begin composting if it is kept damp and in a month or two it can be turned at the same time that it is removed to the main compost pile. If properly maintained, there is really no need for a compost bin or structure.

The rabbit hutches are best hung from the rafters of the barn (hangers can be simply fashioned of baling wire removed from bales of hay) and manure on the floor beneath them can be easily removed periodically. Baling wire is still common in the West; twine is more common elsewhere. Be sure the barn door is wide enough for bringing in a cart to haul off the manure.

Volume two of *Fundamentals of Carpentry* by Walter E. Durbahn, revised by Elmer W. Sundberg, (American Technical Society, Chicago, 1963) contains an excellent plan of a backyard laying house for chickens in the section on farm buildings. This plan can fit well next to the barn on the side opposite the goat yard, thus keeping all the animals in close proximity and making chore time more efficient. A plywood box, topped with rolled roofing, can be made to contain a metal trash can for laying mash. This should be located near, or even built as part of, the chicken house.

The purchase of livestock is not something to be left to chance. Do the homework before setting out on a buying expedition. Learn what qualities to expect in a good dairy goat, meat rabbit, or laying hen. Then seek animals that meet your requirements. Shop around. Do not settle for the first animal that you look at, even though it may well be the one you return to and finally purchase. Most livestock buying guides suggest that it costs as much to feed and keep a poor producer as a good one and sometimes even more. Better animals are usually a better bargain in the long run, though they will probably be more expensive intially.

It is to be recommended on such a small scale homestead that only commercial feeds be fed to the livestock. Growing feed for the animals, aside from an occasional handful of comfrey or a few carrots, is not practical unless a large land area is available for its production. (Do not forget, however, that chickens often relish kitchen scraps in addition to the laying mash.) One can be discerning in the choice of feeds purchased. It might be worth a few trips to agricultural areas that generally surround a large city to locate a mill that produces quality feeds. If organic feeds are available, so much the better.

Small feed stores located close at hand will probably charge considerably more for hay, grains and rabbit pellets, but they may also deliver to your home and if you've no truck or other method for hauling your own from a greater distance, this may be the more reasonable course to pursue.

A veterinarian who will treat, and has some knowledge of, small livestock may present another problem in an urban area, due to the difficulty in actually locating one. It is often easier to find a vet with experience related to exotic animals such as ocelots and flamingoes than one who understands goats! Begin the search for a good vet before the need arises and learn as much as possible about handling health problems yourself. When a veterinarian is located who will treat small livestock, it might be a good idea to visit his office and make yourself known to him personally.

A homestead of any size is a great deal of work. Do not expect everything to come together and function smoothly at once. Set yourself one project at a time and as it begins to work well, begin another. The necessity for planning is great. It may take a year or two before you are really ready for goats, and that garden may not supply as much food for the table as hoped for until much experimentation and experience have taught you what and how much to plant and where. With witnessing neighbors on all sides it is best to go slowly and do a good job in each area, keeping in mind that your property speaks in its part for the entire neighborhood and that you are also speaking for a way of life.

Be willing to share your experience and knowledge with your neighbors. Children are especially vulnerable to your influence and you, in this way, are in a fine position to encourage a new lifestyle in a future generation. Do make children aware of certain rules around your property, however. Discourage their visiting the animals unless in your company and absolutely forbid feeding of animals, explaining that many foods can cause illness in livestock and that you know the special foods they require to stay healthy. Older children who may be interested can be taught to milk goats and care for gardens, chickens, and rabbits. This attention may come in handy with an especially responsible adolescent who could possibly be trusted with the care of the homestead when city living gives way to an occasional weekend in the mountains or in the country.

Get started. Many of the joys of country life are available in your own back yard. If homesteading is a dream worth waiting for, it is certainly a dream worth *not* waiting for!

CLEARING LAND

You say you've been looking at land to buy, and you've found an area that suits you well. The neighbors are friendly; water is pure and plentiful. The land you've looked at, though, is completely wooded—no fields, no meadows. You don't have enough money to hire a bulldozer at $20 or $30 an hour to clear away trees and stumps. What to do? Well, here are some exciting and challenging suggestions.

You can go out into the forest and clear plenty of land for a garden, a home, barn, pasture, pond, whatever. The most important tool is confidence in your own ability. Combine that with good health, and you're set to begin.

After some initial sore muscles, your energy level will pick right up as you see your new space grow and widen and the sun begins to pour in. All your planning should picture what the future will look like. Get inspired what it will be when it's done, rather than fretting about how much work it will involve.

This age of heavy machinery and labor-saving gadgetry may try to dissuade you, but in most cases you can throw that propaganda out the window. Once in awhile, a particular situation of large trees might prove too difficult. Each person has to learn his or her limits. Techniques explained here are flexible and open to substitution of chain saws, bulldozers, or whatever each person feels is needed.

But most clearing can happen very simply and quietly. Clearing land is hard work but highly rewarding. Above all, *believe* that you can do it.

You can accomplish just about any clearing project with three simple hand tools. These are a good *axe,* a *bow saw,* and an *axe mattock.* The axe must be razor sharp. A 48" bow saw is useful only when cutting up large logs. A 30" saw is adequate for most uses.

An axe mattock is also called a grub axe or a pick axe. You should be able to find one at a junk store or a tag sale for a couple of dollars. Keeping the axe mattock sharp is considerably hampered by the fact that you'll be crunching into stones and rocks with it. Keep it as sharp as you can. A dull mattock is no fun to chop tree roots with.

Cut the first few trees in a spot where they won't land on each other. Cut all the trees off at chest height. This leaves a "handle" which will be most important when you get around to pulling the stumps out. It will provide tremendous leverage.

You may like to cut down six or eight trees in a row. Use the axe or the saw, whichever feels more comfortable. Axe off all the limbs and the top, and put all this slash into a pile that will later be burned. Cut the top off where the trunk is about 2" in diameter. Anything smaller takes too long to move and cut for firewood.

Cut the trunks into manageable lengths, drag them off, and pile them according to eventual use: firewood, building logs, fence rails, etc. Don't let too many trees fall into the same space or you'll soon have an impenetrable jungle.

Cut up softwoods as expediently as possible and throw them onto the rapidly growing brush piles. This brush pile (and others like it) will become a thing of wonder, wilder and taller than you might have imagined (Fig. 1-6).

The better you stack your brush piles, the less work you'll have to do in burning. You want it to grow upward, not sideways. Keep piling branches and tree tops and softwood stumps on top of it, as high as you can throw. All that weight will compress it nicely. Large, centralized brush piles are easier to burn and make an awesome blaze.

Try to put off burning these looming piles for two reasons. One is to keep adding to it, especially roots dug out of the ground. The other reason is to let things dry in the sun and the wind.

24

You should find out if a burning permit is required where you live. If so, they're usually free. Their purpose is to control the amount of burning when conditions are dry or windy. Also the fire warden is aware of who is burning and where, so that when he gets a phone call from a neighbor who has spotted smoke up on East Ridge, the warden knows that the fire is under control.

Burn only in the rain or with snow on the ground. This is extra insurance, but it's worth it. If your brush piles have dried for a few months, even the heaviest downpour won't bother the fire.

It's a remarkable experience to burn on a dry, windy day—little ground fires racing away toward the the nearby forest, and neighboring brush piles exploding into flame from wind-borne sparks.

After not too many days you'll be grinning to see a new space in the forest, one or two very scraggly brush piles you've saved and what seems like thousands of 4' high stumps. Stumps are the hardest part of clearing. But you can't do much with that land until they're gone.

If you can afford the time to let them sit there for a year, many of the roots will partially rot, and the remaining work will be much easier.

Fig. 1-6. The land clearing operation has begun (photo by John Grant).

25

Remember to cut off any green shoots that sprout from the stumps. Once a month will suffice. After three or four such "haircuts," most stumps get the message and die.

You'll likely want to dig the stumps out as soon as possible. So the time has arrived to become intimately acquainted with your axe mattock. Pick an average-sized stump and scrape all the soil 6" away from it. This exposes most of the surface roots.

After this minimal scraping, you'll be able to sever almost all the roots. Chop through one at a time until you've completely circled the stump. Then put the mattock well off to one side and try pulling the stump over until it's lying on the ground. If all the major roots are cut, and if there are no large tap roots (ones that go straight down), the stump will pull down.

After you pull it over once, you've won the battle. Raise it upright again, and pull it down in the opposite direction. After three or four directions, the stump should pull free.

Smaller stumps and ones whose roots have rotted don't have to have any roots cut at all. Just pull them down and wrestle them right out. Trial and error will teach you what sizes and types of trees have sufficiently shallow root systems to allow themselves to be weeded in this fashion.

You use a different method to get larger trees and stumps out. Any large tree (let's say 6 inches and bigger) should not be cut down as the first step. Instead, cut off all the roots you can reach. When you have cut most of them, a good push will cause all that top weight to pull the tree over and rip the remaining roots right out of the ground. Then you can chop or saw the roots off and deal with the main log as you wish.

It is very important to envision the finished product in your head. See how the broccoli and the corn will look in the sunshine, and how much fun it will be to put a picnic table on that little knoll.

Sure, there's a lot of hard work left to do. You'll probably cut your finger and bang your shin more than once. Keep thinking of how good it will be when it's done (Figs. 1-7 and 1-8).

Once your stumps are out, you can congratulate yourself because you're close to the finish line. The root sections of your stumps will burn

Fig. 1-7. About 1½ acres have been cleared from the forest (photo by John Grant).

Fig. 1-8. The house and the garden in the forest clearing (photo by John Grant).

exceptionally well in a fireplace or in your stove if the door is large enough. This pile of stumps will take up lots of room because they stack so loosely. Give yourself plenty of room.

Some sunny morning you'll gaze out over a cleared area with some smoking piles of ashes and a primitiveness that conjures up images of early white settlers. Congratulations, you did it. Your work still might not be over, though. If you hope to use that land for pasture, it may be fine the way it is. If your plans include amber waves of grain or little beds of onions and cabbages, there is no rest for the weary.

Most likely you can see some rocks here and there, and severed roots sticking up at crazy angles. The roots come out with much slow, frustrating spading and chopping, if you attack right away. A year's wait makes the whole process five times easier.

If you intend to plow the land with a tractor, it can probably rip all these roots right out. Otherwise you'll want a couple of new tools: a shovel and crowbar. Start turning the soil over a shovelful at a time, beginning to define the shape of the garden.

This will instantly prove to be an arduous task, because beneath those leaves there is a tremendous web of roots. Almost every shovelful of soil will have to be put aside while you chop away the roots in that one little space. Pull out all you can, and try to eliminate them down to 10" deep. Large surface roots can be pulled out by hand.

This rooting can be exceptionally frustrating and slow. It's the only time you'll ever have to do it in that spot. Throw the roots on top of the brush pile you saved, and they'll dry out just fine.

You'll most likely encounter thousands of rocks, from pebbles to boulders. Throw them outside the garden into a pile that evolves into a scraggly stone wall. This seems efficient because all of them are then exposed for future selection for masonry projects.

Most gardens harbor two or three subterranean giants, boulders that will not yield to mere human efforts. Dig a very large grave right next to the monster, considerably deeper than you think necessary. Once it rolls into its final resting place via the crowbar, your garden won't see it any more.

How long does it take to clear land? How much land? These questions depend on the size of the trees, your physical stamina, how many people are working on the project, the weather, and your state of mind.

One important ingredient to clearing trees and stumps should be to have help. A partner or two makes the work flow so much more smoothly. Have a clearing party or a stump pulling bee. Make a game out of it. Don't be overly serious. Clearing is hard work, but let it bring out the child in you. Eat plenty of good food. We can guarantee you'll sleep well.

It's quite a ambitious adventure, this tree clearing business. It surely is a joyful experience to see the full moon streaming down onto your new garden, or maybe glimpse a doe nibble young shoots at the edge of the forest (Fig. 1-9).

SMALL-SCALE FARMING

Not everyone who dreams of a small farm is going to make it. Most farmers would be surprised to learn that anyone could be shocked by having their small farm dreams shattered by an introduction to agribusiness. After all, everyone must certainly know that our farm population has been cut in half since the 1940s, and that the exodus is continuing even now. Everyone (and certainly anyone interested in starting farming) should be aware that only the larger and more efficient farms are surviving.

If you haven't heard that wheat is selling for less than it brought in 1949, that cattlemen have been selling below the cost of production for more than a year and a half, or that dairymen have been skirting the same situation for several years, you probably haven't done enough homework to be ready to farm. If you don't know that the average U.S. farm encompasses 400 acres and represents an investment of about a quarter of a million dollars, and that the USDA predicts that it will take half a million dollars to break into farming by 1985, you might want to reconsider.

It's important to understand the distinction between home-steading and farming. You mentioned producing your own food and preparing for the hard times ahead. That's homesteading. It can be accomplished on a large farm, a small farm, or in town, and since many people in rural homes do not produce their own food or prepare for the future, they are not homesteaders. Farming, on the other hand, involves producing food for sale or barter.

A chicken farmer, then, could be one who has 100,000 birds in cages in climate-controlled light-regulated buildings, or it could be a person who sells a dozen eggs occasionally from the surplus produced by a backyard flock. It shouldn't take much imagination to figure out which one is going to produce eggs at the least cost.

Dreamers and Dollars

This leads us to the fact that farming is a business. Obvious, you say, but it's not obvious to the dreamers. People who don't have enough business acumen to run a popcorn stand envision themselves as farmers, but it won't work. In fact, without knowing and adhering to business principles, even homesteading won't work! The difference, of course, is one of scale. The loss of a couple of dollars on a homestead can be written off as entertainment or exercise or education or any number of others, but a loss on a farm is a loss, period. This, perhaps, is at the heart of your concern, so let's examine it in closer detail.

Any business, in any field, requires capital. You can't even start a lemonade stand without a lemon (or today, perhaps, a synthetic substitute). Farming takes thousands or hundreds of thousands of dollars, depending on the location and type of enterprise. The average Wisconsin dairy farm today represents an investment of $180,000.

In the lemonade business, you'd probably borrow the lemon from your mother. She might not even make you pay her back and almost certainly won't charge interest. Farm debt today stands at more than $1 billion, and those who lend that money expect to be paid back, with interest. Because they expect to be repaid, they examine the borrower's qualifications closely.

So you need training and experience in the business. With the lemonade stand, you must know how to make lemonade, how to make a sign, how to select a location and a nice hot day, how to make change. Certainly no one would start a grocery or hardware store without knowing something about groceries or hardware, without making some type of market survey, and a great deal more. If anyone thinks farming entails nothing more than buying some land, getting on a tractor and going to it, they're dreaming.

Will you raise cash crops or livestock? Will your crops be corn or soybeans, apples or celery, cabbages or artichokes? Why? Will you raise pigs or sheep or cows? Will your cows be beef animals or dairy animals, your pig enterprise a farrowing operation or a finishing operation or a farrow-to-finish operation? How much experience do you have in whichever you choose? How much capital will it take to get started, how long will it be before you can expect any income, how much money will you need to carry

Fig. 1-9. The hard work is well worth the effort (photo by John Grant).

you through that period, what will your cash flow be, what kind of price will you need to make enough money to make a living, and what kind of price can you expect in the future? What kind of machinery will you need, and what do you know about buying, operating and maintaining it?

What about marketing? Is there a local market for your pigs or fat lambs, or will you have to ship them a long distance? Is the goat cheese co-op you'll be selling milk to established and well managed, or will it fold just about the time you get your herd built up? If you intend to market milk yourself, how thoroughly have you investigated regulations governing such activity, how closely have you figured costs, just how certain are you of your potential market? If you sold a few gallons to the parents of a baby who's allergic to cow milk, a guy with an ulcer, and a health food nut, and assume that counts as valid market research, we can guarantee that you won't be farming very long. All of this is only the rawest beginning; yet many who dream of the countryside ignore even these most basic steps.

Economics of Scale

Then we come to the question of size. Is it really necessary to have hundreds of acres if all you want is a small farm?

Average size varies with location and type of enterprise (Fig. 1-10). An acre of strawberries or asparagus near a major population center might be profitable; an acre of wheat probably would not.

In most cases a small farm is at a competitive disadvantage if it produces the same products that the large farms in the area produce. The larger farm can make better use of labor and equipment, and can more easily acquire operating capital. We have seen some exceptions.

If a dairy farmer milks 100 cows with an average production of 10,000 pounds and sells that million pounds of milk per year at $9 a hundredweight, he grosses $90,000. The farmer who milks 10 cows of the same caliber grosses $9,000.

If both farmers had the same lineup of equipment, those costs would smother the smaller of the two. If the large farmer had large, fast, new equipment, he would accomplish much more than the smaller one with small, slow, old equipment that constantly required repairs. There could be compensations. If the larger farmer's equipment and other costs were such that his expenses came to $85,000 a year, he'd only have $5,000 left. If the smaller farmer could hold his costs down to $1,000 a year, he'd have $8,000 left.

A few years ago it would have been tough to find examples of this. New equipment was relatively cheap, there wasn't as much old equipment available, fuel was inexpensive, fertilizers and chemicals constituted a much smaller portion of the farm budget, land costs were lower, taxes were lower, and so forth.

Today a new combine costs $40,000 or more; an old, smaller one, can often be found for $100. Big farmers need eight, 10, and 12-bottom plows costing thousands of dollars. They have no use for the old two-bottom out

Fig. 1-10. A small-scale farm.

behind the shed, and they're sold for scrap metal prices. An average size tractor (now about 85-hp) will cost more than $10,000; old, smaller ones can often be had for under a thousand.

You'll have to be a mechanic if you own the old stuff, and you won't work as many acres in a day. You'll get the job done however. You won't need nearly as many bushels or gallons or pounds to cover the cost of capital to repay loans and pay interest.

Large farmers are extremely shrewd managers. They have to be. They have large equipment because they know exactly what it costs them and what the alternatives are, and because they make money with it.

Small farmers have to do the same. A piece of equipment is not necessarily "right" just because it's old and small and cheap. Small farmers require the same type of management skills as large farmers; they only apply them differently.

View of the Future

There are several other angles here that often get us off the track. For the most part, we believe in organic farming, and we're concerned about chemicals in our food and soils. We can see ecological webs that others ignore or are blind to. We are, perhaps, more deeply aware of the real meaning and nature of the energy crisis and its relation to food. We're uneasy about megafarming and disdainful of the middleman with his processing and packaging and advertising and hauling. We think that somehow this is all wrong and that we can make it right.

Perhaps we can, but you don't go into a burning movie theater and munch popcorn as if nothing were happening. You either wait outside until the fire has burned itself out and then start rebuilding, or you get a hose and *put* the fire out. If you want to farm but without chemicals and without huge

31

sums of capital and vast acreages and gargantuan machinery, you have those same two choices.

If you're serious about farming but lack experience, homesteading is certainly one of the best places to begin learning. You might consider formal training, and then working as a hired hand. With more experience, you might be able to farm as a renter, or on shares. In all of these, you'll have to act like an agribusiness farmer unless you'd be fortunate enough to find organically-inclined people to work with. It's getting easier all the time.

Perhaps the best alternative of all might stem from this encouraging note. Fully two-thirds of all American farmers earn more off their farms than they do from farming.

Golden Opportunity

In organic and other ecological circles, this is generally taken as bad news. More than half the farmers of the 1940s have been forced out, and only one-third of those remaining can be said to be full-time farmers. Ninety percent of our food is produced on 10 percent of our farms. If part-time farming is actually twice as common as megafarming, isn't this a golden opportunity? If we can continue to earn a living in town, it doesn't really matter if the farm makes enough money to support us or not. We can learn. We can improve our soil. We can build up our herds and flocks, settle in with machinery that's proper for each individual farm, build up equity, be organic.

It's not the ideal, because proper farming requires close timing and full-time supervision and surveillance, but it's a good second choice. For most, it's the only logical choice. With study and practice, with good management and sound financial planning, a part-time farm can become a full-time one. If our fears about agribusiness should prove to be right, such small farms will be in an extremely enviable position.

One thing more. Most organically-inclined people know that it takes three to five years to convert a chemical farm to organic methods. What many do not know is that many farmers believe that it takes five years, even for an experienced farmer, to get to know how to work a particular farm. Every place is different, every situation is different. This is only additional reason for the greenhorn to be cautious.

Yes, it's possible to make a living on a small farm. But it probably takes about as much training and preparation as a career in law or medicine or any other worthwhile profession.

Chapter 2

Homestead Business Management

Properly caring for livestock, gardening efficiently, and using homestead produce are all facets of management. Many homesteaders are confused about the broader aspects of business management. This chapter has information about successful homestead management, accounting procedures, taxes, and life insurance.

MANAGING THE HOMESTEAD FOR SUCCESS

What is the secret of homestead success? How do some people carve a satisfying and productive life for themselves from the same raw materials that simply crumble into dust at the hands of others who appear to be equally qualified? Why do some homesteads seem to prosper while others stagnate and still others disappear altogether?

It would be easy to point a finger at specific causes: trying to go too far too fast, ignorance in specific areas of crop or livestock production, lack of capital reserves to meet emergencies—the list goes on and on. There is a common thread which, when pulled, untangles the whole mystery. Homesteads succeed or fail on the basis of management.

The idea may be jarring to some people. Homesteads, they say, are not businesses. They homestead to *get away from* the rat race that business implies for them. We will see why they're mistaken.

Others will be saying that the need for management is obvious. You won't get eggs from your hens without proper feed and housing (management); you won't get milk from your cow or goat unless you can detect heat periods and get them bred, and unless the animal has the genetic potential to produce milk, and unless adequate nutrition is provided—all of which are parts of management.

Overall management—homestead business management—involves a great deal more. It can, in fact, rival the management requirements of a good-sized, money-making business!

Before we attempt to discuss details and specific examples, it will be important to agree on several general assumptions. After all, business methods *do* seem far removed from homesteading. Since many surveys have shown that Americans in general have little knowledge of how businesses operate, it will be helpful to share some common background.

To begin with, if the word "business" immediately makes you think of General Motors or Bell Telephone, rest assured that that's not what we're talking about. Not only does "business" in its broadest sense mean "a particular field of endeavor" or "an immediate task or objective," but even if we use it in the sense of a livelihood, or even a commercial endeavor, it can still apply to homesteading. In fact, everyone is involved in business and business management, even on a personal level. We make daily decisions on how to earn or save or spend money, how to use our time, what to eat, and what to wear. There are alternatives; we must take choices; we have to manage our resources as we go about the business of living.

From the economic standpoint usually associated with business and which we'll spend a great deal of time discussing, it isn't necessary to deal with large sums. A youngster with an allowance, no matter how small, must make decisions. Should it be spent on a toy or on candy? Which toy or which candy? Should it be saved for a more expensive purchase, such as a baseball glove or even a bicycle? Maybe a portion should be saved, and the rest spent to meet immediate needs and desires.

This same process is obviously more complicated for adults (Should I buy a Ford or a Chevrolet? Rent an apartment or buy a house?); more complicated yet for homeowners (Should I heat with gas, oil, wood or electricity? Paint the house? Put on a new roof?); and even more complicated for homesteaders who by their very nature own many capital goods that are necessary to their way of life and to their way of doing business. Should the homesteader have livestock, and if so what kind and how much? What kind of housing will be used; what kind of fencing and equipment? What's the best feed to use, juggling animal health and productivity with cost factors? What kinds of tools does the homestead need to meet its objectives, and what *are* those objectives?

These are not one-shot decisions. We all make them every day. Even if we *don't* make them, we have, in effect, made a negative decision which will affect our productivity and our life, as well as a thought-out positive one.

What we're getting at here is that we *are* involved in homestead business management whether we know it or not . . . whether we want to or not. Too often, homesteaders neither realize that, nor do they want to get involved. The very life of their homesteads depends on their approach to this key consideration.

It's true that some people do quite well at muddling through as if by instinct.

What we're going to do here is to present a practical plan which anyone can use to improve the chances for homestead success or to make an already successful homestead even better.

Finally, don't be afraid that managing your homestead intelligently is going to take a lot of tedious bookwork, accounting knowledge, or a computer. After all, if you're homesteading now, you're already involved in management, as we've pointed out. All you have to do now is *improve* that management.

If we operate our homesteads blindly, without positive management, we're courting disaster. If we rely on our luck and instincts, we're playing Russian roulette as surely as if we cut through a large tree without notching it first, hoping it will fall somewhere other than on our heads.

It makes sense to know what's involved so we can make wise decisions, and so far as possible, guarantee the attainment of our goals. It makes sense to work smarter instead of harder.

What Is Management?

One of Webster's definitions of management is "the judicious use of means to accomplish an end." For the homesteader, it might be the conscientious raising of rabbits to provide meat for the table or goats for milk.

That sounds simple enough. Managing the rabbits, then, would consist of getting them bred, having them kindle litters of reasonable size, bringing the litters to butchering weight without undue feed waste or consumption, preventing the doe from eating or killing her babies, and so forth. All of this is wisely using means and resources to accomplish a certain goal, namely, a rabbit dinner.

It's simple, but there's a catch. Almost every step of the way is marked by a crossroad: decisions must be made. The basis of homestead business management is making those decisions wisely, based on facts. The more experienced we become, the more seriously involved, the more important those decisions are.

Why did the doe fail to kindle after 31 days, the new rabbit raiser asks? Answer: because the two newly purchased animals are *both* does. Solution: find a buck.

This is beginning management and serves to demonstrate some of the basic elements. First, the problem arises. (No babies.) Second, the problem is defined. (No male rabbit.) Third, a solution is found. (Get a buck.)

In real life, even a simple problem like this one is more complicated. Recognizing the problem may be simple because no babies appear in the nest box, but discovering the cause may not be so simple. In our example, it required knowledge on someone's part to determine that the two "parents" were both does. Many other possibilities existed, and a knowledge of them would have been necessary, too.

What if the pair actually was a pair? Then it would be necessary to know if they were old enough to breed, if the buck was sterile; the doe too fat; the doe aborted . . . and on through many other possibilities. Our definition of management would necessarily become more complex. Then our approach might look like this:

1. Recognizing the problem.
2. Gathering the information relative to the problem.
3. Considering the available alternatives.
4. After analyzing the data, making a decision on the basis of the finding.
5. Taking action.
6. Observing the results.
7. Going back to step four if the desired results aren't achieved, and keeping the results on hand so that similar decisions can be made more quickly and effectively in the future.

Has the rabbit raiser who goes through all seven steps really done any more work than one who goes only through four or less . . . and either "rebreeds" the two does or quits immediately? Sure. In this over-dramatized case, it's the only way to reach the desired goal: the rabbit dinner. When you consider the small amount of time involved, compared with the daily watering and feeding and cleaning, the cost of feed, and the original investment, the extra work is insignificant. What's more, it's productive: it's putting meat on the table, whereas the actual care of the animal was not.

Perhaps this is all too obvious. It doesn't hurt to refresh our memories on the obvious once in awhile, and certainly not, when we're going to move into more complicated areas. It goes without saying that moving from a two-rabbit example to an entire, complex homestead introduces many complicating factors (Fig. 2-1). Starting from the beginning and taking them step-by-step, they become a great deal less complicated, and certainly less confusing. Moreover, it's necessary to learn to walk before attempting to run or dance.

Fig. 2-1. The business of homesteading requires coordinating a large number of complex factors.

36

The Role of Manager

What does a manager do? He uses means judiciously to accomplish an end, but we can get more specific.

Imagine a homesteader getting out of bed in the morning. Many homestead chores are fairly routine and are done almost without thinking—maybe that's why we so often fail to acknowledge the importance of management. The goats are milked, the chickens and hogs fed, waterers checked or filled, breakfast made and eaten; most of these could almost be done blindfolded after awhile.

What's next? Is the woodbox getting low? Does the garden need weeding? Is it time to plant corn, or is this the day to make pickles? What gets done, and on what basis is the decision made?

That's management. Since there are so *many* decisions to be made on homesteads, it's essential to have a rational, painless way of making them. It's not enough to get out of bed and face the new day without a plan, not if we want to use our time and energy to get the most satisfaction out of life.

Some homesteaders will say this is somehow distasteful; it's too regimented, they feel. They *do* manage their time, perhaps without thinking about it and probably without a clear course of action. Then they probably wonder why they don't seem to make much progress.

Let's say that the homesteader in our example is delighting in the fresh breath of spring, and on the way back to the house after chores, stops to check the garden and finds it ready for planting. The seeds have been selected and purchased in anticipation of this eventful day. The garden was enriched with compost to have it ready. The gardening tools are close at hand. All that remains now is the actual work.

What sort of management decisions were made? The homesteader is following the same five major areas of management that the executives of any large company are following on this fine spring morning. They are as follows:

1. Planning (think, judge, decide) (Fig. 2-2).
2. Organizing (developing ways to implement the plan).
3. Directing (carrying out the plan).
4. Coordinating (getting together the resources: people, tools, etc.).
5. Controlling (measuring the success of the plan).

The planning involves deciding to have a garden in the first place. It entails deciding what vegetables to grow, what varieties of each, and how much.

Organizing means deciding where to get the seeds and how to pay for them.

Directing involves actually buying the seeds, spading the soil, and planting.

Coordinating is having the seeds and tools on hand when the soil is dry enough to work.

Controlling is evaluating whether the project was a success: whether

Fig. 2-2. Successful small farming requires skillful planning (photo by Jean Martin).

too much or too little of any given crop was planted, whether some plants were too close together or too far apart, whether the right varieties for the soil and climate were chosen, and so on.

This is all still basic, and we do it almost unconsciously. It's important to recognize the principles of management as our homesteading becomes more involved and more sophisticated, because the principles underlie the more advanced business management techniques we'll be looking at next.

HOMESTEAD ACCOUNTING

Since it's likely that many homesteaders are still a trifle uncomfortable with the entire idea of *business* and *management* being an integral part of homesteading, let's spend just a little more time discussing the differences between "normal" accounting and homestead accounting (Fig. 2-3).

As an example, Farmer Jones owns 80 acres of rolling land: 75 acres are tillable, but 25 of those 75 acres are steep enough that erosion is a serious problem.

It's possible to plant corn on them. Using normal accounting and business management methods, he comes up with these options:

He can plant corn on the entire 75 tillable acres, expect an average of 100 bushels per acre, pencil in a price of $2.50 a bushel, and expect a gross return of $18,750. Or, he can keep the 25 hilly acres in hay and plant the other 50 to corn. His estimated return then looks like this:

50 acres corn @ 100 bu./acre = 5,000 bu. × $2.50/bu. = $12,500
25 acres hay @ 3 tons/acre = 75 tons × $45/ton = $3,375

Note that $18,750 gross can be compared to $12,500 + $3,375 = $15,875. Since there is a difference of $2,875 in favor of the all-corn program on the surface that might look like the best way to go.

In planting those hills to corn, he loses a great deal of his topsoil to erosion. The loose, unprotected soil (which is a part of row-cropping)

38

enables rain to wash that topsoil, and its nutrients, into the roadside ditches and even into nearby lakes and streams.

That $2,875 might well mean the difference between profit and loss, which for most small farmers could mean the difference between staying on the farm or going back to truck driving, teaching or some other city job. How do you make the decision on what to plant?

In this very simplified example (and we'll be looking at some of the realities later), it appears to be a matter of economics in terms of dollars and cents. To the economists and accountants and bankers, the choice is clear.

To the homesteader, however, there is another very important consideration. What is the true value of that lost topsoil?

The problem, under normal accounting procedures, is that we can't place a dollar value on that soil fertility because it doesn't have an established market value. The banker can't plug it into his computer; the accountant can't put in into his assets column. We homesteaders know it *does* have a value. We have to find some way to assess the worth of that fertility, and place it on our balance sheets as an asset . . . in which case it could well offset the additional cash to be realized from mining those hills for their production of a profitable crop.

Let's look at another example, not at all uncommon in the best agricultural regions of our country. Farmer Jones has 5 acres of woodlot. He may or may not take wood out of this parcel for firewood, fenceposts, or timber, but his accounting tells him that the most economically productive use of that land is to graze cattle on it.

The cattle trample the soil and eat the tree seedlings. The woodland

Fig. 2-3. A successful homestead requires hard work, knowledge, and skill, but most of all it requires good management.

takes on a park atmosphere and eventually provides very little in the way of cattle nutrition.

If that woodlot were preserved as a woodlot, it would grow trees. These trees could be used as timber, and firewood and wildlife habitat. With management (selective cutting and so forth) it would become a self-sustaining source of lumber and energy that could outweigh its value as second-rate pasture.

What we're getting at is simply this: immediate profits may not be at all comparative with long-range profits. Furthermore, the residual assets of soil fertility and woodlot productivity are hard, or impossible, to write up on a balance sheet or profit and loss statement.

Is this any reason to eschew accounting and business management altogether? Emphatically not. That soil fertility *does* have a cash value, as well as the more esoteric value most homesteaders ascribe to it. That woodlot *does* have a cash value.

Let's look at one more, even more far-out example. Assume this farm contains several acres of marsh. There are cattails, muskrats, and pheasants, but nothing of any real "economic" value. If the marsh were drained, it could yield fantastic amounts of potatoes or celery or other high value crops. Farmer Jones might just *enjoy* the muskrats and pheasants, or the variety of marsh marigolds and other flora, or the idea of preserving a bit of wilderness.

That has a price tag, too, because to achieve similar satisfaction, he might have to spend a considerable sum to travel to the South Pacific to watch the sun rise over an atoll, or to Scotland to experience the mist o'r the moor, or whatever. The problem is, how do you enter such esoteric things into your homestead balance sheet?

We're dealing with economics, with the real world. We may choose to ignore the economics, but they're there.

Economists, accountants, and bankers have their finger on the pulse of the real world, but they tend to ignore some very basic and fundamental truths. Homesteaders can see those truths, but since they're often in conflict with traditional accounting, they tend to ignore traditional accounting.

Both views are wrong. They will have to be changed to make any real progress in saving our planet.

Let's go back to the first part of our example, the corn versus the mixed cropping. Organic farmers and homesteaders are notorious for saying it's not the gross, but the *net* that counts. This is sound accounting. It takes a great deal more input to produce an acre of corn than an acre of hay, and that complicates our example considerably. When we consider other possible crops, the machinery required to produce them, and the marketing factors (either direct sales or the livestock required to sustain that crop production), it becomes even more complicated.

But the object of this lesson is simply this: are we going to look only at this year's cash receipts—or are we going to look at longer term benefits?

Are we going to put only actual dollars on our balance sheets, or are we going to take into account those other values that our way of farming—our way of life—enriches us in?

This gives us the basic tenets of homestead accounting. We're going to be hardnosed about the financial aspects of it all, but we're also going to be very realistic about the true benefits and values which, in traditional accounting, are swept under the table. You probably won't be able to sway the thinking of your accountant or banker, but you're going to have a much better picture of what your homestead, and your farming methods are really worth.

SETTING AND REACHING GOALS

What are your homestead goals? Some people have no greater goal than to make it through the day, or so they claim. If they should happen to achieve anything worthwhile, it would be by sheer accident.

Most of us, however, do have long term goals and desires. Maybe they aren't well thought-out or carefully defined, but we have *some* idea of what we'd like to do with our lives.

The very act of homesteading implies long range goals, but these aren't always well defined or thought out. What's worse, too often the major goal isn't broken down into more easily attained and more immediate ones, and there is no plan. The homesteader sees nothing but work and financial distress, with few rewards in sight, and eventually gives up.

The successful homesteader, on the other hand, need not work any harder, be any smarter, or spend any more money than the one who fails. The successful homesteader's secret weapon is a long-range goal, and a plan for achieving it.

More often than not, this goal is the dream homestead, the ideal place that exists in every homesteader's imagination, and perhaps only in home-steader's imaginations. Creating a dream homestead is very much like creating a beautiful painting from a blank canvas and some tubes of oils. In both cases, the artist has an end in mind, a vision no one else can see or even comprehend. Step by step, sometimes making revisions, sometimes even modifying the ultimate vision, the masterpiece becomes reality. A homesteader without a goal would be akin to a painter splashing color on a canvas while still trying to decide whether the picture is going to be a portrait or a seascape.

Homesteaders are not a uniform lot, and many goals are possible within the framework of homesteading. One family might dream of a paid-for retirement place that would provide food and recreation. Another might dream of becoming self-sufficient enough to be able to leave a city job. Still another might set as a goal the establishment of a profitable small farm, while yet another may wish for nothing more than a pleasant home and life in the countryside while continuing to work in town. Every goal is different and tailored to the individual who dreams of it, but the important thing is that it's there.

Setting Goals

Homestead goals are set in many ways, but most often they evolve, over a long period. In most cases they are family goals, and therefore involve discussion, and compromise. Long-range goals should be altered as little as possible, once they're set, and therefore should not be determined arbitrarily or hastily. Instead, they should be developed, slowly and carefully, and examined from many angles before being solidified.

Reaching Goals

There is nothing mysterious about setting out to attain a goal, no matter how lofty or far away. As with any journey, the first step is the most difficult. After that, it's just a matter of putting one foot ahead of the other. There are, however, two techniques that seem to be used by successful people in any field of endeavor.

The first is psychocybernetics. This simply means that their dream—whether a painting or a homestead—becomes such a part of them that it becomes real. They can actually feel it, hear it, see it, taste it, and their every thought and act is in some way directed toward the achievement of that goal.

It isn't necessary to go off the deep end and become a crazed fanatic. The subconscious can be a powerful ally.

The second method of attaining even seemingly unattainable goals is to break the process down into shorter-range, more easily reached goals. Picture an apartment dweller dreaming of the ideal homestead. No amount of money can buy the perfect homestead: part of the cost is time itself, and the experience and knowledge it takes time to acquire. So this future homesteader must break the major goal down into smaller, more easily manageable parts. It might look something like this: find the right piece of land; make the house habitable, learn to garden; repair the barn and sheds; start raising chickens and rabbits; learn to butcher; start raising goats; become proficient at making cheese, yogurt, and butter; raise a hog; learn to cure ham and bacon and make sausage; retrofit the house to provide solar heating; raise a steer, etc.

The long-range goal is the North Star; it remains a constant beacon. Shorter-range goals are more easily altered. They are also more easily attained, and each is a minor triumph that provides a sense of accomplishment and satisfaction along the way. With each minor goal won, the big one is closer and more realistic.

Attaining Smaller Goals

If you were driving from New York to Los Angeles, you might have a map of the United States. You'd also want maps of the states you were passing through. Your immediate goal wouldn't be California, but perhaps Pennsylvania.

On the homestead, your goal is not the ideal, but one portion of the ultimate ideal.

42

In addition, the map would not only tell you in which direction to go, but it would help indicate if you were indeed making progress, and how much. Certain signs along the way might lead you to suspect you made a wrong turn somewhere, and a check of the map could show you're headed not for California but for Vermont!

On the homestead, one of the most used and most useful tools to indicate progress is the recording of activity in individual projects. These records, taken alone, may seem insignificant, just as a distance of a few miles doesn't look like much on a map of the entire country. They're a largescale map, where progress is more apparent and therefore more encouraging.

A homestead cannot succeed without adequate records. What is "adequate?" This can vary with the individual and many other factors. In general, the beginner especially will make much greater progress by keeping detailed accounts, and by analyzing and using them.

As a simple example, let's say Farmer Jones has purchased 25 straight-run day-old chicks. What types of records would be useful, and how would they be used?

Half the chicks will probably be roosters and will be used as meat. The other dozen or so will be kept for egg production. Even this simple example, then, has two goals: meat and eggs. Even these will be more complex in the homestead setting. The likely goal isn't *just* meat and eggs, but better tasting meat and eggs than can be purchased, or fertile eggs, or roasters rather than the fryer and broilers usually found in stores, or inexpensive meat and eggs. It's also possible that cost and flavor are secondary to such concerns as the desire to be independent of the supermarket or the pleasure of caring for a small flock of poultry.

No matter what the goals, primary and secondary, two important points stand out. One, you must know what those goals are, just as you must know that your journey will take you to California, and not Vermont. Secondly, you must have some method of tracking your progress in order to determine if those goals are being reached.

The most basic records in any enterprise are financial. Often, homesteaders feel that, since their primary goals are not financial, such records are useless. They aren't.

The financial records of the poultry enterprise will include the initial cost of the chicks, the cost of feeders and waterers, the expense of housing and brooder lamps and outside runs and nests, feed, and any medications that may be necessary—in brief, everything spent on the chickens. The other side of the ledger would show the amount of meat and number of eggs produced.

At this point it might be worth mentioning once again that a homesteader doesn't necessarily have to be an accountant, any more than a homesteader needs to be a vet or a carpenter. A successful homesteader needs to know a smattering of many arts and sciences, and a basic understanding of financial management is important.

The records, therefore, need not be in any specific form. They aren't going to be audited by an accountant. They are simply a tool to show the homesteader what's being done right and wrong, what progress is being made toward the stated goals, and most importantly, how to improve the situation.

On a very elementary level, when the last of the laying hens goes into the soup pot, the small flock owner will be able to determine exactly how much each pound of meat and dozen eggs cost, in dollars and cents. Records will also help pinpoint mistakes, so that the next batch of chicks will provide even more "profit"—which to homesteaders means not only cash but "goal-value" that might not be readily defined in financial terms.

FARM BOOKKEEPING

Bookkeeping, the bugaboo of farming, is certainly never a favorite task. Computers are presently taking over much of the book work for the bigger farms, but the small independent family farms still must care for their own books in such a way as to know their financial standing throughout the year.

Today even the smallest farm business which has dealings with credit must be able to show cash flow for the year and have accurate figures for the annual income tax forms.

One bookkeeping method can give an up-to-the-minute picture of the farm financial status with the minimum of effort. The system is based on the use of five by eight file cards. The tools needed are a copy of the current farm income tax blank, and a packet of five by eight lined cards.

To set up the file, take out of the white lined cards and copy off the expense items which pertain to the farm operation from the income tax form. You may combine some of the items such as insurance and taxes, and then separate the items at tax time.

The list is numbered from one to whatever number it takes to cover the list of expenses. These numbers will correspond to the index card. Thus, if hired labor is number one on the list, hired labor expenses will be filed behind card number one.

The next step is to take one of the lined cards and in the upper left hand corner write 1 HIRED LABOR. Every time a bill for hired labor is paid, the receipt is filed in that slot and the amount is noted on the white card.

Continue in this manner for the other items of expense, making a card for each and using the consecutive numbers. Behind the expense files, the various income categories are listed. The cattle sales file not only has the price received for the cull cows and calves shipped, but additional cards are labeled COMMISSION and TRUCKING. In this manner, the costs of selling the cattle are also tabulated and available at a glance.

The final numbers of the index file are used for such items as capital expenses for the year, a file for income tax returns from previous years, ASCA papers, and other items which must be consulted during the year.

Each month, when the checks are written the bills which are paid are sorted according to category, each noted on the appropriate card as to amount only and filed in the proper spot. When a column of figures reaches to the bottom of the card, the total of that column is added and noted.

When the financial condition of the farm is needed, it is a simple matter to finish the addition on the cards with a small calculator. Subtract the expenses from the income.

Income tax preparation is simplified as the receipts are stored in a large envelope with the year indicated on it. The cards are once again figured with the totals and noted in the proper places on the income tax farm form.

The only time consuming portion of the income tax is figuring the depreciation schedule for the farm property. This can be figured from the previous income tax forms, readily available in the file, and the new capital investments also noted in the files.

The shoebox method is still used to some extent as all the bills and receipts not filed are placed in one desk drawer with the check book. Another drawer holds the five by eight file. File boxes of this size are available at a reasonable cost.

With this method, bookkeeping chores have become much easier, though certainly not a fun thing to do. The bills and receipts are easily found and the income tax headache each year has vanished.

THE COMPUTER

Does your homestead need a computer? Probably not. But does it want one? You might be surprised. You can purchase a TRS-80 from Radio Shack which will be fun, challenging, useful, and, of course, expensive.

Home computers have been selling rapidly for about a year, and new models and brands are being introduced all the time. The Radio Shack is lower priced than many. The stores provide easy service if problems arise. You can upgrade your system gradually as finances allow. Programs are readily available to buy or, if you have a program to sell, the potential market is larger.

If you are a novice to programming, start with a TRS-80 Level-I 4K. It comes with a manual that explains in very simple terms the computer language the machine understands. Once you understand the manual and have grown fond of your machine, you will begin to get frustrated by lack of sufficient memory to run large programs and lack of more complicated basic commands. So take your computer back to Radio Shack and ask for Level-II conversion and also 16K of memory.

Level-II is much more powerful than Level-I. Programs load and run faster on Level-II, and programs are more easily written, once the new commands are learned.

Computers are not cheap, so why would you want one? Well, for fun. A computer is the ultimate toy, since after a game gets boring, you simply load in a different one.

It is endlessly versatile. Games may be played with the computer alone or with two or more players against each other and the computer as referee. There are games of dexterity and skill or games of challenge. Consider using a computer to help you keep records. Storing and analyzing data is what a computer does best.

You don't take the time to turn on the computer, load a program, and enter data just for one item. Minute-by-minute records must still be made by hand, as they happen. The computer is for sorting and tallying the data, and giving useful, permanent totals, year after year.

If you have a home business, the computer is great for inventory, mailing lists, and accounting. Many business programs are already written and available. You need to make only minor changes to get the computer to handle records for your business.

Specific homestead programs must be written by you to meet your own needs. More general programs are readily available for such things as checkbook balancing and budget maintenance. Such programs are purchased from firms which handle "software" ("software" runs the computer, "hardware" *is* the computer) for about $8 to $25. There are many interesting programs available; the only limit is your budget.

These software businesses are also a source of potential income from your computer. A program you write which you think may be of interest to others can be sent to a software firm. If the publisher likes it, it may be purchased outright or you could receive a percentage of sales.

All programs for larger systems are stored on cassette tapes or "floppy discs." Therefore, a "publisher" of software actually is selling and buying cassettes which have complete programs on them, in a form which sounds like so much noise to the human ear.

Tempted? You can see a TRS-80 demonstrated at a Radio Shack. If you want to learn more about other brands and what software is available, take a look at a few microcomputer magazines, where you will find ads for software and hardware. It is a brand new field and much software has yet to be written. New TRS-80 machines cost about $699 for Level-I 4K and $999 for Level-II 16K.

Are there any problems? Sure. Sometimes cassettes are hard to load. The computers, at first, were very sensitive to having the right volume on the cassette player, but machines for sale now have largely corrected this problem.

The machine should be treated with care, protected from dust and crumbs, and never placed in a carpeted room, as static electricity can do grave damage. Microcomputers are state-of-the-art machines, too new to be totally without "bugs." On the whole, though, they are very reliable and relatively trouble free.

There is one additional problem that should be mentioned. The machine is addictive, frustrating, fun, time-consuming, and exciting—the wave of the future.

HOMESTEADERS AND TAXES

To be fully equipped to take on the Internal Revenue Service (IRS) on an equal basis, you should obtain the following, free, from your nearest IRS office: Publications 17, 225, and 334; Form 1040 with Schedules A & B, C, D, E, F, and SE; and Forms 2106, 3468, 4136, 4562, 4797, and 5695. If you don't have a nearby IRS office, look them up in the phone book. They'll list a toll-free number you can call to get the forms and publications.

Are you thinking to yourself that you couldn't possibly need all those forms? You'll find that you really do need most of them. You probably could get by without some, but using them is actually easier for you. You may only fill out a couple of lines on some, but their use will help to organize your thinking. Also, if the IRS didn't like their forms, they wouldn't print them; so make them happy.

There are even other forms you may want as well. The elderly will want Schedules R and RP. You might want to income average on Schedule G, or revise a previous year's return on Form 1040X. Maybe you just moved and need a Form 3903, or maybe you're trying to figure all of this out during lambing and need a Form 4868 to request an extension of the time to file your return.

A mysteriously incomplete list of forms is given at the back of the instructions for Form 1040. A visit to an IRS office will allow you to browse through *all* of the forms and is recommended if you can arrange it. As a last resort, you can get Publication 900 for a list of all publications.

You can probably figure out the basic Form 1040 without any coaching beyond that provided in the various IRS publications. You may want to invest in a privately published income tax self-help guide as well. Lasser's *Your Income Tax* is useful, and the others on the market are helpful as well.

If you make part of your living from artistic, craft, or writing activities, you probably should also get a copy of *Making it Legal* by Davidson and Blue, McGraw-Hill, 1979, for both income tax advice and general legal information. Both of the books will be either deductible or depreciable as a business expense, and the second one can even be used to claim investment credit. It's on to the various schedules which go along with Form 1040.

You probably should not use Schedule A, the one where you can itemize deductions from your income. Most people are much better off taking the standard deduction rather than itemizing.

If you've had unusually costly medical expenses, interest payments, theft loss, alimony costs, or whatever, then it may be that Schedule A is for you. Lasser gives a list of about 300 things you can deduct. Keep in mind, though, that usually you are much better off deducting many of those costs which *could* be shown on Schedule A as a business or farm expense.

If you receive any income from interest or dividends, enter it on Schedule B, which is the flip side of Schedule A. Don't yield to the temptation to cheat anywhere on your return, but certainly don't do it here as this sort of income is very simple for a tireless computer to trace. If you had any income of this sort which can be treated as capital gains, be sure to do so. Don't treat it as ordinary income.

Don't list interest or dividends from tax-free sources such as municipal or state bonds or the like. Similarly, don't list so-called dividends from a life insurance policy, as these are just refunds of your money.

Schedule C should be used to show all income and expense of doing business except those better treated as farming activities. Much of this form is self explanatory, but here are a few tips.

On line E you probably want to indicate a cash accounting method because that is a simple way for the nonprofessional accountant. If you have an inventory of finished items or raw materials at the end of the year, then check a box on line F and show your inventory value on the other side of the form.

In Part II list the costs of doing business, here called *deductions*. This is the place to list the items you might otherwise have put on Schedule A. You should also show here a fair share of expenses such as telephone, power bill, insurance, property taxes, and other costs that are part personal and business. Don't try to deduct office space in your residence unless the space is a separate room used exclusively as an office in your business.

Add any categories that you need under lines 32a, b, c, etc. If you travel in connection with your business, list the expenses on a Form 2106, listing mileage on your personal auto for business use on the back side and transferring the total to the front side, line 3. Write a note on line 8 of 2106 that you are transferring the item to line 29, Schedule C, and do so. You can use another Form 2106 for farm auto expenses and transfer that to Schedule F. If you travel in connection with another job, use yet a third 2106 and transfer that to Form 1040.

Schedule D is the place to put any income that is allowed to be treated as capital gain income. Such income is taxed at lower rates than ordinary income, so you should try to use this form if you can. Income that can be treated as capital gain is any income (or loss) that you make from investments made with the primary intention of making a profit. You could have bought common stocks, land, an antique car, a bull, a work of art or virtually anything which was not purchased for your own personal use. Profit from selling your residence, personal car, jewelry, etc. cannot be treated as capital gains income.

Incidental personal use of an item doesn't disqualify it, however. If you bought a painting with intention of later selling it as a profit, then it's okay to have the painting hanging in your home in the meantime. The same reasoning would apply to almost anything, although it may happen that you and IRS don't see eye to eye on some items. It costs nothing to try, so don't hesitate to list an item if you think it belongs in this category.

If you've sold breeding stock (except horses) that you previously purchased rather than raised, then report those profits (or losses) on Form 4797 and transfer the numbers to Schedule D. Do the same for sales of equipment or machinery used in business, including farming. This provision can be a nice loophole for you.

For example, you buy a tractor or a potter's wheel to use in farming or in your craft business. You use it for a year or more, during which time you've taken an investment credit, depreciated it, deducted costs of maintenance and repair, and then you sell it at a profit. This profit is taxed as a capital gain, at less than half the usual rate.

Do note that this does not apply if you are in the business of buying, repairing, and reselling equipment, but only if the equipment is used in another business. There is a fine line between the two activities, and many a farmer buys, repairs, and resells equipment all the time and gets capital gains treatment of the profit, while in effect getting free use of the equipment in between. You draw the line where you think it should be.

In situations like this, there is room for honest disagreement between you and IRS, so make the decision which is most favorable to you. If you're not intentionally trying to defraud, then the worst that can happen to you is that you'll owe the additional tax at some later date, plus interest at a modest 6 percent. That's a pretty cheap loan these days!

On Schedule E, try to list anything you can possibly justify. The reason is that income from Schedule E is not subject to self-employment tax, which is a fancy name for social security payments for the nonsalaried. Some annuities are in this class, as are rents received, royalties from mineral deposit leases, certain income from partnerships, estates, and trusts, and small business corporations.

Check with the payer of the annuity, if you have one, to see if it qualifies. A tax adviser can help you with the other categories. For that matter, go to the IRS office and ask them to help you decide, or go ahead and claim any item in doubt and argue later if your return is selected for audit.

Schedule F is an important one for many homesteaders who show a profit from farming activities. Even if you don't show a profit every year, you should use Schedule F because the loss can help to cancel income from another source, provided the farm doesn't lose all the time. It is a remarkably simple form, especially if you use cash accounting. The Farmer's Tax Guide, Publication 225, is a very good one and will help you a great deal if you read and study it carefully. Do remember not to list sales of breeding stock on Schedule F because they're subject to capital gains treatment and should be shown in Form 4797 like that tractor you rebuilt.

What about depreciation and tax credits of various kinds? Depreciation is a way of spreading out the cost of a piece of equipment or a farm animal over the years of its useful life, rather than deducting all of the cost at once as one would do with items such as feed, medicine, fuel, and other items which are used up rather quickly or at least in less than a year.

Credits are amounts which serve to cancel part of your tax obligations; they apply directly against the tax, rather than just diminishing your taxable income as a deduction would. There are credits for the elderly, credits for child care expenses, credits for purchases of equipment, credits for fuel and lubricant tax, and even credits if you earned less than $10,000 under certain circumstances, and credits for saving energy by insulation or installation of solar heating, or other renewable energy sources on your residence.

DEPRECIATION AND INVESTMENT CREDIT FOR HOMESTEADERS

If you are making income from your homesteading activities, then you should know about depreciation and investment credit. As a matter of fact, there are also credits you may be entitled to even if you're not earning income from the homestead.

What's depreciation? It's a way to deduct costs of items used in business that have a useful life of more than a year. Such items include equipment, farm animals, buildings, books, fences, and such. The useful life of an item is for you to decide, because the life of anything depends on how well it is made in the first place, and on the sort of use to which it is put.

There are tax advantages to be gained from both short and long lifespans, depending upon your situation. It is usually advantageous to depreciate as rapidly as possible by assuming a short useful life. As you will see later though, it is useful to assume a useful life of seven years or more to receive the maximum investment credit. You'll have to decide for yourself which course is best for you.

Depreciation can be done in any reasonable way, but I recommend you stick to one or both of two methods. The simpler of the two is called the *straight line method.* With this method the item is assigned a useful life span and a salvage value at the end of the useful life. The salvage value is subtracted from the cost, and the remainder, called the *depreciable balance,* is divided by the number of years of useful life. If an item cost $1500 and had a salvage value of $100 and a useful life of seven years, the depreciable balance would be $1500 − $100 = $1400. The $1400 divided by 7 years gives a depreciation of $200 per year.

There are other methods which allow more rapid depreciation. The simplest of these is called the *declining balance method.* With this method, no salvage value is assigned. The depreciable balance is reduced each year by an amount that is either twice (200 percent) or one and a half times (150 percent) the straight line rate. The rules, greatly simplified, state that you can use the 200 percent rate for new items, and the 150 percent rate for used items and new buildings.

Let's do an example. Suppose you bought the same $1500 item as above with a useful life of seven years, and it was a new item eligible for the 200 percent rate.

	depreciable balance	depreciation
first year	$1500 × 1/7 × 200% =	$429
second year	$1071	$306
third year	$765	$219

Notice the problem with this method. There is an undepreciated balance left over. The way to solve this problem is to change to the straight

	depreciable balance	depreciation
fourth year	$546	$156
fifth year	$390	$111
sixth year	$279	$80
seventh year	$199	$59
undepreciated balance $140		

line method at some point. Generally, you should change when the straight line method gives a larger annual depreciation than the declining balance method.

In the example that would be in the sixth year. You'd subtract the $100 salvage value from $279 leaving $179. With straight line you'd deduct $90 the sixth year and $89 the seventh year. Also, at the time you change to straight line is when you estimate the salvage value which you might decide was more or less than $100.

One additional form of depreciation remains. You can also take additional first year depreciation of 20 percent for any item (except buildings) with a useful life of six years or more. This 20 percent is taken before the salvage value is subtracted. Here's an example. Suppose you bought the same item as above. First you would take 20 percent of $1500 or $300, leaving a depreciable balance of $1200.

	depreciable balance	depreciation
first year	$1200 × 1/7 × 200% =	$343
second year	$857	$245
third year	$612	$175
fourth year	$437	$125
fifth year	$312	$89
sixth year	$223 change to straight line	$62
seventh year	$61	$61
salvage value $100		

Note the change from declining balance to straight line in the sixth year by subtracting $100 from $233, leaving $123 which is then divided between years six and seven. By the way, an important rule is that you can not change depreciation methods without written permission from IRS, except that the change from declining balance to straight line can be made without permission.

You might consider taking the additional 20 percent first year depreciation and use the declining balance method. The reason is that you normally will want to depreciate as rapidly as possible. The reason for this is that you pay for the depreciable item with 1979 dollars. In an inflationary economy you'll be taking your depreciation deduction in future years in inflated dollars, so you won't recover your costs in terms of 1979 dollar value.

You may have perfectly good reasons to depreciate more slowly. Each individual taxpayer is unique, so judge your own case or get advice from an experienced tax consultant.

You should buy a big, wide ledger to keep track of depreciation through the years. You can model your ledger after the example in Publication 225, or even buy preprinted ledger sheets from a good stationery store. Some tax advisors have printed ledger sheets for sale.

If you bought an item on July 1, then you could only depreciate for half the annual rate because you only had it half the year. The additional 20 percent first year depreciation can still be applied in full.

On Form 3468 you can obtain credit against your tax bill. Notice that credits are not deductions. Deductions are subtracted from your income. Credits are subtracted from your tax.

You are entitled to a credit called an investment credit for any item of equipment you buy from a screwdriver to an oil tanker. Farm animals (except horses) are considered equipment in this context. The tests are that the item must be depreciable, have a useful life of at least three years, is tangible property, and is placed in service during the year. All manner of things qualify.

Buildings don't qualify except those built especially for production of food such as greenhouses, lambing barns, chicken coops, confinement feeding facilities, and the like. Buildings used for bulk storage of agricultural products also qualify. The test of these buildings is that the material stored must be fungible. What it really means is that one part of the commodity is the same as any other part. A hay barn would qualify, because, in the view of IRS, one hay bale is the same as another hay bale. A grain bin would qualify as long as it was filled with bulk grain. If you had a building to store bags of seed of various kinds, it would not qualify because oat seed is not the same as buckwheat or clover.

Livestock qualify for investment credit, but there are limitations. The test here is whether or not you sold essentially identical stock during the year beginning six months prior to the new purchase. In other words, if you sold a milk goat for $200, then three months later bought a similar milk goat for $200, you can't claim credit on the second one. If the first one died, or had to be disposed of because of infertility or sickness, then you could claim credit for the second one. Publication 225 has some examples to help you figure out your case.

Investment credits can be as much as 10 percent of the purchase price so they are a very nice credit, indeed. You should also be aware that if you sell an item before its assumed useful life has expired, then you must pay back some of the credit you previously took. There's a form for this, Form 4255.

Credits are also available for taxes you paid on fuel and lubricants used in your farming business or certain other uses off the highway. This credit won't amount to much for most homesteaders, but every little bit helps.

Credits are also available for a percentage of money spent on insulating a home built prior to April 20, 1977. You can also get credits for solar collectors, heat storage units, wind generators, and other items that capture natural energy. Credit is not allowed for woodburning heaters, heat pumps, carpet, and some other items. This credit applies to either old or new homes. The limits are $300 credit for the insulation of an older home and $2200 for the renewable energy units.

The renewable energy credit is a dandy. It is 30 percent of the first $2000 you spend, and 20 percent of the next $8000 to give the $2200 maximum credit. Naturally you first have to come up with $10,000 to get the credit, so there's no such thing as a free lunch. If you build your own units you are entitled to credit for cost of materials, but not the value of your labor. Use Form 5695 for these energy credits.

Schedule R and RP is the place for the elderly to get credit just for being elderly. Who says the elderly get no credit?

What can you do if your income is low or even negative? You can get *earned income credit*. If your adjusted gross income on line 31, Form 1040, is less than $10,000, and you had one or more children living with you during 1979, you may be eligible. Check the inside cover of the instructions for 1040 for details. Even if the amount on line 31 is zero or negative, you may be able to list gross profits (profits before losses are subtracted) on Schedule SE and have some money credited to your social security account, plus some refunded to you in cash, even though you owe no taxes at all.

Finally, suppose you find that you have deductions and credits resulting in your owing no tax at all, or even have an excess of credits over taxes owed. Perhaps your income is negative. What then?

Get a Form 1040X and carry your losses or credits back two years, and get a refund of taxes you paid then. You can get a refund even if you lost money in 1979. You can apply the loss or credit to either of the previous two tax years, or can apply them to the future five years.

Form 1040X is a simple one and can be really useful. It allows you to revise previous returns, using your 1979 losses or credits. It seems almost designed for new homesteaders who quit salaried jobs to move to the country, and need a few years to turn a profit from their labors.

Get all of those forms, sit down with your records, and dig in. You will probably want to invest in a small electronic calculator to help you do all the number crunching needed for all the options open to you. The calculator is depreciable and entitles you to an investment credit.

When you have a doubt about whether you are entitled to a given credit or deduction, or if you have two or three reasonable ways to do something on your return, choose the one most advantageous to you. There is room in all tax matters for honest differences of opinion.

If your return is audited, and the examiner decides against you, you can request a hearing. If you still lose, then all you have to do is pay the back tax plus low interest, so stand up for your rights as you see them. Be honest.

LOOPHOLES FOR HOMESTEADERS

If you still have reportable income after disregarding your alimony, Nobel Prize, and railroad retirement benefits, then you should at least avail yourself of the loopholes available to you. These loopholes are the same ones available to anybody, homesteader or not, but perhaps you're not making use of all of your rights under the law.

You are entitled to the usual exemptions for self, advanced age, dependents, and the like, and can also take deductions for a variety of types of expenses. You are probably better off taking the so-called standard deduction (now included in the tax tables) unless you have unusually high deductible *personal* expenses such as large charitable contributions, alimony, interest on a home loan, high medical costs, and so forth.

The homesteader's loophole is that you may have expenses which really should be treated as business expenses rather than personal ones. These expenses are a cost of doing business and should be treated as such. They may be used to reduce your taxable income *before* you take your personal exemption, either itemized or standard. You need to have a business.

First of all, and most important, is to clearly define your business venture or ventures. Unless you are very successful indeed, don't define your business unit as Happy Rabbit Farm and try to call everything, including the mailbox, a business expense. Be realistic, and honest, and separate out portions of your homestead which are actually producing income, or at least have a really defensible possibility of producing income in the near future. You can treat each of these as a unit, or lump then together, but avoid lumping everything. An example might be helpful.

Suppose the owners of Happy Rabbit Farm look over their operation and conclude that what they are really doing is raising rabbits, goats, and bees for their own use and for fun, but that Cecelia's handspun-handknitted goods, her chickens, and Riley's weathered wood window boxes and hand-made weathervanes are the actual moneymakers. What to do? A simple approach would be to operate four businesses: Cecila's Knits, Egg-On, Windowboxes Unlimited, and Whither the Wind. This would be fine, but you would need four sets of books, four sales tax permits, and have to subdivide expenses such as telephone, use of your car, and such in a complex way. An easier way would be to combine all of them under the umbrella of Rabbit Run, and pool all of the costs and income. There are more advantages to this than you might think.

First, you need only one set of books. Second, you can share facilities such as file cabinets, stationery, stamps, tax permits, business licenses, etc. Third, the grouping allows you to shelter a weak member under the arms of the stronger, income-rich members of your micro-empire. You may have a good idea which will take a couple of years to show a profit while you develop a market or learn a new technique. Shelter it under the wing of Rabbit Run's more established, and profitable, parts.

The trick here is to define your business areas narrowly. Group as many as you wish together, but have each one clearly in mind before the grouping. Be tough with yourself, and don't allow a loser to become a part of *your* company.

The reason that you should operate as a formal business is that it makes you have the right attitude about keeping proper records, and simply gives you a framework to channel your thinking in a businesslike way. You'll be able to take advantage of those almost legendary things such as depreciation, travel expenses, investment credit, and deduction of business expenses. You have easy access to a variety of income-reducing devices by this route.

How do you demonstrate to IRS that Rabbit Run is really a business? That's easy. Just show a profit every year and pay income tax on that profit. Too tough? Then show a profit for at least two out of five years and pay tax on that. Still too tough? Then you must show evidence that you are in business with the intention of making a profit. You must be able to demonstrate that you have really tried to make a profit even if you failed.   For evidence, you should be able to show that you did such things as changing aspects of your business in an attempt to make a profit. You consulted experts, you abandoned totally unprofitable activities, your losses decreased through the years, and you acted in a businesslike way. The proof will be left up to you, but if you really did try you should have little trouble convincing IRS. Recently a tax court ruled that an artist had been trying to make a profit, and allowed deduction of business expenses even though she had never made a profit in a lifetime of painting, so it can be done.

Every homesteader has some activity which produces a profit. Sit back and analyze all of your activities, and sift out the ones which can be used to reduce your tax obligation.

To start your business, all you have to do is to do it. You might ask your local banker, city clerk, county clerk, or some other knowledgeable person as to whether you need a permit or license to do business. In rural areas and small towns you probably won't need to do anything formal, but be cautious and inquire first. Apply to your state's Department of Revenue for a sales tax permit so you can buy supplies for resale tax free, and can collect and report sales tax on things you sell. Keep receipts for *everything* you buy for your business, and record the expenses in an accounting book of some sort. You don't need elaborate records, but you do need accurate records. Also, get a receipt book with duplicate pages and give a receipt to everyone who buys anything from you. This is handy because you then have a copy of every sales receipt for both income tax and sales tax records without really having to work very hard at it. You'll also want an inventory of supplies and unsold items at the end of each tax year. Open a business checking account, too.

Expenses of doing business include cost of raw materials, feed, dues to organizations, books, magazines, insurance, legal services, postage, travel, a portion of telephone and utilities costs, and a host of other items. You can even deduct the cost of an office in your home, but IRS is very tough on this one because too many taxpayers were cheating on offices. The office must be used exclusively for business uses and be equipped as an office for whatever business you are in. A corner of your bedroom or some similar arrangement won't do.

Get Publications 225, 334, and 552 free from an IRS office. Also ask them for copies of Schedules C, D, F and SE and Forms 1040X, 2106, 3468, 4255, and 4562 for future use.

LIFE INSURANCE

Where does life insurance fit, or not fit, into a homesteader's economic plans? G. Richmond McFarland, president of Retirement Plan Administrators, Inc., Valley Forge, PA says "Much life insurance seems to me to be a ripoff unless purchased for death protection only. Determine what dependents will really need should you die. Do not insure for any more, and then buy term insurance to cover the greatest need and examine it each year to see if you have too much. Shop for the lowest term insurance coverage. Don't be boggled by an agent trying to sell you a lot of frills—just seek term insurance.

Use Capital on the Homestead

McFarland says, "Don't put more money than necessary into life insurance. You can use the excess capital in your homestead to get a greater return and build up values greater than any insurance company will give you in returned cash values."

McFarland concludes, "Obviously I do not sell insurance and I get concerned if people tie up money in nonproductive assets such as cash value life insurance. Keep as much money as possible and use it to build up cash values in things important to you."

Another professional advisor, Glenn Cole, a partner in the CPA firm of Elmer Fox, Westheimer & Co., Bakersfield, CA, "I recommend to my clients the book *The Great American Insurance Hoax* by Richard Guareno and Richard Trubo (Nash Publishing Corporation). This excellent book differentiates between those who need and don't need insurance and covers well the faulty thinking associated with such practices as borrowing the cash surrender value of a policy. It also helps guide the reader to the proper type and amount of insurance to buy and discusses types of insurance other than life."

R. Arthur Gindin of Midland, MI, suggested that the best source of information is the booklet *Life Insurance from the Buyer's Point of View* by E. P. Welker. It's available for $2 from The American Institute for Economic Research, Great Barrington, MA 01230.

People Have Different Needs

David W. Barnard, an agent for Mutual of Omaha in Oxnard, CA, had this to say about insurance for homesteaders, "The home-steader should buy enough life insurance to cover any financial problems that would be caused by his or her (including children) death, that could not be solved by existing assets, or that *might* not be able to be solved by the survivors. Moving back to the city and getting a job may or may not be a solution depending upon the possibilities for that person, their future health, etc.

"These things are vastly different for each person. A good agent who is trying to help you will be able to ask the right questions to find your real needs. Then he will suggest a plan to solve those needs at a price you can afford. One of the forms of term insurance will probably be part, if not all, of this plan because these offer the most pure insurance coverage for each dollar spent. Cash outlay must be kept to a minimum for the homesteader. His investments must first be in land, animals, and equipment. Later the term coverage can be converted if an investment in cash value insurance is called for by your planning for the future.

"Some questions to be answered: what will burial expenses be in your area? Do you have enough health insurance or will there be final medical bills? What taxes will have to be paid upon your death? How soon will they have to be paid? Will your family have to make mortage/taxes/insurances payments, or rent payments? What would happen if they lost the rental? Will the survivor have an income producing job or business that can be managed without you? What additional expenses will the business or homestead have if you aren't around to help? What do you want to provide for your children's future if you aren't around to help? Do you feel you need to help your children with their education, buying a home, etc.? If the survivor would have to return to the city, will it be necessary to provide funds for schooling and living expenses during the schooling so that he or she can get a good job? Will social security be enough to live on in the late years of retirement? How much will social security help, both at the death of one partner and later during the retirement of the other? Are you eligible for social security benefits? What other assets do you have that could be used for these purposes?

"These are but a few of the questions that need to be asked, and every one of these will lead to many sub-questions. The questions are the same for anyone in any walk of life. The answers are different for every individual.

"Your insurance representative can help you reach a decision on these questions, and determine how much money will be required to solve them. Some of the money won't be needed for years—old age retirement for instance—so part of the need can be funded by interest earned on money invested at death from the insurance proceeds. Thus, less insurance is necessary than might be expected.

"Insurance deals in discounted dollars. If you die tonight, you can leave your survivors the money they will need, if you will spend just a few dollars today, and if your health qualifies you for a policy. Your family must spend the money it will take them to continue to live without you. Where will it come from? If you don't already have enough set aside for this purpose, see your life insurance agent. He is the only person in the whole world who can provide those dollars that must be available to your family when you die, at a price your family can afford today. It must be done while you are healthy, it is too late when you are dead!"

Against Insurance

Bruce Jenkins of Holualoa, Hawaii, says, "Insurance is, in essence, gambling with your premium that disaster will strike and you don't want the risk of covering your own disaster. The insurance company gets the value of the policy that disaster won't strike often enough to impair the profit made from your premiums and investment of your premium dollars. As home-steaders, you should think more in terms of self-sufficiency and carry more risks yourself. The test of all insurance is to weigh the premium cost against the policy value and its benefit to you after disaster.

"I'm against life insurance in general. In our home, we promote good investment policy in land, home and business. We promote good health, so spending money gambling on our death doesn't seem to make much sense. The only life insurance we carry is a policy covering the declining value of our mortgage indebtedness (mortgage life insurance). This relieves my spouse of that additional financial burden if I die. It does not pay her any cash proceeds when I die.

"Remember, never make yourself beneficiary of your policy or the proceeds will pass through probate at your death instead of directly to the beneficiary. In our case, the savings and loan is the beneficiary. They are paid the balance of mortgage due at my death and my wife is issued the warranty deed as survivor.

"Encourage agents to expose you to all possibilities without smother-ing you. Read all small print. What appears to be a good policy can be whittled down to a poor policy and a small gamble on the company's part."

In summary, there seems to be general agreement that home-steaders should consider only term life insurance and then only as much as absolutely necessary.

Chapter 3

Zoning and the Homestead

The last thing in the world that a homesteader needs is a law which says that he can't raise animals or produce on his own property. Families who moved out of the city for that very purpose often are finding themselves stymied by ordinances and regulations which dictate the ways in which they can use their land. Usually, these laws come under the heading of *zoning* (Fig. 3-1). Frequently the suburban and semirural homeowner doesn't learn about them until he's already sunk a small to sizable fortune into acquiring, stocking, planting, equipping, and fencing his homestead. Then it's too late!

Although most people have heard about zoning, few really understand what it's all about—not that it's a new idea. It's been with us for thousands of years.

Zoning is really part of a larger field called *planning*, which is a branch of the law concerned with the systematic development of communities. The ancient Hebrews practiced a form of planning when they relegated *harlots* to a designated region outside the city gates. The ancient Romans had laws controlling the height of all buildings which fronted on public streets. Napolean III is said to have appointed a planning commissioner to regulate the development of Parisian boulevards in 1853.

EUCLID CASE

In the United States, however, zoning was rather slow to develop. This was probably due to our passion for individual freedom and to our law's traditional protection of the rights of private property. When the Supreme Court considered the case of *Euclid vs. Ambler Realty* in 1926, everything started to change.

The *Euclid* case involved a local law which required all buildings in a certain zone to be set back a given distance from property lines. The plaintiff, who owned property in the affected district, was unhappy with the law, contending that it diminished the value of his land by limiting its use.

Fig. 3-1. Ordinances dictate how homesteaders can use their land (photo by Paul Clark Landmann and John Davel).

The court agreed that the statute interfered with the owner's general right of dominion over his property, but upheld it anyway. Such interference, it wrote, had become necessary as a result of the problems of modern urban life. Among these were the possibilities of fire, building collapse, and overcrowding. Setback requirements designed to alleviate these difficulties had to be viewed as a necessary evil.

Much has happened since 1926. Cases which followed *Euclid* expanded the scope of permissible zoning legislation. Today, some zoning laws exist for no other purpose than to preserve neighborhood beauty, to protect the character of historical landmarks, or to promote the interests of legitimate business. Their application has grown geographically as well, moving—as the people have—out of the cities and into the countryside. In fact, it is probably true that there is now no inhabited place in America which is not controlled by some kind of zoning or planning regulation.

In general, modern zoning laws divide a given area into regions or *zones,* prescribing the uses to which property may be put in each of them (Fig. 3-2). Frequently, the zones established are labeled *residential, agricultural, commercial,* and *industrial,* the permitted uses depending on the classification of the region involved. Ordinarily, no gas station will be permitted to operate in a residential zone; no factory is built in a region designated "agricultural."

DEFINITION OF FARMING

In the law, words do not always mean what they appear to mean. More often than not, this is what gets the homesteader into trouble. While most people will not have any problem at all with a term like farm or farming, the courts might spend weeks, years, or even decades attempting to determine its significance.

In a recent Pennsylvania case, for example, one court defined farm as "a place of several acres" on which crops, vegetables, and animals are raised. "The principle use of the produce," it said, is "to maintain the farmer and his family, only the excess being sold." A California tribunal arrived at a different understanding. "A farm can be of any size," it wrote, "of any shape, of any boundaries." It may even comprise less than one lot. Furthermore, the court concluded, farming may include "gardening, fruit growing, the raising of vegetables, trees, shrubs, plants, and similar products."

A New Jersey court refused to get technical about the definition, ruling, in 1952, that the classification would have to depend on the way a particular piece of land was used. In the matter before it, the court was asked to direct a township to issue a permit for the construction of a chickenhouse by a man named De Benedetti, who raised poultry on a part-time basis. The township argued that because he didn't give the enterprise all of his time, De Benedetti couldn't refer to it as a farm. The court disagreed. Farming is farming, it said, no matter how much time the farmer spends doing it.

Sometimes courts try to establish specific requirements, in an attempt to clarify the zoning law's meaning. In 1971, for example, an Iowa tribunal

Fig. 3-2. This rural homestead is being surrounded by a subdivision. Note the road cut at lower right (photo by Paul Clark Landmann and John Davel).

found that a particular enterprise was not a farm because there were "no barns, shed, or buildings for the housing of livestock," and "no part of [the] land is to be used for production of crops, fruits, or vegetables." A Massachusetts court declared, in 1943, that a certain piggery was not a farm because, "Not a pound of the food furnished to the hogs is produced upon the premises."

TYPES OF AGRICULTURE

In order to avoid the narrow construction which these and other courts have placed on the word farm, many legislatures have shied away from its use. Instead, they write zoning laws which refer to *agriculture*. This is a somewhat more flexible concept; for while farming is said to involve the cultivation of the earth and the growing of crops, agriculture is not so narrow a term.

A Pennsylvania court, in the 1962 case of *Fidler vs. Zoning Board*, held that two types of agricultural activity were generally recognized. These it referred to as *arable agriculture* which involves "the cultivation of the ground," and *pastoral agriculture*, which is "the feeding and management of the flocks and herds." The distinction, it said, has existed from the earliest times: "Abel was a keeper of sheep, but Cain was a tiller of the ground."

That Pennsylvania judge concluded that raising turkeys was an agricultural enterprise, even though none of the feed used to fatten them was raised on the land. Similar reasoning led a Kansas court to rule, in 1958, that "The raising of canary birds is . . . commonly regarded as an agricultural pursuit." In a dissenting opinion in the Iowa case of *Farmegg vs. Humboldt County*, it was argued that modern egg production is agriculture, although mechanization has given it a "commercial countenance."

A recent Texas court has decided that where arable agriculture is concerned, crops and food production need not be involved. Defining *horticulture* as "the art of growing flowers or ornamental plants," it ruled that "Horticulture is a branch of plant production, which is one of the main divisions of agriculture." A recent Kansas court added other specialties to the list. "Agriculture," it said, includes farming, dairying, pasturage, apiculture, horticulture, viticulture, animal and poultry husbandry, and the sale of such products by one engaged in agriculture as herein defined.

Some zoning laws go even further than the Kansas court, allowing land in certain areas to be used for any "agricultural purpose." At first glance, this may seem like nothing more than another way of saying the same thing. The courts have not interpreted it that way. For in jurisdictions which use such language, it has been held to authorize a multitude of agriculture-related activities.

An Ohio court once extended the meaning of "agricultural purpose" to include the keeping of polo ponies by a private recreation club. In 1973, an Illinois jurist applied the term to the storage of processed sewer sludge. The odiferous substance was to be kept in a 4 million gallon holding pit which the plaintiff sought to build on a 60-acre tract in Grundy County.

From there it was to be pumped to neighboring farmlands, where it would be used for fertilizing the soil.

Although the county Zoning Board objected, the court permitted the pit to be constructed. It concluded, first, that the spreading of "liquid organic fertilizer and soil conditioner" on farmland is an "agricultural purpose." Then it went on to find that "it logically follows" that the use of land for the storage of such materials "is also a use for an agricultural purpose."

Some jurisdictions prefer to call such agriculture-related activities "accessory uses," permitting them on that basis. An example can be found in the 1958 Pennsylvania case of *Gaspari vs. Board of Adjustment.* Gaspari, who raised mushrooms on land in an agricultural zone, was charged with violating the local ordinance by using his property for "manufacturing" instead of agriculture. The activity referred to involved the grinding of corncobs, hay, and chemicals in the production of "synthetic manure" in which he grew his fungi.

Eulogizing the disappearance of such institutions as the U.S. Cavalry, the mounted police, and the horse-drawn brewery wagon, the court referred to the "shadow of a manure famine" which had spread over the land. As a result, it concluded, mushroom growers like Gaspari had no choice but to turn to science for an acceptable substitute. Thus, it ruled, the production of "synthetic manure" was a use "accessory to agriculture." As such, it was permitted in an agricultural zone (Fig. 3-3).

A similar finding was made in the Massachusetts case of *Petros vs. Inspector of Buildings.* The plaintiff in that matter sold dressed chickens in

Fig. 3-3. This land is zoned agricultural (photo by Paul Clark Landmann and John Davel).

an area zoned to allow such activity. The inspector sought to close him down, contending that local zoning laws did not permit his operation of a "slaughterhouse." In rejecting the inspector's arguments, however, the court found that killing chickens was not the plaintiff's main activity, but was merely "accessory" to the permitted conduct. Under the circumstances, there was no reason to prohibit him from continuing.

THE MEANING OF ANIMAL HUSBANDRY

Although "animal husbandry" is generally accepted as a branch of "agriculture," there has been some judicial disagreement as to *its* meaning. Most courts apply the dictionary definition, referring to husbandry as "that branch of agriculture which is concerned with farm animals." An animal husbandman, they rule, is "one who keeps or tends livestock." Even terms like animals or livestock can present judges with a problem.

In Connecticut, for example, one 1964 court wrestled for three pages with a definition of livestock before coming to a suitable conclusion. The word, it decided, has a "plural connotation," always referring to "more than one." For this reason, it found the defendant's pony to be a "household pet."

An Ohio court wrote, in 1965, that *animal husbandry* included the raising of mink, and, therefore, that mink were livestock. Four years later, a Massachusetts tribunal declared that "mink are not included in the phrase 'domestic or other animals,'" Raising them, it held, was not an agricultural pursuit.

Another Ohio court found that chickens were not animals, since the term means "A quadruped, not a bird or fowl." Yet it was held in Missouri, just a few years later, that animal meant "any member of the group of living beings typically capable of spontaneous movement and rapid motor response to stimulation." A Virginia court specifically held it to apply to "domestic turkeys and poultry."

If any rule emerges from a review of these decisions, it is that the law is never simple, rarely clear, and not often easy to understand. For this reason, a homestead family has to be especially careful in selecting a place to live. There is always the possibility that zoning ordinances will prohibit the very activities which made homestead life so attractive in the first place.

If you've already bought a place, and are facing trouble from the local zoning commission, building inspector, or *gendarmerie* on account of an alleged violation, don't give up without a fight. None of these agencies is the final authority on how the law should be enforced. Only courts can decide that. Until they rule against you, you haven't lost.

If you're looking for a homestead, play it safe. Make sure to find out what the local zoning ordinance says. Don't stop there. Find out what it means, too! It isn't enough to ask the realtor; he may not know, even though he thinks he does. Go directly to the zoning board. Tell them what you have in mind, and ask them what they think. If their answer doesn't satisfy you, consult with an attorney. It might cost a few bucks, but in the long run, it might save a few thousand.

THE PIGGERY AND THE LAW

Most folks who live in the country are well aware of the advantages in keeping a pig or two around the homestead. They're lazy animals and not much good as sentries or beasts of burden. They do have at least one attribute which recommends them to the food producing family. There is a special process by which garbage and table scraps can be converted to juicy, succulent pork. Only a pig can master its secret.

Lots of homesteaders capitalize on the swine's natural ability. Some of them feel pretty smug about it, certain that they have uncovered one of life's lesser mysteries. By recycling what they don't want, they can get what they do want. Things aren't always that easy. Uncle Remus, the philosophical old slave created by J.C. Harris, is credited with saying, "Watch out when you're gittin' all you want. Fattenin' hogs ain't lucky as they think."

What a homesteader has to "watch out" for is the law. Of all the animals which get its hackles up, probably none does it as consistently as the swine. A Pennsylvania judge once wrote that: "It is recognized by all authorities ... that the keeping and raising of hogs . . . is likely to be offensive, and has a tendency to endanger the health and destroy the comfort of residents in that vicinity." As a result, the law struggles valiantly to draw a line around the pigs (Fig. 3-4).

Many reasons have been advanced for this rather intolerant judicial attitude. Some relate to the way pigs smell, others to the way they sound. A few judges make reference to the slovenly appearance of pigsties and hog pens. A New York court once closed down a piggery because, "Rats are living on the property in numbers, and they would tend to stray onto the public highway and onto adjoining lands."

Whatever the reason, however, the keeping of pigs has been closely regulated by Anglo-American law since prerevolutionary times. As early as 1765, Blackstone—a British legal philosopher whose *Commentaries* are known to every American law student—wrote that: If a person keeps his hogs so near the house of another that the stench of them incommodes him and makes the air unwholesome, this is an injurious nuisance. For every "injurious nuisance," the law provided a remedy. A more modern approach involves zoning legislation which prohibits the keeping of swine in all but specially designated areas.

Often these laws contain provisions which allow homesteaders to have a limited number of pigs, even outside the special regions. Most of the time the limits are strictly enforced, with any attempt to exceed them resulting in swift prosecution. In a recent Massachussetts case, for example, a defendant named Murphy was prevented from using a building which he had constructed, although its cost was quite substantial. The structure, designed as a hog barn, consisted of nearly 2500 square feet. Since the local law restricted residents of the zone to three hogs per land-parcel, the court issued an injunction against him.

A California version of that law, which prohibited "the keeping and maintenance of more than five hogs," received an interesting test in the

Fig. 3-4. The law is rather intolerant toward pigs (photo by Jean Martin).

1955 case of *People vs. Johnson*. The defendant in that matter was in the business of buying and selling pork on the hoof. He would purchase hogs from homesteaders and other small breeders in his vicinity, keeping them in pens until he had enough to fill a truck. Then, usually after a day or two, he would cart them off to market in Los Angeles.

When he was charged with violating the law in question, Mr. Johnson took a shot at the section's phraseology. "Sure, he admitted. "I had more than five hogs on my place. But I didn't 'keep and maintain' them. All I did was store them for a little while." The court, however, was unimpressed with his reasoning.

His offense, it said, consisted of "locating a prohibited number of hogs on the premises over a period of months." The fact that not one of them stayed there for more than a few days was held to be irrelevant. After all, "If the stench was still perceptible to the olfactory senses of the adjoining neighbors, the identity of the individual offending hogs would become unimportant."

In both of these cases, the courts were dealing with laws which set forth a particular numerical limit to the animals kept. Some jurisdictions are less specific, using more flexible terminology to express the prohibition. A recent Missouri litigation involved an ordinance of the City of Versailles which simply prohibited the keeping of a "pig pen" within the city limits.

The plaintiff, Joe Kays, kept 29 hogs on four and one-half acres of pasture. He had been visited one day by the local authorities who charged him with violating the law. They contended that any enclosure could be classified as a "pen," but Kays argued that the word could not be applied to a tract as big as his. Taking a middle ground, the court concluded that the definition of "pig pen" was a relative one, based upon the size of an enclosure as related to the number of animals kept within it. Kays' pasture, it ruled, was not a pen with only 29 animals in it, but could become one if their number was increased.

Frequently, commercial hog growers attempt to get around the zoning law's numerical limit by establishing their operation in regions reserved for farming or for agriculture. Sometimes, these efforts are successful. A 1962 Kansas court, for example, in the case of *Carp vs. Board of County Commisioners,* held that the zoning administrator had no right to interfere with the operation of the plaintiff's hog feeding business. Although Carp kept between 2000 and 2500 head of swine on his property, the court concluded that he had not violated a zoning regulation which classified the region as agricultural.

On the other hand, there are many jurisdictions which place the raising of pigs in a class by itself, barring such activity from even the agricultural area. A 1943 Massachusetts tribunal rules that "the maintenance of a piggery is different from ordinary farming," and cannot freely be conducted in an agricultural zone. Zoning boards, it said, had the right to confine such operations "to a particular part of the city or town, or to prohibit them altogether."

In order to sidestep the distinction between "piggery" and "farm," some swine breeders argue that their main occupation is the tilling of the soil. Feeding pigs on their surplus, they contend, is a permissible accessory use, incidental to farming. Courts which accept such reasoning, however, are usually quick to place limitations upon it.

A 1954 New York decision illustrates this point. In it, the court recognized the realities of rural life by agreeing that most farmers keep a "reasonable number" of chickens, sheep, and other livestock. It went on to hold, however, that, "The extensive raising of pigs to be sold and disposed of shortly after birth is not among the usual accessories to a farm." A Pennsylvania court in the same year defined "piggery" as "a place where swine are kept or bred," adding that the mere fact that some of the feed which the animals consume is raised on the grounds does not make a "piggery" a "farm."

Perhaps the most interesting dispute over the language of a zoning statute can be found in the *Appeal of Abernathy,* decided in 1962. The appellant in that case was the owner of a 47 acre tract of farmland on which he kept 50 head of swine. He also had a contract to collect garbage in the neighboring towns and maintained a fleet of trucks for that purpose. Although he didn't make much money in the garbage business, his swine enterprise was really cleaning up.

After collecting the garbage, Abernathy would cook and sterilize it in accordance with state health requirements, and then feed it to the hogs. The local zoning officer didn't like it much, but since piggeries were not excluded from the district there didn't seem to be anything he could do about it. Then, after rereading the zoning law, he came up with a new twist.

Rushing right over to the Abernathy place, he issued a "cease and desist" order. "What you're running," he said, "is a commercial garbage disposal. And the law says you can't do it." Abernathy hit the ceiling, taking his case to the Board of Adjustment for review. They backed the zoning officer, affirming his order to stop. Finally, the matter ended up in court.

After reviewing all of the evidence, including the fact that most of Abernathy's income came from pigs and not from garbage, the judge reversed the finding of the board. The man's business is clearly "pig farming," he said, "as distinguished from garbage disposal," The mere fact that "some garbage may be disposed of in the process of raising swine" does not change it one iota. If the zoning board doesn't want pigs there, they'll simply have to change the law.

Even that step might fail to clear the air, however. This is because of the constitutional principle of "due process," which prevents the arbitrary taking of a citizen's property rights. A piggery which has been in business legally for any time at all cannot suddenly be kicked out because legislators have decided to alter the character of a neighborhood. Zoning changes may not prohibit people from continuing to use their land as they lawfully used it under the old statute.

On the other hand, they will clearly not be permitted to expand or increase the "nonconforming" use. A Massachusetts court, in 1950, refused to allow a petitioner to erect a new building on his pig farm, even though he had been there eight years longer than the zoning law. The court said that because the business was "preexisting," it was protected from the operation of the statute. The new barn he was building, however, was not entitled to that protection, since the law had come first.

A similar ruling was made 14 years later in the case of *Bowes vs. Inspector of Buildings.* The plaintiff in that matter had raised pigs since 1914 in an area which was since zoned residential. At first, there had been only "three or four shacks" on his property. Somewhere along the line these disappeared, being replaced by eight wooden buildings. One of them contained a boiler for cooking slop. Finding that the structures had obviously been erected after the law went into effect, the court declared them to be in violation of its provisions. Bowes was enjoined from using them for the purpose of keeping swine.

Under some circumstances, a judge may order a homesteader to get rid of his pigs in spite of a zoning law which permits him to keep them. Generally, this kind of judicial action is based on the government's right to protect the public health and welfare. Often it occurs because of the manner in which the animals are kept.

In *State vs. Primeau,* a recent Washington court considered the case of a family which had been raising "pigs, goats, dogs, and other farm animals" for 10 years before a zoning law reclassified their neighborhood. Ordinarily, the court declared, the new ordinance would not interfere with activity which preexisted it. In the Primeaus' case, there were other factors to be considered.

Summarizing the evidence presented at trial, the judge described the defendant's yard as: "A malodorous pigsty, bounded by sagging, decrepit, patched up fencing festooned with garbage, enclosing hogs wallowing in muck and mud—a pen littered with garbage, refuse, debris, and filth against a backdrop of junked automobile bodies occupied by numerous dogs as sleeping quarters—a place from which . . . a stench would naturally be deemed to emanate." Under the circumstances, he concluded, Primeau could not avail himself of the zoning law's protection to continue maintaining a "public nuisance."

On the other hand, a Missouri court in 1972 came to the opposite conclusion in a litigation which involved 29 swine being kept within the city limits. In that matter, though, the evidence showed that the defendant's lot was "reasonably clean." His nearest neighbor testified that she had never been bothered by odor, dust, debris, or noise. As a result the pigs won, there being no good reason to banish them.

Don't try to keep more pigs than your local law allows. If you keep any pigs at all, make sure their quarters are clean. The hogs will appreciate it and so will your neighbors. In fact, the only one who might not is your lawyer. That's likely to be one less fee that he'll be collecting.

CHICKENS

The homesteader is quick to learn that in raising chickens, as with nearly all food producing enterprises, nothing comes easy (Fig. 3-5). There are natural problems like poultry lice, chicken hawks, skunks, and predators. There are a few man-made ones as well. High on the list of these is the zoning law, since most municipalities have regulations which strictly control the places where chickens can be kept.

Zoning, as we have seen, is the branch of law which concerns itself with defining and delineating the ways which land in various regions can be used. In doing so, it seeks to determine those uses which are most appropriate for each given community. Obviously, this involves decisions which are not likely to receive the approval of all the community's members. For, as a New Jersey court indicated, this determination depends: " . . . not only on all the conditions, physical, economic, and social, prevailing within the municipality and its needs, present and reasonably prospective, but also on the nature of the entire region in which the municipality is located and the use to which the land in that region has been or may be put most advantageously." To paraphrase one of our greatest presidents, you can't please all of the people all of the time. It is for this reason that a homesteader must be particularly careful when selecting a place to live or when planning development of the place which he has already acquired.

Different people have different ways of looking at life—and the law is not always kind to chickens. Even regions which have been set aside for "farming" or "agriculture" may be controlled by ordinances and statutes which exclude the keeping of poultry. In a recent New York case, for example, one court concluded that raising chickens for eggs and for mean was not "farming" within the zoning law's definition. In justifying his decision, the presiding judge wrote that the term "farm" was a relative one, depending for its definition on a consideration of "all the surrounding circumstances."

To some extent, this concept of relativity exists in most American jurisdictions. As a result, courts are likely to refer to all manner of seemingly irrelevent details in deciding whether or not a particular flock of chickens may stay. In the matter of *Barkmann vs. Town of Hempstead,* for instance, a 1944 judge concluded that a defendant who kept his birds as a "pastime" was not farming. Yet just a few years later, another judge ruled, in the case of *DeBenedetti vs. River Vale Township,* that chickens raised as a part-time hobby *were* protected by the local law's "farming" provisions.

In DeBenedetti's case, the court concluded that chicken-raising was "agriculture," no matter how it was conducted. Arguments to the contrary have frequently been advanced. In one 1962 case, a Pennsylvania Common Pleas court denied a building permit to a poultry grower on the grounds that his activity was commercial rather than agricultural. The applicant owned 42 acres in "an essentially rural area" of Upper Macungie Township, and sought to use it for the raising of 40,000 to 50,000 young fowls. He was stymied, however, by a ruling that an operation of that size could not be referred to as a farm.

On the other hand, a Kansas court; just four years earlier, ruled "without equivocation" that "the raising of chickens . . . is an agricultural pursuit." An Arkansas court, in 1962, flatly rejected the contention that

Fig. 3-5. Nothing comes easy in raising chickens.

chicken raising was a commercial activity. The Arkansas case, *Franklin vs. McCoy,* involved a ranch on which some 75,000 chickens were kept, and 1,000 sold each week. The appellant claimed that the state's legislature never intended to include such an operation in the terms agriculture or farming.

The court vehemently disagreed, carefully tracing the history and derivation of both words before coming to its conclusion. Ruling that the chicken ranch was indeed a farm, Justice Ward, who wrote the decision, stated that he was "unwilling to say the legislature . . . meant that raising chickens is not an agricultural farm activity." If the lawmakers disagree, he said, then they must say so "in unmistakable terms." To date, they have not.

In coming to its conclusion, the Arkansas court relied heavily on the well-noted case of *Fleckles vs. Hille* in which an Indiana judge held that agriculture referred not only to the tilling of the soil, but to the raising and management of livestock as well. Even the word livestock has doubtful meaning in some jurisdictions when an attempt is made to apply it to chickens or other poultry. In the 1975 *Appeal of Krechovitz,* for example, a Chester City court wrote that the word was to be interpreted in light of the surrounding community's popular usage. In that case, because the Chester City area relied heavily on the meat packing industry and the raising of beef, it was held that chickens simply weren't livestock.

A similar conclusion was reached by an Ohio court in the case of *Del Monte vs. Woodmansee,* wherein it was held that chickens weren't even *animals.* "An animal," said the court, "is, in common sense, a quadruped, not a bird or fowl." Many jurisdictions disagree, however.

A Missouri court, for example, in 1957, wrote that animals are "all living creatures not human." A recent Virginia tribunal stated that the term *animal* includes all inferior living creatures with the power of self-motion. Both courts ruled specifically that chickens are animals.

Even courts which recognize a difference between chickens and animals may have difficulty telling a rooster from a hen. In an interesting New York case, a defendant named Filactos was sentenced to 10 days in the county jail for having a rooster on his property—even though the local ordinance permitted the keeping of chickens! When Filactos appealed his conviction to the state's Appellate Department, the judge had to go to Funk and Wagnalls for a definition. Concluding, finally, that the word *chicken* referred to "a cock or hen of any age," the court set his sentence aside, sending the prisoner home to feed his flock.

Unfortunately, however, the chicken problem isn't always solved quite so easily. In many jurisdictions, farming and agriculture are words which apply only to the tilling of the soil. In these states, chickens are permitted in agricultural zones only if their maintenance is closely related to the cultivation of crops. This concept can be made clear by looking at two leading New England cases, both decided in 1931. Both involved small flocks of chickens kept in areas zoned agricultural.

In one of the cases, *Winship vs. Inspector,* a Massachusetts court permitted the poultry to stay. The birds belonged to a farmer who owned 18 acres which he used for the cultivation of grain and vegetables. This led the court to conclude that the raising of chickens was "incidental" to his lawful use of the land.

In the other case, *Chudnov vs. Board of Appeals,* a Connecticut tribunal came to a different conclusion, banning the birds. That flock was the property of a defendant who owned a three acre tract which he had never plowed or cultivated. Under the circumstances the court found the keeping of chickens to be his "primary" land use. Since it wasn't agricultural, it could not be permitted.

Even in areas which do apply the term agriculture to the keeping of chickens, a poultry grower is not completely in the clear. The courts are likely to take a long hard look at the ways in which his operation is conducted in determining whether or not it violates other zoning provisions. One court attempted to justify this practice by noting the differences between poultry enterprises and those involving other types of livestock. "It is a matter of common knowledge," said the court, "that fowl are often killed and dressed by poultry raisers" while "no such widespread practice exists with respect to cattle, sheep, or swine."

Recognizing this basic difference, an Ohio court recently permitted a defendant to go on butchering chickens in a zone from which "slaughterhouses" and "abattoirs" were excluded. Although neighbors contended otherwise, the court ruled that the defendant's principle business was raising chickens, not killing them, and that the slaughtering was only incidental to that "agricultural" activity.

A 1971 Iowa court ruled that raising chickens was a non-agricultural activity, when conducted on a huge, mass production basis. The operation in question belonged to the Farmegg Products Corporation, which maintained buildings and facilities in various locations throughout the state. One of these, located in a "suburban residence district" in Humboldt County, was to be erected for the purpose of raising chicks. The birds would be hatched at another location and brought to the Humboldt County facility when they were one day old. There they would be kept in cages and fed by machine until the age of 22 weeks, at which time they were to be transferred to laying houses located in another county.

In denying Farmegg's application for a permit, the court referred to the circumstances of the proposed operation. The land, it noted, was not to be used at all. No feed would be grown on it; no barns or sheds would be erected on it; no implements would be drawn across it. Instead, modern factory-type buildings would be constructed and "equipped with vent fans, automatic feeders, watering equipment, and manure removal equipment." Under the circumstances, the court concluded, the corporation's activities cannot be characterized as farming or agriculture.

Many one-horse homesteaders agree with the Iowa court, and are glad to see a blow struck for good old down home dirt farming. Be careful not to miss the point! The court may have talked about machinery, but in effect it ruled that raising chickens isn't agriculture and that egg production isn't farming. So check the zoning laws carefully before you build that henhouse or, better yet, before you buy that farm.

GOATS

One of the by-products of our present economic condition seems to be an American rediscovery of the dairy goat. Intelligent, clean, and easy to handle, a single doe can produce enough milk for a fair-sized family on a fraction of the feed that a cow would require. Goats are inexpensive to purchase and relatively simple to house and care for. They are recommended highly to the homestead family seeking self-sufficiency (Fig. 3-6).

To some folks, goats are special; their milk is the most healthful and sweetest on earth, their bleating is symphonic, and their fragrance is a heady perfume. Even the manure is held to be golden, a rich harvest of earth-nourishing elements all packaged in a conveniently pelleted form.

On the other hand, there are those who fail to share this point of view. Many of our legislators seem to be amoung this group, for there are laws and ordinances throughout the United States which closely regulate the keeping of goats. In some areas they are restricted to regions zoned agricultural. In others, they are excluded altogether.

Many reasons have been given for the existence of these regulations. Some are probably valid; others based on misinformation. Much of the time they are subjective, involving individual esthetic reactions to the species' natural traits.

One Los Angles prosecutor wrote, for example, that, "The offensiveness of the goat lies in its persistent and nerve-racking bleat, and in the foul odors which emanate from the animal and its abode as ordinarily kept." Others have complained of an insect problem, or of excessive noise at kidding time.

Neighbors Held Sway

Attempts by "goat people" to dispute such accusations have usually terminated in shouting matches, each side contradicting vehemently the conclusions and claims of the other. An illustration can be found in the case of *Ex Parte Matthews,* a proceeding brought by a woman convicted of keeping 12 goats in violation of a local zoning law. In her efforts to change the ordinance, Mrs. Matthews produced a veritable parade of witnesses, all anxious to discuss the relative merits of goatkeeping.

First the editor of a goat magazine testified that the female goat is a quiet animal, making no noise at all once she becomes accustomed to her surroundings. Then several other "goat people" stated that there isn't any smell from a female goat "except when she perspires, and that then it is not seriously objectionable," Finally, an expert goatkeeper swore that in his experience goats are not especially attractive to insects.

Fig. 3-6. Goats are easy to care for (photo by Jean Martin).

In response to Mrs. Matthews' proof, a few of her neighbors got on the stand to tell it as they saw it. Four of them testified that her animals made "a terrible noise . . . described as "baa" all the time, and that they stamped, jumped, and bleated regularly during the night. Others referred to the stench which emanated from the Matthews' place as "something fierce," claiming that it drove them to keep their windows shut at all times, and that it could be smelled from two blocks away. Still others told of screen doors that were black with flies.

In response to the conflicting testimony, the court dismissed Mrs. Matthews' petition, allowing her conviction to stand. A law, it said, which sought to protect property owners from the conditions complained of at the trial was undoubtedly a reasonable one. Its provisions were upheld and the goats were ordered out of the neighborhood.

Many jurisdictions agree with the findings of the *Matthews* court, maintaining statutes which show no mercy to the cud-chewing moneysavers. Sometimes these laws mention goats by name. Others simply include them among the animals classified as "neat" or "bovine." In one early North Carolina case, they were even held to be included in the statutory definition of "cattle."

The judge in that matter went all the way back to the book of Genesis for his precedent, citing the contract between Laban and Jacob as authority. According to its terms, Jacob was to receive of Laban's cattle, "every speckled and spotted goat" as payment for tending the herds. This, said the court, was an indication that "in the scriptures, the word 'cattle' ordinarily and usually embraces goats." It was enough to justify an affirmance of the defendant's conviction.

There are many ways in which zoning laws deal with the keeping of goats, the most drastic involving their total exclusion from areas characterized as residential. In a recent Connecticut proceeding, a homesteader named Lawrence attacked such a law, claiming that it interfered with his ability to feed his family. Lawrence, who lived on 1½ acres in North Branford, was the father of five children. He claimed that because the goats were kept for milk, their presence was a legitimate "accessory" to residential use of his property and that he could not be required to get rid of them. The court disagreed.

Whether the keeping of goats was an accessory use, it held, depended on what was "customarily incidental" to dwelling in the area involved. This determination could only be made by the local zoning board, which, in theory at least, was familiar with the needs of the community. Since the board had already ruled against Lawrence, the court concurred in ordering the removal of his animals.

Some juridictions have taken a more flexible approach to the problem, limiting the number of goats which can be kept instead of banning them absolutely. Generally, these ordinances are strictly enforced, on the theory that a violator who is given an inch may end up taking a mile. In one prosecution a numerical limit of that type was enforced in spite of the fact that some of the animals involved were not yet mature.

Kids Counted

The case, known as *Ex Parte Lusher,* involved a woman who was convicted of keeping more than four goats in violation of a local limiting ordinance. In defense, she argued that two of her six goats were no more than kids and should, therefore, not be counted. Her contention failed, though; their age held to be of no moment. The purpose of the law, reasoned the court, was to help control odor and noise. In this connection, "the young may well be as great, if not greater source of discomfort than the more mature." Mrs. Lusher's herd was disbanded by order of the court.

Still another legislative approach is based on an attempt to balance the rights of goatkeepers with those of their neighbors—to give each of them as much freedom as life in a congested society will allow. Laws which fall into this category may regulate the distance which must be maintained between one person's goats and another person's home. A Kansas zoning law, for example, prohibits the keeping of any goat in an enclosure "closer than 25' to the dwelling house of another."

A much litigated California statute varied the distance required depending on the number of goats being kept. A pen containing one goat was to be located at least 50' from a neighbor's house. For two goats, 100' was required. Anyone wanting to keep four goats had to see to it that at least

300' separated them from a dwelling, while 1000' were necessary for a herd of five. The law was attacked more than once by goat people who called it unfair and unrealistic, but the court vindicated the law, describing it as reasonable and holding it to be valid.

A few jurisdictions direct their legislative prohibitions against buck goats only, apparently recognizing that it is the sexually mature buck alone who produces the infamous "goaty" smell. Zoning laws in such areas are likely to read like one recently tested example which provided that: "It shall be unlawful to keep or maintain any male goat exceeding the age of six months within the limits of the city." This particular law was declared valid in spite of attempts by goatkeepers to have it stricken down.

Reasonable and Flexible Approach

Perhaps the most reasonable approach is the one taken by a recent zoning board in the state of Kansas. Instead of arbitrarily limiting the number of animals which might be kept, it enacted a regulation flexible enough to fit any situation. According to this law's provisions, the keeping of goats was prohibited only if done in an "unclean" manner which resulted in "the annoyance of any citizens."

In the case of *State vs. Johnson,* a defendant who was accused of violating its provisions argued that the terms "unclean" and "annoyance" were too vague to be constitutional and too subjective to have any validity. The court disagreed, however, writing that both of these words were "within the understanding or comprehension of a person of ordinary intelligence." The statutory description, it said, was clearly applicable to Johnson's goat pen, in which "manure or other filthy refuse" had been allowed to accumulate. He received a $50 fine.

The ordinance involved in Johnson's case is one with which few real "goat people" would disagree. Clean pens are not only better for the neighborhood, they're better for the goats. In addition to assuring that the milk will remain sweet, regular cleanup goes a long way toward safeguarding the health of the stock.

Some of the other statutes considered do seem a bit arbitrary. Perhaps this is evidence of a general misunderstanding concerning the nature of the animal. Perhaps it is the result of a few slovenly enclosures and a few inconsiderate breeders who have allowed their own laziness and lack of concern to tarnish the image of the goat in the eyes of those who make the laws.

In any event, it's time for concerned "goat people" to begin working to restore their favorite animals to their rightful place in society. For many of us, this work must begin in our own barns and pens—with a rake, a shovel, a pitchfork, and an eye to the future of America's dairy goats.

HORSES

Many people think of the horse as a four-legged plaything of the wealthy—a sleek and shiny thoroughbred animal that runs six furlongs with startling speed, or pursues a fox over miles of rolling countryside with a human being on its back. Anyone who has ever had to round up a dozen nervous calves on foot, or who has tried to plow a field without relying on fossil fuels, knows that a horse can do a lot more than that. With the proper breeding and the right kind of training, a horse can be an extremely valuable member of the homestead ecosystem (Fig. 3-7).

For this reason, a homesteader ought to keep informed on the laws which regulate the keeping of horses, just as he stays in touch with all matters potentially affecting his lifestyle. As can be expected, zoning ordinances are frequently found among such regulations. They can prove to be a thorn in the side of anyone seeking self-sufficiency on the land.

Most courts agree that horses are permitted in regions zoned for farming, even where the animals are not used for draft. This judicial attitude dates back to a day when horsepower was measured by counting hooves and dividing by four. It is still very much in effect today.

In a recent New Jersey case, for example, a man named Mitschele relied upon it to help save his farm. Mitschele had been in the milk business for more than 12 years, operating his dairy enterprise on a 23-acre spread in a farming zone. When the price of feed went up faster than the price of milk, he found that he just couldn't make it any more.

In an effort to hold on to his land, the cowman switched to horses, applying for a permit to construct a 40-stall barn on his property. The local zoning board granted his request, but a neighbor objected, protesting that raising horses isn't farming. When the matter ended up in court, Justice Bodine disagreed with the complainant. The management of livestock is properly classified as farming, he decided, no matter what the purpose for which they are kept. The zoning board's conclusion was affirmed, with the court permitting Mitschele to make the transition.

Other New Jersey courts have not always been in agreement, however. In another of that state's recent decisions, it was held that the stabling of horses is not an "agricultural" pursuit. The case, entitled *Borough of*

Fig. 3-7. Horses are beautiful animals (photo by Jean Martin).

Demarest vs. Heck, was decided in 1964. It involved a stable owned by the zoning inspector himself. In it, he kept 18 horses and three ponies, some of which he owned, and some of which he boarded at a fee.

When the municipality tried to close him down, Inspector Heck balked, declaring that his sideline was perfectly legal in an area zoned agricultural. A judge who decided the case ruled against him. Agriculture, he said, refers only to the tilling of the soil. Heck's horses had to go.

Perhaps if he had gotten rid of them in the first place and stuck to ponies, he would have fared better. For in at least two recorded cases, ponies were given special consideration by the courts, being allowed to remain in areas from which horses were excluded. One such dispute, *Zoning Commission of Danbury vs. Grandieri,* revolved around the Connecticut law's definition of livestock.

Grandieri, who lived in a residential zone with his wife and four children, owned a Shetland pony which he kept in a large fenced corral. The zoning commission, citing an ordinance which prohibited the keeping of livestock in residential areas, ordered him to dispose of the animal. When Grandieri refused, legal action was instituted.

In rejecting the commission's argument, the court considered the fact that all four of the defendant's children played with and had a "deep affection" for the pony. Under the circumstances, the judges decreed, the beast was not "livestock," but a "household pet." As such, it was permitted to stay.

In a similar proceeding an Oklahoma tribunal compared *Shetland ponies* to dogs, and ruled that they had not been excluded from a residential zone. The case, *Simons vs. Fahnstock,* came up on the complaint of a neighbor who objected to the construction of a barn for housing such animals. Although the community was zoned "residential," the court found that because of their "diminutive sizes" and "general habits," the law had not been intended to bar Shetlands.

In the main, however, horse ownership in a residential and other nonfarming areas is severly limited by legislation. Some municipalities require application for a special permit by anyone seeking to keep a horse on his property. The city of El Paso, Texas, has gone even farther, declaring that anyone asking for such a permit must consent to regular inspections of his premises. According to one of the statute's provisions, failure to remove manure at least twice a week or to drain water troughs to prevent insects from breeding in them will result in revocation of any such permit issued.

In 1971, a group of concerned horseowning citizens tested the El Paso law, arguing that it violated their constitutional rights by authorizing warrantless, and therefore unreasonable searches. A federal judge disagreed. Writing for the Fifth Circuit Court of Appeals, Circuit Judge Skelton called the requirement a "reasonable" one holding it to be entirely constitutional.

Other jurisdictions require similar sanitary precautions, although not necessarily including them in zoning codes. The town of Seekonk, Massachusetts, for example, allows the keeping of horses only upon issuance of a permit by the Board of Selectment. When Robert Flynn, the plaintiff in a 1967 lawsuit, sought to have a neighbor's permit removed, the court made it clear that it would grant his request if unreasonable stench or odor could be shown to emanate from the quarters of the horses. A special "master" was appointed to visit the premises in question to conduct an objective smell test. Fortunately for the defendant, the wind was blowing in the other direction and Flynn's complaint was dismissed.

Many localities have gone so far as to ban horses completely from residential areas, making no provision for the issuance of permits or the granting of zoning variances. Greenville County, South Carolina, recently passed such a law, prohibiting horse ownership in any area designated "R-15" or "R-20" in the zoning scheme. Wayne Finley, a resident who already owned a horse, opposed the new restriction. He expressed his protest by purchasing two more horses and stabling them on his land. It wasn't long before he and the zoning administrator were standing face to face before a Supreme Court justice.

Finley called the law unconstitutional, contending that it discriminated against people who lived on less than one and a half acres. His argument fell on unsympathetic ears. The horses simply must go, the court decreed, except for the first horse, the one whose presence predated the statute. He, and he alone, may remain.

The latter aspect of the court's decision was based on a concept known as the "prior nonconforming use" rule. In theory, this principle of law provides that no zoning ordinance can affect activities which were in progress before its enactment, even though they now violate its provisions. In actual practice, it has been used to save the day for many a homesteader.

Take John Bobinski, for example, who, in 1965, bought a nine-acre parcel in Saddle River, New Jersey. The place had a horse barn on it which hadn't been used since 1940, but all previous owners had kept it in good repair. Soon after moving in, Bobinski stabled a few horses in the barn, in spite of a 1963 ordinance which made such activity illegal. Local officials tried to stop him, but a court backed up the homesteader. In doing so, the judges concluded that the barn constituted a "prior nonconforming use," even though it hadn't seen a horse in 27 years.

Even where horses are declared to be legal, however, a homesteader is not completely in the clear. Unless the animals are kept in a way which does not unreasonably inconvenience neighbors, they are still liable to become the subject of court issued injunctions against keeping them at all.

In a 1972 Colorado case, for example, one Arlene Hobbs was enjoined from keeping horses on her Jefferson County property in spite of a zoning ordinance which permitted two equines per lot. Finding that the animals attracted large numbers of flies, and that they produced a noxious odor which permeated the area, the court said that legislative authority notwithstanding, no citizen can be allowed to pursue an activity if it is a nuisance to neighbors.

The message should be clear. The best available weapons in the legal battle of the horses are not an attorney or a law library. They are rather a wheelbarrow, a pitchfork, and a shovel.

BEES

According to several well-known principles of aerodynamics, the bee cannot fly. It seems that his body is too heavy, his wings are too short, and his overall construction is simply not adequate for the job. Fortunately for the beekeeper, the bee knows nothing about aerodynamics. So he flies merrily along, kissing the neighbors' flowers and filling his keeper's hive with the only predigested sugar available to man.

All isn't sage and clove, though. For once in a while, the honeymaker's peculiar nature brings him into stinging contact with the law. When this happens, the bee usually loses. A California court recently commented that, "The business of bees keeps them on the wing most of the time," and for this reason special laws are necessary to control the places and ways in which they are kept. In 1963 a Florida judge agreed, holding that a beekeeper's liability to his neighbors is based on "the location and manner of keeping them" rather than on more traditional principles of law.

Century of Regulation

The regulation of beekeeping is not new to American jurisprudence. In fact it dates back almost a century. The first case on record is probably that of *John Olmstead vs. Robert Rich,* decided by a New York tribunal in May of 1886. The plaintiff in that matter owned a house adjacent to the defendant's property in the town of Hobart. He complained that the defendant kept over 140 swarms of bees and that many of them were hived only 60 feet from his residence. He alleged also that the insects frequently stung members of his family, soiled articles of clothing which were left on the line, interfered with the enjoyment of his home, and made his property "unsafe" and "unfit for habitation." He demanded $1,500 in damages and asked the court to stop the defendant from continuing his offensive activity.

The jury was apparently unimpressed with Olmstead's claim of injury, awarding him only six cents in damages. The trial court issued an injuction directing Rich to move his bees. The judge conceded that beekeeping was a legitimate occupation. He added, however, that, "When a business, although lawful in itself, becomes obnoxious to neighboring dwellings, the carrying on of such business is a nuisance which [the law] will restrain."

Nearly 70 years later another court referred to the *Olmstead* ruling in deciding the case of *People vs. McOmber,* which was based on very similar facts. The defendant in that proceeding had been indicted for maintaining a public nuisance and appealed to a higher court. He claimed that his 30 swarms were properly housed and that he was not to blame for their activities on his neighbor's property. The appeals court ruled against him, however, concluding that, "Keeping bees in such a manner as seriously to interfere with the rights of neighbors may constitute a nuisance." The hives were banned.

In regulating the keeping of bees, the state generally relies on its broad "police powers." These powers—reserved to the states by the U.S. Constitution—are extremely flexible and may cover a multitude of legislative areas. A 1933 California court summed them up by saying that, "In the exercise of its police power, the state may prescribe regulations tending to promote the public health, safety, morals, and welfare of the people." Other courts have specifically related these powers to the regulation of bees.

A Michigan judge, for example, in the case of *Wyant vs. Figy,* wrote that "The state, in the exercise of its police power, has the right to regulate the manner by which bees may be imported into Michigan." Another court, in the case of *Graham vs. Kingwell* ruled that, "Where the exercise of police power is applicable, the provision of the Constitution declaring that property shall not be taken without due process of law is inapplicable." The *Graham* case involved several colonies of bees which were confiscated and destroyed because their owner violated a local regulatory statute.

Case-to-Case Basis

Until recently, legal bee control was conducted by the courts on a case-to-case basis, zoning laws rarely concerning themselves with the problem. This was probably due to an early Arkansas dispute which resulted in a temporary victory for beekeepers. The case—*Arkadelphia vs. Clark*—was decided in 1889, and involved a municipal ordinance which had been passed early in that year. The law in question made it a crime "to own, keep, or raise bees in the city of Arkadelphia," and imposed a $5 to $25 fine for its violation. The defendant was a homesteader who refused to get rid of his swarms in spite of the legislative prohibition.

Ruling in his favor, the Arkansas court stated that "Neither the keeping, owning, nor raising of bees is itself a nuisance." The judges recognized the possibility of an improperly maintained hive becoming obnoxious and thereby being subject to legal intervention, but they refused to allow the city council to condemn beekeeping on a wholesale basis. In striking down the law, they wrote that: "The ordinance under consideration undertakes to make each of the acts named [owning, keeping, or raising bees] a nuisance, without regard to the fact whether it is so or not. It is therefore too broad, and is invalid."

This judicial attitude prevailed for many years. As population growth led to greater urbanization, it gave way to a less tolerant point of view. Finally, in 1938, a California court expressed the "modern" philosophy which led to inclusion of bee regulations in most contemporary zoning plans.

The petitioner in that California proceeding was one Edna Ellis, a town-bound homesteader who lived on about a third of an acre in Los Angeles county. Her street, Goodwin Avenue, was divided into small building lots, all about 50 to 150 feet. Ellis kept goats, rabbits, and other domestic animals on her property, but it was her bees to which the neighbors objected. Demanding her arrest, they pointed to a Los Angeles law which restricted the keeping of bees to Beverly Hills and the San Fernando Valley.

Ellis contended that her constitutional rights were violated by a law which discriminated against those who did not live in the specified areas. The court did not agree. Even a discriminatory zoning law is valid, it maintained, if it bears a reasonable relationship to "public health, morals, safety, or general welfare," and if its districts are created according to a "fair and rational" plan. Referring to the San Fernando Valley as an area primarily set aside for ranching and to Beverly Hills as a district of ruggedly mountainous terrain, it concluded that the ordinance had been "well patterned."

Then, addressing himself more specifically to the problem at hand, the writing judge said that: "City people, unaware of the inherent proclivity of bees to attend strictly to their own business, and not understanding that bees are by nature retaliatory rather than aggressive, become excited and apprehensive of unprovoked assault when bees appear."

Stating it more simply, he added, "Bees annoy them." This, he suggested, could lead to all kinds of trouble. As an example, he cited "the unlikely combination of a bee and an excited motorist in the same auto," and called it a "major traffic hazard."

Under the circumstances, he said, the law of nuisance does not provide enough protection. It is no longer sufficient to require that beehives be kept at a safe distance from a neighbor's abode. It has become necessary to ban them completely from population centers. The law under which Edna Ellis had been prosecuted was declared to be a valid one. Her conviction was sustained. Ever since, zoning boards have been enacting bee regulations.

For this reason, you'd better check the zoning law before investing in a hive. If it doesn't get in the way, remember the law of nuisance. Anything can be excluded from an area if it consitutes an unreasonable annoyance to others who live there.

As a New York court decided, "The right to keep animals carries with it an obligation to use reasonable efforts to prevent them from injuring the public." So choose your location wisely and make sure the bees don't get out of hand. If a neighbor gets stung in his yard, you might get stung in a courtroom.

DOGS

Where would the happy homestead be without dogs? Some earn their keep by herding sheep and cattle. Some protect hearth and home by keeping the wolves away from the door. Others don't work for their meals at all, but still manage to eat well. Sometimes we cuss them, sometimes we scratch them behind the ears. Sooner or later most of us end up keeping one or two (Fig. 3-8).

Usually they're nice to have around. Most dogs have one troublesome

Fig. 3-8. The dog is still man's best friend (photo by Stephen M. Barrett, Jr.).

trait in common—wanderlust. Rarely content living life in the same surroundings every day, they tend to go roving in search of greater knowledge. This means that unless that urge is controlled, your dog is likely to go visiting your neighbors, and their dogs are likely to come visiting you. Frequently, this leads to legal problems.

In 1932 a Michigan judge wisely wrote that, "While some dogs are justly regarded for admirable qualities, others are dangerous, mischievous, little better than a public nuisance." Unfortunately, it isn't usually possible to tell which is which until it's too late. For this reason, most states and municipalities have laws which prohibit unattended dogs from "running at large" or wandering without human supervision.

In a few states, these laws permit—or even direct—the summary destruction of unattended dogs caught running at large, An early Massachusetts statute, for example, provided that, "Any person may, and every police officer shall kill or cause to be killed all such dogs whenever and wherever found." In support of this kind of provision, one court noted that, "Dogs have, from time immemorial, been considered as holding their lives at the will of the legislature." Another judicial body—in the case of *Finley vs. Barker*—ruled that while the destruction of a roaming dog might deprive its owner of property, it was not a violation of his constitutional right to due process.

Many more states allow the killing of a dog which is trespassing or attacking livestock. An Iowa law, for example, permits a homesteader to shoot a dog caught in the act of "worrying, maiming, or killing any sheep or lamb or other domestic animal." A Michigan statute enacted in 1929 provided that any dog which entered a field or enclosure unaccompanied by its owner was a "private nuisance," and entitled the owner or tenant of that field to kill it "without liability for such killing."

The law doesn't stop at authorizing the keeper of livestock to protect his property from raiding canines. It also provides the means for collecting damages from the dog's owner. In all jurisdictions, this type of recovery is available through a negligence lawsuit. Often these can be brought in the small claims court or before some other informal adjudicating body.

In order to win a negligence case, the damaged party had to prove that his losses were the result of the dog owner's failure to act like a "reasonably prudent person." This is a rather elusive term, and sometimes one which a jury is called upon to interpret. Often, the injured plaintiff tries to show it by proving that the defendant knew that the dog had a propensity to do harm and failed to confine or restrain him.

Allowable Presumption

This isn't always easy to establish, However, particularly over a dog owner's protest that "Rover never attacked animals before." So several states' courts allow certain presumptions to be used in helping a plaintiff to prove his case. A Wisconsin tribunal once ruled, for example, that there are some things about dogs which everybody ought to know.

The matter before it, *Matthews vs. Scannell,* involved a complaint that the defendant's dog broke into the plaintiff's hutch and killed 14 *Chinchilla* rabbits. The dog owner's lawyers contended that their client was not guilty of negligence since he had no way of knowing that the dog was a killer, and therefore had no reason to keep him confined. But the trial judge rejected their arguments, holding that "To require proof that a dog might kill rabbits would be to require proof of the most natural trait of the animal." The defendant was ordered to pay for the damages.

A few states have gone even further, allowing recovery in attacking dog cases to be based on a concept known as "strict liability." This principle of law holds that anyone who engages in a dangerous activity ought to bear the burden of damage which results, even if he does nothing "negligent" or "unreasonable." Dogs, in these jurisdictions, are considered "wild" or "dangerous" animals.

In Ohio, where a strict liability statute exists, it has been held that the dog owner's conduct is completely immaterial to the question of his liability. In fact, the courts have written, "It is the conduct of his property [i.e. the dog] which renders him liable." A Maine tribunal agreed, explaining that "the gist of the action is simply the keeping of the dog." All else, it ruled, is irrelevant.

In effect, this means that the owner of a dog is financially responsible for any harm which the animal does. He thus becomes an "insurer" of the public safety, at least insofar as that particular dog is concerned. Because this point of view varies drastically with more traditional concepts of negligence and "fault," many states have been unwilling to take this step. In most of these, another approach makes it just as easy to recover compensation for damages done by a trespassing dog.

Tough Trespass Laws

Anglo-American law has always placed land in a position of reverence. The person who occupies it has special rights to privacy and physical security. Even an unauthorized footprint in the grass is considered an affront to the one who owns or possesses it. The trespasser is liable for damages, even if they amount to nothing more than a symbolic "peppercorn," or a judgment for the sum of "six cents." A landholder who sues for "trespass" need prove only that the defendant came onto his property without invitation.

By way of extension, the law in many places had come to hold that the owner of an animal is automatically responsible for any damage which it does while trespassing on the property of another—whether he was guilty of negligence or not. This rule was applied to dogs as early as 1897, by a New York court in the case of *O'Connell vs. Jarvis*. The plaintiff in that matter alleged that the defendant's dog had killed some of his flock while intruding on his land. The defendant denied any wrongdoing, contending that none of the losses were his fault.

The court ruled that "fault" had nothing to do with it. Ordinarily, it said, dogs, unlike cattle, are not likely to damage land merely by trespassing on it. For this reason, courts rarely concern themselves with dog-trespass cases.

Where the trespassing dog attacks and injures animals belonging to the landowner, an action for trespass is quite appropriate. The defendant in the *O'Connell* case paid the cost of his wandering dog's depredations and presumably learned a lesson.

There are times, though, when money is small compensation to a homesteader who loses his best breeding doe to a neighbor's vicious dog, or whose chickens are in a constant state of uproar because of canine intruders which make them nervous. Nobody wants to shoot a dog if he can help it. Anyway, most of the time that's like locking the barn door after the horse has been stolen. The best answer is to keep your roving pal at home and to insist that your neighbors do the same.

Chapter 4

Building Projects

Instructions for constructing a mini-barn, compact barn, various shelters, a woodshed, a fruit and vegetable bin, and other projects are included. Plus, there is a section on salvaging old buildings.

MINI-BARN

This mini-barn will add rural charm to any small homestead. The barn has 64 square feet of floor space.

Framing consists of 2″ × 4″s, with each frame 24″ o.c. No studs are required on the rear wall due to the vertical siding.

Note the arrangement of the brooder, feed, grain, etc., which only takes up 16 square feet of floor space. Forty-eight square feet are left for a goat or pony.

The mini-barn may be mounted on a concrete slab, or a dirt floor may be used. Use double 2″ × 4″s for the bottom plate (Fig. 4-1).

COMPACT BARN

This compact homestead barn is large enough for two standing stalls for horses, cows, goats, etc. It has a lean-to shed for many uses. The loft will hold about a ton of hay or grain and can be built for about $350 if some scrap or salvaged material is used. To reduce cost, the concrete floor may be omitted if the barn is placed on concrete piers. The bottom plate should be 4″ × 6″.

The lean-to may be added later. You can add one on each side for a total floor space of over 400 square feet. Windows and doors may be the sizes of your choice.

The barn may be extended in length to 14′, 16′, or 18′. It is not advisable to extend the width or height due to load factors.

Trim strips around the edge of the roof are optional. If you want

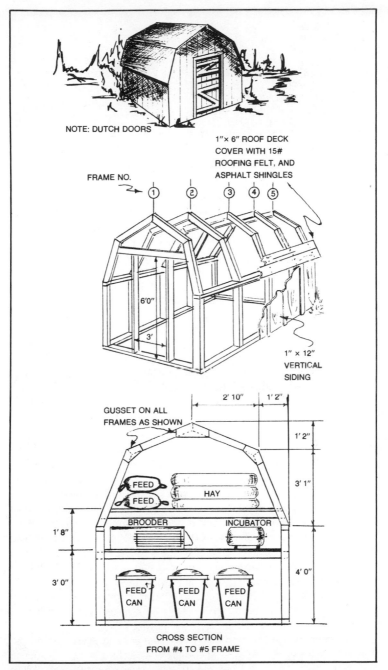

NOTE: DUTCH DOORS

1" × 6" ROOF DECK
COVER WITH 15#
ROOFING FELT, AND
ASPHALT SHINGLES

FRAME NO.

6'0"

3'

1" × 12"
VERTICAL
SIDING

GUSSET ON ALL
FRAMES AS SHOWN

2' 10"   1' 2"

1' 2"

3' 1"

FEED
FEED   HAY

BROODER   INCUBATOR

1' 8"

4' 0"

3' 0"

FEED
CAN   FEED
CAN   FEED
CAN

CROSS SECTION
FROM #4 TO #5 FRAME

Fig. 4-1. Construction details for the mini-barn.

2"×4" 150 BF
2"×6" 240 BF
4"×4" 20 BF
1"×6" 500 BF
½"×4'×8' PLYWOOD
EXT. GROOVED
90# ROOFING 200 SQ FT
CONCRETE READY MIX 4 YDS
MISC. NAILS, HINGES, AND
BEAM STRAPS, ANCHOR BOLTS
PAINT IF DESIRED

**Table 4-1. Materials List
for the Compact Barn.**

shingles for the roof, then omit 90# roofing and use 15# roofing felt under the shingles. It will take 234 square feet or 2⅓ squares of shingles to cover a barn without a lean-to, and 3½ squares of shingles to cover a barn with a lean-to (Table 4-1).

After the concrete floor and piers are complete, assemble the sides (studs, top and bottom plates, and diagonal bracing) and brace temporarily. The rafters are assembled with a 2" × 6" joist nailed across the bottom. Toenail to the top plate. Then cut out and install special studs. Cover each end of the barn with plywood siding. Cut out for a window and door in the front, and only a window in the rear of the barn. Cover the sides with plywood. Then install a post and rafters for a porch shed or lean-to.

Install the floor for the loft and roof decking on the lean-to and a barn, leaving 6" overhang. The rear end of the lean-to should be sided in for weather protection. Cover the roof area with 90# roofing extending over all edges 1½", which will cover the trim strip.

Install the door and windows. Cut out a 2' × 3' hole in the second floor near one corner. Then install a ladder to the first floor (Figs. 4-2 and 4-3).

SMALL CABIN

Recent years have witnessed a veritable mushrooming in new designs in architecture from geodesic domes, A-frames, permanent tipis and yurts to plastic inflatable structures, sod houses, and icosahedron eco-cabins. Many of these structures have been dealt with in a number of alternative lifestyle magazines, but the present is geared to frame construction in its broad sense. It's been with us since the middle ages, in a cruder form, and since then has been refined into what we know today. The chief fault of this type of construction is viewed in the poor design and waste of the modern three-bedroom ranch house. To the unpracticed eye, much of the visible waste is cosmetic touches. Waste is less apparent to the untrained eye in the form of excess material. Poor design is a little more complicated matter.

Methane, wind-generated electricity, and solar heat are beyond the reach of most people today who want to homestead for reasons of expense and technology. We don't have time to wait around for an "ecologically sound" house (is there such a thing?) the way land prices are advancing. That leaves the here and now—using good old wood for frame construction and wood heat. What is needed today is sound thinking on how to gear modern materials to homestead needs.

If for some reason you need to construct a small building—a house to live in until your homestead begins to really take shape, or a milkhouse so you can ship Grade A rather than Grade B—here's a small cabin-type building that can be erected by anyone with a little ambition (Fig. 4-4). This cabin shouldn't cost more than $1,000 to complete, even if all the lumber is bought from a lumber yard. It could cost considerably less if used or rough-sawed lumber is available.

Start out with a post foundation spacing the posts about 5' to 6' apart on the eave edges of the house and about 7' to 8' apart on the gable ends. Railroad ties are perhaps the best bet, either new or used, but other choices could include old telephone poles or cedar or pine logs treated with a preservative. Green cedar logs should be good for about 10 to 20 years. If you have access to standing fir or pine trees, they can be cut to length and treated on the building site with a preservative.

A good method is to dig a trench to fit the posts, line it with *visqueen,* fill it with creosote thinned 50/50 with kerosene, and roll in the posts—one at a time unless you want to dig a lake. The longer the posts are treated the longer they will last, but even a quick dunking will give you a good five years or so before they start to rot. If you wait until you've got the money to do it the so-called "right" way (e.g. continuous poured concrete footings reinforced with steel rebars etc.), you've got a lot of patience. Don't be

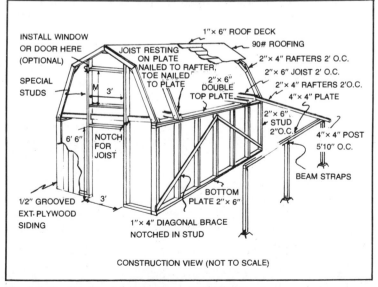

Fig. 4-2. Construction details for the compact barn.

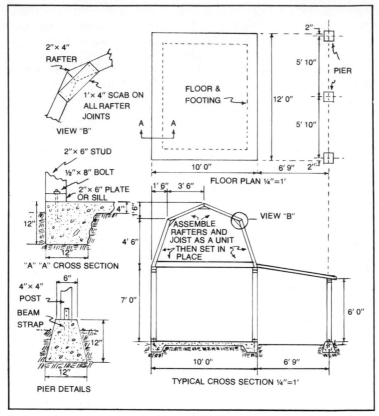

Fig. 4-3. More construction details for the compact barn.

afraid of a wooden post foundation. If can be replaced if the posts do give out in the years to come, and you'll probably have enough money by then to afford concrete piers.

After the posts are in the ground, build the floor. Don't worry if the tops of your posts aren't dead level. Use a builder's level and a two by four to lop them off as close as you can. The finishing touches can be done by shimming (leveling with the use of a tapered piece of wood, metal, or stone) between the posts and joists. A good, strong floor can be made by spacing 2 × 10s 24″ on center and securing them with four spikes at each end. Conventional building practices dictate spacing the joists 16″ on center, but unless you're going to be storing pianos, it's a needless extravagance. Rough-sawed pine and a layer of ¼″ Masonite is probably the cheapest deck. Other possibilities include shiplap or ½″ CDX topped with Masonite, particle board or plywood.

The least expensive way to build the wall is to use 2 × 4 studs 24″ on center topped with ½″ insulating sheathing. This sheathing is cheap but not

90

very good for shear strength, so cut in 1 × 4 diagonal braces after squaring the wall and before sheathing it. To build the walls, lay the top and bottom plates alongside one another and mark the stud locations; spread the plates and nail in the studs. Now snap a chalk line 3½" along the edge of the deck where the wall is to be placed. While the wall is down, toenail the bottom plate to the deck holding it to the line. This assures that the plates will be straight and enables you to square the wall by measuring it diagonally. Move the top plate until both diagonals read the same. Then put one toenail into the top plate. Cut the braces, sheath the wall, and raise it. The toenails in the bottom plate will keep it from sliding off the deck. When it's up, you'll be able to see the chalk line on the deck. Push or pull the bottom plate to the line and nail (Fig. 4-5).

Build the walls in opposite pairs and when they are all up, double up the top plate using your scrap 2 × 4s. Try to stagger the breaks in the plates. Now the walls are up and by squaring them while horizontal, the corners will come out plumb but the walls will be crooked along their length. Sight down the top plates and nail braces where needed to straighten the walls. These braces are temporary as the ceiling joists and roof will hold the walls when they're in place. Nail in the ceiling joists spacing them 48" on center and decking them with plywood. The 48" spacing will have a little spring to it, but it won't collapse. Study the plans and keep in mind that the ends of the joists will have to be trimmed to follow the pitch of the roof. The deck will have to be cut to allow the ends of the rafters to pass through it and rest on the wall plates. Both of these operations are best done after the deck system is in place.

Follow the plans to lay out the rafters. Cut one of each. After making sure they fit the chalk line, use them for patterns. Cut all the pieces using the patterns and when done, lay the pieces one set at a time along the chalk lines and nail them together with the collar ties. As you complete a set, raise it into position and secure it with toenails into the plate and joist. When they're all up, brace the end sets plumb and cut in the gable studs by holding them in position and marking. Sheathing grade or used 1" boards

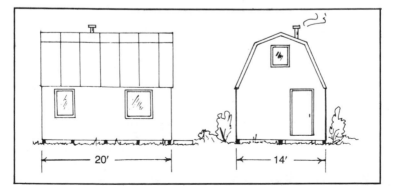

Fig. 4-4. Two views of the cabin.

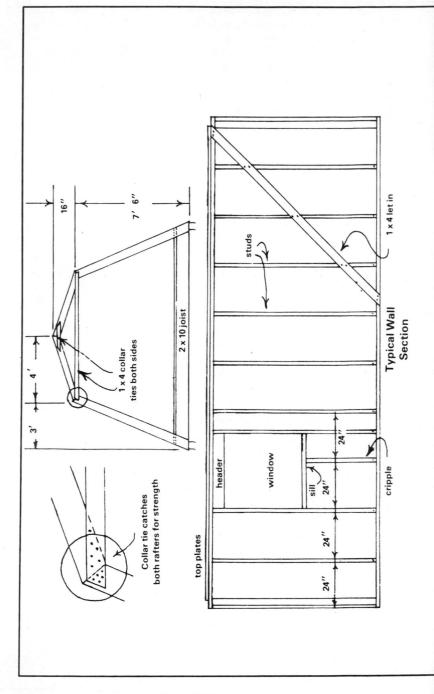

16"

7' 6"

2 x 10 joist

1 x 4 collar
ties both sides

3'   4'

Collar tie catches
both rafters for strength

studs

1 x 4 let in

header

window

sill

cripple

24"

24"

24"

24"

24"

top plates

**Typical Wall
Section**

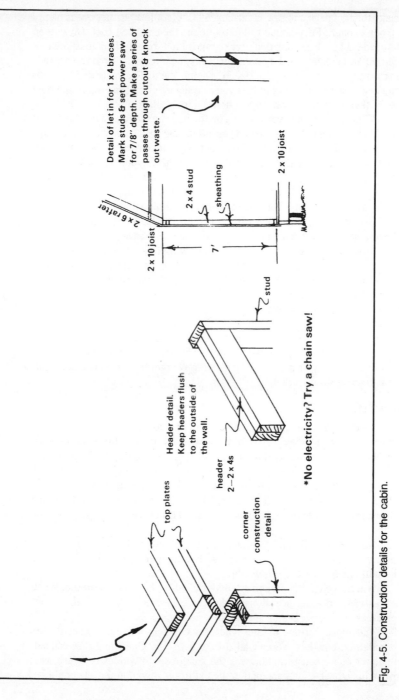

Detail of let in for 1 x 4 braces. Mark studs & set power saw for 7/8" depth. Make a series of passes through cutout & knock out waste.

2 x 6 rafter

2 x 10 joist

2 x 4 stud

sheathing

7'

2 x 10 joist

Header detail. Keep headers flush to the outside of the wall.

stud

header 2 – 2 x 4s

corner construction detail

top plates

*No electricity? Try a chain saw!

Fig. 4-5. Construction details for the cabin.

93

make the roof deck unless you can buy ½″ CDX for less. Either one is plenty strong enough. Fifty-pound rolled roofing is the cheapest roof. On a steep pitched roof such as this, don't try to put it on horizontally unless you're a demon for punishment. Lay it on vertically, lapping away from the prevailing winds and tarring the lap. Use ¾″ roofing nails. The gable ends have to be sheathed from a ladder unless you're real clever and can figure out how to do them the same way as the downstairs wall.

This pretty well covers putting up the house except for a few hints that will help out along the way. When you put in your windows or doors, always place them alongside a stud in the layout. This necessitates only one more stud for the other end instead of two which is what happens if you drop them into the walls anywhere. If you keep the windows 4′ or less in width, you can get by with two 2 × 4s on edge for headers, and that means more money. Use a ladder to the loft. Don't build stairs in a building this small. Put a hatch on the opening, or all the heat will go up there. Insulate the building. Shave the foundation posts with a chain saw so it can be skirted; and you'll have a snug little place. As you can see after studying this and the plans, all the structural members are 2′ on center. So if you measure the layouts from the same direction, all the members will stack. A rafter should be directly over a stud which is directly over a floor joist. The upstairs joists should fall alongside every other rafter.

The whole point in a small house like this is that it can be put up with a minimum of expense. While no one would like living in a place this small for too long, it beats buying a used trailer or paying rent. It provides a quick way to start living on a piece of land. After a bigger house is erected, it can be converted to a workshop.

GEODESIC DOME

When Jerry Belanger began to plan the ideal house for the ideal homestead, he knew exactly what he wanted: everything his house lacked. The kitchen lacked space for the quantity of often bulky tools used in a homestead kitchen. The cheese kettle and press, canning kettles, lard press, and other large items were stored in the basement. There really wasn't decent storage room for them there, either. All the smaller tools were a problem too: the noodle maker, butchering tools, bread pans, and so forth.

No modern kitchen has a decent place to attach hand grain mills or sausage grinders or Victorio strainers. The countertops are too thick, and the pull-out boards are too wobbly.

When an old farm kitchen is "modernized," it has to be carpeted. What homesteader doesn't occasionally dump a gallon of milk or a pail of soft tomatoes or a few eggs on the kitchen floor?

The more serious of these defects could have been corrected by remodeling, but they weren't all that was wrong. One thing that caused Belanger major consternation was the lack of south windows. There was one in his closet-office, and one in the bathroom, and neither one could be used for starting bedding plants in the spring. If *both* could have been used, they wouldn't have begun to meet the needs for sunny window space.

Equally serious, because of the design, there was no way Belanger could effectively utilize solar heat or a woodburning stove. He wasn't interested in running a stovepipe out a window, or any other makeshift solution.

The basement was fully cemented and damp, and served as a poor root cellar. Besides, it was very small, so even major remodeling to provide a decent root cellar wouldn't have helped much, because Belanger would have lost the kitchen tool storage space.

The final decision to build a new house was made when the state announced that the highway Belanger lived on would be widened. Balanger didn't like living on a highway in the first place, but it was almost a necessity when he ran a print shop on the homestead, because the trucks that delivered paper were restricted from many back roads, especially in the spring. When he learned that the highway would come practically through his front room, and would require the destruction of several ancient trees in his yard, he knew it was time to move.

There were a number of potential building sites on his land. He wanted a location that would allow solar heating and protection from the bitter northwest winds that rip through the area. Economy was a factor. He didn't want to have to pay for a long road, or stringing power lines.

The location he settled on was on the southeast slope of a hill on the "back 90." It wasn't too close to the barn, but it wasn't really too far, either. There was a well and a good garden spot. The crest of the hill was the highest point for miles around, and especially to the west, where most of the winds come from—an ideal place for a wind electric converter.

Going underground appealed to Belanger because of the obvious heating and cooling efficiencies, but perhaps even more so because of how such a house can be integrated into the landscape. It seemed ideal for one who despises lawns and other features of conventional American yards. At that time, though, there was almost no information available on underground structures.

Geodesic domes had also interested Belanger for a long time. Prefab domes were available, in use, and proven.

Domes cost about 15 percent less than conventional construction. They're stronger, use less material, and are extremely heat efficient. Since the frame is self-supporting, design possibilities are unlimited. Different configurations, sizes, and stud systems are available from a number of manufacturers. One firm claimed that a crew of three could erect a shell in a single day, with resulting labor cost reductions.

Belanger decided on a 6/12ths (a half sphere) 40' diameter model from The Big Outdoor People in Minneapolis, MN. One of the deciding factors was that they had the only 40' dome available at the time (Fig. 4-6).

Belanger designed a number of features into the house that would be of particular concern to a homesteader. Number one was to make sure he had

Fig. 4-6. A passive, solar geodesic dome.

some southern windows. The four southern sides are glass, providing a greenhouse that's 30′ long and more than 10′ wide at its widest point. The four sides of the greenhouse account for about one-fifth of the main floor walls.

He didn't want windows on the north or west sides, both to avoid winter heat loss and, in the case of the west side, to keep the summer sun out. The dining room is well below the crest of the hill, so even though it faces north, he did put in three triangular windows.

There are also four triangular windows on the southeast, at the upper level. The kitchen, on the east, has one square window.

The play of light through the day, and through the seasons, is probably one of the most enjoyable things about this house. The placement of the windows and the interior walls is such that every room has natural lighting. On summer mornings, Belanger has direct sunlight on the western wall . . . coming in through both the north and south windows. Sunbeams coming through the skylights march across the floor, sweeping the greenhouse in summer, and reaching well into the interior during the winter when the sun is lower. In the winter, the greenhouse is in sunlight from the main windows, but an overhang keeps out the higher sun of summer.

The large expanse of glass to the south was designed for plant propagation. Belanger also thought it might do a little for passive solar heating; it does a lot.

The house has electric heat which he had hoped to utilize the windmill for. The windmill isn't operating (that's another story), so the electric heat is turned off and Belanger heats with wood.

There is a great heat loss through those windows at night. The answer to that is the window wall. Nightwall clips are available from Zomeworks, P.O. Box 712, Albuquerque, NM 87103. These are small magnetic strips with double faced adhesive backings. Belanger cut 1″ Styrofoam to fit the window, removed the backing from the magnetic strips, and pressed them onto the Styrofoam. Then he removed the backing from each complementary strip, and put it in place over its magnet. He pressed each piece of

Styrofoam onto a window. The result was four clips on each window, and four clips on each piece of insulation.

When the sun goes down, Belanger stokes up the fire and puts each window wall in place, the magnets holding them up. In the morning, he simply takes each one down and lets the fire go out.

Wood heat was designed into the place. Belanger uses a Timberline TLF, the largest fireplace type model. Naturally, the doors are usually closed, but it's nice to have an open fire on occasion.

Belanger's interest in underground wasn't stifled entirely. To get at least some of the benefits, he built the house "upside down." Instead of going up to bed, his family goes down, the bedrooms being in the basement.

This has worked out extremely well. These rooms have been comfortable even during the hottest weather, far cooler than upstair bedrooms. During the winter, being underground, they stay reasonably comfortable even without much heat.

The living room is on the upper, or third, level. The solar and wood heat from the main level rise, and Belanger has never had to turn on the electric heat upstairs. During the summer it gets quite warm, but what homesteader sits in a living room in the summer?

Actually, there is a remedy built in. A duct at the top of the dome pulls hot air off the ceiling. In the summer it exhausts it outside, and in the winter, if the passive solar is really cooking, he can direct it downstairs to the bedrooms.

If Belanger overcompensated on the greenhouse windows,—from zero in the old place to 30', he also overreacted in the kitchen. It has 270 square feet, with more than 30 linear feet of cupboard space, 15 of that floor to ceiling storage. There is room for all of the homestead kitchen equipment.

There is also a second kitchen, which will be the real homestead kitchen. It will have decent work surfaces for such things as cutting meat and making sausage. There will be a deep sink . . . large enough to be able to get a 21-quart pot under the faucet or to wash a decent load of fruit or vegetables at canning time. The canning stove will be there, keeping the heat and steam away from the rest of the house. It's also the place where dairy utensils are washed and stored, where the cheese press isn't in the way when someone's cooking dinner, and where all the clampdown tools actually clamp down.

Below that is the root cellar, convenient to the keeping room, the garden, and the kitchen. It's still lacking the shelves and bins of a proper root cellar, but it does hold Belanger's canned produce, grain, potatoes and onions, and so forth. The grains are stored in new garbage cans. A minimum-maximum thermometer showed that the temperature hardly varied from 45° throughout the winter, and as of this date (late January) the potatoes and cabbages are still in fine shape.

Among the unfinished projects, even after two years of construction, is one of the bathrooms. It was designed for a composting toilet.

The garage, also still under construction, will support three solar panels for water heating. The eaves will direct water into a cistern for emergency garden use.

Certainly Belanger would do a few things differently if he was starting over again. All in all, he's satisfied. His experience so far indicates that a proper house can make an important contribution to homestead success and satisfaction.

A-FRAME

Chet Plonski and his wife Alice have been homesteading since they met more than eight years ago. After renting several farm acreages and struggling with rundown buildings, faulty plumbing, and hazardous and inefficient electrical wiring, the Plonski's knew that the only way they could homestead the way they wanted was to design and build their own home from scratch.

The Plonski's were lucky. They found a small acreage (3.2 acres) which had been used only for pasture for the past 35 years or so. It even had a windmill standing on it. Somehow, they found a bank willing to loan them 90 percent of the money they figured it would cost to built their dreamstead.

For various reasons, they decided that the house would be an A-frame (Fig. 4-7). One reason was because of the dramatic effects which can be achieved with them aesthetically. The other, main reason was because A-frames are easy to heat and are so cozy in the winter. By this time, they had been through enough Iowa winters to know what to expect.

Since staying warm was their primary concern, they placed no windows at all on the north side of the house. The roof on the north side reaches to within a foot of the ground. That foot of exposed concrete block is covered with 1½″ of Styrofoam insulation. If he had it to do over again, Plonski would insulate the entire outside of the basement walls, all the way down to the footings.

The Plonski's have an outside entrance to the basement on the north side, but they made the entryway in the form of an annex, much like an enclosed porch. Under the stairs which lead to the basement, they have a storage space for root crops. A second door at the foot of the stairs lets them into the basement (Fig. 4-8).

Fig. 4-7. The A-frame is designed for energy efficiency.

Fig. 4-8. The basement entrance to the Plonskis' A-frame.

The Plonski's installed two large windows on the east side to catch the morning sun in winter and for ventilation in summer. On the west end, they have one window over the kitchen sink (they can keep an eye on the pasture while they do dishes). The other west window is in the back bedroom in the loft. This was a necessity for light and ventilation. They were able to use a minimum of windows because they didn't chop the house up into a dozen rooms. As a carpenter, it has always bugged Plonski that most modern homes start with a large floor area, which gets divided into bedrooms, living rooms, utility rooms, family rooms, television rooms, dining rooms ad infinitum. Each room must have a window (and the consequent heat loss and expense) as well as its own heat supply (another heat "run" or a baseboard unit).

In the Plonski's house, the ground floor is all one open room, with the exception of a small (almost a closet by contemporary standards) room which houses the stool and some floor cabinets for toiletry supplies. The loft is divided into two bedrooms for their son and daughter.

The basement is used primarily for food and tool storage. Plonski and his wife sleep there, but as yet, their "bedroom" is just an area unenclosed by walls.

They wanted a house big enough to comfortably support their homestead activities, but small enough to heat cheaply and efficiently. They settled on a ground floor dimension of 26' × 36'. The loft dimensions work out of 14' × 30'. This gave them 1,356 square feet of house proper, with an additional 936 square feet of basement. This seems small when compared to most new homes, even if you include the basement, but when you figure the cubic feet of space that you have to heat, compared to a conventional vertical-walled house of the same dimensions, you realize that there is a considerable saving in heating space.

How It Works

There was never any question in the Plonski's minds as to what their primary heating fuel would be: wood. They have always loved the pleasant heat they get from their stoves. In their area there seems to be an abundance of dead wood (mostly elm and box elder, but increasingly, oak) free for the cutting.

Their major heat source is an Ashley, which is roughly centered in the basement. The stove pipe extends up through the main floor and through the loft floor and finally exits through the ceiling via a double insulated pipe. This gives us about 19" of hot pipe inside the house.

For cooking, once again the fuel is wood. The Plonskis use primarily scrap wood that is left over from construction projects and repair work. This wood would normally be heaped up and burned. Instead of heating the great outdoors though, they use it for cooking, baking, and canning. In addition to this, it is also their supplier of hot water.

The hot water for dishwashing is heated on top of the stove or in the reservoir which is built into the old range. There is always water on the stove, so that whenever there is cooking being done, there is also the hot water to do the dishes.

When the Plonskis lived on rented acreages, their major expense always seemed to be electricity. At times, their bill was as high as $50 to $60 per month. For a while the reason for this was a real mystery to them. Besides lights, all the appliances they owned were two freezers, a refrigerator, and a wringer washing machine. They finally figured out what was eating all the kilowatts; the electric water heater and water pump.

Since these had been their biggest users, they decided to just eliminate them on their homestead. That is where the windmill came to the rescue.

After reading some old farm design books, the Plonskis decided that the windmill, with an adequate storage system, would suit them just fine. They poured a concrete cistern in the basement. It has a capacity of about 128 cubic feet of water, roughly the size of a medium sized stock tank. The kitchen sink is directly above the cistern and is fitted with a hand pump. They installed a new, double-action force pump (one that will force water uphill under pressure as opposed to "lift" pumps which just spill water out of the spout) under the windmill, and ran a 1" plastic line underground to the cistern (Fig. 4-9). So much for cold water. They find that a full cistern will last them anywhere from six weeks to two months. This includes all the water for drinking, cooking, and for washing dishes.

For bathing, they use water heated by a stovepipe water heater. In the west end of the loft they installed a 35-gallon tank which is pumped full by their windmill. In the event that there is no wind when the tank needs filling (something that happens occasionally even in Iowa) the water can always be pumped manually. It takes 212 up and down strokes to fill the hot water tank. It may be a little taxing on the old muscles, but it is a viable backup system. The water in this tank flows by gravity down to a coil in the stovepipe. From here, the water rises naturally as it is heated. It continues to circulate as long as the stove is in use.

From this tank they have a line that runs by gravity to the kitchen sink (for hand washing) and another line to a tub and shower in the basement. For this water line, the Plonskis used ¾″ iron pipe, and the pressure is excellent.

The last major complaint they had about rented farm acreages was the fact that the bathroom stool never worked properly. When they weren't running all the time, they were plugging up and overflowing. When Plonski wasn't monkeying with the float, he was on the working end of a plunger. He knew there was a better way.

The answer was a composting toilet. After writing to Abbey Rockefeller, they located a dealer for Clivus Multrum in Iowa. In their case it was a life saver, because when they finally moved into the basement of their not nearly completed dream house, it was the middle of December, with the temperature sitting at −6°, and the old pump had frozen solid and cracked wide open. No water. At least with the Clivus, they didn't have to worry about flushing the toilet. The Clivus unquestionably cuts down on their water consumption, and enables them to have the convenience and comfort

Fig. 4-9. Trying out the newly installed pump.

101

Fig. 4-10. In the kitchen area there is a hand pump at the sink.

of an indoor toilet and still have their "weird" water system. The Plonskis now use less than half the electricity they used before they moved to their new home.

The Balance Sheet

The cost in dollars and cents for installing these energy-saving systems runs about the same or somewhat less than the comparable "standard systems." The Clivus cost the Plonskis about $1400, or about what it would have cost to put in a water stool and septic tank with laterals. The water pump with two new cylinders set them back $230. The Ashley woodburner sold for $250, and cookstove (Home Comfort) was acquired at a farm auction for $135. There Blazing Showers hot water heater cost $50 plus another $20 to have the fittings welded and cut in the recycled hot water tank (Fig. 4-10).

Their home so far, including land (3.2 acres), fencing, outbuildings, and all materials (new and used) purchased so far have come to about $18,000, certainly not an excessive amount of money for a comfortable new home. The actual building they did themselves, except for electrical wiring which was done for them by a friend in exchange for help in pouring a concrete floor in his new barn.

What would normally be the sewage waste is instead turned into a small amount of rich compost. The waste (gray) water flows out through a tile line and is dispersed under the orchard. The household cleaning products which are in this water are biodegradable within 24 to 36 hours. The

102

Plonski's kitchen garbage is fed to their livestock or cycled through the Clivus. Either way, it is returned to the earth along with wood ashes to enrich the soil of their homestead. They have yet to purchase or apply any kind of chemical fertilizer to their food crops or to the crops they raise for their livestock. In fact, by burning wood for heating and cooking, they are not only saving energy by not purchasing fossil fuels, but are at the same time salvaging heat from materials that would otherwise be wasted (scrap wood) or performing a service by eliminating disease-harboring wood (elm and oak).

The Plonskis love to work within nature and let nature work for them. It is a real thrill to watch that old windmill pumping away. It is better than magic. The wind power is free. It is a beautiful thing to watch your cattle grow and thrive on homegrown feeds like mangels, carrots, comfrey, rutabagas, cornstalks, and hay instead of pumping them full of feeds which have been fertilized, cultivated, dried and processed with enormous amounts of fossil fuels. It is nice to know that you are not supporting the energy-intensive processed foods industry at your own table.

The other cost is, of course, the inconvenience. Someone has to keep an eye on the hot water tank so that it doesn't overflow while it is being filled. The windmill won't shut itself off. Someone has to carry water to the chickens and ducks. Someone has to pump water for the cattle when there is no wind. There is wood to be cut, split, stacked, and kindling to be chopped. Ashes must be hauled out and spread on the garden. Someone must remember to fill the washer and rinse tubs the day before the clothes are to be washed so the water won't be ice cold. Sometimes it is annoying when you need a shower and the water isn't hot yet. So you either take a chilly shower, heat the water on the stove for a bath, or go without. They've alleviated this problem somewhat, at least in the summer time, by building an outdoor, solar shower.

The Plonskis were able to design and build their house from scratch. They are still not finished. A few things are left yet to do in the house. The solar-heated pumphouse is only started, and the combination summer-kitchen-greenhouse-wood storage-facility is only a plan. The garage-workshop is still in the idea stage. The big root cellar is still several summers away. Water in the barn would sure be nice. The solar panels on the south side of the roof will have to wait. They're getting there, though.

BACKYARD BIOSHELTER

If the sink in your house is overflowing with vegetables that need caring for all summer long and your mate is wondering who will ever eat all the vegetables you bring in, you're probably compulsive when it comes to growing things. Seized with an insatiable passion to plant, you've already begun to consider ways of extending your growing season, much to the chagrin of those around you. Cold frames and hotbeds are one alternative; for the really serious, a greenhouse is another.

103

If you're a born tinkerer and like to experiment as well, you might want to look at a backyard bioshelter which incorporates not only a flower and vegetable growing solar greenhouse, but a shelter for animals as well (Fig. 4-11). The rationale for it is simple. Plants benefit from the carbon dioxide, manure, and heat animals provide. The animals in turn appreciate the oxygen generating features the plant has as well as the occasional food it provides—a fair trade, it seems.

The vital link in this whole scheme is the lowly earthworm. In ecological parlance, the worm is classed as a *decomposer*. His role in the cycle of nature is to break down wastes. The result of his efforts is a rich, vital plant growing medium.

Techniques for growing the red (manure) worm are well advanced. The red worm even thrives on chicken and pig manure. Within a year, a mere 1,000 earthworms can convert 1 ton of manure into ample supplies of rich castings and fertile potting soil.

Models of different but related "miniecosystems" exist and have performed well. The one Ron Poitras relied on most for his planning was the facility constructed by the New Alchemy Institute. Its bioshelter on Prince Edward Island incorporates fish, plants, and people all relating in a symbiotic way. John Todd, creator of N.A.I.'s bioshelter, says, "It's inspired by biological systems capable of providing its own energy and climate, treating its own wastes and growing food for its residents as well as the community which surrounds it." The concept remains highly experimental, but Poitras felt there was enough information for him to begin his own construction.

The shape of the facility Poitras built was dictated by a combination of the site and the requirements of activities taking place inside. The earthworms and composting bins are underneath the animal housing area and on the same level as the greenhouse. This arrangement simplifies handling of the manure-growing medium. Running the length of the building is a wall of

Fig. 4-11. The bioshelter is a mini-ecosystem, providing a solar greenhouse and an animal shelter.

55 gallon drums which separates the earthworm composting area from the greenhouse and serves as thermal mass for heat storage. In addition to the 22 water barrels for storing solar heat collected during the day, 17 tons of concrete and stone which serve as wall and floor for portions of the building also store heat.

Another important part of the heating system for the building is the animals themselves. Rudy, Poitras's 200 pound pig, gives off nearly as much heat as a solar collector of equal surface area. With his two goats and a dozen fowl, his animals provide over 20,000 Btus of heat per day.

The biggest problem he faced in combining all these things in one tight, well insulated building, was providing adequate ventilation. Animals and plants contribute considerable moisture to the air, and fresh air is essential in keeping everything healthy. Conventional facilities for housing animals and plants introduce tremendous quantities of cold air from outside to provide the ventilation needed. The heat lost, as a consequence, is tremendous. Fresh air for Poitras's bioshelter is introduced via a solar air collector on the roof which preheats the air introduced for ventilation. So far this seems to work well, although he has recently had to add a small fan to circulate and increase the amount of air that is brought in.

On a larger scale, facilities such as these may form another important link in the effort to strengthen the economic viability of the small farm. In Poitras's part of the country, the short growing season is a major stumbling block the small grower faces in achieving an adequate, year-around income. by devising innovative solar facilities that extend the growing season and combine, to advantage, a variety of operations typically undertaken on a small farm, we may soon experience some of the changes an increasing number are saying is essential for the survival of our agriculture.

Who knows, bioshelters may be the new farms of the future—energy conserving, diversified, "miniaturized", serving a local market and providing useful creative work for a new generation of intensive market gardeners.

BUILDINGS WITH SAWMILL SLABS

When you consider the high prices of plywood and framing lumber today, building even a small, simple shed 8' square can easily run you over $100 in wood costs alone. If you feel you have to shelve some of your building plans, remember slabs. Slabs are the half-rounded pieces trimmed off a log when it is squared up to cut into lumber. They are available at lumber mills.

A pickup load of these slabs costs only $5. Cedar slabs can be 6" to 12" in width and mostly peeled of bark. The cut side is as smooth and flat as any unplaned board.

Slab stringers are suitable framing material, similar to studs, and called *slab stringers*. They're usually a little thinner than 2 × 4 studs and are seldom squared on all four sides, but they work just fine for framing material.

Fig. 4-12. Slabs give a building a log cabin look (photo by John McDowell).

To make a slab outhouse, simply build a frame of slab stringers and cover it horizontally with short pieces of slabs. The total cost for the outhouse is about $6, almost all of which is for nails and hardware.

Fashion a 8 × 16' goathouse from slabs, building sections of wall 8' long and then joining the sections together. Build these sections by laying the slab stringers out on level ground, with 16' centers between studs. Then put the siding on these sections with wide slabs, starting at the bottom, working up, overlapping them slightly like shingles to shed the weather. Then, standing the sections up, join them together with large spikes, add a roof (also of slabs and stringers), and the basic shed is completed. The cost is about $10 for wood, $16 for nails.

The rounded sides of the slabs give the building a log cabin look (Fig. 4-12). Add another 8 × 8' section on one side, and then join an 8 × 12' hay shed to the original structure.

Anyone interested in slab building should reconnoiter their area for sawmills and mill dumps and check there. The East has plenty of hardwood forests; the West has the pin and the fir softwoods; and the South generally has both. Those who live in the treeless section of the Great Plains and the Southwest won't have much luck finding slabs, but you have a wealth of sod and adobe.

Slabs are a very reasonable, economical way to build some good looking sheds and outbuildings, ones that fit in quite nicely with the back to the earth type of homestead. If you have a power table saw handy, you could even dress these slabs up and use them for siding on a regular house. At any rate, any time you spend more for nails than lumber, you've probably got an A-1 source of building material you can't afford to pass up.

As for the mills, well, if no one comes for the slabs, they either burn them as waste or let them rot away. What a waste! That is another good reason for you to save money by building with slabs.

CHICK BROODER

Most small homesteads require the use of a small chick brooder to raise a few fryers or young pullets each year. You can build this one for less than $5.

Cut out two sides from 1" × 12" pine board. After the windows are cut,

106

nail ½″ hardware cloth over the opening on the inside of the brooder.

Cut out two 1″ × 2″ × 12″ pieces and one piece 1″ × 12″ × 12″. Assemble as shown in Fig. 4-13. Nail ½″ hardware cloth over the bottom. This should cover the area between the 1″ × 2″ × 12″s, which will be covered from the inside later with aluminum wrap and used as a chick feeder. To clean, just remove the aluminum wrap.

After all pieces in Fig. 4-13 have been cut out and assembled, cut out ¼″ × 9″ × 14″ plywood and nail in place. See Fig. 4-14. Cut out the ¼″ × 14″ × 20″ lid which is hinged to open as shown. The 1″ × 1″ × 3″ legs are nailed in position after all else is assembled.

A chick feeder is provided in one end. It will be necessary to use a small portable water container as none is provided. A 25-watt lamp will maintain a temperature of 95° to 98°F.

CHICK WATERER

An automatic waterer will provide clean water for your flock if you are away for a long weekend. Construct the holding rack to fit the size of the can and pan available to you. Figures 4-15B and 4-15C show the completed assembly. Figure 4-15A shows the can's nozzle or spout just below the top of the pan where the water level will be maintained. The spout should be the only opening in the can.

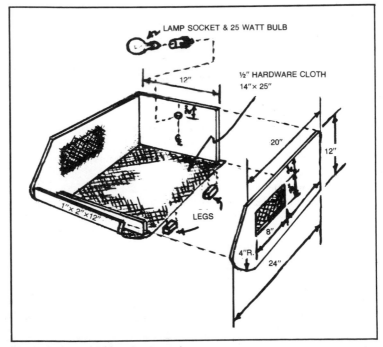

Fig. 4-13. Assemble the pieces as shown.

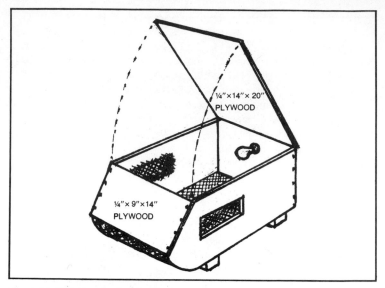

Fig. 4-14. Nail the plywood in place.

Figure 4-16 shows a remote automatic chick watering setup for use when floor space is at a premium. Water will only run out when the water level drops in the drinking pan below the spout or the end of the hose. Any 5-gallon can may be used as long as you can adapt a spout or hose. Several hoses may be run to different cages or coops from one can.

A-FRAME HOUSE FOR THE HOMESTEAD HOG

There are two different ways to get started raising livestock. The first way is to jump in with both feet and buy several animals. The second method involves buying only one or two to start with, then gradually increasing the number as you gain more experience. Although the latter method is a slow process, it's the one Herbert Huff and his wife have chosen for many reasons.

By utilizing the slowpoke method, they've managed to prevent some rather costly errors. Although they have made numerous mistakes over the past four years, they haven't cost them nearly as much as if they had started out on a larger scale.

The cost of permanent livestock housing is usually more expensive than the livestock themselves. Therefore, Huff feels that it's best to start out with a small, low-cost shelter built primarily from recycled materials. Later on, if you're still interested in raising that particular type or breed of animal, a more expensive, permanent shelter can be built.

The temporary hog house shown in Fig. 4-17 is a perfect example of starting out small. Rather than build a large house for several hogs, Huff built a shelter to contain only one. He did this primarily because he didn't

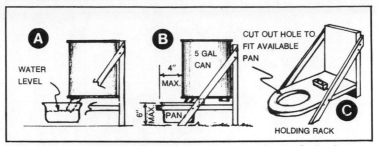

Fig. 4-15. The automatic waterer will provide clean water for your flock when you are away from home.

know how many hogs his family would eat in a year. Had he built a large, permanent house for three or four hogs, he would have wasted a great deal of time and money.

After raising his first hog last year, Huff's original idea of a good hog house has changed considerably. The shelter has enabled him to raise pork immediately, plus given him the time to carefully plan a permanent house.

Obviously, Huff's hog house isn't exactly an architect's dream. In fact, such an eyesore sitting in the front yard might be cause enough for neighbors to call City Hall for its removal. Huff placed the house out back and over the hill.

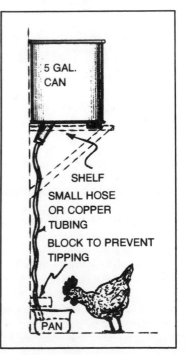

Fig. 4-16. A remote automatic chick watering set up.

Fig. 4-17. A temporary hog house.

Since the house is completely open in the front and not insulated, Huff considers it suitable only for spring to fall hog raising in cold climates. The shelter could be insulated by leaning straw bales against the walls and tacking one end of a burlap sack over the door opening. However, since the house and pen aren't portable, Huff would have to walk through snowdrifts to bring the hog his daily rations during winter months.

Huff chose an A-frame building because they are easy to build and use a minimum of materials. Triangular buildings are also incredibly strong and have the ability to shed snow and resist wind that would tip over other buildings. This ability, of course, is due to the steep pitch of the walls.

With the exception of the 2 × 4 lumber framework, the entire house was built from recycled materials. The ¾″ plywood floor had previously been used as a sign to advertise sweet corn. Roofing tin came from a similar A-frame hog house that had rotted years ago. The nails and ⅜″ plywood end piece were recycled from other projects.

The frame is built from three triangular-shaped ribs which are connected by one side brace on each wall and two on the floor (Fig. 4-18). The 2 × 4 ribs were built so the widest part of the board runs parallel with the wall, providing more room inside the small house.

110

For a larger house, Huff would have turned the boards the other way, so the edge of the board lay against the wall. In addition, he would have used plywood gussets and collar beams (Fig. 4-19). Ribs built in this manner would be much stronger than Huff's, but his pig house is so small it doesn't really matter.

To make the ribs, Huff started by cutting three 2 × 4s to 4' in length. The boards were then laid out on the floor in the shape of a triangle. Once he obtained a uniform shape, the boards were marked and cut at the proper angle, then used as templates for cutting the boards for the other two ribs. Huff nailed the three ribs together with two 3¼" nails at each point.

The ribs were then connected by nailing one 6' long side brace on each wall, plus two more on the bottom for a floor support. His wife held the front and back ribs upright while he nailed the braces on, then the center rib was positioned an equal distance from the front and back ribs.

The plywood floor and back wall were nailed in place with large shingle nails. Rather than add any more weight to the structure, Huff hauled the framework back to its present location and applied the tin sheeting there.

To provide ventilation and protect the floor against rot, Huff felt that a simple foundation was necessary, so he set the house on top of several concrete slab chunks. The only time a foundation isn't necessary is when pressure-treated floor members are used.

One problem with small A-frame houses is trying to fill the gap between the first vertical fence post and the sloping walls of the house. Huff solved this problem by allowing the extra long sheets of tin to protrude 16" beyond the front of the house. The overhanging portion was then bent at a right angle and nailed to the fence posts on each side.

For the pen, Huff used two 16' long pieces of heavy duty hog fencing. He bent the last 3' of fence at right angles so they would meet, thereby eliminating the need for an extra piece of fence at the end. All together, the pen measures about 6' wide by 13' long.

Also, he was able to save four fence posts by building the hog pen alongside a horse pen. He saved money and labor by simply nailing the

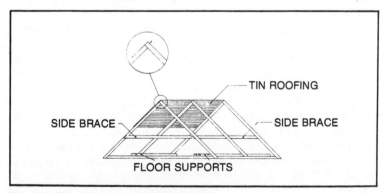

Fig. 4-18. The side braces connect the ribs.

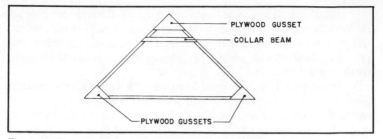

Fig. 4-19. The use of plywood gussets and collar beams.

fencing to the posts that were already there. For the other side and the end, he used four fence posts which he bought at a sawmill.

Total cost for the hog house and pen came to about $4. At last year's low market price of pork and high cost of commercial feeds, Huff's hog raising venture didn't break even. However, this year it will, since he's now grinding and mixing his own feed.

When it comes time to build a permanent hog house, Huff will reuse the expensive hog fencing from the old pen and salvage the fence posts as well. Chances are, he'll also use the house for some other type of small animal.

LOW-COST RABBIT SHELTER

Up until last fall, Herbert Huff and his wife were provided with a fairly constant source of meat from a healthy herd of Red Satin rabbits. Due to a lack of housing space, they elected to temporarily phase out the rabbits. They had underestimated both the number of rabbit cages needed to provide a constant source of meat and the amount of space needed for the cages.

Originally, Huff's rabbits and goats were raised in the same building. The problems began when the rabbits started doing what they're best at—multiplying. Soon, three of the four barn walls were covered with rabbit cages. With the addition of three more goats, there was scarcely a place left in the barn where the goat could rest.

Huff couldn't justify the expense of building a conventional rabbitry. So he decided to butcher the rabbits.

About March (a month after Huff's supply of frozen rabbits had run out), he began to crave home-raised fried rabbit. Luckily, the materials for a low-cost rabbitry became available shortly afterwards. One morning a large canvas tarp fell off a truck as it passed by his house.

The shelter requirements for rabbits needn't be elaborate. Being hardy animals able to withstand very cold weather, the basic considerations are a dry, draft free and well-ventilated environment. With these three things in mind, it seemed to Huff that a heavy tarp was able to meet these requirements as well as a conventional wood frame structure (Fig. 4-20).

Huff actually had all the materials on hand to build his miniature rabbitry. Two 8' long 4 × 4s were recycled from a hog hanger (which didn't work too well). The few 2 × 4s, nails, and wire were leftovers from other projects. A sheet of Masonite (sometimes called hardboard) had been bought for another project that never evolved.

Since the 4 × 4s weren't pressure-treated, Huff started by painting the lower portion of the posts with creosote paint to prevent wood rot. After measuring the length of the cages, he dug two holes (with a post hole digger), spacing them at the proper distance so the cages would fit between the two posts. He then used a carpenter's level to make sure the posts were plumb, then packed the dirt tightly around the posts using a section of water pipe as a rammer.

Next, he nailed a 2 × 4 to the top of both posts. This horizontal board acts as a brace and a support from which to suspend the cages. Huff wrapped a piece of wire around the 2 × 4 and threaded it through the top of the cage at both ends. For additional support, he nailed both sides of the cages to the 4 × 4 posts. See Fig. 4-21.

Fig. 4-20. A low-cost rabbit shelter (photo by Herbert Huff).

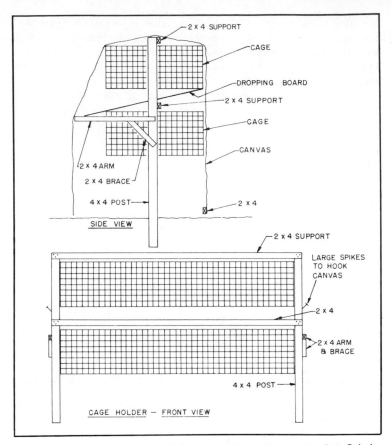

Fig. 4-21. Side and front views of the cage holder (drawing by Bob Schein-koenig).

About 9″ below the bottom of the upper cage, he nailed another 2 × 4, running from post to post. The lower cage was installed in the same manner as the upper.

Huff then cut a sheet of ¼″ Masonite the same length and about 9″ longer than the overall depth of the cage. This was so the bottom cage would be completely covered. The masonite was then painted with several coats of exterior grade Varathane to waterproof it and prevent it from warping.

To mount the board, Huff drilled two ⅛″ holes (spaced apart by 1″) along the front edge of the board. A short piece of wire was run through the bottom of the cage, then through both holes in the board and twisted underneath. All together, Huff made eight pairs of holes along the front edge of the board and fastened them in the same manner.

Next, Huff nailed a length of 2 × 4 to each post (running perpendicular to the post) long enough to extend 6″ past the rear edge of the dropping board. The boards hold the canvas tarp away from the dropping board so the droppings can fall to the ground without interference. Shorter lengths of 2 × 4 (with one end cut at a 45° angle) were nailed under the arms to serve as a brace.

The tarp was then draped over the frame and moved around until it was even on all sides. Starting at the top, Huff stretched the tarp tight between the two posts and tacked it down with shingle nails. He repeated this procedure at the back of the cage holder where the canvas meets the 2 × 4 arms which hold it away from the dropping board.

To aid in rolling up the front portion of canvas, Huff nailed a 2 × 4 along the bottom edge of the tarp. Two large spikes were then partially driven into each post. Small holes, cut at appropriate places in the canvas, allow the sides to be covered by wrapping the canvas around the sides and over the protruding heads of the spikes.

Although Huff's tent-style shelter is exceedingly simple, he feels that it has some advantages over a conventional rabbitry. Ventilation, for example, is accomplished by rolling up the front and pulling back the sides of the canvas to allow air flow. Since it's located outdoors, excess moisture soaks into the soil under the cages.

For those who are mixing their own feed, an outdoor shelter like Huff's will allow the rabbits to be directly exposed to sunlight. Therefore, they can produce vitamin D naturally, without the help of commercially produced vitamin supplements in their ration.

Probably the best advantage to this type of rabbitry is the low cost compared to a wood frame building. Even a small wood frame structure will cost a few hundred dollars (unless recycled materials are used) plus the cost of a building permit. If you can find a tarp at a reasonable price, a rabbitry similar to Huff's will cost much less than a wood building. Also, a building permit shouldn't be necessary, since it's not a building at all, just a cage holder.

New tarps are usually quite expensive. If you're unable to find a large used tarp at a reasonable price, it might be cheaper to nail a simple 2 × 4 frame to the poles to serve as a mount for hinged plywood panels. The hinged panels on both sides and front could be opened for ventilation. Obviously, a roof would also be necessary.

Since the small rabbit shelter will only hold two double cages, Huff keeps two more inside the goat barn. A few cages in the goat barn never caused any major problems.

This rabbitry is another example of how Huff has managed to provide shelter for his animals at low or no cost. If, in the past, you've decided against raising livestock on the pretext of high housing costs, think again. There's nearly always a low-cost alternative.

BUILDING THE HOMESTEAD HOG HUT

Many new homesteaders decide against raising animals the first few years, assuming that the cost of building an animal shelter would be prohibitive. There are a few homesteaders who have "beat the system." Bill Cox of Bancroft, Michigan, is a perfect example.

While building his own house, Bill had a lot of other things to spend money on besides a hog house. Still, the thought of a few hundred pounds of home-grown pork in the freezer was tempting. Instead of deciding not to raise a hog or spending money when he ought not to, he elected to build a low-cost hog hut from mostly natural materials.

Bill started by cutting down several post-size locust trees that were on his property. With the posts, he built a pen large enough to accommodate the few feeder pigs he buys each year. More posts were installed inside the pen at one end to serve as the walls and roof support of the house.

The posts were laid out in a rectangular configuration. At the top of each post, Bill nailed a board running horizontally to the next post. These boards serve as a brace to hold the posts straight and a support for the roofing materials. Small diameter poles were laid on top of the supports, then tar paper and loose straw on top of that to serve as a roof (Fig. 4-22).

Instead of having a level layer of straw, Bill heaped the straw in a big pile. Its curvature allows much of the rain to run off the roof, rather than soak in and cause excessive weight on the framing members.

Bill installed fencing around the entire perimeter of the pen and around the posts of the hog house. On the other side of the fence, he stacked straw bales around the poles of the shelter for walls. Obviously, the fencing attached to the poles of the shelter prevent the walls from being knocked down by rambunctious pigs.

The sight of a straw bale shelter is pretty rare nowadays. Similar structures were commonplace many years ago in the wheat belt of this country. Homes, animal shelters, and even large barns were often built of

Fig. 4-22. Building with straw bales helps beat the high cost of materials.

straw bales, since they had an overabundance of this natural renewable resource.

Construction techniques varied considerably. One method was to lay the bales up like blocks or bricks, with the upper bales overlapping the lower by one-half of the length of the bale. Then small diameter stakes were driven into each end of two or more bales to keep them from shifting. Sometimes the outer face of bales were coated with stucco to waterproof them.

Bill's hog hut has seen service for two years now. Although one wall did fall down, it appears as though the shelter could stand for another year or two without extensive repairs. Bill plans to replace the roofing with another bale of straw next year. Unlike most roofing jobs, the waste from this shelter can be used as compost in the garden.

Like many homesteaders. Bill raises his pigs from spring to fall to keep chores during the winter months at a minimum. It seems that a slightly modified straw bale shelter would make an excellent winter hog house, since straw is a very good insulator. A four-wall shelter with a burlap sack tacked at the top for a door would be adequate.

No doubt there are some disadvantages to raising a hog during the winter months. Raising pork year 'round eliminates the need for extra storage space in the cellar or freezer. Although weight gains would be slower during the cold months (more food is required to keep the animal warm), the additional cost for feed would be less than the cost of another freezer plus the electricity it would use.

Bill estimates the total cost for his hog hut at $15. So for the price of a dinner for two at a decent restaurant, Bill Cox built a hog hut that will enable him to provide his family with a year-round supply of pork. If he ever decides to build a more permanent hog dwelling, he'll undoubtedly be able to justify the expense, considering all of the years he's been able to raise pork in his low-cost hog hut.

SALVAGING OLD BUILDINGS

A year ago Jim Woehrle's township in northern Minnesota put the old town hall up for sale on bids. The highest bidder would have the privilege of tearing it down.

Woehrle's $250 bid for the hall was accepted and he became the owner of a 30′ × 75′ monster with a gable height of 30′. Inside there was an expanse of maple flooring. Narrow tongue and groove white pine boards covered its walls and ceiling. Outside were a sea of metal roofing and enough drop siding to cover a large barn.

Since Woehrle and his wife Janet had moved from the city less than a year before, they had plenty of building plans that required lots of building material for their 80-acre homestead. They knew the $250 town hall would supply them with everything needed to complete their homestead projects—without having to go in debt (Fig. 4-23).

If your finances are anything like the Woehrles' one trip to the local

Fig. 4-23. The town hall will keep Woehrle's homestead supplied with building materials for a long time.

lumber yard will bring tears to your eyes. Example: One 2 × 4 8' long costs $1.80—2 × 6s cost $2.80 for an eight footer, $4.20 for a 12 footer and $5.84 for a 16 footer. One-inch boards 6" wide cost $2.16 for an 8 footer, $3.24 for a 12 footer, and $4.32 for a 16' board (northern Minnesota prices).

Any building project larger than a bird house will cost you a bundle at these prices. These are prices for planed lumber: rough sawed lumber costs less, about $175 per 1,000 board feet. (A board foot is 1 square foot of wood 1" thick or its equivalent; one 2 × 6, 8' long is 8 board feet.) To have rough sawed lumber planed costs about $35 per 1,000 board feet.

Is salvaging building material worth the time? You probably won't be paying yourself $5 per hour for your time, but you'll get an awful lot of good stuff for next to nothing.

How much should you pay for an old building? Try not to pay anything. Woehrle bid $250 for a town hall that produced a mountain of boards, siding, metal roofing, maple flooring, 2 × 4s and 2 × 6s—enough stock to keep his homestead projects supplied for quite awhile.

How long will it take to tear down a building? It will probably take about three times longer than you think. This was Woehrle's experience. What he thought would be a two month job ended up taking about five months of part and full time work over a cold Minnesota winter. Time is a big consideration especially if there is a deadline for having the building down (as was Woehrle's case). Also, if you have other commitments or deadlines, remember that salvaging takes a long time espcially if you plan to save as much as possible. There's a big difference between salvaging and demolition.

Another factor that determines whether all that nailed together lumber is worth the work depends on what kind of wood it is. Know your wood! The structure that Woehrle bought was built with six different kinds: basswood, poplar, white pine, red pine, balsam fir, and tamarack. If you're not sure what kind of lumber the building is made of, find out. Ask an old-timer to help you identify it. The softer woods—poplar, basswood and balsam fir—tend to dry rot after awhile. Even though a board may look sound, there's a chance it may be rotten where it crosses supports. To test for dry rot, stick a sharp nail into a suspicious board. If it's like poking a piece of Styrofoam you've found dry rot. If you find a lot of this punky wood you'd better start looking for another organized assortment of boards to dismantle.

Is rough sawed lumber okay to use? If your prize is made of rough sawed boards and dimension material (2 × 4s and 2 × 6s), the stuff won't be uniform. It will vary in thickness and width. This can cause problems when using the lumber for studs and wall sheathing—the inside walls will be uneven because of the variation in width since it isn't planed to a certain dimension. If you're thinking of getting your used material planed at a local mill, you'll probably find the mill won't plane used lumber because one little nail can really mess up a planer. Used rough sawed lumber is still great for outbuildings and other homestead projects.

Before the nails fly, here's another thought. How about moving the building? If the structure is a type and size you can use, maybe you should just move it. Woehrle's town hall had an 18 × 24' addition that was moved to his place one mile away (Fig. 4-24).

What's required? You need timbers to put underneath the thing to be moved, blocking to put under the timbers, and a jack (hydraulic jacks work best). Woehrle met a man in a neighboring town that moved buildings as a sideline. He dropped off the timbers, and Woehrle jacked up the building so the timbers could be slid underneath. Then the timbers were jacked to a height of 3' so dollies could be place under the 12 × 12 timbers. It took about a week to prepare for the move home. On moving day a neighbor and his truck were hired to pull the "soon to be garage-workshop" home. So for one week's work the Woehrles got a garage-workshop complete with chimney. Moving saves a lot of time—no salvaging, no building. How much did it cost to move? It cost a pickup load of firewood for the truck and drive and $35 for the use of the timbers and dollies.

Here are the necessary tools of destruction (Fig. 4-25). A nail puller is required. Nail pullers are a real headache to use because the jaws must be whammed down on either side of the nail head, and then the handle is pulled toward you. If you're working on walls, your arms will hold out for about 10 minutes of whamming and pulling at a time. Nail pullers are really designed for working on horizontal surfaces. They're great for pulling nails out of subflooring and roof boards. Although nail pullers are really slow, they do make a neat little gouge in the board where the nail was. They reduce the chance of splitting the board.

The nail claw and hammer are ideal for pulling nails out of wall boards and siding. The claw does leave a larger gouge than the nail puller but it's two to three times faster and a lot easier on the body. The trick is to bang the claw under the nail head and yank it so the head is a little above the surface of the board. Then finish pulling the nail out with a hammer.

The crowbar is your basic salvaging tool. It's best to have a couple of them, one large bar for prying apart dimension lumber and a smaller one for

Fig. 4-24. The building will make a fine garage-workshop.

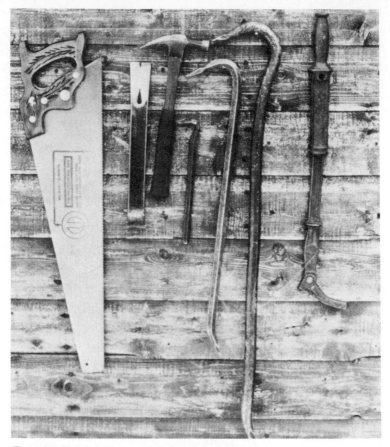

Fig. 4-25. The tools used to salvage a building.

boards. Woehrle borrowed an old hand-made 36″ crowbar that worked wonders for prying apart 2 × 4s and 2 × 6s.

Another prying tool that's handy for removing windows and door frames is a "wonder bar." It's a piece of flat steel with a slight curve at one end and a 90° bend at the other. The wonder bar's thin, wide blade allows you to pry without doing much damage to the wood.

A chain saw works great for cutting out floor joists and beams, but watch out for nails. If you're working on a tall building get a 40′ wooden ladder. There's nothing like a sense of security when you're working 30′ in the air. A wooden ladder has a wide base and its weight gives it some stability.

For removing shingles, a shovel with a square edge works the best. Push the shovel underneath the shingles and then down towards the roof; up come the shingles.

120

A good place to start removing board is on the inside of the building. That way the boards won't get wet. If there are tongue and groove boards, remember to always start prying on the tongue side (that's where the nails are). The tongue side of the board is generally the top of the wall if the boards are horizontal. After the wall boards and ceiling have been removed, the toughest job remaining is the hardwood flooring (if you're lucky enough to have it).

When it comes to removing hardwood flooring, the easiest way Woehrle found to get the stubborn things up is to start on the side of the room that has the tongue as the leading edge. Woehrle wired a piece of flooring to the handle of the wonder bar so he could work in a standing position. Since hardwood flooring is tongue and grooved on three sides, special care must be taken to get it up without splitting out the edges. By using the wonder bar's 90° prying edge Woehrle carefully worked up the entire 30′ run of boards from one end of the room to the other, and worked them up a little more on the way back until they popped loose.

Make sure you get the floor up before you take the roof off. If the flooring gets wet and warps, all those little grooves won't match, or once you've installed it you'll be listening to a symphony of creaking nails as the flooring dries.

After the flooring is up, take out all the windows. If you don't you will wind up breaking them when you start working on the outside. With the inside finished, you're ready to start on the roof.

When it comes to removing the roof, especially a steep one, use an extension ladder laid flat on the roof with a good rope tied to its top rung. Tie the other end of the rope to something sturdy on the other side of the building. This will make working on the roof safer and easier. Whatever you do, don't anchor the rope that you have tied to the ladder to your car or truck.

Woehrle's town hall was topped with a truckload of metal roofing— 3,500 square feet of it. Use a nail claw and a hammer for pulling nails out of metal roofing and be careful not to tear the metal when pulling out the nails. Beneath the metal roofing on his hall, Woehrle found a layer of cedar shinges—3,500 square feet of it. Here the square bladed shovel came into play.

Once all the roofing is removed, start taking the roof boards off beginning at the bottom. After you get the first row of the boards off, you'll be able to stand on the edge of the board. About 3′ up the roof, take the second row of boards off and so on all the way to the peak. You've made yourself a ladder all the way up the roof! Now you can work your way back and forth across the roof removing boards as you go.

With the roof boards off, the next step is to remove the rafters. Since the span in Woehrle's building was 30′, he cut the trussed rafters at the top of the wall and let them drop to the inside.

With the roof off, all that remains are the walls. With a nail claw and a hammer, remove the siding. When Woehrle pulled the nails out of the siding, he put a piece of plastic on the ground beneath him to catch the nails as they fell. Save as many nails as possible; at 59 cents per pound it doesn't take long for them to add up.

With the siding out of the way, Woehrle was ready to take off the sheathing. This is where he made a mistake. Instead of removing the sheathing the same way, he removed the siding very slowly with a nail claw and hammer, Woehrle decided to speed things up. He cut each wall at the corner and dropped the walls to the outside. He didn't drop them to the inside (which would have been best) because he had piles of scrap lumber lying there and didn't feel like moving it.

Once the wall was down with the studs on top, it meant taking a crowbar and prying the 2 × 4s off the sheathing. He ended up cracking a large percentage of the boards. Time was saved but not the lumber, and saving boards is what salvaging is all about.

After the walls were down, all that remained were the floor joist, foundation blocks and a huge pile of scrap lumber. There is nothing in the world finer than super-dry pine, poplar and basswood boards for starting fires. Woehrle hauled most of the scrap lumber home and used a circle saw to cut it up into stove lengths. He now has a two year supply of kindling.

The final and perhaps most important step is storage for the salvaged building material. Luckily Woehrle had a barn to store the boards. He stacked the dimension lumber outside on skids. He left ½″ board about every 4′ across the top of each layer so air could circulate through the pile. Without air circulation the wood will rot. It's a good idea to cover the top of the pile to keep the rain off your lumber. One important thing to remember when stacking boards is to try and get the skids level with each other so your boards don't get bent out of shape. If you're going to stack your boards inside with no spacers, make sure the boards are dry before you stack them or they will rot.

Would Woehrle salvage another building? Yes, but he'd never tackle another giant alone. Due to the mind numbing task of pulling nails, he would find a talkative friend to help.

Why pay exorbitant prices for new lumber, metal roofing, siding, and flooring when the used variety works just as well? Sure, salvaging is a lot of work, but it's a sure way to keep down the cost of homestead building projects.

BUILDING A WOODSHED

Now that many people heat their homes exclusively with wood, they tend to accumulate a large supply of firewood which needs protection from the elements both before and during the heating season. It is not unusual for an average family's well-insulated house, heated with an airtight stove or two, to require four or five cords of dry hardwood per winter. A supply of that size, stacked and split, calls for a considerable amount of space. A cord alone takes up 128 cubic feet.

The benefits of any woodshed are hard to beat. Besides keeping the fuel dry and rot-free, thus ensuring hotter fires and less creosote formation within the stove and flue, a woodshed's walls allow higher, yet less tippable stacking, an important consideration in the presence of children and pets. Besides, it's a nice feeling to have your fuel supply under roof and ready to use. You can also gauge your rate of usage better.

The ideal location for a woodshed is somewhere near the house— close enough to make an easy walk through the snow with an armload of firewood, yet far enough to keep the various wood-eating bugs (cockroaches, termites, ants, and more) away from the tempting framework of your dwelling.

Here is a large and sturdy, yet inexpensive and pleasingly proportioned woodshed (Fig. 4-26). Use pressure-treated framing members throughout, and a galvanized corrugated roof. The three walls are ½" CDX plywood painted on both sides with a preservative stain. The total cost of materials was $200. See Table 4-2.

Needless to say, all of the pressure treated wood is hand-picked from the lumber yard. The preserving process, coupled with questionable quality control from sawmill to retailer, leaves much of the lumber "crooked as a dog's leg."

Start by choosing a fairly level site and digging four holes 2½-3' deep. Use a tape measure to position the holes and square their alignment by measuring the diagonals.

A shovelful of gravel is placed in the holes for drainage. The posts are inserted, and the earth is tamped tightly around each one as you check and recheck for plumb with a spirit level.

Then the bottom, middle, and back top plates are toenailed level across the three sides. When you determine the exact height of the roof and its pitch, saw and notch the four posts to accept the 2 × 6 side beams.

Fig. 4-26. A large woodshed.

Table 4-2. Materials List for the Woodshed.

2 pieces 4'×4'×12'
2 pieces 4'×4'×10'
6 pieces 2'×6'×14'
4 pieces 2'×6'×10'
3 pieces 2'×4'×12'
8 pieces 2×4'×8'
7 pieces ½" CDX plywood
7 pieces 2'×10' galvanized corrugated roofing
3 lbs. 16d nails
5 lbs. 8d nails
5 lbs. lead-head roofing nails
1½ gal. preservative stain (available in many colors)

Now you were ready for the roof rafters. By lining up the six of them on sawhorses, you can square up, measure, and notch all six at once.

Place the rafters crown-up, at right angles to the pitch, 24" on center. Then drove their notches snugly onto the side beams and toenail each juncture with six 16d nails.

Measure and cut the rake boards and nail them into the butt ends of the rafters. The roof system fits together perfectly.

The plywood gives the shed its final structural integrity. Each of the seven pieces, three sawn square and four sawn on pitch, is tacked up with 8d nails every 6-8". Additional blocking at each seam is added: 2 × 4s cut to fit between the plates, toenailed top and bottom and tacked from the plywood side. A small brace is placed midway along the back wall, tying in the first and second roof rafters with the top plate.

Installing the galvanized roofing is a cinch. There are a few rules to remember: nail through the corrugation crests, never the troughs, space nails every three or four crests, and overlap at least one crest between panels. Naturally, the edges of the roof are nailed tightly, every 6" or so, to keep wind lift from tearing away the panels. Apply a thick coating of preservative stain inside and out.

FRUIT AND VEGETABLE BIN

A considerable amount of time and effort is spent on growing fruits and vegetables, so why not construct a special storage bin which will aid in prolonging shelf life by eliminating bruises and providing air circulation?

This storage bin only takes up 4½ square feet of floor space and may be stacked as high as desired. Each set of three bins will hold about 75 pounds of apples, potatoes, onions, etc (Fig. 4-27). If you wish to paint your finished bins, be sure to use nontoxic paint.

Cut out four pieces of pine board 1 × 12 × 18". Drill four ¾" holes as shown for ventilation. Then cut two pieces, 1 × 12 × 36", and nail in place for top and back. Next cut out and nail a 1 × 6 × 36" front panel in position; then cut out a ¼ × 19½ × 36" plywood bottom (Fig. 4-28).

Fig. 4-27. A storage bin for fruits and vegetables.

To reduce costs, scrap lumber or other materials may be substituted, as long as the strength is not diminished. This is important for stacking.

Three sections stacked will be about 37″ high and will hold about four bushels of fruit and vegetables.

COMPOST PRIVY

Privy building requires the application of common sense and science, according to the Farallones Institute, designers of a do-it-yourself compost-

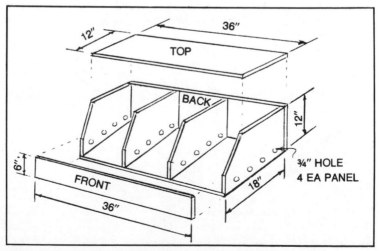

Fig. 4-28. Construction details for the fruit and vegetable bin.

Fig. 4-29. The compost privy can be used where sewer hookups or septic tanks are unavailable or not practical.

ing toilet. Unlike the famous *Ecolet* and *Clivus* composting johns, The Farallones concept is strictly a privy, an outdoor toilet. Farallones is an appropriate technology research group, not a manufacturer. Plans for their composting privy are contained in "Technical Bulletin No. 1" from Farallones, 15290 Coleman Valley Road, Occidental, CA 95465 for $2.

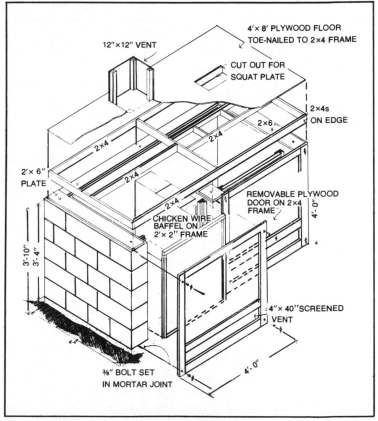

Fig. 4-30. Construction details for the compost privy.

Table 4-3. Materials List for the Compost Privy.

⅔ cu. yard concrete for slab and grout
one sack mortar
concrete blocks:
    40 8″×16″ stretchers
    20 8″×16″ corners
    10 half blocks
two 2′×6′×8′ redwood plates
two 2′×4′×8′ redwood boards
fourteen 2′×4′×4′ redwood boards
two 2′×2′×4′ redwood boards
forty linear feet rebar ⅜″, 4′ lengths
eight 7″×⅜″ diameter galvanized
    carriage bolts with wingnuts
one sheet 4′×8′×⅝″ plywood
eight 10″ foundation bolts, nuts, washers

The compost privy is designed to decompose human excrement and organic household waste in a safe and sanitary manner without the use of water or plumbing. The compost privy takes the place of the flush toilet, the septic tank, and the garbage can. It can be used where sewer hookups or septic tanks are unavailable or not practical and it saves water normally flushed through the toilet—about half the annual domestic water consumption—7,000 to 10,000 gallons per person is saved each year (Fig. 4-29).

The compost privy designed by Farallones can be built by amateur builders using common materials and common tools for less than $300, a savings of up to several thousand dollars over the usual flush toilet/ plumbing/septic tank combination. The compost privy returns valuable nutrients and humus to the soil. Between 1 to 2 cubic feet of humus are produced from each person's excreta in a year.

The compost privy does not receive waste water other than urine. Household waste water from sinks, bath, and shower may be diverted into the garden, recycled through a solar still, or emptied into a sump pit and leaching lines. The proper operation of the privy requires your attention: a simple ritual, 30 minutes twice a month to turn the pile. You are managing a complex biological machine that has no moving parts.

The privy consists of a two-chamber concrete box 4′ by 8′ by 8′ outside dimension. Each chamber has a capacity of 1 cubic yard. The plywood top is fitted with an opening "squat plate" over one chamber to receive excrement, household wastes, and additional high carbon content organic matter. The front of the box has two removable plywood doors with screened air inlet vents. A 12″ square plywood vent stack, screened on top, allows passage of exhaust gases up and out (Fig. 4-30). Once or twice a month the pile is turned and mixed with a pitchfork and/or a flat shovel stored within the compost chamber and used exclusively for this purpose. After six months, the pile is turned to the storage compartment to the left (or right) for at least six months of final composting and aging before it is removed for use in the orchard or flower garden. As an added factor of safety Farallones researchers recommend not using the compost directly in the vegetable garden but on fruit trees and shrubs or ornamental plantings. Following is the construction sequence. See Table 4-3.

- ☐ Level site, layout, place vertical rebar.
- ☐ Pour the slab.
- ☐ Lay blocks, cure 24 hours.
- ☐ Fabricate the top, access panels.
- ☐ Place the vent stack.
- ☐ Make a squat plate.
- ☐ Build the enclosure.

Chapter 5

Ways with Water

Homesteaders must have an adequate water supply. Water is required for many tasks, and homesteaders must use it wisely. Read on for some interesting information regarding water.

DIGGING WELLS

Of the three main types of wells, dug wells are the oldest and the most widespread. Their main disadvantages in the United States are the constantly lowering water table and increased pollution. These two factors usually necessitate going down to water-bearing rock far below the range of pick and shovel (although there are dug wells that go as deep as 400').

In certain favorable locations or where machinery cannot be used, digging may not only be useful; it may be the only method. Hand-dug wells are usually circular for reason of economy and strength. Experience has shown that a diameter of about 3-4' is necessary for one man to work comfortably. Two men can work in a hole 4-5' in diameter. Since it has been found that two men working together are more than twice as efficient as one man working alone, the larger size is probably more common. There appears to be no advantage to making the well larger than necessary.

A lining of permanent materials is necessary to keep the ground water from seeping into the well and contaminating it. Built as the well-digging progresses, linings also protect against cave-ins. The lining also serves as a foundation for the well cover and the pumping or hoisting mechanism.

Reinforced concrete is plainly the first choice for linings, although masonry or brickwork can also be used. Uneven pressures can make the latter two bulge and weaken. Therefore, they must be thicker than concrete linings. They are also more difficult to work with in the confined space of a hole in the ground.

Concrete forms can be precast at the site. A thickness of 3" in good ground, to 5" in bad, is usually considered sufficient. (Bad ground would be shifting sand, shales, etc.)

For the actual digging, a hole about 4' deep is dug first, and shutters are set in place. These lining shutters extend about 6" above ground level, and earth is tamped in solid around them. The purpose is to prevent rounding of the edges of the excavation, which not only makes extra work, but might also be dangerous to anyone working in the hole. The shutter remains in place during the sinking of the well and until the section is concreted.

The experts then construct plumbing rods so they can make sure the hole is going down vertically. This consists of a crosspiece that can be fitted into an exact position over the center of the well. A hook over the exact center supports the trimming rods. These rods are the exact diameter of the well. When lowered into the excavation, they enable the digger to not only keep the sides straight and even, but they also ensure the hole is the right size from top to bottom. (A variation of as much as 1" will result in 33 percent more concrete being used.)

Then, with your miner's pick, bar and short-handled shovel, you dig. In reasonably hard and dry ground, it should be possible to take the first "lift" (that's well-digger talk for sections of the hole) to about 15'. Then you're ready for lining.

The hole is 15' deep. The bottom is leveled. The mouth is still protected by the shutters. The next step is setting another shutter (a form, really) at the bottom of the hole. This should be about 2' high and is usually made of metal. This first form is of extreme importance: if it isn't exactly centered and leveled, the entire hole will be thrown out of kilter. Push loose earth behind the forms. Twenty-foot lengths of reinforcing rod are pushed into this earth, so they extend 5' above the top of the well. The number of rods required varies with the type of ground. Under normal conditions, seven is the usual number, but as many as 19 may be required in shifting ground.

The rods are supported 1½" from the face of the well, throughout their length, by pins fastened or twisted to the rods and forced into the earthen sides of the well.

A second set of shutters is then placed in position above the first. The space behind is filled with concrete. (Be sure to coat the shutters with old engine oil to prevent the concrete from sticking to them.)

The concrete is mixed at a proportion of 5:2½:1 of gravel, sand, and cement. A convenient way of measuring is by constructing two wooden, bottomless boxes. They should be 30" by 30". Make one 12" deep for measuring gravel and the other 6" deep for sand. When mixed with 100 pounds of cement, the proportions will be correct. This quantity should be just about right to fill behind one 2' high shutter. The gravel should pass through a ¾" mesh, and the sand should be sharp river sand. Both should be clean and free from soil or clay. (Likewise, the water used should be clean.)

Tamp the concrete carefully into the shutter to avoid air spaces, but be careful not to disturb the reinforcing rods. Leave the top of the concrete rough, so it makes a good bond with the next layer.

When the pouring behind this second shutter has been completed, then make the first curb. This is a groove in the earth side of the well immediately above the top of the second shutter. The groove should be about 8″ high and cut into the side of the well about a foot. One pin for each reinforcing rod is driven into this groove, and a hooked end of the pin is fastened to the reinforcing rod. A horizontal rod is put in place and fastened to each pin and vertical rod. Concrete is then handfilled into the curb all around. The third set of shutters is put into place, and concrete is poured behind it. With the fixing of the third shutter, the top will be too high to reach, so subsequent stages will have to be reached from a bosun's chair suspended with a ½″ rope from the winch.

Then set two more sets of shutters in place and cement. The top is now 5′ below ground level. The concrete should be left overnight before proceeding.

The weakest part of the well is at ground level. For this reason, the top section is made 6″ thick. To do this, excavate to a diameter of 5′ (if the well is 4½′ in diameter).

The shutters below are left in position (leave them a week at least, so the concrete cures), but the one at the surface must be removed. Be careful not to disturb the plumbing pegs, which hold the plumbing rods. Three more shutters are added and concreted, one at a time. Before concreting the top lining, bend the tops of the reinforcing rods around the well at about 2″ above ground level. Pour concrete to 6″ above ground level to keep surface water out and protect the well from falling debris.

The first lift is now complete—you have 13′ of the concrete lining supported on the curb, 6″ of wall above ground, and the bottom 2′ of unlined excavation.

The process continues until the aquifer is reached. The only problem you might run into in subsequent sections is where the top of the second lift meets the bottom of the first. One solution is to make precast tongued bricks. These can be forced into concrete in the opening, forming a snug fit.

When the aquifer is reached, it's impossible to pour concrete. Then precast caisson rings must be used. These rings, cast on the surface some weeks before use, have an inside diameter of 3′, 1″ and an outside diameter of 3′ 10″. Each cylinder is 2′ high. The rings are made with four equidistant ⅝″ rods embedded in the walls, and four equidistant holes to accept the rods from the caisson, immediately below. The rods project 2′ above the top surface (for 2′ caissons) and the holes have widened tops so the rods can be bolted and still be flush. The first ring is lowered into the well. When the second is lowered, it has to be maneuvered so that the rods from the ring below penetrate the holes of the ring above. These are bolted tightly together. When four or five rings are firmly bolted together, sinking continues by hand digging inside the caisson. As the caisson goes down, more rings are added until water is entering at such a rate that bailing with the kibble is no longer possible. You've hit the bottom.

The space between the lining and the caisson must not be filled with cement mortar or stone. The caisson may settle later without breaking the lining.

According to the nature of the aquifer, water may enter the well through the bottom or through the walls. When the latter method is preferred (and it usually is), the caissons must be made of porous concrete. This is accomplished by mixing the concrete with no sand (which fills air spaces) doing little tamping, and mixing with as little water as possible. Obviously, such concrete is not as strong as that made with sand, and proper curing is even more essential than usual.

Sound complicated or like more work and bother than you were prepared for? Well, if you were a pioneer—or if you happen to have land in one of the few remaining areas where you can get water without going to great depths—the pioneer's method might just work for you.

Just dig a hole of the desired diameter and depth. The material excavated is put into boxes or buckets and hoisted out of the hole with ropes. When water is reached, bail out the water with the solid material. The drier you can keep the hole, the deeper you can go, and the more water your well will produce.

When you have gone as deep as possible, lay round stones around the perimeter of the bottom, 2' to 3' high. From there on up to the surface, just lay a stone (or brick) and mortar wall. This method will not make a well as strong as the one formerly described and it's harder to make the walls waterproof (to keep out contaminated groundwater).

Concrete or clay tiles make excellent well casing and can be placed quickly and easily into the well by the use of a simple A-frame or other temporary structure for lowering tile into a well. Note the outside, protective layer of concrete which extends down to a 3 m (10') minimum to ensure watertightness of the upper walls (Fig. 5-1).

Figure 5-2 shows a dug well and an outside protective cover of concrete. At the well bottom are two different types of construction: one, built-up, round stones offering a filter wall, and the other, a concrete shoe. Stones must be laid up after the wall is completely excavated and are practical only in areas of coarse sand and gravel. The concrete shoe is employed where the well casing is sunk as the excavation progresses and is usually more practical in fine sand. A protective, graded sand filter should be built up in the bottom of this well.

CISTERNS

When planning your water requirements, don't forget the water from the sky. Rainwater can have many uses around the homestead. It's ideal for laundry, because it's softer than most ground water. It can be used for irrigation and might be especially useful during dry periods when your well water is rationed for more important uses. Rainwater shouldn't be used for drinking, either for humans or livestock. Besides not being clean, it lacks the minerals of ground water.

One inch of rain falling on 100 square feet of surface is about 62 gallons. Allowing for evaporation and other losses, about 50 gallons can be expected to reach storage. So if the roof area is 450 square feet and annual rainfall is 28", you could theoretically collect 6300 gallons of rain water a year.

Roofs are dirty, so you have to devise a means of allowing the surface to be flushed before water is diverted to the *cistern*. There will be light rains where no water at all will reach storage. Also, precipitation falling as snow is largely lost. It's a rare cistern that is 100 percent watertight. So the actual water collected will be much less than the theoretical volume.

The most common kind of cistern is built below ground and is constructed of masonry, although it seems concrete would be more practical in most cases. It must be watertight, both to prevent the contents from seeping out and to prevent ground water from seeping in. It will have to be

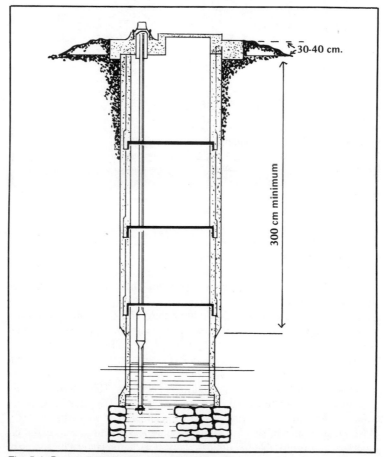

30-40 cm.

300 cm minimum

Fig. 5-1. Dug well lined with concrete or clay tile.

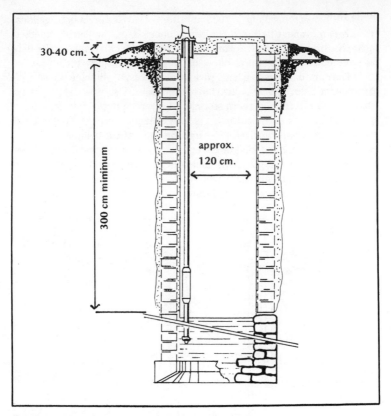

Fig. 5-2. Dug well with protective casing and platform.

cleaned occasionally, and all but the best manhole covers will admit mice, toads, and similar delectables you don't want in your water supply.

Water in a new or repaired masonry cistern is likely to be hard because of dissolved lime from the plaster or cement. Thorough curing will help prevent this problem.

Some authorities advise deducting a third of the rainfall for leakage, roof washing, etc. If you want to store water over the winter months, take that into account. Since 1 cubic foot holds 7.5 gallons, you can easily determine the size of the cistern you need (if you know how much water you want).

There is always some sedimentation in cisterns. This, along with the bugs and things, make annual cleaning a necessity. This should be done when the water level is lower. Since this is likely to be when the water is most valuable, it will require some planning and discretion. In cases of emergency, it is possible to eliminate foul odors in the cistern by adding a quart of water mixed with a tablespoon of chloride of lime.

RAIN TRAPS

Rain traps have been used for providing water for livestock in areas of light precipitation (Fig. 5-3). It has also been suggested that they may have uses for domestic and irrigation water in areas of heavier rainfall.

The trap is much like a cistern, but instead of relying on a roof, the "catchment liner" (made of watertight sheeting) is spread on the ground, enabling rainfall from a much larger area to be utilized.

The liner is usually made of butyl, a synthetic rubber, which resists aging from heat, sunlight, and ozone. It is tough, flexible at low temperatures, and resistant to damage from most chemicals. Liners up to 54' by 54' are available in one piece, and it's possible to cement two or more together.

A 54' square catchment liner will trap 1,557 gallons of water for each inch of rain. Storage bags may be made from two pieces of butyl cemented together.

DRIVEN WELLS

Driven wells are an alternative that many people forget about. All you need is a driving point, pipe, and a special hammer for driving. Diameter is most commonly 1½" so don't expect to use an old oaken bucket with this type.

There are many methods of driving wells, but basically all you're doing is sticking a pipe into the ground as far as possible and then adding a new section that's driven. Keep up the process until you hit water (and then some, for a steadily producing well).

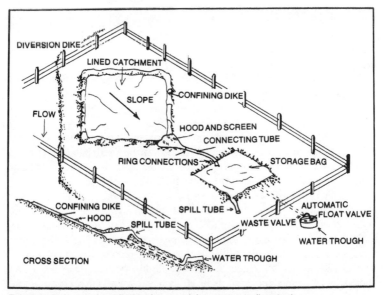

Fig. 5-3. Rain trap installation for supplying water to livestock.

135

Fig. 5-4. A driven well.

When the pump is installed, it's necessary to fill the suction column with clean water and to exhaust the air in it. The water coming out will be muddy at first, but should clear up after an hour or so of pumping.

To ensure a steady flow of water, "open" the well by removing the fine earth or sand particles around the drive point. If you're using an ordinary pitcher pump, raise the handle high for a moment, thus allowing the water in the column to drop suddenly. Then resume pumping immediately and vigorously. This process should be repeated several times.

If you hit rock, pull the rig and start some place else. You might have to pull the pipes, however, if you don't hit water within the depth limits you've set or if you hit a boulder or something (Fig. 5-4).

FILTERING WATER

There are three ways of purifying water for household use: *boiling; chemical disinfection* (chloride, iodine, or potassium permanganate); and *filtration* either through a sand or ceramic filter.

A simple household sand filter can be made wherever fine sand is available. The essential points to remember are that the water must pass through at least 2' of sand (and more if possible), and the rate of flow should not exceed 4 gallons per square foot per hour.

Cut the head out of a steel drum. Place the drum on a stand, and drill a 3/32" hole in the bottom. Fill the bottom few inches with pea-size stones, then fill to within 4" of the top with fine sand. Make a hole just below the top rim for an overflow, connecting a pipe to carry off excess water.

To operate the filter, keep a continuous flow of water running in at the top, just sufficient to keep the filter filled, with a slight overflow. (It might be necessary to put something under the inflow to keep from washing a *hole* in the sand.) A 30" high, 24" diameter drum should deliver about 12 gallons an hour. This water is just filtered: chlorination may still be necessary.

Covering the filter to keep it dark will eliminate green algae. The filter should not be cleaned too often, as its efficiency results from bacteriological growth in the sand. When it becomes necessary to clean it, just scrape off a

136

¼" layer of sand. After several such cleanings, additional clean sand should be added.

BALANCING THE SMALL FARM POND

A problem which often confronts homesteaders is one of finding their ponds becoming ecologically unbalanced in terms of the fish population. This becomes apparent when the water looks murky, turgid, and generally unhealthy. Although there can be several reasons for this condition, a common one is an over-abundance of fish relative to the breeds found in the pond. If small ponds are not fished hard and frequently, this unbalance can occur quite rapidly.

When George Jerman moved to his present homestead in Texas, some five years ago, he was confronted with just such a situation. Being a city bred soul, with little knowledge of fishing and its related problems, he soon found that his three ponds were in trouble ecologically, thanks to the help and knowledge of local farmers and the state biologist. His ponds are roughly ¾ of an acre, ½ acre, and ¼ acre in size. If ponds of this size are not fished hard and regularly, the fish population can explode in numbers, with devastating results. The fish start fighting for food and space. Due to an inadequate balance within their ranks, they become dwarfed in size and fishing can become quite poor.

"Wild" fish (which are usually introduced into the pond through feeder streams), runoff and eggs (brought in mainly by birds) can further complicate the situation. These fish can be anything from bottom-feeding *shad*, carp, or catfish to bluegill or bream. Bottom feeders are one of the main causes of muddy, stirred water when over population occurs. When the food chain in relatively small-sized ponds is disturbed, the stocked fish such as bass and bluegill, which the bass prey upon for food, begin their population explosion! The bass are natural harvesters in this situation. When the food chain is thus interrupted, the bluegill proliferates at an alarming rate, starting a chain reaction which results in the dwarfing effect on the fish. The results are pitiful to see. Jerman has observed bass with 2 pound bodies and heads that would indicate that they should in fact weigh more than 3 pounds!

The solution is to kill off all existing fish and restock the pond with the proper ratio of bass to bluegill. One of the safest and most efficient ways to accomplish this is to use a nontoxic powder called *rotenone*. A 5 percent solution of rotenone may be found at most feed or garden stores. Jerman used the powder at the rate of 10 pounds for his ¾ acre pond and divided 10 pounds between the two smaller ponds. Scatter the powder on the surface of the pond and stir it in with a couple of paddles or, better yet, use a small outboard motor. It is important to distribute the powder as evenly as possible, so it reaches all parts of the pond. The results will be dramatic. Within 10-15 minutes the smaller fish will rise to the surface, grasping for air. Rotenone paralyzes a nerve in the fish and they are unable to breathe. Within 18 hours the entire population of fish should be floating on the surface of the water. If you net the larger fish *immediately* upon seeing them surface, and before they die, then you can have one heck of a fish fry. The rotenone is not toxic to mammals and will do no harm to the other pond inhabitants. The dead fish may be composted or used as fertilizer in the garden. Some fish will sink to the bottom and help to refertilize the pond. If you have ducks or other animals that eat fish, do not allow them to eat any of the decayed fish. Jerman was not aware of this and lost many fine ducks to a case of *botulism*.

The ponds will be safe to restock in about two-three weeks. This should be done as soon as possible in order to start the natural balance back on course again. The local parks and wildlife agent can advise you as to proper proportions and quantities of fish to stock for the size of your particular pond. Many states will supply free fish for the asking.

There are other methods of harvesting overstocked and un-balanced ponds, including seining, draining the pond, etc., but for ease and effectiveness, rotenone is hard to beat!

WINTERIZING A SPRING

In rural areas of the country everyone has to have some source of water to supply their own needs. There is a variety of choices open to the homeowner when he begins to develop his water source and supply. Some choices have high costs, either initially or in the long run; deep-drilled wells, cisterns and ponds all have high initial construction costs. Other choices may not be feasible for your geographic area. If, however, you are fortunate enough to live in an area with shallow aquifiers (water-conducting channels in the earth's subsurface), then you are probably in a situation where these aquifiers can easily be tapped to supply your water needs.

According to the *Encyclopedia Britannica*, springs and seeps are the normal discharge points for water reappearing from the "groundwater phase of the water cycle." A spring is differentiated from a seep by the way the water reaches the ground's surface. A spring has a perceptible current where it emerges onto the land or into another surface water system. Water without a perceptible current is called, quite appropriately, a seep. When one develops a seep, it is commonly called a shallow or dug well or tapping a spring.

Deep wells will not freeze in the winter. A spring, if its water output is sufficiently great, also will not freeze in the winter. What about your common dug well?

It has likely been the experience of many rural residents to have to chop a hole in the ice on top of the water in their spring or seep before being able to use it in the winter. Not only is this a nuisance, it can also be a real trial on a windy, below zero day.

Argie Healey's water source is a seep, dug 8' deep to turn it into a shallow well. In order to keep the water in the pump from freezing, and to make life easier, Argie's husband Dennis decided to build a combination spring and pump house. They already had a wooden, square 4'×4' box sunk into the earth to define the space of the well, to keep it from silting in, and to provide a 900-gallon storage tank. The wood provided a good foundation upon which to begin building.

Dennis purchased a supply of rough-cut lumber. Getting hardwood instead of pine, he considered himself lucky, as he believes that hardwood has better insulating value. He constructed a small 4×4' building extending upwards from the spring box itself (Fig. 5-5). Between each vertical board, he placed another smaller diameter board. This board and batten siding looks good, effectively shuts out drafts, and compensates for shrinking that the unseasoned wood would do.

The Healeys' wood has not shrunk as much as some woods will, though. They used elm which had died several years previously from Dutch Elm disease. This wood, then, was fairly dry, even though it had just been cut into lumber.

The roof on the little building was sloped to the south and covered with black tarpaper to catch the sun's rays. The entire inside of the structure was insulated with sheets of polyurethane foam, and all the cracks were caulked. The door was made to be particularly tight-fitting and also insulated on the inside.

Do you think that this was enough to keep that spring from freezing? It was not. When the temperature dropped into the 'teens and then hovered around zero, a 2" thick layer of ice formed on the water's surface. The insulation was not enough. The Healeys also needed a heat source.

An electric line was run to the spring pump house and a light socket installed, using a regular 100 watt light bulb. With the good insulation, this small amount of heat proved sufficient to keep the spring from getting more than ¼" ice on it.

The Healeys later installed a regular shallow well electric jet pump. The light bulb was not sufficient to keep the air temperature in the building high enough to prevent the water in the pump's storage tank, and the water in the pump mechanism itself, from freezing. An automatic, thermostatically controlled heat tape was wrapped around these parts.

Fig. 5-5. A way to winterize a spring.

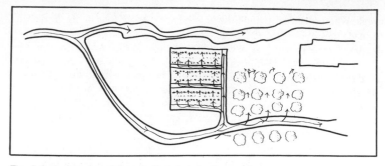

Fig. 5-6. A diagram of Bonnie Bahn's irrigation system.

IRRIGATION BY FLOOD AND FURROW

Bonnie Bahn's homestead has one thing in common with other homesteads everywhere—there is always something that needs doing. The Bahn's have horses, cows, goats, chickens, and dogs. Caring for the animals is only one phase of their homesteading operation. One of the chores that Bonnie Bahn really likes is irrigating her large garden, yard, and a 20 tree orchard. It takes her about ½ hour a day.

The method of irrigation she uses is a form of flood irrigation. Surface irrigation controlled by ditches generally falls into this category. The other major category of irrigation is the use of sprinklers. Sprinklers need pumps and pipes and lots of money to make them run.

In flood irrigation, the water is ditched and when released from the ditch is allowed to run in a sheet over a field. The hay field is irrigated in this way, and this is basically what is done in the orchard. Ditches are necessary because a creek will flow down the lowest channel it can find. By ditching a nearly level channel following the contours of the land, water can be made to flow at a level that is usually considerably higher than the creek. The land below the ditch can be irrigated.

In her garden Bonnie uses many small furrows between the planted rows. This is usually called furrow irrigation and allows very precise control of the water flow and distribution. The experts say that the cost of labor for furrow irrigation is prohibitive. Rows in the garden must be lined up for planting, though, and it is very little extra work to make definite furrows between the rows.

A diagram of the system is in Fig. 5-6. This particular plan wouldn't work for everyone. In Bonnie's case, the orchard is quite a bit higher than the creek which flows parallel to it. She had to walk up the creek until she came to a point as high as the top of the orchard. There must be a slight downhill slope to the point where the water is needed. A gradual slope is much better than a steep one as it will not erode as severely. Determining if you are above the spot to be irrigated can be done visually or by using an engineer's level. Bonnie's husband Alan uses an engineer's level and surveys uphill from the point where he wants the water to go from the creek. When you are digging the ditch by hand, corrections in the grade can be made to some extent while you are actually digging. A ditch that is to be dug by machinery must be accurately laid out before starting to dig.

A combination of laziness and Bonnie's inaccurate surveying caused her ditch to go below the top row of trees in the orchard. She was quite sure that she should go up the creek further to start the ditch, but that would make a longer ditch. Besides, there was a brush-free spot, and she could start the ditch without clearing brush first. The top row of trees are apple trees and don't need a great amount of water. The soil absorbs some water even though it is above the ditch, and this seems to be adequate.

The ditch should open into the creek at a point where it is easy to divert water into it. A concrete or metal headgate is usually used to divert water from a creek to a ditch, but she uses a large rock as a diversion in the creek and controls how much water enters the ditch with several small rocks.

Once one starts digging the ditch, the trick is too keep going downhill without any quick drops. A fall of more than 4" per 100' will tend to cause erosion due to the faster flow of water. If you are into surveying, a fall of about ½" per rod (16½' or 5½ yards) makes a good ditch.

If there is no fall to the ditch, the water will move sluggishly or not at all. This is often called a dead spot. Bonnie's ditch ended up with a dead spot in it. Such a spot will leak more easily and soak up more water. Luckily, the dead spot in her ditch is right above the garden, and in addition to causing more surface moisture, it helps provide subirrigation.

The Bahns get quite a lot of subirrigation which is great for deep-rooted plants, but makes for a wet basement. Subirrigation occurs when water travels below the ground by capillary action. The water is held at a certain level in an underground water table over a layer of clay, hardpan, or rock. Ditches are sometimes lined to prevent loss by seepage. This would also decrease the amount of subirrigation, but it is expensive. Besides, the asparagus would miss the deep moisture, and the pasture along the upper ditch would miss the seepage.

Controlling how much water comes from an outlet in the ditch can be done in many different ways. Because the Bahn's soil is relatively stable, Bonnie can merely make small breaks in the sides of the ditch with a shovel. To prevent washing, these breaks should be lined with sod, gravel, or plastic. A rock, large clump of sod, or portable commercial diversion is placed in the ditch on the downhill side of the break. With practice, you'll get so you can control quite accurately how much water comes through each break. Until you get used to it, though, it's better to release too little water than too much.

For a more unstable soil, Bonnie would probably use siphons rather than breaking the ditch wall. These can be commercial siphons, made just for this purpose, or pieces of garden hose. They must be anchored securely and will have to be started by being filled with water. This can be accomplished by suction or by laying the siphon or hose in the ditch until it is

Table 5-1. Normal Root Depths of Some Mature Plants.

crop	feet	crop	feet
Alfalfa	5-10	Potatoes (sweet)	4-6
Asparagus	6-10	Potatoes (Irish)	3-4
Tomatoes	6-10	Beans	3-4
Deciduous Orchards	6-8	Strawberries	3-4
Grapes	4-6	Turnips	3
Citrus Orchards	4-6	Squash	3
Cantaloupes	4-6	Celery	3
Watermelons	6	Spinach	2
Corn (field)	4-5	Cabbage	2
Corn (sweet)	3	Cranberries	1-2
Grain	4	Lettuce	1-1½
Mint	3-4	Onions	1
Peas	3-4	Radishes	1

full, then closing off the ends while it is put in place. Also, pipes or boxes with covers that open and close can be installed to release water from the ditch. These devices can be bought or made by the irrigator and usually are referred to as turnouts with gates.

Because erosion is always a problem with any sort of irrigation, the Bahns' garden is slightly terraced and irrigated on three levels. This gives Bonnie maximum use and control of the water. Contour rows are ideal for this type of irrigating, but the short up and down rows give Bonnie the north-south orientation that she prefers and, on this gentle slope, the terracing prevents washing. For steep hills, a contour garden with ditches going across instead of up and down the slope is best to prevent erosion. Usually the worst causes of washing are either too much water for a small ditch or the level of the ditch is too steep.

To cut off water to a specific furrow, Bonnie blocks the inlet with rocks and mud or a piece of sod. Remember, though, that cutting off the water in some furrows will increase the amount in the remaining ones, so be careful not to have too much water going to one spot.

To make efficient use of irrigation, one must know something about the water needs of the plants. Plants with shallow roots will have to have frequent, shallow irrigations. Plants with deep roots will need less frequent but heavier irrigations (Table 5-1). Mostly because of evaporation from the soil and transpiration from the plants, the need for water in the garden reaches a peak in midsummer and then starts to taper off.

Seeing plants grow and flourish, thanks to your efforts at irrigating, is most rewarding. Flood and furrow irrigation are perfect for people who can't afford sprinklers and don't really believe in them anyway. Although the Bahns have a deep well and occasionally use sprinklers on the lawn, flood irrigation is the method they prefer. There is no need for an expensive pump using electricity and/or expensive, awkward pipes and sprinklers. All one needs is a shovel and a leftover urge from childhood to play in the mud.

GARDEN SPRINKLER

Garden irrigation is usually done best by means of furrows or basins. This method gives more economical use of water and better control of the area to be covered. In addition, overhead watering sometimes, due to the residual water left on leaves, seems to encourage certain insect pests and diseases.

Sometimes, however, overhead watering is the only practical answer. One of the most useful overhead sprinklers is the impulse or "machine gun" type. They will cover a wide area and some of them will operate on quite low water pressure. They can be purchased either as assembled units or just the sprinkler heads alone. The bases on some of the commercially available units are a bit wide to fit between close-spaced garden rows, so you can buy just the heads and assemble your own stands.

A stand is easy to assemble. You may have most of the parts on hand—most are standard pipe fittings. Figure 5-7 gives just about all the necessary construction details. The height of the upright pipe can be varied

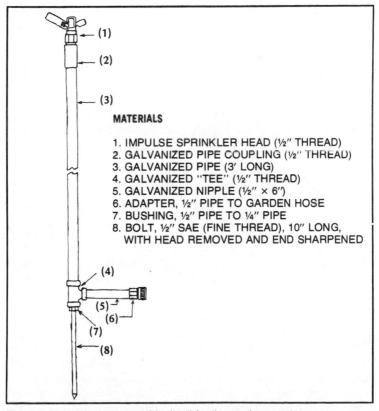

MATERIALS

1. IMPULSE SPRINKLER HEAD (½" THREAD)
2. GALVANIZED PIPE COUPLING (½" THREAD)
3. GALVANIZED PIPE (3' LONG)
4. GALVANIZED "TEE" (½" THREAD)
5. GALVANIZED NIPPLE (½" × 6')
6. ADAPTER, ½" PIPE TO GARDEN HOSE
7. BUSHING, ½" PIPE TO ¼" PIPE
8. BOLT, ½" SAE (FINE THREAD), 10" LONG, WITH HEAD REMOVED AND END SHARPENED

Fig. 5-7. Materials and assembly detail for the garden sprinkler.

Fig. 5-8. As many as 1200 planted containers can be watered at once from a single drip line.

to suit the area you need to cover. Just a word or two about the construction. The threads on the ½" SAE bolt are not a perfect match with the threads on the ¼"×½" pipe bushing. Coat these threads with gasket cement or pipe dope and just run them up good and tight.

To place the finished sprinkler, just push the spike into the soil by pushing on the side outlet with your foot. Not only does this stand work well, but if you have some or all of the parts on hand, it will cost quite a bit less than a commercially assembled unit.

DRIP IRRIGATION

This summer most country dwellers can count on being confronted with a dry spell in the middle of the growing season. This generally requires some form of supplemental watering for a varying period if the season's garden, fruit trees and berries are to be saved.

144

Until the introduction of *drip/trickle irrigation*, a progressive new development in economic agriculture, trying to do a hurried job with supplemental watering was a headache. Available methods were wasting water and required a considerable capital investment when extra pumping was necessary.

This is not the case with drip irrigation. Specifically, drip irrigation is the frequent, slow application of water to the soil at very low pressures through mechanical devices called *emitters, spitters*, or *diffusers*. They are located at selected points to provide direct watering to the roots of plants without flooding the surface. It is pinpoint, precision irrigation, a drop at a time. The volume of soil wetted by drip is much less than that wetted by sprinklers, flooding, or row watering. It is much less messy.

For gardeners who need only supplemental watering, it is by far the most simple and inexpensive method. The water pressure required is so low that a gardener with a windmill pumping 5 gallons per minute and a storage tank can water 1 or 2 acres of garden or orchard directly from the tank without a pump if gravity pressure is 3 psi or more.

Garden watering is a snap with a drip hose which resembles a soaker hose (Fig. 5-8). The drip-soaker is a dual plastic tube. The main tube carries the water supply and has small orifices every few inches which release water into a smaller outer tube. This tube has orifices which drip or ooze water out directly to the base of the plants. The double tube configuration keeps the rate of drip balanced the length of the tube.

This type of hose is laid alongside each plant row. It requires only a plastic pressure reducer at the hose bib to reduce the pressure to a drip rate. The only other fitting required is a regular 40-mesh washing machine screen washer at the outlet. This screens out sand particles and sediment which might clog the tiny orifices. As the tube is extruded, the orifices are punched with laser beams to insure positive water metering.

The soakers are inexpensive and come fitted with regular garden hose connections, the screen and an assortment of various size plastic reducing discs when bought in kit form (Fig. 5-9). Otherwise, the various individual

Fig. 5-9. Pressure reducing kits are available with different size openings.

parts can be purchased separately and the hose bought by the foot if you want to customize. Liquid fertilizers can be used with this system.

With a water pressure of 3 to 4 psi, you can water 600′ of garden row at once from a single hose bib. By using Ys at the bib, you can water an acre in a few hours with one outlet. The soaker will wet an area 36″ wide in porous soil or 12″ in heavy soil. In clay soils more of the subsurface is wetted.

The drip tube can be cut with scissors. Ordinary flexible plastic pipe tees, elbows, and unions can be used with it. All that is needed to fasten tube and fittings together is a wrap of garden mending tape around the joints. The open ends of the tubes are sealed by doubling them back and wrapping with a turn of the mending tape.

For watering trees, shrubs, or vines, a different type of drip system does the job. Soakers are just about perfect for watering lilac hedges and rows of perennials.

For individual plant watering, a ½″ supply tube is sufficient to water 100 to 300 bushes, vines, or trees. The same tube can be used to water mixed plantings of bushes and trees at the same time.

The supply tube is punched anywhere along its length to allow a microtube (emitter or spitter) to run from it to the base of each plant. If it is a large tree, two or more of the tiny tubes may be run to the tree, about halfway in from the drip line. These tubes are normally regulated to drip from 1 to 2 gallons per hour at the root of the plant. This forms a moisture reservoir of about 4 square feet. For the first watering, it is advisable to leave them on for 24 hours to establish the pattern. After that, using for two to four hours every second or third day in dry weather should be adequate. Like the soakers, emitter drip systems are available in kit form.

John L. Parker had an excess of garden hose around as the result of using soakers and used it to make a drip system of his own. His lot is long, rocky and narrow. He has planted a long row of blackberries and dewberries followed by dwarf fruit trees. He ran the garden hose along the rocks. At each berry bush he ran a 1/32 micro tube with the end a couple of inches from the base.

While there are punches available to make the hole to insert the micro tubing in the garden hose, Parker prefers to use a drill with a bit one size smaller than the micro tubing. This makes a tight seal. To hold the tubes in place at the base of the plant, he cuts 3″ lengths of garden hose and drills the same hole in the center of each piece to insert the end of the tube. This holds it firmly and prevents clogging. If he needs to shut off a drip, he can just double it and shove it in the end of the piece. At the tree end of the run, Parker used two of the micro drippers off the garden hose, one on each side of the tree.

Parker has cut his watering requirements 62 percent compared to when he ran it down the rows. He runs the line at four psi so that it drops approximately 2 gallons per hour as checked in a bucket. He runs the system an average of 3 hours every third day.

While Parker's drip line is only a few hundred feet, a drip system of this

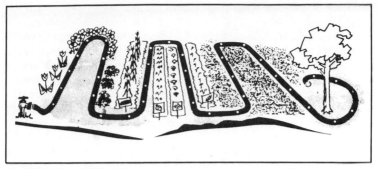
Fig. 5-10. Up to 600' of drip/soaker garden hose can be run from one.

type can run from one hose bib 1,200 to 1,500' if the ground is level or slightly downhill (Figs. 5-10 and 5-11). Parker has found it invaluable for hillsides since he can run emitters to each plant, watering without erosion and with water savings up to 90 percent. Also, he does not need to disturb the ground on the hillside to create watering basins.

Parker starts tomatoes, peppers, and other tender plants early in his northern Arizona section and uses lots of plant containers. One firm makes hanging baskets and 4 gallon containers with the spitter-emitter built in. All that is needed is to run a micro tube from the supply hose laid along a row of containers to each container.

Another firm has a similar emitter-spray in the form of miniature pointed stakes which can be struck in any container and connected to the supply tube with microtubing. Using either one, Parker can water all of his planters and containers at once in just a few minutes. Further, they all get exactly the right amount of water for optimum growth.

As with garden soakers, Parker uses a pressure reducing disc and a washing machine screen at the hose bib. He uses a manual timer to water them 10 minutes each day.

SUNFLOWERS FOR IRRIGATION

You can equip your entire farm with historically approved irrigation gauges for a mere $1.15 plus labor. These gauges will tell you when to irrigate almost as quickly as if you had a sophisticated installation of expensive tensiometers. Spend your $1.15 for half a pound of sunflower seeds, or if your place is small, buy a packet of seeds for only a few cents.

Plant a hill of sunflower seeds here and there among the crop you want to water. Like most other plants, sunflowers wilt when they are deprived of water, but they do so a few hours, maybe a day, ahead of other plants (Fig. 5-12).

Sunflowers collapse dramatically when they are thirsty. Nor do they give much warning. When your sunflowers look sad, it is time to get water on that crop you hope to raise. Don't worry about the sunflowers. When you start slopping water around, they will spring back to attention with dramatic

147

suddenness and stand there brightly until the next time you let things get too dry down under.

Sunflowers are a splendid tool for learning about permanent wilting percentages and field capacity. This can be money-making information that a lot of farmers don't know how to use. You don't need to be much handier with a pencil than you are with a shovel to discover this useful knowledge, either. First flood the soil where you have sunflowers standing guard. Let the area drain for a day or two, and then find out how much water is down around those roots. A good tool for the job is a shovel. An easier way to do it is with a soil auger.

Don't make any estimates until you have dug below the sun-dried earth at the surface. Squeeze a wad of the wet soil you have dug up. Even if your soil is sandy, it will press into a ball with all that water in it. Really study that ball of soil until you know what it looks like and how it feels. Do this with soil from different depths, down to the bottom roots of the crop you are cultivating. You have just found out what the field capacity is on your old homestead.

What is *field capacity*? It is a soil scientist's way of saying you can't put any more water in a particular patch of land. As surely as any jug, a given soil is limited in the amount of water it can hold. But you can be fooled, for every different soil has its own unique water retaining properties. So, too much water dumped on some land means expensive runoff or excessive penetration that sinks below the thirsty roots.

Fill up the test holes you dug to check soil moisture. Don't irrigate again until the sunflowers wilt. When they scream for water, dig new test holes before irrigating to find out what has happened to the precious water. Surprisingly enough, you will probably find quite a bit of moisture, even though the sunflowers have wilted.

The amount of moisture present when the sunflowers droop is the permanent wilt point (or percentage). That is why your sensitive sunflowers are sad. If you do not irrigate soon, your crop will also wilt or die. Even

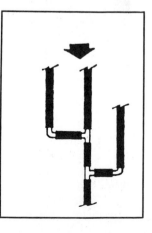

Fig. 5-11. The hose can be branched and teed to fit the garden configuration.

Fig. 5-12. Sunflowers help you do a better job of irrigating.

with that moisture down there, you will still get drought reactions from
your plants.

When an irrigation engineer says a soil has reached the permanent wilt
point, he is expressing an exact situation. He means that most farm crops
can't suck any more water out of the ground. This is generally 10 to 15
percent of field capacity.

It's a waste of water to irrigate beyond the field capacity of your
ground. You'll lose the crop if you don't irrigate when the soil has reached
the permanent wilt point. You must move promptly when the wilting begins
to punish your sunflowers.

Sunflowers, and other instruments, can be damaged. Most farm animals love to eat the heads off sunflowers, and decapitated sunflowers don't

lend themselves to water mensuration. Expensive *tensiometers* seldom survive when a cow steps on them, either. Sunflowers can help you do a better and a cheaper job of irrigating. They are especially good on small farms where the owner is also the farming expert. After harvest, you can eat the sunflower seeds yourself, or let the farm animals have them.

Chapter 6

Septic System Installation

If you've sworn never to go through another winter shivering in that little house out back, but don't think you can afford to have a tile bed installed, don't despair. You can do it yourself and save hundreds of dollars. See Table 6-1.

HOW IT WORKS

Let's take a look at how a conventional septic system works. The effluent is piped into the septic tank. This is a large concrete tank divided into two chambers. As the first chamber fills up, the solid matter rises to the top and forms a crust. Protective baffles keep incoming material from disturbing this scum and prevent it from entering the second chamber. This portion of the tank is really a safety measure because in theory it only contains relatively clear water. It is important that no solid matter leaves the tank, traveling along the header and out through the runs of perforated tile. Eventually, such material would plug up the tile bed and ruin the whole system. The solid matter trapped in the first chamber is continually munched on by bacteria which reduce it in volume and transform it into a uniform gray mass.

Only clear water, then, reaches the header which divides the flow as evenly as possible to the runs. These are lengths of plastic pipe with holes on their underside that have been buried in gravel. All this serves the purpose of spreading the sewage water over a large area and allowing it to seep slowly into the ground. Mother Nature's own purifier—earth—takes over, and ordinary water is all that gets down to the water table.

COST

What's a system like this going to cost? An 800 gallon tank goes for about $300, 600 gallons about $75 less. Three hundred feet of perforated

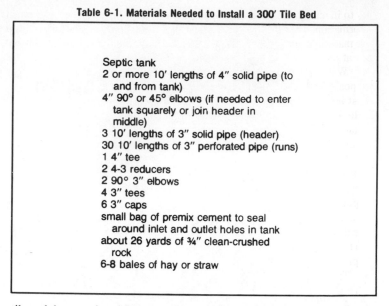

Table 6-1. Materials Needed to Install a 300′ Tile Bed

Septic tank
2 or more 10′ lengths of 4″ solid pipe (to
   and from tank)
4″ 90° or 45° elbows (if needed to enter
   tank squarely or join header in
   middle)
3 10′ lengths of 3″ solid pipe (header)
30 10′ lengths of 3″ perforated pipe (runs)
1 4″ tee
2 4-3 reducers
2 90° 3″ elbows
4 3″ tees
6 3″ caps
small bag of premix cement to seal
   around inlet and outlet holes in tank
about 26 yards of ¾″ clean-crushed
   rock
6-8 bales of hay or straw

tile and the associated fittings will run another $150-$175. Add on a couple of tandem loads of crushed rock at $70-$85 apiece, and it totals up to between $600 and $650. That is just for the tile bed. Any fill you may have to have brought in will be extra. Every situation will vary, but you could easily save as much as $400 by installing your own tile bed.

GOVERNMENT REGULATION

Sewage disposal has become a big concern in the past few years, and rightly so. As a result, the government is increasing its control of septic bed installations. This is good in that it stops a lot of people from putting in inadequate and potentially polluting tile beds, but it brings with it the problems of all bureaucracies: red tape, mindless adherence to regulations in the face of common sense, and a generally dehumanizing attitude.

Nevertheless, most tile beds are pretty straightforward. Most of the rules are reasonable, and most health officials are just people with a job. Remember that and you should get along all right. Unless you live in a remote region or have very understanding neighbors, you're going to have to deal with your health department, so make it a pleasant relationship.

The installation of private sewage systems is reasonably consistent across the United States and Canada. The figures that we've already used and the rules we'll be mentioning apply specifically to eastern Ontario, but will be fairly close to what will be required of you.

GETTING STARTED

The first step in your project is to call the health department. It's their job to investigate all installations, and their visit can be a source of much information. They'll show you the best spot to put your bed and fill you in on the materials you'll need. Ask questions! You'll find them very helpful and not at all scornful of do-it-yourselfers.

While there, they'll be evaluating the environmental effects of your proposed bed. The most important factor they look at is depth of soil—you must have at least 5' of soil before hitting either bedrock or the water table. In addition, they'll make sure that the pollutants are released a safe distance from your well, your neighbors' well, and any open or standing water.

Once your site has been approved, it's time for some more phoning. Look in the Yellow Pages under concrete products and decide who you want to buy your septic tank from. Call him up and ask him questions. The health inspector told you what size tank you need. Find out its dimensions and how big a hole you need to bury it (generally 10″ deeper and 6″ bigger on each side than the tank itself). Also, determine the height of the inlet hole and get him to give you a price on the plastic pipe for the tile bed. If he sells it at all, he probably deals in big enough quantities to give you a discount.

There's no putting it off any longer. The only thing left is to get out there and start digging.

A word here about shovels. If you don't have a good dirt scooper already, go out and buy one. Look for a sharp angle between the handle and the blade. The flatter that joint is, the more bending over you'll have to do. Find a good balance between heavyweight construction and a lightweight and, most important, find a handle that is comfortable in *your* hands.

THE TANK

Stake out the dimensions of your future hole and dig in, so to speak. As you are piling up dirt from the excavation, remember that the truck that delivers your tank has to back up to your hole *squarely*, so don't leave a pile in front of that side. Consider, too, that you're going to lay a pipe into and out of the tank.

Square off the sides of your hole and measure its bottom to make sure it's the same size as the top. How deep? It's nice to have a shovel's depth of soil over the tank, but you can always mound that up later. The tank shouldn't be any deeper than it has to be, so that the tile bed can be kept shallow. Aside from the digging this will save you, shallow runs allow more evaporation of water. The most important thing about the depth of your septic tank is that the sewage from the house flows downhill to it.

When you've dug down to what you think is a good depth, measure up the side nearest the house to the bottom of the inlet hole. Dig a trench to where the pipe comes out of your house. Does it fall away from the building? Put a straight board in the bottom and lay a level on it. You want a visible drop but not an exaggerated one—about one fourth of a bubble off level. You can have a much steeper slope than that, but usually an effort has to be made to keep things shallow rather than deepen them.

Fig. 6-1. This trench was dug with a backhoe.

Now level up the bottom of the hole, again using the board and carpenter's level. It should be perfectly horizontal from side to side, but a drop of up to an inch from inlet to outlet won't hurt. Make sure there are no stones where the tank will sit, and place your order with the concrete man who will deliver in a couple of days.

Be sure you're there when he does. See that he puts it in properly. The inlet hole in the tank is higher than the outlet, and the larger of the two manholes in the lid goes over the first chamber. He knows his business, but everyone makes mistakes. It's you that would have to live with it. Check and double-check the level.

Run some ABS or PVC 4″ pipe into the tank and cement around the inlet hole. Make sure that the hole is free of anything that would impede the flow of sewage. For instance, use fencing pliers to cut out any reinforcing wire.

THE HEADER

Stake out the area reserved for your bed. A standard installation of six runs of 50′ each on 6′ centers will be 30′ wide and 50′ long. Lay the pipe nearby. Be sure you pick a smooth spot, because especially in hot weather it has a tendency to warp.

Have a load of clean ¾″ stone delivered and dumped to one side of the bed or the other. By postponing delivery of the second load until this one runs out, you can better judge how much more to order. You will be starting on the far side and working towards your pile of stone.

Dig a trench from the tank to the line of the header using the same gentle slope you used to go into the tank (Figs. 6-1 and 6-2). Hopefully, your

154

Fig. 6-2. Checking the slope on the pipe to the header.

crosspiece will be centered on the tank. If not, you are required to arrange some turns so that you enter the header in the middle. Dig out where your sewage distributor will sit in both directions, keeping it perfectly level and a couple of inches lower than the trench from the tank.

Now make up the header (Fig. 6-3). Start by inserting a piece of 3″ solid pipe into a 90° elbow. Cut the pipe off with an ordinary hand saw so that when a 3″ tee is fitted on the end, it will be centered 6′ away from the elbow. Repeat with another tee. Make a mate for the whole thing so that you have two 12′ lengths of pipe, each with an elbow and two tees ready to receive a total of six runs of tile.

Wheel some gravel over to the header trench and, starting in the center, fill in those couple of inches where you were too deep. Lay a 4″ pipe

Fig. 6-3. The first run where it joins the header.

155

Fig. 6-4. Checking the header for level.

from the tank and put the stem of a 4″ tee on its end. Reduce the arms of the tee to 3″. Set the two halves of the header in the trench and plug them into the reducers using enough extra 3″ conduit to make the inside tees 6′ off center as well.

Check every section of the header for level and adjust (Fig. 6-4). It is absolutely essential that this distributor be as horizontal as possible, or only the downhill side of it will ever see any use. Recheck it and readjust.

Fig. 6-5. If the solid pipes are warped, lay them with the "banana" on its side. The weeping tile must have the holes on the bottom regardless of curvature.

156

The gravel that you are scratching away or adding will provide a good base to keep your crosspiece from settling. Keep checking each of its parts until you get it right. Cement around the outlet hole.

THE BED

It's finally time to begin on the runs of weeping tile (Fig. 6-5). Dig a trench 18″ wide and 6-8″ deeper than the header along the full length of a 50′ run. The downwards slope should be almost imperceptible. Start wheeling over enough stone to fill up the trench to the height of the header. Fill in the length of one 10′ pipe and then put it in place and adjust it for level before proceeding (Fig. 6-6). While making sure that you have some drop, keep it as little as possible. The idea here is to let the water trickle out the full length of the run instead of rushing down to the bottom and collecting there.

Cover the pipe as you go with just enough gravel to hide it (Fig. 6-7). Keep the top flat, not mounded up in the middle. When the whole thing is

Fig. 6-6. A whole line of perforated pipe laid in the trench but not covered.

Fig. 6-7. The first pipe in a run partially covered.

buried in gravel, spread a bale of hay or straw over its length (Fig. 6-8). This is not insulation, but serves to keep dirt from sifting through the stones and plugging things up. By the time the hay has rotted, the soil will have settled in place. Don't forget to fit a cap on the end of the line. Complete this procedure opposite each of the tees in the header.

It's time to call the health department again. They'll want to come out and make sure you did what they told you. If you've done something wrong, they can make you change it.

Fig. 6-8. A cross-section of a run showing 6-8 inches of gravel under the 3″ pipe which is covered by more stone and then straw.

THE LAST DETAIL

After the inspector approves, it's time to cover up all your hard work. The header and runs already have lots of support, and you should take care to see that the larger pipes are held up, too (Fig. 6-9). Shovel dirt alongside them until just the top part shows. Walk their length with your feet right next to the curve of the plastic, so that the dirt is squished under the pipe and thoroughly tamped down. If the soil should settle, the plastic tube could break and create a very nasty mess to have a clean up. For the same reason, never drive heavy trucks or tractors over your tile bed.

VARIATIONS

Remember to quiz your officials about all aspects of their specifications (they may prefer building paper instead of straw to cover the stone or other such differences). Should you be pressed for space, they may have you put in an open pit bed.

This involves one large square hole instead of a series of trenches. The runs are closer together, requiring less room. The open pit method means shoveling more dirt but wheelbarrowing less gravel. If you dig out a short ramp, a truck can back down it and dump the crushed rock right in the excavation. After smoothing it over, shallow trenches are scratched out of the stones. The pipes are laid and covered. Straw is then spread over the whole thing (Fig. 6-10).

CARE AND FEEDING

You've just gone through quite a bit of work to get this job finished, so it would behoove you to show some concern for the finished product. This is a

Fig. 6-9. An overall view showing four of the runs installed. The pipe from the tank is visible in the center foreground.

Fig. 6-10. Spreading the straw.

biological system. Nonorganic materials should not be introduced into it. If you have kids, it's inevitable that the odd toy truck is going to get flushed down the toilet, but please keep it to a minimum. Don't feed clothing or plastic, rubber, or metal materials to your septic system.

Have the tank pumped out regularly. On the average it'll need it every three years. At $30 or $40 it's still cheap insurance on the life of your tile bed. Also, don't plant trees on or near the bed, because the fine roots will seek out the nutritious water and can plug up pipes.

Chapter 7

Heating

An energy-efficient heating system is a necessity for the home-steader. This chapter has plenty of information concerning woodstoves. There is a section detailing construction of a hot water heater to fit around a stove. Plus, there is material on using heat from the sun to keep animals warm.

OPERATING A WOODSTOVE

All parts shown in Fig. 7-1 are not necessary for a stove to operate properly. There may be three separate warming oven doors; or there may be only two hinged on the outside edges and swinging out from the center; or there may be only one, which is curved and lifts up from the bottom of the warming oven.

Some models have a reservoir, indicated by the dotted line on Fig. 7-1. Reservoirs can only be used for heating water if the inside is relatively free of mineral scale and does not leak. There is always a liner inside the reservoir, generally made of copper, cast iron, or galvanized tin. If the stove is old enough, the outside will be heavy tin, lined with a porcelain liner. Water must be kept in the reservoir at all times when there is a fire in the stove. Otherwise, the heat from the oven will warp, and in time, burn out the liner.

Parts absolutely necessary for a cookstove to work properly include a lid for every hole in the cook top of the stove. Some stoves have two lids and a french griddle. Others have either four or six holes. Generally, one of those in the back will have a grilled top which sets into the center of one lid for simmering stew or keeping the coffee pot hot without boiling.

A *firebox* draft on the left front is necessary. If the back draft, next to the pipe is missing, it can be made to heat by putting a damper in the pipe directly above the cook top, to force the heat back over the oven.

161

Fire back, fire walls, and grates must be in place. These are removable and may be replaced if parts can still be purchased for the particular make. Sears & Roebuck and Montgomery Ward are good places to find replacement parts. As little as 25 years ago, they handled parts for almost every known make and model of woodburning cook stove.

There must be a door on the ash box, either functioning separately from the inside ash box or built directly on the ash box. If the door operates separately, an ash box is not necessary, but is a convenience.

Check inside the oven for holes in the walls, especially next to the fire wall. This is generally the first place the oven walls will break. If it is rusted or burned out and the damage is not extensive, a workable patch can be made from a piece of car body tin, spotwelded into place. Do not use stove cement, supposedly made for the purpose of patching ovens, as the high temperatures cause it to crumble and fall onto the food being baked.

It is best to empty the ashes each day before starting a new fire. The ashes may be cleaned away from the top and bottom of the oven at regular intervals, but it is absolutely necessary to do the job anytime the top doesn't brown as quickly as it should. The bottom of the bread or cake won't brown properly by the time the food is baked.

Never install a wood cookstove without putting a secondary damper in the stovepipe or using two elbows. The reasons are simple. The two elbows give you more heat from less fuel. The damper is preferred because you not only save fuel, but have better control of the fire. Also, you don't have to clean stovepipes as often.

The firebox damper is generally a sliding affair on the side of the stove near the bottom of the firebox. This regulates the quickness of your fire. It must always be open until your fire is burning well.

At the back of the stove somewhere close to the pipe outlet (especially if your stove doesn't have a reservoir for heating water), there will be a handle at the side near the back of the stove to control heat flow up the pipe. (If a reservoir model, this draft handle might be located between the oven and reservoir, just in under the stove top. If your stove has a damper at the pipe outlet, don't look for this particular handle.) To heat the oven or hold heat on the cook top, this draft must be either partially or fully closed, depending upon how quickly you want the oven or cook top to heat.

In general, the draft at the top back lifts up to close and pushes down to open. The draft at the side away from the firebox pulls out to close and pushes in to open. Either type is commonly referred to as the "back draft," because it controls the heat flow up the chimney.

If you don't want to make some unbelievable messes, it's best to spread a couple sheets of newsprint under the ash drawer and remove the ashes each morning before starting a new fire or kindling or mending an old one. It's best to learn this while first getting acquainted with your stove. It's so easy to forget or put off when you're busy.

Once a week remove the little ash cap below the oven and scrape out everything that will come out from under the oven. Occasionally ashes will

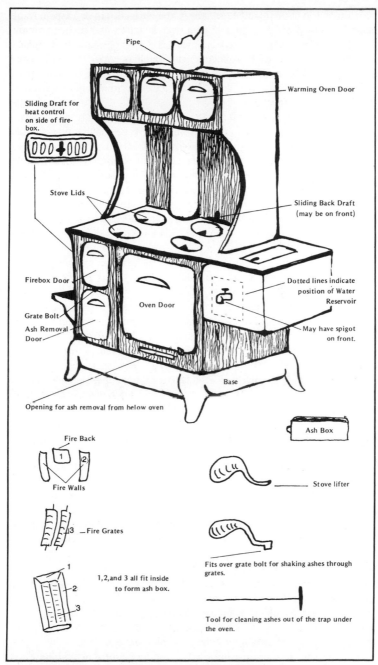

Fig. 7-1. Woodstove diagram (drawing by Margot Mayr).

Labels on diagram:

Pipe

Warming Oven Door

Sliding Draft for heat control on side of firebox.

Stove Lids

Sliding Back Draft (may be on front)

Firebox Door

Dotted lines indicate position of Water Reservoir

Grate Bolt

Ash Removal Door

Oven Door

May have spigot on front.

Base

Opening for ash removal from below oven

Fire Back

Fire Walls

Ash Box

Stove lifter

Fire Grates

1,2,and 3 all fit inside to form ash box.

Fits over grate bolt for shaking ashes through grates.

Tool for cleaning ashes out of the trap under the oven.

build up on top of the oven, especially if you burn a lot of dry aspen. More than a 2″ buildup will prevent both your oven and the water in the reservoir from heating properly.

There are special little gadgets made to clean under the oven. They are expensive and hard to obtain. A 3′ long stick, about ¾″ through, and a piece of scrap metal or a tobacco can lid tacked onto the end, makes an ideal, inexpensive oven cleaner.

With both the side and back draft open, place some crumbled newsprint, an egg or milk carton in the bottom of the grate, having first worked all the ashes down through the grate holes. (The wax on a milk carton does not explode. First, step on the carton to smash it flat before putting it into the fire box. Thus, the wax melts and keeps the paper burning until the kindling catches fire.) Always start with a clean grate unless you have coals enough left to rekindle a fire. If there are coals, rake them ahead carefully, lay the kindling wood on top, and you are in business. Next, lay a few very small pieces of dry wood on the paper, add a couple larger pieces of dry wood and you're ready to light up.

Some people rarely ever use the door on the firebox. There's too much chance of a spark popping out without being noticed. Watch your side draft for the same reason. Use a kitchen match and simply reach in through the front lid hole and let the starter material catch before letting go of the match. If you're also new to kitchen matches, remember to be quick about it, because you are holding the match, head down. It will flare rather quickly and, because of the wooden stick, the heat will be much more intense. It will cause burned fingers.

There are two alternative methods to lighting with a match held head down. The simplest and least expensive is to fold 4 × 8 pieces of newsprint into fan-like pieces, storing them in a can handy to the stove. Light one of these and reach down through the lid hole. Set the end of the lighter stick against the end of the starting material and leave it there. In a minute the starter material will be burning.

You can take a gallon size metal can, fill it two-thirds full of really dry sawdust, add about a cup of fuel oil, and mix the lot with an old spoon until all the oil has been soaked up by the sawdust. Leave the spoon in the can. When you want a fire simply spoon a couple spoonfuls onto the clean grate, add small pieces of kindling, working up to larger pieces and light through the front door, with a match. No need to worry about flying sparks here. There won't be any.

Once the fire is burning well, add larger pieces of wood. For the major part of the time, it is advisable to have plenty of green cook wood available. Ask a neighbor which green woods burn best or experiment.

The reason for using green wood is that it gives better control of the heat and less ashes in the ash pan. All dry wood will force you to fill the firebox constantly or it will heat the stovepipe beyond controlling with a draft. (This could lead to a fire hazard if stovepipes instead of a chimney are used to vent the stove through the ceiling, because the pipes will get red all the way through the roof.

Generally, you can use birch, oak, maple, and white ash for green wood. Be careful using white ash, however, because it burns like coal. Two fireboxes full can ruin, beyond saving, any thing you may have in the oven. For dry wood almost anything, but many people prefer dry balsam or cedar for kindling, since either can be shaved on the end with a thin knife and the shavings lit with a match. Thus, you need not save newsprint or cartons. If you need kindling material, ask a neighbor to save milk or egg cartons or go to the local dump for the milk cartons. A bit of drying in the sun will make even the rained on ones burnable due to the wax.

A thermometer on the oven door is nice but not a necessity. You can soon learn to judge how hot the oven is by simply sticking your hand in for a few seconds. If the oven gets too hot, it can be controlled two ways. Adjust the side draft, closing it for less heat or add less wood to the firebox.

If your stove has a reservoir, always keep it full of water. Not only does it provide hot water for all purposes, but it keeps the oven temperature more steady. Once a week, use or drain out the water while the fire is low and wipe out any rust, mineral deposits, etc. If you do, you can use the water to cook with, also. Keeping it full of water prevents it from burning out and causing leaks.

It is also a good place to temper salvaged jars or heat canning jars. Place the clean jars in the reservoir and leave them in there two or three days. They'll heat and cool as the stove does and provide you with extra strength canning jars that will stand pressure canning better than regular jars.

If hard water and mineral deposits in the tea kettle or reservoir are a problem, here's a simple solution to most of the problem. Tie a small rock or a marble in the corner of a clean piece of old handtowel. Drop it into the tea kettle or reservoir. It will sink to the bottom and collect all the lime, rust and mineral deposits which boil out of the water. When it becomes quite heavy with deposits, throw it away and replace with a clean cloth. (The weight in the corner prevents the material from floating up, which can be a distinct problem in a tea kettle when it shuts off the spout.)

MORE HELP WITH WOODSTOVES

How do you start a good fire? First check the ash box for an overaccumulation of ashes. If the box is full, this will affect the "draw" of your stove. Clean the ash box out and open up your damper all the way. Next, in the front of your firebox place small pieces of paper. On top of that, try some twigs or wood splinters. Last, but not least, comes a few sticks of hardwood. Now you're ready to light it up. Once a good fire is established gently close the damper, not all the way, but enough to lower your flame and maintain a more even heat.

How do you use a minimum of wood? If you are burning wood with the damper wide open, you can't help but use a lot of wood. If, however, the damper has been mastered, the next possibility is the wood burned. Soft varieties will be consumed rapidly, and the value of them as heating and cooking agents will be very inefficient.

The soft types are excellent fire starters, but they are inferior for use as consistent cooking and heating fuel. Hardwoods must be used for good, steady fires. They not only put out more heat, but they'll save you a lot of trips to the woodshed, as less wood will be required for the task at hand.

How do you keep your stove from smoking you out of house and home? Smoke is a common gripe of used woodstove purchasers. Cracks and holes of even the smallest proportions can cause untold misery. Before buying a wood cookstove, check it over thoroughly. If there're any leaks, you would do best to shop elsewhere. If the cracks aren't too bad, you might seal them with some sort of plaster or by welding.

Smoke is often caused by the uninitiated cook and is not the fault of the range. As with burning reasonable amounts of wood, the damper again comes into play. If it's open too much, you'll have too much fire. If it's not open enough, then there will be too much smoke. It's as simple as that.

Certain woods burn with more smoke output than others. Experimentation is the only way to figure this part out.

Lastly, be sure your stovepipe is not clogged with soot or debris. If your pipe runs horizontal across the ceiling before going outside, that could be your problem. Much has been said lately about using long, horizontal extensions of smoke pipe to warm your dwelling. By the time the contents of the stovepipe have traveled less than halfway its heating capacity will have dropped below reasonable levels. If particularly resinous wood is being used, a mass of residue could accumulate which could prevent you from using your stove without producing smoke. It would also assure you of a lot of extra stovepipe cleaning.

SAFETY TIPS FOR WOOD AND COAL STOVES

The U.S. Department of Agriculture's Extension Service warns families turning to use of cast iron stoves that they can burn wood safely, but only a firebrick-lined stove should be used for burning coal. This is among the safety tips passed along by extension agents as many families try to ease costs of other home heating fuels by using wood and coal. Other suggestions include:

☐ The stove should be on a brick platform or fireproof asbestos stoveboard, at least 24″ from side walls and other burnables. Even a fireproof stoveboard might conduct too much heat for safety if the stove's legs are shorter than 6″ to 12″.

☐ Never use a pipe labeled "vent" as a chimney. A vent pipe—a single thickness of metal—can get very hot and start a fire in combustible materials in wall or ceiling. Use, instead, an "all fuel" chimney with a U.L (Underwriters Laboratories) label. This chimney is either a double thickness of pipe with asbestos between the pipes or a triple-walled pipe with an air gap between the pipes.

☐ If you have doubts about the way your stove is installed, ask your local fire department to inspect it.

☐ Keep the stove door closed while the fire is burning to prevent accidents caused by sparks flying, etc.

☐ Never leave small children unattended where the stove is in use.

☐ Clean the stove regularly, but maintain ashes 1″ deep to improve fuel efficiency.

☐ Never stoke up a wood or coal fire so hot that it changes the color of the stovepipe. *A glowing red stovepipe signals danger.* Cool the fire as quickly as possible by closing the stove's dampers and partially closing stovepipe damper. If that doesn't do it fast enough, bank the fire. Put a few coal shovels full of ashes on top of burning wood or coal.

☐ Routinely check to be sure no wood, kindling, newspapers, furniture or anything else have been left close to the stove. Three feet away is a good safe distance.

☐ With cast-iron stoves, gases may pass out through the chimney without being burned. Some gases may condense in the stovepipe and chimney, especially if wood is damp. Dangerous deposits of creosote can cause a chimney fire. Make sure all wood used is dry.

☐ Take down the stovepipe several times during the winter and clean out the soot.

☐ Make sure the chimney does not have heavy deposits of creosote or soot. To clean, drop a line with rag attached down chimney.

☐ Don't keep kerosene or other flammable liquids in the same room with the stove. Never use any of these to start a fire.

☐ Do not transfer ashes from the stove to a cardboard box. A live coal may ignite. Place ashes in metal container only.

☐ Before you open the firebox to add fuel, or just to look at the fire, always open the stovepipe damper first. This allows accumulated gases to escape up the chimney. Otherwise, they might flare up or even explode when air suddenly comes in through the firebox door.

SAFE HEATING WITH WOOD

Imagine a 5-gallon bucket filled with heating oil. Light a piece of paper and drop it in the bucket. Try adjusting the burning bucket of oil to the desired temperature for heating your living room. This may sound strange but this is what you do with any wood heating system.

Most heating fuels are easily controlled because exact amounts of fuel are burned to reach a desired temperature. Then the system shuts off. Wood is uncontrollable. You can increase or decrease the air flow, but with the average fireplace you can't even do that. Even with some control over the oxygen, you can't always get the desired results. Masonry chimneys should be sturdy and freestanding.

A wood fire is like a pet. It needs constant attention, and it will work for you if you provide it with the right things at the right time. Stove design is important, but the way you feed the fire, the size and the condition of wood, and how tightly you pack the firebox make more difference than the stove.

Some states have stringent laws regarding wood heat. Insurance rates may increase with secondary wood heating systems.

Others are more lenient. Your homeowner's policy may be adjusted to your prime source of heat. With oil or gas, set rate determines what you pay. If your home is heated only by wood, your rates will probably be higher. Your payments for an existing oil or gas system that are supplemented with a wood burner will not increase.

You are not required to have a building inspector or insurance agent approve your wood heating setup in some states. Normally, your insurance agent makes periodic inspections with a homeowner's policy. If your agent finds the setup unsatisfactory, you will have to correct it or lose your coverage.

Save yourself some trouble and have a voluntary inspection before you light that first fire. Why take chances with your insurance policy or your family's safety?

Unsafe Installation

Legality aside, unsafe installation is the major cause of fire. Here is an example. A man installed his grandmother's old pot-bellied stove in his home. The job looked first rate.

The first few fires charred the wood which came in contact with the pipe. On a crisp day he stoked up a roaring blaze and a fire broke out in the second story. Everyone escaped in time and the damage was minimal—a cheap lesson.

The man made several common mistakes. First, clearances from all combustible surfaces were improper. Required clearances are based on stove type, size operating temperature, and type of protective coverings.

Asbestos millboard on surfaces near the stove is best. Sheet metal can also be used. Both need nonflammable spacers to break contact with the wall, because heat can be conducted.

Masonry is exempt from clearance requirements. Since it also conducts heat, keep combustibles out of contact with masonry walls.

Situate your stove in a central location away from walls and exits. This way is safest and most efficient.

A simple test will assure you of proper clearances. Place your hand on the closest surface. If you can keep your hand there comfortably with the stove in operation, the location is safe. If not, you need added protection.

Some assume that the smoke pipe is the chimney. A smoke pipe is a chimney *connector*. It serves to hook up the heating device with the chimney and should not pass through exterior walls.

These connectors should be as short as possible with no more than two right angle bends. A 6″ pipe is the most common household size. A heavy metal, at least 24 gauge, is recommended. Clearance must be three times the pipe diameter or 18″. See Fig. 7-2 and Table 7-1.

Chimneys

You've probably seen chimneys that are secured with guylines. They look like they'll topple over with the first strong wind. Nothing could be more dangerous. Chimney design and installation are important in guarding against a chimney fire.

Two types of chimneys are safe for woodburning use: a lined masonry chimney and a prefab class A chimney. These are designed to withstand high temperatures. Chimney fires can reach temperatures up to 3,000°F, so the proper chimney is essential.

Clearance, again, is important. Two inches should separate the chimney from combustibles. It must extend at least 3' above the highest point where it passes through the roof and 2' above any point within 10'.

Inspect your chimney if it hasn't been used lately. Make sure the fireproof clay liner is intact. The linear makes the flue airtight and protects the masonry from moisture damage.

Wood is a mixture of charcoal, hydrogen, tars, resins, and volatile gases mixed with water vapor. It is not a refined fuel like heating oil or gas which burns with oxygen in a uniform mixture. The woodstove gets different types of sizes of wood which are haphazardly dumped into the firebox.

Incomplete burning results from this arrangement. Some of the gases are consumed, some escape, and some condense in the cooler regions of the

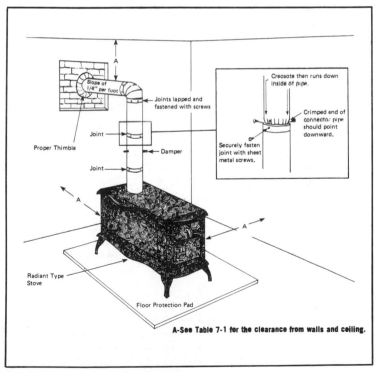

Fig. 7-2. Proper woodstove installation.

Table 7-1. Clearances for Wood Burners with No Added Protection.

	radiant[2]	circulating[3]	supplemental[4]	cookstove or range	pipe
Ceiling	36"	36"	36"	30"	18"
Front	48	48	48	-	18
Side	23-36	18	36	24	18
Rear	36	18	36	24	18

[1]Information adapted from NFPA bulletin No. 89M, 1976 edition.
[2] A radiant stove is one with a single layer of metal enclosing the fire, such as a Franklin stove.
[3] A circulating stove is one with a second metal jacket enclosing a space for heating and circulating air.
[4] A supplemental heating device is one such as the Add-A-Furnace.

stovepipe and chimney. This condensate is commonly called *creosote*. It can accumulate in your chimney and, when conditions are right, ignite.

The result is a stack fire which can really get hot. Increased heat will increase the draft which will stimulate the main fire in the firebox. The stovepipe can glow red igniting walls and ceiling. Showers of sparks can rain down onto the roof.

Ideally, you would like all these gases to burn. This rarely happens even with efficient systems. You should realize that if you burn wood, you will have a creosote problem.

Decrease the moisture problem by using insulated piping and avoid attaching more than one heating device to the flue. Double venting decreases the stack temperature which adds to the creosote problem. The danger of carbon monoxide seeping into the home also increases with multiple venting.

Build the chimney within your house, not on the outside. Naturally, some house designs prevent you from doing this. An inside chimney will throw off more heat and keep dry better.

Remove creosote deposits before they build to a dangerous level by using chimney brushes, tire chains, chicken wire, or a weighted burlap bag filled with straw. To use a bag, attach it to a rope and work it up and down the chimney.

Some stove manufacturers suggest setting small chimney fires on a regular basis. Crumple up a couple sheets of paper and toss them on a hot fire. This should reduce the buildup if done often enough. You can buy chemical soot removers too. If you have some extra change in your pocket, hire a chimneysweep.

Efficiency Is the Key

Who doesn't like a fireplace? Its flames are as warm as the mood it creates. If you sit close enough, it even keeps half of you warm. Unfortunately, the fireplace is only 10 percent efficient.

You can install a glass door in front of your fireplace. It works well if you like staring at a picture of a fire.

If you close the doors when you go to bed for the night, you can save heat and money. As the fire dies, strong drafts continue sucking up heat from the room.

Heat vents or "stack robbers" can be installed to recirculate some of the heat, but they are difficult and costly to install.

Inexpensive heat-circulating grates draw cool air through the bottom of the "U" tubes, warm the air by the flames, and recirculate the air into the room.

The *chunk* or *simple box* stove is the most common and least expensive. This stove is inefficient, though, and lacks control over the air above the wood which burns the escaping gases. This incomplete burning results in heat loss and creosote buildup in the chimney.

Airtight stoves are more sophisticated and more efficient. You control the rate at which you burn the wood and the air flow. A secondary air flow allows the volatile gases to burn above the wood. The fuel is consumed more completely. The efficiency of the simple box stoves is estimated roughly at about 30 percent: air tights estimate around 50 percent.

There are many designs for woodburning stoves. Some are better than others and newer designs are probably more than 50 percent efficient. The market is growing rapidly. One of the best sources is the *Woodstove Directory,* published by Energy Communication Press, and available at most bookstores.

Fuel values of wood depend on species, its density, and moisture content. Denser hardwoods, properly dried, are best. Conifers, such as pine, have a high resin content which causes creosote buildup. Dry pine split into small pieces makes excellent kindling.

You can get up to 40 percent more heat from wood by allowing it to air dry before you burn it. Wet wood requires heat to drive off the moisture. This causes a lower fire temperature which also leads to more creosote buildup.

If you cut your own wood, stack it in a sheltered place. It's best to plan ahead by cutting wood at least a year before you use it.

A good source of information on wood heat is the National Fire Protection Association. Write to them at 470 Atlantic Avenue, Boston, MA 02210 and ask for their catalog of publications.

For safety and efficiency, do some homework. It will pay off in the long run.

FINDING AND REPAIRING THE JUNKYARD STOVE

With the ever increasing shortage, woodburning cookstoves are once again becoming a popular item. Unfortunately, modern cookstoves are expensive (not to mention lacking nostalgic appeal) while repairable old cookstoves are becoming as rare as frog fangs. If you're willing to look hard and long enough, though, you can find a repairable cookstove at a very reasonable price. Consider an old woodburning cookstove a wise investment, since prices are sure to rise before too long (Fig. 7-3).

Fig. 7-3. An old woodburning cookstove is a wise investment (photo by Herbert Huff).

After you buy a cookstove, all that's needed is time, a few materials, and a bit of determination to convert your rusty "monster" into an attractive and efficient cookstove. Hopefully, this section will provide some helpful hints on where to find cookstoves, prevent you from buying 500 pounds of junk, and explain a few inexpensive methods of repair.

Unfortunately, old cookstoves aren't exactly the most widely advertised product around. In our modernized world of fast food restaurants and microwave ovens, anything that involves physical effort is considered "old fashion" or "primitive." Consequently, you won't find full page advertisements featuring old cookstove sales. For best results, look in the smaller ads of your local newspaper.

Antique shops, flea markets, and swap shops occasionally carry old cookstoves. The cookstove in Fig. 7-3 was one of four cookstoves found at a swap shop.

Farm and antique auctions are a good source and will usually sell a cookstove for less than a dealer. You should give yourself enough time to inspect the stove before the auction starts.

Call auctioneers in your area to ask if they have any auctions with cookstoves scheduled. If not, ask them if they'll give you a call or send a card when they do. Most auctioneers will be glad to help you out.

You can advertise for free with signs at every place in your area that has a bulletin board. Write your phone number or address in vertical rows on the bottom and cut these rows in sections that can be torn off. Give it a try before you pay for advertising, it's worked quite well for me.

Scarce but Available

Scarce as they are, old woodburning cookstoves *are* still available. Don't get in a hurry and buy the first stove you see. Look around until you find the type of stove you want at the right price.

Can It Be Fixed?

Don't squander your hard-earned cash on a cookstove that's about as worthless as a burp. You can save yourself a lot of grief by knowing whether major parts are missing or repairable. It's possible to make some parts, but the total investment in time and/or money may exceed the value of the stove. Most stoves are sold "as is—no refund," so check it out right the first time.

Important parts that are sometimes overlooked are the grates, oven damper, and stove top. Grates are sometimes warped, broken, or burned out. Stove tops may be cracked, warped, or broken. Occasionally, oven damper supports are broken. Depending on the extent and location of the damage, repairing these parts may be expensive and time-consuming if not virtually impossible.

First, inspect the stove top for broken or cracked parts. To check for warpage, lay a straightedge across the outer edge and check for gaps. Make sure the lids sit flat in their seats and won't rock when you push on them. Next, remove the lids and lid supports and inspect the other side of the parts. Broken cast iron can usually be repaired by an experienced welder, but if the top is warped you should find another stove.

The oven damper regulates the heat within the stove. When closed, the heat flows under the stove top and around the oven. When open, the heat escapes up the stovepipe. Before you buy a cookstove, make sure you can repair the oven damper, or be prepared to eat a lot of raw food.

If the damper itself is broken, it can be repaired by welding. Repairing the damper mounts inside the stove may be difficult. Seek the advice of an experienced welder before you buy a stove with broken damper mounts.

Clean the grates with a wire brush and inspect them for warpage and breaks. Broken grates can usually be repaired unless they're broken at the ends where they mount on the stove. Welding the ends back on may be tricky, so speak with a welder first.

The grates should move freely when turning the handle on the front of the stove. If the grates or shaker mechanism is rusted and won't move, penetrating fluid and light tapping and prying will usually free them. If the mechanism is broken, determine how much work will be involved in disassembling and welding the part before you buy.

Although the majority of parts can be repaired, a stove in bad shape will require a great deal of work. Sometimes the total investment in repairs will exceed the value of the stove. Determine how much time and money you'll need to spend on repairs before you buy a cookstove.

Before you make any repairs on an old wood cookstove, you'll want to clean it first so you won't have to wallow around in filth. Once, when faced with several years accumulation of dirt, rust and ashes, Herbert Huff figured the easiest way to remove it would be to blow it out with the air hose at the local service station. Apparently, the station owner didn't approve of Huff blowing debris across his landscape—he threatened to rip out Huff's "gozzel pipe."

Here's a safer method that works almost as well. Knock loose all of the old furnace cement and other debris, and sweep it towards the firebox. Sweep out the remaining dirt, then carefully tip the stove on end with the firebox on the bottom. With a stick, scrape away the debris under the oven (through the small cleaning door). Block up one end of the stove and scrape the dirt from the sides and back of the oven.

Tip the stove right side up and clean the remaining dirt and rust from the stove interior with a wire brush. Do an especially careful job around the areas that will need repair later on. Go over the whole area with a damp rag to clean up the dust. After all repairs have been made, this area can be painted to prevent further rusting.

A most helpful tool is a portable drill. With a wire brush attachment installed, you can clean your stove with a minimum of effort. Also, you can reach small areas that otherwise couldn't be reached with a hand-powered wire brush.

Observe a few safety precautions when using a portable drill. Keep the spinning wire brush well away from you to prevent the drill motor from becoming tangled up in your clothing. Also, hold the drill so the brush or sanding disc rotates away from you. Otherwise, you may wind up with wire bristles or sandpaper stuck in your skin (burns and smarts). It wouldn't be a bad idea to use safety glasses, either.

Removing Parts

The avid stove restorer would completely disassemble a stove in order to restore each part to a "like new" condition. Disassembling a stove requires a great deal of work, time and sometimes money. Also, you may end up damaging the part or the adjoining area considerably when you remove parts. The majority of parts can be inspected and repaired without removing them. If you're not experienced, don't remove parts unless it's absolutely necessary.

Bolts that won't come loose can be drilled, broken, or cut. When they're tight and won't spin, break the bolt by tightening the nut with a wrench, vise grips, or a socket and ratchet. When loose, hold the nut and drill through the bolt head with a drill bit slightly larger than the bolt. Bolts that are out in the open and stick out far enough can be cut off with a hacksaw.

Don't drill, break, or cut screws or bolts that are screwed into a stationary part or fixed type of nut. Unless the nut is removable and accessible, use lots of penetrating fluid and be patient.

The majority of cookstoves have two types of fasteners, rivets and stove bolts. Rusty bolts or parts that won't come loose can be sprayed with penetrating fluid by mixing 10 parts of mineral spirits with 1 part of 10-W oil. Spray the area, allow it to set for awhile, and all but the most stubborn parts will come loose.

Avoid removing rivets if at all possible. Rivets can be removed by drilling, but they are hard to hold on to and will usually spin with the drill bit. Also, it's not at all practical to install new rivets, so stove bolts are normally used as a replacement.

Basically, repairing old cookstoves, involves repairing two different metals—cast iron and steel. Gray cast iron (most commonly used in old cookstoves) is very brittle yet easy to machine. Drilling or grinding cast iron is easy, but do handle parts carefully. One drop on a hard surface, and you'll be presenting a jigsaw puzzle to the local welder.

Steel is a tough metal which bends rather than breaks under shock. Like cast iron, mild steel is also relatively easy to machine. The characteristics of steel include a low rust resistance and the tendency to become bent or dented. In most cases the main steel destroyer is rust.

Welding Is Best

The best way to repair broken cast iron or relatively thick steel parts is usually by welding or brazing. Welding steel is a fairly simple matter, however, welding cast iron can—at times—be difficult. Unless you've had experience welding cast iron, it's best to leave it to the professional.

When sending parts out to be welded, advise the welder of the type of conditions to which that particular part is subjected. Exterior parts that are seen should be brazed or welded with nickel. Since both metals are soft, the weld can easily be ground down, making the weld barely noticeable. On parts that are under stress (grates, oven damper), it may be better to use a stronger filler rod such as steel. Whatever the case, find a welder who guarantees his work and let him make the decisions.

If nonremovable parts needed welding, have it done before you start to repair the rest of the stove. Otherwise, you may end up repairing the same area twice. Welding close to sheet metal panels may warp or burn holes through them. So after the stove has been cleaned, carefully inspect the stove and have all of the heavy parts welded first.

Welding is usually the best way to repair broken parts; however, sending parts out to be welded is time-consuming and expensive. Sometimes it's possible to repair heavy parts without welding. Simply cut a piece of mild steel (thickness and overall size depends on the amount of stress) and lay it across both broken pieces. Next, drill holes through both the steel and the broken parts. Use metal screws or bolts and nuts to hold the parts together. Obviously, this isn't the most attractive method of repair. It will however, join broken grates and other internal parts in a strong manner without welding.

REJUVENATING THE JUNKYARD WOODSTOVE

After all the welding on the old cookstove has been completed, you can start repairing the rest of the stove (Fig. 7-4). Begin by repairing the exterior sheet metal panels. Since the outer panels are visible, you'll want to repair them in the most attractive manner possible. Usually this involves removing inner panels so patches or new panels can be installed from the inside. Damaged areas that are located in areas that aren't normally seen can be fixed from the outside with less trouble.

To repair large holes, make a patch from 26 gauge sheet metal and (when it's feasible) remove inner panels or other parts for access. Clean the inner side of the panel with a wire brush. Apply furnace cement on the area that'll be covered by the patch. Hold the patch firmly in place and drill holes through both the patch and the panel. Now the metal can be fastened with either small sheet metal screws or pop rivets.

A patch installed in this manner will have a gap between patch and the sheet metal panel that you may wish to fill in. Probably the most popular filler used for repairing old stoves is furnace cement. It's inexpensive extremely heat resistant and easy to use. It should be used on parts that aren't seen since it's hard to sand smooth and its porous appearance doesn't match well with metal.

There is a better material to use when appearance counts. "Muffler Mender" by Victor products doesn't contain the abrasive material found in furnace cement. When properly applied and sanded, it blends in well with metal.

When filling areas, clean the metal with a wire brush first. Apply "Muffler Mender" about ¼" higher than the surface metal. Try to work the air bubbles out of the material. After a few hours, the filler should be hard enough to sand down. Start with medium coarse sandpaper and sand the material until it's almost at the same level as the surface metal. Then use finer grit sandpaper to make the area as smooth as possible.

Small holes or cracks can be repaired without using a patch. Clean both sides of the metal with a wire brush. Slightly indent the metal around the hole with a ball peen hammer. This indentation will allow the filler material to be spread out over a larger area, thereby making a stronger bond. In addition, more filler can be applied to the inside of the panel for more support.

When sanding "Muffler Mender," avoid breathing the dust. There's no list of ingredients on the tube, but it probably contains asbestos. So wrap a towel around your beak first.

Interior panels can be repaired with less trouble than the outer ones.

The large holes can be repaired with patches and the smaller holes with furnace cement. Panels that are rusted out can be replaced with a new piece of 26 gauge sheet metal, or just place a new panel over the old one and seal it with furnace cement. Obviously, there's no need to install patches from the inside or sand filler materials, since the inner parts of the stove aren't seen. Inspect the inner panels well. Excessive air leaks will cause the fire to burn too fast.

To inspect the oven for holes, stick your head right in there and pass a strong light over the exterior oven panels. Fix holes with a patch covered with furnace cement. Wipe the furnace cement from around the edges of the patch, or it may turn up later in your food (tends to spoil the whole meal).

Inspect the bottom of the stove. Repair the bottom panel in the same manner as the interior panels. As an optional safety feature, you can install a

Fig. 7-4. This stove needs rejuvenation.

heat shield on the bottom of your stove. Carefully tip the stove on its side, lay a sheet of asbestos over the bottom panel, and cover with a sheet of 26 gauge sheet metal. If a heat shield isn't used, it's a good idea to mount the stove on some type of nonflammable surface.

The Warming Cabinet

The warming cabinet is simply a sheet metal box with one or two doors that's mounted on a cast iron or mild steel frame. Repair the warmer box as you would the exterior panels. If the cabinet is in extremely poor shape, it may be better in the long run to have a new box made by the local tinsmith. The back panel can be repaired or replaced, and the frame can be repaired by either welding or brazing.

When the stovepipe and hand damper assembly are missing, or if the pipe is rusted out, you can buy new parts at most hardware stores. Some stoves have an oval-shaped pipe flange and require a reducer pipe. Still, all three parts should cost no more than $6 or $7.

To assemble a new pipe and damper, first snap a section of stovepipe together and place it (along with the reducer when necessary) on the stove. Position the seam in the back and offset by 1″ or so (otherwise the damper rod will run into the seam). Mark the pipe where the damper handle will be easy to reach and remove the pipe from the stove.

Remove the damper rod from the plate and push the pointed rod through the pipe with a firm twisting motion. Measure (on the inside) from the top of the stove pipe to the hole. Mark off the same distance directly opposite the hole and push the rod through there. All that's left now is to remove the rod, hold the damper plate inside the pipe and insert the rod through the plate.

When you place the stovepipe and damper through the warming cabinet, the damper rod sticking from the pipe may hit the back panel of the cabinet. Rather than cut the rod off (a short rod may come out of the hole and cause the damper to fall inside the stove), remove the rod and push the stovepipe through the warming cabinet. With the stovepipe in position (check by putting the cabinet on the stove), put the damper rod back in the stovepipe and push it through the back panel. Remove the assembly and set it aside until all of the parts have been painted.

The Heat Indicator

Often the heat indicator on old cookstoves will have a cracked viewing glass or the gauge itself won't work. The heat gauge on Herbert Huff's stove had a cracked glass, so he decided to replace it. In his case, the overall investment in time and money wasn't worth the slight improvement in appearance. Before you attempt to disassemble a heat gauge, read on and then decide for yourself.

The outer ring on Huff's stove was frozen in place by several decades of accumulated rust. After the first few hours of trying to tap the ring loose, and several applications of penetrating fluid, Huff was ready to give up. Penetrating fluid mixed with dirt and rust had seeped inside and smeared all over the face of the gauge.

After a few more hours of tapping, the ring finally came loose. The constant pounding caused a small part inside the gauge to break. Fortunately (after another hour), Huff was able to make a new part from a stiff piece of wire.

With the gauge repaired, Huff drove to the nearest glass shop to have a new viewing glass made. All together, he went to three different glass shops and was informed—by all three—that he needed a heat resistant glass (which they didn't have). Finally, he found one shop that stocked the special glass, but had to wait another week before they could get to it.

The real shocker came when Huff got the bill: $9 for a 2″ diameter piece of glass. This doesn't mean that you'll have so many problems, but it's something to consider before you get too involved in the whole project. The glass in your area may not be that expensive, so call around and price different shops before you start.

When all the necessary repairs have been made on the old woodburning cookstove, you are ready for the final touch: painting on the fresh, new finish. The cleaner and smoother the surface of the stove, the better the finish will turn out. Painting over dirt and rust is a no-no. Not only will the rough area show up in the finish, but the paint will peel off before long. Take the time to clean the surface well, and your efforts will show up in the finished product.

Start out with the rough work first, such as grinding welds and sanding heavily rusted parts. If you need to do a lot of grinding or sanding, pick up a grinding disc at an auto paint supply store. One grinding disc will outlast several packages of the paper-backed discs. Buy a coarse grit disc for grinding welds and a medium grit for sanding rusty parts. Later on, you can go over these areas with a finer grit sandpaper to make the surface smooth.

After the rough work is completed, use a wire brush to clean up the surface rust and dirt. Baked-on grease can be removed with a putty knife or scraper (a propane torch may prove helpful). Once the stove is clean, sweep up the working area and use a damp rag to remove any dust on the stove.

Inspect the nickel or chrome-plated parts. Unless the plating is rusted through and peeling off, you can clean and polish these parts to a high luster. First, carefully scrape away the dirt and grease, but don't mar the surface. Depending on how rough the plating is, whether it is rusty or simply discolored, use either 500 or 600 grit sandpaper or one of the many chrome cleaners available to polish the part. Be sure to cover all of the plated parts with masking tape and newspaper before you paint.

Plating Parts

You may wish to have certain parts of your stove plated or replated. The shiny parts will enhance the beauty as well as increase the value of any stove. Plating parts is expensive—$100 or more for some of the larger parts. Have a few of the smaller parts priced first, rather than go the trouble of removing the large ones. Then you should have a good idea what the cost will be for the big parts.

Most of the older stoves were nickel plated. Nickel will shine almost as well as chrome, but requires polishing periodically.

Like nickel, brass plated parts require polishing. It's best to brass-plate parts that are in the low heat area, since heat causes brass to tarnish faster. Only one plating shop in Huff's area did any brass plating, and they charged more than for chrome plating (again, fewer steps involved).

Probably the best choice for an old cookstove is chrome. The hard finish doesn't need polishing, and it looks better than nickel. Since prices are all about the same, chrome is the best bet.

Painting the Stove

To finish the stove, you'll need stove black and heat-resistant paint. Stove black is used on the stove top and inside the warming cabinet where pots and pans would scratch the finish if paint were used. Heat-resistant (sometimes called engine or barbecue) paint is used on the rest of the stove. Both items are available at most hardware stores.

Start by painting the inside of the oven and warming cabinet with stove black. You should use stove black before painting the rest of the stove, since it contains petroleum distillates that will stain or dissolve the paint. Clean up any spills with a rag and solvent before you paint.

Huff used three different types of heat-resistant paint on his stove. The stove body was painted with dull black paint. The dull paint covers up all kinds of minor metal flaws that would otherwise show up in high gloss paint.

The warming cabinet was painted with high gloss paint. This paint was used because the shiny hard finish will resist grease stains better than dull black.

As an alternative to plating, Huff painted some of the parts with white paint to make them "stand out." Start by painting the white parts first. When it's easy to do so, remove the parts and paint them individually. When not, mask the area around the part with masking tape and newspaper to prevent overspray. Spray the parts well with two or more *thin* coats and allow the paint to dry. Then mask all of the white parts (and the heat gauge glass). Paint the rest of the stove black (Fig. 7-5).

Fire It Up

Set up your stove in a well ventilated area (the paint will stink at first). Start out with a small fire. If you notice any leaks, allow the fire to go out and repair the hole before going any further. Very slowly, work your way up to a hot fire. After the stove has been used a few times, the paint will cure and the odor will go away.

Old woodburning cookstoves are really simple to repair. Obviously, if you're more interested in efficiency than looks, you can save money by

Fig. 7-5. This stove is ready to be fired up.

repairing only the vital parts. Still, you should be able to buy all of the necessary materials (including stovepipe and damper) for less than $25.

The majority of old cookstoves sell for $25 to $400, depending on size and condition. At first, $400 may seem like a lot of money for an old cookstove. An old cookstove in good shape, though, will outlast several electric ranges since there are no elements or burners to burn out. It's not at all uncommon to find an 80-year old cookstove still in service.

A cookstove is a much sought after antique, so prices are sure to rise as time passes. If for some reason you decide that you don't like using an old cookstove, chances are you can sell the stove and make money in the process. Any way you look at it, you can't go wrong with an old woodburning cookstove.

CONSTRUCTING THE HEAT REFLECTING STOVE BOARD

Anyone considering the installation of a woodburning stove would be wise to carefully select a *stove board*. They vary in size and type of materials used in their construction. The primary function of stove boards or wall boards are the same—to prevent excessive heat or sparks from catching the floor or walls on fire.

There are three different types of *stove boards: heat insulators, heat absorbers,* and *heat reflectors*. Naturally, each of the three types have their distinct advantages and disadvantages.

Heat Insulators

Of the three types, heat insulator boards are probably the most popular. Commercially made boards are usually a thin sheet of metal packed with asbestos. The main advantage of insulator boards are that they are lightweight and can be used on any type of floor.

A homemade version can be made by using a sheet of asbestos board. Unfortunately, asbestos board is quite brittle and will often crack under the stress of a heavy stove. A protective cover made of sheet metal or aluminum might help to prevent cracking.

Either version will protect floors and walls from combustion. A considerable amount of heat will travel through the board, which can cause discolored or warped flooring materials.

Heat Absorbers

Heat-absorbing stove and wall boards have the ability to not only protect floors and walls, but also store heat. Long after the fire has died, the heat absorber continues to radiate stored heat into the room. Of the three types of stove boards, heat absorbers are undoubtedly the most efficient.

Heat absorbers are made of heavy materials such as stone or brick masonry, or ceramic or cement tiles. For this reason, heat absorbers are best suited to basement installations. Building a heavy heat absorber on a wood framed floor would cause the floor to warp if not give altogether.

The latest idea in stove and wall boards is the *heat reflector*. Rather than insulate or absorb heat, this type of board reflects heat away from the floor and walls. Consequently, the heat is reflected back into the room where it's most needed.

Since this type of board can't store heat, it's not the most efficient. Considering that it can reflect heat back into the living area instead of losing heat through a cold wall or floor, it would seem to be more efficient than an insulator board.

Like insulator boards, reflectors are lightweight and can be used on wood floors. Unlike many commercial insulator boards, an air space can be provided between the board and floor, thereby preventing warped or discolored flooring materials.

Construction

The project began by measuring the stove and figuring the size of board needed. Then four 2 × 4s were cut to the appropriate size to form a frame around the board. The 2 × 4s were then trimmed ½″ on one edge (for appearance) so they measured 1½″ × 3″. See Fig. 7-6.

A ¾″ wide dado groove was cut in each 2 × 4 about ½″ from the top edge of the boards. Three of the 2 × 4s were then nailed together, and a ¾″ plywood board was slipped into the dado groove. The fourth 2 × 4″ brace was then centered and nailed underneath to help support the plywood.

Buy a thin sheet of shiny aluminum to serve as a reflector. This was nailed on top of the sheet of plywood with small aluminum nails. It's best to use aluminum nails, since some nails will cause corrosion.

The wall board was even easier to make, since it holds no weight. It consists of a 2 × 2″ frame with a thin sheet of aluminum nailed on top. A small piece of bent metal running from wall board to wall serves as a brace.

Here's another way to build the stove board without cutting a dado groove in the 2 × 4s. Just nail a 1 × 2″ strip along the edge of the 2 × 4s to

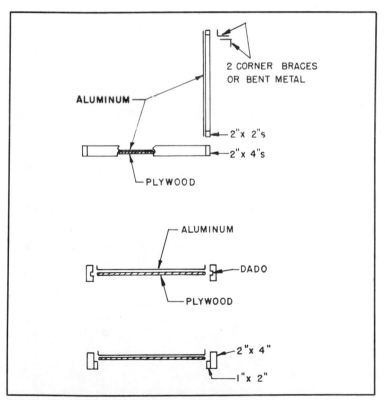

Fig. 7-6. Construction details for the stove reflector.

183

serve as a ledge for the plywood to rest on. Nail all four 2 × 4s together along with the brace, then lay the plywood on top and tack it down with finish nails.

An attractive alternative to aluminum for a wall board might be mirror tiles. Nail a piece of ⅜" plywood (good on one side) to the 2 × 2 frame, and glue the tiles in place. Not only will it look nicer, it'll also be a more efficient heat reflector than aluminum.

The only maintenance the stove and wallboard require is an application of aluminum polish once every two years or so to keep them shiny. For wood floor installations, the reflector stove board is the best choice.

PIPE CLEANER HELPS REDUCE CREOSOTE PROBLEM

Everyone with wood heat has experienced some sort of problems with creosote. Problems are kept at a minimum by burning well-seasoned, dry wood, but it isn't always possible to cut far enough in advance.

The major creosote problems come from the new controlled-combustion, wood space heaters of the Ashley type. Mr. Jefflin Farm has a Siegler and wouldn't part with it for anything. Wood burns slower with a more complete combustion than the old potbelly wood stoves. He can fill it infrequently and keep up with a busy schedule without worrying about the fire going out. Farm can control the temperature relatively accurately and can burn either green or seasoned wood with great efficiency. All of this makes the furnace invaluable, but it also makes for great quantities of highly flammable creosote.

Creosote is a natural by-product of wood. In the old potbelly stoves, fires burned hotter and the creosote was largely burned up right along with the wood. What little creosote did collect in the chimney would occasionally catch fire, but there is rarely enough of a buildup to harm a tile-lined, concrete block chimney.

The newer furnaces, however, burn more slowly and allow the creosote to evaporate in the form of a vapor into your chimney. When the vapor hits the cold air at the top, it condenses into a gummy liquid and runs back into the chimney. Over a short period of time, it builds up into a thick, gooey mass. The right conditions, such as a windy night or a particularly hot fire, will dry this goo into a highly flammable material which burns with tremendous heat. You've got yourself a bad chimney fire.

Farm has often heard from oldtimers in his area that potbelly or wood kitchen stoves, as a rule, cannot burn out a clay-lined chimney. The new space heaters can, and do, and occasionally burn down houses as well. The slow baking of the creosote in the chimney is ideal for building up a tremendous mass of the stuff and can make your home a pretty unsafe place to be.

After many bad chimney fires, Farm continued to work on a solution with little success. His first attempt was to clean the stuff out with chains. You can and should do this regularly. A clump of old tire chains tied in a loose mass by a heavy rope run up and down the inside of the chimney will

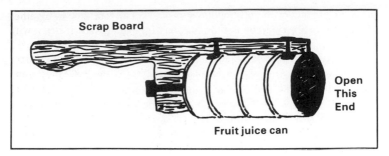

Fig. 7-7. Make a pipe cleaner out of an old fruit juice can.

scrub it out pretty well, unless your creosote is wet. If it is, the chains won't budge it.

Farm then tried running the stove at hotter temperatures. This forced the stove to burn up much of the creosote right along with the wood. Farm was in the process of building a house and now has his furnace in a small space. Even with the windows open, the excess heat was too much for comfort. Farm also had to use more than the usual amount of wood and, though he had less of a creosote problem, he still had the problem.

The biggest danger point is the connecting pipe from your stove to your chimney. Farm reduced that danger by setting up his cleanout door directly across from it on the outside of the chimney. He made a pipe cleaner out of an old fruit juice can and bolted a wooden handle to it (Fig. 7-7). The lip of the can makes a great scraping edge for cleaning the creosote off the inside of your connecting pipe and is just the right size for the job. With your cleanout door located directly across from your connecting pipe, you can reach right into your pipe with the scraper with no effort (Fig. 7-8). The creosote in the pipe is almost always bone dry because it's so close to the fire, making it a ripe place for a fire to start.

Still, the chimney buildup was Farm's greatest worry. On several occasions he has had a fire shoot 10′ above the chimney in the middle of the night. He no longer had the fear of the connecting pipe burning out as it had once. The chimney might crack, though, if the fire went undiscovered. Whenever he did discover one, he'd dash up to the roof in record time and pour quantities of salt down, which put out the fire.

Farm chained the chimney out as thoroughly as possible. Then he stuffed about four loosely crumpled sheets of newspaper into the chimney just above the cleanout door and set fire to it. Standing by with two 5-pound bags of salt, the rest of the family watched the flames lick at the top of the chimney weakly. He set it off three times in a row to make sure it burned clean, then chained out the thoroughly dry residue. A perfectly controlled fire made the chimney clean.

It works fine. Farm uses this method once a week now and has had no unexpected fires since. His chimney stays perfectly clean, and the creosote never gets a chance to build up to a dangerous level.

Should you decide to try this method, there is some advice:

☐ Make sure your chimney is as clean as you can get it with chains first. If chemical cleaners help in your chimney, use them just before you try the first deliberate fire.

☐ Be prepared to climb the roof with lots of salt on your first try. If the fire gets overly hot, you can put it out easily.

☐ Make sure all wood or shingle surfaces near the top of your chimney are protected from fire by flashing.

☐ Keep your furnace turned low to insure it will not add its fire to your fire.

☐ Be sure to clean your connecting pipe first.

☐ Don't try this method with a metal stovepipe. They can and do burn out easily. Your claylined chimney should be in good shape as well.

It may not be the easiest way to clean out a chimney. It's a lot better, though, than sleepless nights.

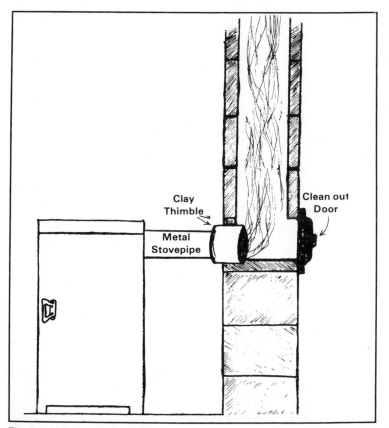

Fig. 7-8. Note the cleanout door.

186

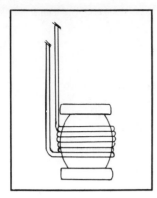

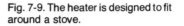
Fig. 7-9. The heater is designed to fit around a stove.

GRAVITY WATER HEATER

During the coldest spells Julianne Kuhl's bedroom was usually down to 39°F by morning, even with a fire in the stove all night. Because the Kuhls couldn't afford to heat their house with oil, they put in a woodburning pot-bellied stove to heat three of the eight rooms in their home. The other rooms were blocked off with heavy canvas. Julianne's husband designed a gravity hot water heater to fit around the stove. The Kuhls figured the monthly cost by dividing the number of months they used it into the expense of materials purchased. Figures 7-9 through 7-13 show the actual

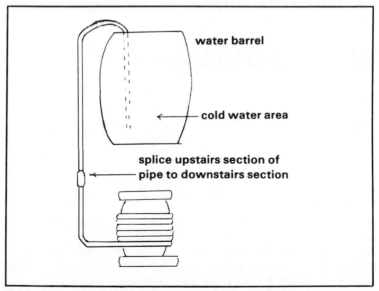

Fig. 7-10. Place the water barrel at least 10′ above the spigot.

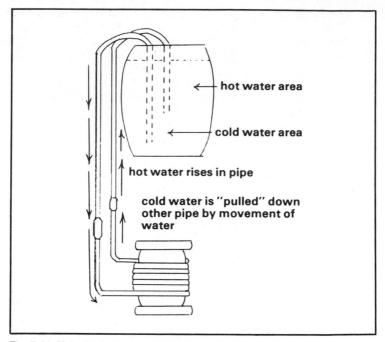

hot water area

cold water area

hot water rises in pipe

cold water is "pulled" down other pipe by movement of water

Fig. 7-11. Note the hot water and cold water areas.

construction of the thing, and it works on a proven thermodynamic principle: hot water rises, cold water falls.

Take copper pipe and wrap it around the firebox of your stove six or seven times. The Kuhls used 7/16" plumbers' tubing; ½" tubing will give better recovery. Be careful not to put a kink in your pipe.

On the second floor, or at least 10' above your spigot, place your water barrel. The Kuhls used a wooden hogshead barrel, but even a conventional water tank could be used. Line the water barrel with at least 1" of foam rubber or fiber glass insulation.

Take at least three heavy-duty (three mil) plastic bags. Put one inside the other to make one bag out of them. Then insert the whole unit into your insulated barrel. Don't use thin plastic; the water comes up at about 212°F and will melt thin plastic. You will probably want to secure the bags to the barrel with duct tape because the wet bags tend to slide down into the barrel.

Open-ended cold water pipe should stop seven-eighths of the way down into your water barrel.

Now run your hot water line from the barrel to your stove. Be sure this splice is soldered well because if your fire gets very hot you will occasionally have steam running up that line. The open-ended hot water pipe should be three-fourths of the way down the barrel's depth.

188

Now run a pipe from the water barrel to your sink. The Kuhls used copper pipe because the copper curves are no problem. Again, take care not to kink the pipe. The open-ended faucet (spigot) line should be in the upper third of the barrel. That way when the hot water is drained out, you still have some warm water left in the barrel to take the chill out of the icewater from your well. This makes it that much faster to heat the whole barrel of water up again. Atmospheric pressure will force water down the faucet line once you cause the water to drain out by applying suction. You may use your mouth on the spigot; it is a bit awkward to do that while bent over a sink, but it works quite well. You would install a faucet in the faucet line to shut off the water.

Now make an air pipe, just a short length of about 16″ to hang over the barrel. It should not touch the water inside the barrel.

Final steps are to make an insulated cover for your barrel to keep the water hot (plastic covered wood or foam are good), and to provide some means of refilling your barrel.

Sophistications could be an automatic filling device, similar to a toilet bowl float. The Kuhls had to fill their barrel by hand, using buckets of cold water from the bathroom on the second floor. The Kuhls were surprised at how often they had to refill their barrel, two or three times a day. Yet this was their only source of hot water for washing themselves, their dishes, and their laundry.

A further improvement could be hooking up pipes to a tub, provided it is located lower than the water barrel. You could also hook up your hot water line and your cold water line onto the same faucet, thereby "stretch-

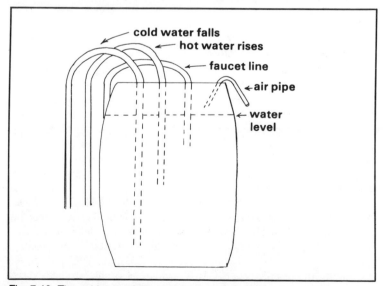

Fig. 7-12. The cold water falls, and the hot water rises.

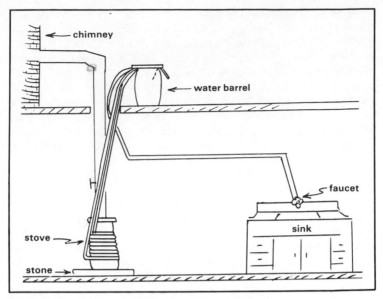

Fig. 7-13. The system when it is completely hooked up.

ing" your hot water to accomplish more. Figure 7-13 shows what the system looked like when it was completely hooked up.

One drawback may be keeping a fire going during the summer. There is no reason your stove couldn't be located in the cellar. You would just need a lot more pipe because the water barrel has to be higher than the sink outlet to provide decent water pressure.

LET THE SUN WARM THE ANIMALS

With the continuing rise in energy and heating costs, the cost of providing a minimal amount of heat for livestock during those periods when they need it is becoming prohibitive. Believing that sunlight could provide part of the heat required for warming a pen during birth or for a brooder area. John Parker began looking for an economical, simple way of capturing the sun's heat—one that anyone could build and use. After considerable experimenting, Parker settled on a solid concrete block wall as the most satisfactory and least costly method of heat storage, since a constant flow of heat is not necessary for animal warmth.

The blocks Parker used are 8 × 16" solid concrete blocks, 4" thick. This selection was based on information provided by the Portland Cement Association in its bulletin, "How to Calculate Heat Transmission Coefficients and Vapor Condensation Temperatures of Concrete Masonry Walls."

The heating source was a 4' × 5' window of double strength glass situated 30" above floor level and in the center of a 9' long south wall of a

190

small shed. The wall was laid to receive maximum sunlight. The wall extended 18" longer than the window on either end and was 18" in from the window. The wall was 64" high, 16 4" thick blocks (Fig. 7-14). The blocks were laid on a smoothed section of the dirt floor with heavy plastic sheeting under them as a vapor barrier.

Blocks Locked in Place

Each end of the wall was in the form of a "T", with the concrete blocks extending out 8" on either side. The blocks were laid up without mortar. This leaves an uneven line along the top since the blocks vary slightly in size, but this is of no importance other than looks. While the blocks are not easily dislodged, Parker made the wall more secure by driving a 7' steel post well into the ground tightly against each end of the wall and running a wire with a turnbuckle tightening between the two posts across the top of the wall. This literally locks the blocks in place.

Parker painted the wall with dull black paint on the side and ends facing the window. He also lined the entire window wall with 4" of urethane insulation and sprayed it with reflective aluminum paint (Fig. 7-15).

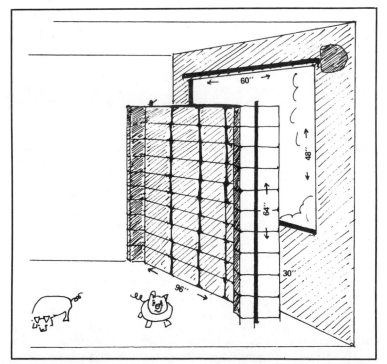

Fig. 7-14. A concrete block wall is a satisfactory method of heat storage (drawing by Gretchen Belanger).

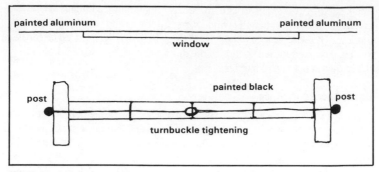

Fig. 7-15. Aerial view of the wall.

After devising and discarding several Rube Goldberg methods of automatically covering the window at night and on cloudy days, Parker reverted to a simple air curtain control which prevents heat loss back through the window. For this he used a 2″ plastic pipe extending across the top of the window and 4″ beyond at each end. He drilled ⅛″ holes in the pipe every ¼″. Since very little air is needed to form the curtain, Parker used an old hair dryer with the heating element removed and the blower tube inserted in the 2″ pipe. The other end of the plastic pipe was closed.

To control the air curtain, Parker used a regular standard photoelectric cell programmed to turn the dryer blower on when no sun was striking the block wall. Depending on how much sunlight strikes the wall to heat the blocks, they can give off adequate warmth for 19 to 28 hours. Even on the coldest days, if it was sunny, the wall absorbed enough heat to register 125°F on the thermometer atop the wall.

Using the block wall as a heat source eliminated about two-thirds the cost of the normal heat required for small livestock and early chicks during cold weather. The solar heating was entirely independent of normal heating arrangements.

Infrared Assist

When the pen was used for lambing or farrowing, two infrared lamps coupled together and hung above the pen were set to turn on when the temperature dropped to 55°F on a thermostat placed at floor level. With baby poultry the brooder thermometer was set to go on normally when heat was needed, while the large pen space along the concrete solar wall provided a warm feeding and exercise area.

Young pigs need a warm dry place if all the litter is to be saved when sows farrow in cold weather. They also thrive better and grow faster with less feeding when they are not forced to endure cold conditions.

It is necessary to have warmth for early chicks, turkeys, and other poultry. While they need maximum warmth for only the first few weeks, all young poultry are healthier and more vigorous under temperate conditions.

192

Laying hens do better in a building that, if not especially warm, is at least free of drafts. If you raise sheep, the lambs born early in the season (February and March) need adequate warmth for the first two weeks.

Parker has found this rather simple system to be the lowest cost supplemental heat he could devise. It is practical for heating a fairly large pen area with little trouble.

Chapter 8

Alternative Energy

A solar collector, windmills, and farmers' alcohol are featured in this chapter. A checklist at the end of the chapter will help homesteaders save energy.

HOMEMADE SOLAR COLLECTOR COMBINES THREE FEATURES

A small, homemade, low-cost solar collector designed by a Nebraska farm couple is the first to combine the features of portability, tiltability, and flexible air flow. Named for its designers, the Young Solar Collector was built with the help of the Small Farm Energy Project and can be used for a variety of farm projects.

Gary and Delores Young used the flat-plate collector to heat their home and dry corn. In 1979 they estimated they saved 190 gallons of propane gas drying corn and 141 gallons heating their home by using the collector. Using available lumber and excluding labor costs, they spent $1,410 to build the collector, including the cost of a used running gear. Their payback is estimated at 5.8 years (figuring in tax credits), while the collector's lifespan is 20 years.

Originally, the Youngs were going to build two vertical wall collectors, one to dry their grain and another to heat their home. They decided they could build one collector to do both after learning about multiple-use collectors.

They spent 84 hours building their 10×24' collector in the winter of 1978. The Youngs used 2×4s and sheathing lumber from an old hog barn to build it. After the frame was built using 2×10" lumber, the other components were fitted into the frame. Starting from the back of the collector, these components are:

—1" sheathing.

—2×4" studs lined with 3.5" of fiberglass insulation, vapor side up.

194

—4-mil vapor barrier.
—Used aluminum press plates nailed to studs.
—3″ battens forming 3″ air channel.
—Layer of used Masonite or plywood wall paneling.
—1×2″ battens forming 0.75″ air channel.
—Corrugated metal absorber plate.
—1×2″ battens forming 0.75″ dead air space.
—Cover plate—5-mil corrugated Filon fiberglass.

The finished flat-plate collector was then hinged to a four-wheel running gear that had been lengthened and framed. The Youngs' used running gear was valued at about $100; a new one would cost about $525.

The running gear is vital to the solar collector, as it gives it its portability and tiltability. Because it can be tilted, the collector can be positioned to receive maximum sunlight. Its portability means it can be used on any farm, regardless of layout. Its third feature, flexible air flow, allows it to be used as either a low temperature/high airflow system for grain drying or a high temperature/low airflow system for space heating.

When drying grain, the Young collector and fan system can produce an airflow of 3,000 cubic feet per minute at 1.2″ of static pressure, according to Walter Heid, Jr., an agricultural economist who wrote the USDA report on the collector. This system produces a temperature rise of 12° F at noon. For home heating, 19,700 Btu are produced per hour at noon, with a temperature rise of about 40°F.

Construction plans for the Young Solar Collector may be purchased from the Small Farm Energy Project, P.O. Box 736, Hartington, NE 69730 for $2 per set. Specify "Portable Solar Collector Plans" when ordering.

SOLAR-WIND SYSTEM

Countryside is well-known for its expertise on small-scale livestock raising, so when an A-frame structure sprouted on the roof of the *Countryside* building in Waterloo, Wisconsin, there was local speculation that the staff was going to raise rabbits, chickens, goats, or **something** on the roof. Not a bad idea, perhaps. In truth, the shed is a solar collector. In combination with a Wincharger 12-volt generator, it heats a portion of the *Countryside General Store* (Figs. 8-1 through 8-3).

The project was a dream for a long time. When the magazine ran a series of articles on alternative energy in 1970, it was a wild dream indeed.

In 1975 the staff moved into a spacious building (a former International Harvester dealership) with a large expanse of flat roof. The idea of solar heat came up again, even before the gas bill for the nine furnaces in the building arrived. There were other priorities, though

In the summer of 1976 things fell into place when we met Steve Schmidt, who was selling and installing commercially-produced solar collectors. He had some interesting ideas (Fig. 8-4).

Fig. 8-1. The windmill and collector sit atop Countryside's cement block building.

One was that solar was ideal for commercial buildings as a supplemental heat source. A major part of the expense, he pointed out, is storage. Heat storage is important in a home because most of the heat is required in the late afternoon to morning, when there is no sun.

A commercial building, on the other hand, is empty during those hours. Thermostats are turned down. He suggested using the heat from a collector directly, without storage.

He also failed miserably as a salesman, admitting that he felt commercial collectors were ridiculously overpriced. He could build one himself for a fraction of the cost.

This was starting to sound good. We understood some of the basic principles, thanks to those earlier articles, and found it rather bothersome that such a simple process had so quickly become so technical and expensive. It would cost even less if we could use recycled materials, he added. That did it.

Recycle and Build

The first step was recycling several large piles of boards, formerly shelving which had been torn out to accommodate the Countryside Print

Shop. Pounds of nails were pulled (Figs. 8-5 and 8-6). Plans were drawn on the basis of the material available.

In addition, it was decided not to make the unit inconspicuous, which is the usual goal, but to have it stand out. Everyone talks about solar heat, but very little is actually used, at least in southern Wisconsin. By calling attention to itself, this unit could prove that solar energy was more than science fiction.

The design called for 96 square feet of collector set into an A-frame which was an equilateral triangle 10' long on each side. The structure is 13' long. The collector itself is 8×12'.

The rafters were made from 1"×12" boards 6' long. With a lot of cutting and some recycled nails, these became 2×6s 10' long. Fourteen of them were used.

Technically, the angle of the collector should approximate the degree of latitude of the location plus 15°, so that the noon sun in winter strikes it at a 90° angle. Waterloo is located at about 43°. Rather than worry about a few degrees and to avoid the attendant problems of measuring, cutting, and fitting, Steve took the much simpler route of making an equilateral triangle with the collector then being inclined at 60°.

One-half-inch plywood, which had formed the backs of the shelves, was used to face the north side of the A-frame and the back of the collector (Fig. 8-7). Six inches of foil-faced fiber glass insulation was installed over the plywood at the back of the collector. Steve thinks 4" would have been sufficient, with less cost. Half-inch tempered Masonite was used to cover the insulation.

Fig. 8-2. Another view of the windmill and collector.

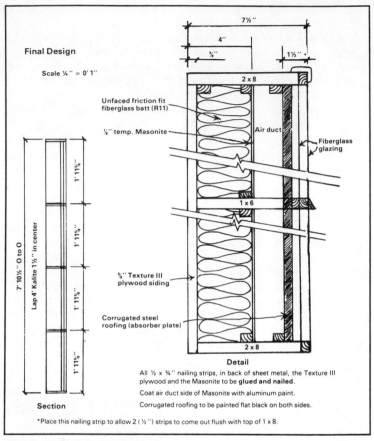

Fig. 8-3. Design for the collector.

Next, 1×2 wood strips were nailed to the Masonite, horizontally. These provide the air space where the heat is collected and moved away from the collector. Ordinary corrugated sheet metal which had been painted black was nailed to the strips.

Paint and Fiber Glass

Steve used flat black *Rustoleum*. A quart should have done the job. He used 1½ gallons. He blames his sprayer, but thinks it might have been cheaper to have a body shop paint the panels. The flattest, most absorbent black paint is *Nextel*, made by 3M.

Next, more strips were nailed to those below to provide another air space. Sheets of *Kalite*, a special grade of fiber glass designed for solar applications, was fastened to the strips. Another layer of strips was added, and a final layer of Kalite installed.

Fig. 8-4. Steve Schmidt designed and built the solar-wind system.

Fig. 8-5. Schmidt's son Phillip helped with the recycling and construction.

199

Fig. 8-6. The Schmidts are working on the project.

There are pros and cons on the double thickness of Kalite, but now Steve thinks one would have been better. With only one layer, the difference in insulating value would be negligible, the cost of labor and materials would be cut in half, and under certain conditions efficiency would actually increase.

Two 12-volt Dayton blowers—the type used in automobile heaters—force air from a cold air return, across the solar collector between the corrugated metal and the Masonite, and into the Countryside Store via a flexible insulated duct (Fig. 8-8).

The first blower turns on when the temperature inside the collector reaches 100°F. The second turns on at 105. The Honeywell thermostats controlling the blowers are the types used in 12-volt motor home furnaces.

The blowers are powered by two Sears Marine Diehard batteries. They're designed for motor trolling, and therefore have a sustained output, rather than the short jolt needed for automobile engines. The batteries are charged by the Wincharger.

Tables 8-1 and 8-2 show what went into the solar collector.

The budget for the collector was $600. Actual cost was $627.33. Neither of these figures includes labor. A total of 111 hours was spent on the project, including erecting the windmill.

The wind generating system more than doubled the cost (Fig. 8-9). A transformer could have been used, greatly reducing the capital expense and only slightly affecting operating expense. The generator does have far more capacity than is being used by the two blowers. Lights, a stereo tape deck, or other 12-volt appliances could be added to the system.

According to calculations (and at present natural gas prices), the solar unit should pay for itself in three years. If this winter's experience comes anywhere near expectations, the system will be expanded. Steve already has changes in mind, and he wants to experiment with other designs.

200

Fig. 8-7. Here's a detailed look at the back framing of the collector.

The reflector in front of the collector added $96.69 to the cost, using new 2×4s and exterior grade plywood (Fig. 8-10). The increase in efficiency is apparent to the naked eye when standing near the reflector. The reflective material is used printing plates from the Countryside Print Shop.

Steve designed the reflector to fold up against the collector during the hot months. He figured this would eliminate possible damage to the collector from intense heat which would build up when the sun is hot and no heat is being taken off the collector.

How effective is it? There is no doubt that it produces heat. One recent sunny day the outside temperature was 50°F. The temperature at the outside of the collector was 90, and inside of it at the vent to the *Countryside*

Fig. 8-8. Inside the collector two 12-volt automobile heater blowers force air from a cold air return across the collector and into the store below.

201

Table 8-1. Collector Materials.

Kalite glazing (4×25 feet)	$65.52
100 sq. ft. Sears glazing	53.67
2 tubes adhesive	5.60
1 roll aluminum foil	11.59
4 tubes silicone caulking	10.00
wood glue	2.88
Visqueen	5.06
Flashing and tar	41.16
Neoprene nails	5.56
4 insulated ducts	35.50
Dampers and diffusers	29.34
2×4s and plywood for reflector	96.69
1½ gal. flat black paint, thinner, etc.	28.55
3 pcs. ¼×4×8 Masonite	24.00
7 pcs. 26"×8' corr. sheet metal	30.94
92 sq. ft. insulation	21.16
6 pcs. 2×8×¾ styrofoam	19.20
weatherstrip	3.82
2 blowers	54.66
blower controls	31.20
wire	5.29
nuts, bolts, staples, & misc.	45.94
Total	**$627.33**

Store the thermometer read 130—the top of the scale. It couldn't go any higher.

Even on overcast days, the temperature reaches 100°F easily. What it will do during the Wisconsin winter remains to be seen but from what we've seen so far, we're optimistic.

WATER PUMPING WINDMILL

If you have a well and want to pump water from it with a windmill, you probably already know that a new steel mill and tower from any of the popular American manufacturers can cost from $2,000 to $4,000 or more. For that price you can have a windmill and tower delivered to your door in a hundred or so pieces.

To turn those hundred parts (with accompanying nuts, bolts, pins, and other fasteners) into a working windmill, you can pay a professional windmill erector (if you can find one) $35 an hour and up for several days to do the assembly work for you.

Instead of spending a minimum of several hundred dollars—much more if, you live many miles from a windmill dealer or well serviceman—you can put together and erect your own mill and tower. In addition to saving money, you'll be at an advantage when it comes to making repairs or performing routine inspection and maintenance if you have first hand knowledge of how the mill and tower go together.

Table 8-2. Materials for the Wind-Electric System.

12-volt Wincharger	$735.00
2 Sears Diehard Marine batteries	110.22
20 ft. ground cable	7.80
ground rod	6.00
ground clamp	2.30
23 ft. cable, pulley, bolts & misc. (for ground-controlled windmill brake	12.53
Total	**$873.85**

Richard Flint and his wife decided to put up a windmill, a 12′ diameter Baker on a 25′ Heller-Aller tower (Fig. 8-11). In preparing to set up their mill, the Flints talked with dealers, manufacturers, and a windmilling instructor. Using many of their instructions and improvising where there were no instructions, the Flints spent about 14 working days assembling and erecting their mill and tower. While a few of Flint's methods for handling problems apply specifically to Baker windmills and Heller-Aller towers, nearly all of them also apply to the other popular modern American mills (Aermotor and Dempster).

Preliminaries

As soon as practical after you receive the windmill and tower parts, they should be counted and inspected. Loo particularly for cracks in the cast

Fig. 8-9. Tom Voigt steadies the newly-raised wind generator while Jerry Belanger climbs the tower to remove the guy ropes.

Fig. 8-10. The finished collector gets an assist from a reflector, made out of aluminum plates recycled from the offset press.

iron gearbox, broken gear teeth, bent bands and leg parts for the tower, and bent blades for the fan. Also, open the ball bearing turntable (which goes at the top of the tower and allows the mill to swing with the wind) to be sure it's greased. If it's not, apply a liberal coat of wheel bearing grease. Next, read thoroughly any instructions furnished by the manufacturer.

As part of the process of familiarizing yourself with the assembly steps, loosely fasten together the pieces making up two adjacent legs of the tower (including horizontal bands) and one arm-assembly on the fan. This can be very important as, for instance, in the Flint's case they discovered two things during the trial assembly. The diagram furnished with the tower didn't match the parts they had. Also, because the legs of Heller-Aller towers incorporate a tension curve (making them slightly concave), they couldn't assemble the tower without mechanical aid in making the necessary slight bow. To allow yourself time to cope with such problems, the trial assembly should be done as far in advance of the permanent set up as possible. In the Flints' case, an interval of a month made it possible to get a correct diagram and to devise a method of bowing the tower legs.

Anchor Holes

To secure the windmill structure against wind damage or toppling from its own weight, the tower must be firmly fixed in the ground. This is accomplished by setting steel anchor posts (extensions of the tower legs) 3½ to 4' into the ground. All modern American towers come complete with anchor posts. Besides digging the anchor holes deep enough, you need to ensure that they have two other important properties. They should be wide enough to allow accurate positioning of the tower (3' square is enough and is also about the smallest convenient size if the holes are to be hand dug). The bottoms of the anchor holes must be level (in the same horizontal plane), so the tower will be plumb when it's upright.

You can easily determine level using an inexpensive sighting level. First, choose a point from which to use the level (the Flints laid a level on the temporary cover welded to the well casing, from where by turning the level on top of the cover they could sight toward each of the four anchor holes in turn). Then stand a post, rod, or piece of pipe upright in each of the holes in turn. The bottoms of the holes are level when the indicator on the lens of the level lines up with the same height on the rod for all of the holes.

The manufacturer of the tower recommends the following method of establishing the location of the anchor holes. Lay out on the ground the four bottom bands of the tower so they form a square with the well at its center. From each corner of the square, measure 6″ toward the well. The four points located in this way are the interior contents of the anchor holes (Fig. 8-12).

Fig. 8-11. A windmill that pumps water.

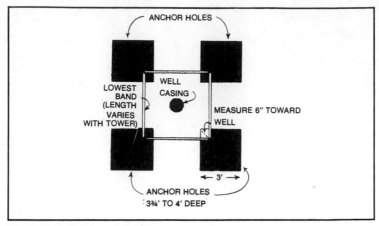

Fig. 8-12. Note the anchor holes.

Tower Assembly

In general, you can assemble your windmill tower lying on its side and then tilt it upright, or you can put it together standing, from the ground up. Unless your tower is very tall or you have to erect it in a confined space, it will be easiest to assemble it on its side. If, like the Flints, you have a Heller-Aller tower, you'll find it extremely difficult to put it together standing because of the problem of bowing the legs. These instructions cover assembly on the ground.

To begin, lay out the leg sections on the ground where the tower is to be assembled. Orient the pieces so as to minimize the amount of maneuvering you'll have to do in raising the completed tower. Ordinarily, this is with the topmost leg sections lying farthest from the well, so the assembled tower will lie on its side with the anchor posts extending over two anchor holes and its apex pointing away from the well (Fig. 8-13).

While laying out the leg pieces, you can position the tower so that when it's tilted up, the furled fan of the mill won't be held directly above the ladder by the prevailing wind. When the wind does stand the fan over the ladder, it's difficult getting onto the tower platform to work on the mill because you have to swing the fan out of the way first. So in assembling the tower, position it so that when it's upright, the prevailing wind will blow from your right as you climb the ladder. It's less preferable, but still all right, to have the prevailing wind directly in your face or at your back as you climb. Avoid placing the tower so that on the ladder the prevailing wind will come from your left.

Begin assembling the tower at the top end by bolting the turntable to the top ends of two of the legs. Until the tower is completely together, leave all nuts only finger tight so there will be play in the structure. Then, working down the same pair of legs, bolt on the truing center. The first horizontal band is next below the truing center.

On Heller-Aller towers this first band is shorter than the distance between the pair of holes in the legs through which it has to be attached. In order to put the band on, the two legs have to be drawn toward each other about 6". To bend the legs on the Heller-Aller tower, they first pulled the lower ends of the two top leg sections toward each other by hand, reducing the distance between the bolt holes by an inch. Then they looped the chain of a ratchet come-along around the legs 10' below the turntable and hooked the chain back to the come-along. By operating the lever of the come-along, they constricted the loop of chain until the holes had been drawn together another inch. The remainder of the bow was made by alternately tightening two loops of ⅜" aircraft cable (using 6" draw turnbuckles). One loop was placed around the legs just above the two bolt holes, the other 18" below the holes (Fig. 8-14).

With the first band on, continue down the pair of legs, attaching leg sections, horizontal bands, and diagonal braces. When three or more parts have to be attached with a single bolt, it's sometimes difficult to line up the factory drilled holes. This can be made easier by inserting a drift pin (alignment punch) through the holes and then levering them into place. Then clamp the parts in place with vise grip pliers, remove the pin, and put in the bolt.

On Heller-Aller towers, the legs have to be bowed slightly more to attach the second horizontal band and have to be spread to accept the band at the base of the tower. The spread can be accomplished without mechanical aid; the additional bow can be forced using a pair of loops of aircraft cable in the same way as described earlier.

Finish the first pair of legs by attaching the anchor posts and shoes. Then assemble and attach the third leg. Connect the bands and braces between it and the adjacent leg. Again, start at the top and work down the leg. Likewise, put together the remaining leg and attach it; then tighten all nuts on the tower so the structure becomes rigid. Although the tower ladder can be attached as soon as all four legs are in place, on Aermotor and Heller-Aller towers there is less chance of damaging the ladder if you wait

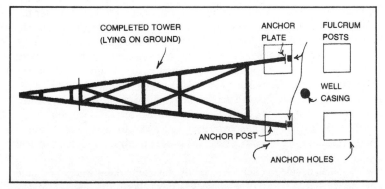

Fig. 8-13. The assembled tower on its side.

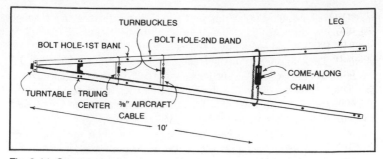

Fig. 8-14. One loop is placed around the legs just above the two bolt holes, the other is 18" below the holes.

to attach it until the tower's upright. This is because the ladders on both these models (wire loops on Aermotor and steel pegs on Heller-Aller) are fastened to one leg and can be bent while maneuvering the tower to raise it.

Raising the Tower

The most common method of raising an assembled tower is to pivot it at the base of the anchor posts and tilt it upright by pulling a cable attached just below the truing center. If you position your tower for assembly as described, the completed tower will be in the proper position to be tilted up. If you don't plan to set the drop pipe, cylinder, and sucker rod in the well yourself, it's easier if you have this done before raising the tower (especially if your tower is 30' or less in height).

When you're ready to erect the tower, begin by forming a pivot. Plant a 6' 4"×4" post vertically in each of the two anchor holes over which the legs extend (Fig. 8-13). Set these fulcrum posts against the side of each hole closest to the the well. Align them with the shoes on the bottoms of the anchor posts. Then slide (drag) the tower so the shoes butt against the fulcrum posts.

Unless you have access to a mast truck or other boom tall enough to lift your mill to the top of the erected tower, set the gearbox and mast of the mill into the turntable while the tower's still on its side. In this way you'll raise the heaviest part of the mill at the same time you tilt the tower up. The only common alternative is to use a gin pole, the "rancher's nemesis," once the tower is up. A gin pole is a very stout wooden or steel pole with a block and tackle attached to its tip. The gin pole is stood vertically on the platform of the erected tower and chained or tied to one leg. Then with the block and tackle, the mill can be hoisted above the top of the tower and then lowered to insert the mast into the turntable and truing center. Because of the large weight (150 to 500 pounds or more) and awkward shape of windmill gearboxes, this is a risky procedure, to be attempted only with the smallest mills.

If you do decide to raise the gearbox along with the tower, you should also attach the tail to the installed gearbox before erecting the tower.

Otherwise, it will be necessary to maneuver the unwieldy tail at the top of the upright tower. When raising a tower with gearbox and tail installed, chain the tail firmly so that as the tower goes up, it will point in the direction opposite that from which you pull to raise the tower. This will ensure that the tail doesn't flop or swing as you lift the tower.

Now the lift begins. Raise the top end of the tower above the horizontal and rest it on sawhorses or scaffolding (railroad ties piled into a short pyramid make an excellent stand). The taller the stand the better, so long as it's stable and doesn't rock or teeter. This small height increases the effectiveness of the pull of the cable during the lower part of the lift, which requires the most power.

Further elevation of the tower should be attempted only when the air is calm, in order to avoid injury or damage that might result from wind twisting or tipping the tower. Allow yourself plenty of time the day of final raising, since the tower should be raised and centered on the well. The anchor holes should be filled on the same day.

Using cable clamps, secure a heavy cable around two legs of the tower (Fig. 8-15). At the same time, attach a guy rope to each leg of the tower at the level of the first horizontal band.

The cable and all guy ropes ought to be at least twice as long as the nominal height of the tower. Fasten the free end of the cable to the boom of a boom truck, the elevated bucket of a front end loader, the hitch of a tractor, or the *secure* bumper of a pickup truck or other vehicle which will supply the power for lifting the tower. A boom truck or front end loader is preferable as

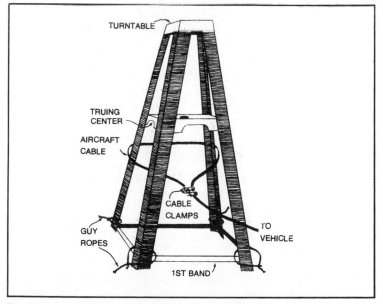

Fig. 8-15. A heavy cable is secured around two legs of the tower.

the elevated cable connection increases the transfer of power to the direction of lift while the tower is near horizontal.

The vehicle should begin its pull from the side of the well opposite the tower. A person should man each guy rope as the vehicle moves away from the well and lifts the tip of the tower. The people handling the guy ropes should maintain a constant light tension on them to keep the tower from swaying or tipping. They should not attempt to help pull the tower up. Take care to elevate the tower slowly, especially as it nears vertical, to avoid pulling it all the way over.

Centering the Tower and Setting the Anchor Posts

You can finish work on the day you raise the tower by centering the tower and then setting the anchor posts. Centering is the process of moving the tower slightly in order to position the center of the turntable directly above the well. This is done so the pump rod will run straight up and down in the drop pipe and not rub against the top rim of the pipe (which not only wears out the rod and pipe but also saps the power of the mill).

The most accurate way to determine the center of the tower is to drop a plumb line from the center of the turntable through the truing center (or from the mast if the gearbox has been installed). When the bob hangs directly over the center of the drop pipe, the tower is in the proper position. A windmilling instructor at New Mexico State University recommends using a sash weight (from a double hung window) suspended on light wire instead of an ordinary plumb bob and line. Because the plumb line used in centering is necessarily long, a heavy weight is preferable so the effect of breezes is minimized.

An alternate method of locating the center of the tower is to string heavy line (mason's twine for instance) between both pairs of diagonally opposite legs. The tower must then be shifted so the point where the two lines cross is directly above the center of the drop pipe.

Only a small shift of the tower (if any) should be necessary in centering. With a person pushing or pulling (as appropriate) each leg, it's ordinarily possible to slide the standing tower the small distance required. If you have to move the tower more than a couple of inches, or if budging your tower takes more power, you can pull it gently with the vehicle used in the raising operation. To pull the tower, attach a cable to one leg of the tower at the level of the lowest band and to the vehicle. If you do use a vehicle to move the tower, the guy ropes should be manned again until the tower is in position.

Once the tower's been centered, it has to be solidly anchored. Tower manufacturers recommend using concrete to form a wide heavy boot on each leg. In putting up their tower, the Flints followed this advice by pouring approximately 1' of concrete into the bottom of each anchor hole, on top of the shoe and surrounding the anchor post. At that rate they used about 1-⅓ yards of concrete in total for the four holes. This was probably more than adequate. One manufacturer suggests a minimum of 6 cubic feet of concrete for each hole. Fill the remainder of each hole with dirt and tamp it firmly.

Fan Assembly

With the tower, gearbox, and tail in position, you can assemble the fan. Since this is done from the tower platform where work can be awkward, as much preparatory work should be done on the ground as possible.

For instance, check to be sure that the blades are firmly fastened in their brackets (chairs). The chairs are riveted to circular bands (rims) at the factory. The blades may work loose in shipment and can later be flung from the mill when it works in the wind. One dealer recommends that all blades be brazed to the chairs before the fan's put together. The manufacturer of the Baker mill has available a set of angle braces which can be used to reattach blades that come loose from their mills. Usually, Aermotor and Dempster blades stay securely in position because each blade is riveted to a bracket on the rim, and one rim passes through a slot in each blade.

When you're sure the blades are fast, use a rope and pulley hung from the tailpipe to raise the fan arms or spokes to the platform. Then attach the arms to the hub (on Baker mills paired arms and angle braces bolt to the hub; on Aermotor and Dempster mills paired threaded spokes screw into sockets in the hub).

Use the same pulley and rope to hoist the blade sections to the platform, one at a time. As each section is raised, attach it to the arms. With all sections except the first and last, it's easiest to first attach the side that does *not* share an arm with a previously attached section (Fig. 8-16).

On small mills with light fan sections assembly is relatively easy. On mills with fan diameters of 10' or more, the blade sections can weigh 50 pounds or more each. This extra weight complicates the procedure somewhat. For example, four people worked on the installation of the Flints' 12' fan: two on the ground to hoist up the parts and man guy ropes to keep the mill from swinging on the turntable, and two on the platform, one to position the blade sections and fasten the bolts, and the other to hold the fan in position while the blades were attached—with an open pair of arms downward.

Because the blade sections were so heavy, one person alone couldn't both hold a section in place and insert and fasten the bolts. The Flints hung each section in place with baling wire while it was bolted on. When a section had been attached, the fan had to be rotated to bring the next pair of open arms into the downward position. This rotation became increasingly difficult with the third through seventh sections as the fan became more and more top heavy. The Flints found that two people pushing only on arms to which blade sections had already been attached could, with effort, rotate the fan into the proper position.

As with the tower, all nuts should be left finger tight to allow small movement of the arms and blade sections until all sections are in place.

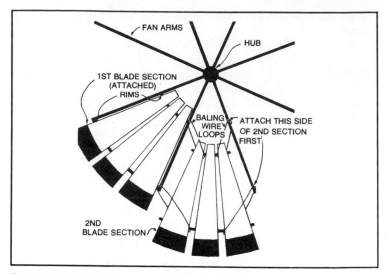

Fig. 8-16. With all sections except the first and last, it's easiest to first attach the side that doesn't share an arm with a previously attached section.

Governor and Pull-Out

To finish putting your windmill in operating condition, you have to attach the governor and hook up the pull-out system. On all modern American mills the rotational speed of the fan is governed by the angle at which the wind hits the blades. This in turn depends on the angle between the fan and the tail (which can vary from 0° to 90°). A very stout spring (the governor) stretched between a projection on the gearbox and a hole on the tail pulls the tail out perpendicular to the plane of the fan, or nearly so. This keeps the fan in the teeth of the wind. When the wind is severe, its force overcomes the strength of the spring, furling the tail part way or completely into a plane parallel to the fan and thereby stopping or reducing the speed of the mill.

There's a series of holes on the tailpipe or strut allowing adjustment of tension on the governor spring. The farther the hole you use is from the gearbox, the stronger the wind must be before the tail furls. When you attach the governor to your mill, start out using the hole nearest the gearbox (least tension). If after several weeks at this setting the mill furls too easily (that is, seems to slow or stop pumping when the mill is in no danger), increase tension on the spring by stages. Leave it at the lowest setting that provides satisfactory water volume.

On the Flints' mill the governor spring couldn't be stretched by hand much beyond the first hole on the tailpipe. To stretch it farther, they hooked it into the hole they wanted to use. With two turnbuckles attached with wire between the free end of the spring and a projection on the gearbox, and a fan arm, they drew the spring out the necessary length and fastened it. A

212

similar system of auxillary power will probably be necessary when you increase the tension on the governor of your mill.

At the time you attach the governor, also install the pull-out lever and cable. This is the lower part of the pull-out system which allows you to furl the mill when water isn't needed or in bad weather. The upper part of the system is integral with the gearbox and mast and is factory installed. The lower part of a reliable pull-out system has three important elements: a *stout lever*, a *durable cable*, and a means of easily adjusting the length of the cable to insure that the tail furls completely. The Flints now use a 30″ length of 1½″ diameter steel pipe as a lever; the wooden lever that came with the mill was broken in shipment and seemed flimsy anyway. The pipe is pivoted on a ⅜″ bolt which passes through both flanges of one of the angle iron legs of the tower. Quarter inch aircraft cable connects the lever and the pull-out swivel on the mast of the mill. Original equipment was 11 gauge galvanized wire which fatigued and broke in less than a year. Proper adjustment of the cable length is made easy by joining the lever to the cable with a turnbuckle (Fig. 8-17). The cable is at the correct length when, with the lever pulled down against the tower leg, the tail is pulled parallel to the fan and firmly against the bumper on the gearbox.

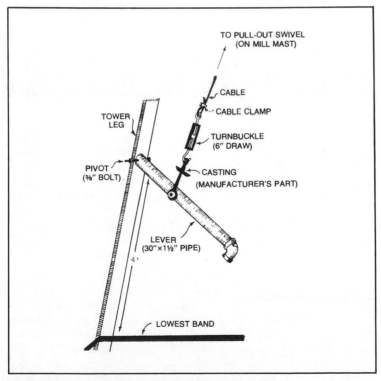

Fig. 8-17. Use a turnbuckle to join the lever to the cable.

With the pull-out mechanism installed, the mill and tower are in operating condition. Go over the entire tower and mill making sure that all bolts and set screws are tight, including any that were factory installed. There are a number of set screws on the gearbox and hub casting. These should be tightened firmly but *not* with a vengeance, as excessive torque can crack the cast iron.

To begin pumping water, it only remains to connect the pump rod to the sucker rod. This is usually done using a "red rod", a length (or multiple lengths) of 2″×2″ lumber which is often painted red. Some people prefer to make the connection using steel pipe. Because of the pipe's excessive strength, if anything goes wrong (a jam in the mill or blockage in the drop pipe) you're likely to end up with a broken mill or snapped sucker rod that will have to be fished out of the well. A good, clear pine 2×4 ripped to 2×2 makes an excellent "red rod."

Maintenance

The pinion and drive gears (which translate the rotational motion of the windmill into the up and down motion of the pump rod) are housed in the gearbox, which you have to keep filled to the recommended level with windmill oil (or 10 weight motor oil mixed with an equal volume of kerosene). Once a year the oil should be drained, the gearbox should be flushed with kerosene or gasoline, and you should refill it with fresh oil. Also, once a year completely inspect the tower and mill, tightening any loose bolts and other connections, checking the pull-out system for soundness, and securing any blades that may have loosened. The Flints think fall is the best time for the annual inspection and oil change, so the mill's in the best condition going into winter when repairs are most difficult.

Safety

Whenever you work on the mill from the tower platform, it's wise to wear a safety belt (such a lineman's or logger's belt). You can fashion a safety line from rope. Whatever you use, make a habit of it. *Never* work on the mill in a strong wind or when you're tired. See Fig. 8-18 for a glossary of windmilling terms.

POWER FROM THE WIND

During the several decades following World War II, it appeared the windmill was spinning into oblivion on the pasturelands of America. Then the early 1970s brought threat of a possible shortage of fossil fuels. Faced with a fuel squeeze and increasingly higher energy costs, many farmers and stockmen are reevaulating the wind machines. So tall towers and spinning bladed-wheels continue to be a part of the grasslands scenery of the Great Plains as old mills are renovated and new machines are erected (Fig. 8-19).

Perhaps no other machine played quite as important a role in the settling of the Great Plains as did the windmill (Fig. 8-20). A water source

anchor plates (shoes)—The horizontal metal plates fastened to the feet of the anchor posts that distribute the weight of the windmill tower on the floor of the anchor holes and hook the tower legs under the concrete anchor boots.

anchor posts—The lower extensions of the tower legs that are set in the anchor holes and secure the tower to the ground.

arms (spokes)—The rods or bars that radiate from the hub of the windmill and hold the blade sections in place.

bands—The horizontal bars that link the legs of the tower.

blades (vanes, sails)—The featherlike elements of the fan that catch the wind (on modern American mills these are truncated wedges of sheet metal fastened in groups of three or four to the rims of the fan).

braces—The diagonal wires or straps connected between the legs that hold the tower rigid.

bumpers—The spring-loaded stops mounted on the gearbox that take the shock of the tail when it swings out behind the fan or is furled.

cylinder—The reciprocating pump used with windmills consisting of a plunger inside a tube equipped with a check valve at the foot end (usually positioned near or below water level in the well).

drive gears—The pair of large gears enclosed in the gearbox that carry the pitman and are driven by a pair of pinion gears.

drop pipe—The vertical water-carrying pipe hung in the well, at or near the end of which the cylinder is attached.

fan (wheel)—The wind-rotated assembly of the mill, consisting of blades, arms, rims, and hub.

gearbox (bowl)—The cast iron oil bowl that houses the gears and pitman (a single casting includes gearbox, mast, and hub housing).

governor—A device that prevents the mill from developing excessive rotational speed (on modern American mills a hinged tail combined with a heavy spring serves this purpose).

hoop—A sheet metal cap that covers the top of the gearbox (removable for inspecting gears and adding oil).

mast—The tube projecting downward from the mill gearbox that is inserted through the turntable and truing center of the tower and holds the mill upright.

pinion gears—The pair of small gears on the axle (hub shaft) of the mill that are powered directly by rotation of the fan (the teeth of these gears mesh with those of the drive gears).

pitman—The metal arm connecting the drive gears and the steel pump rod that translates the rotational motion of the gears into the up and down (reciprocating) motion of the rod (similar in function to connecting rods in an automobile engine).

pull-out mechanism—The device used to furl the tail of the mill manually (design differs with manufacturer).

red-rod (pump pole)—The square wood rod used to connect the steel pump rod and wood sucker rod (so called because it's often painted red).

rims—The circular metal bands that hold the blades of the fan.

sucker rod—The wood rod (often ash) that extends down the drop pipe (from the red rod) to the pump plunger.

tail pipe (strut, bone)—The horizontal structure that carries the tail vane or fin and is pivoted at the gearbox casting.

truing center—A cast element of the tower located below the turntable near the top of the tower that squares the tower and holds the mill mast.

turntable—The fixture at the top of the tower on which the gearbox sits and which contains bearings, allowing the mill to swing easily with the wind.

Fig. 8-18. A glossary of windmilling terms.

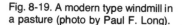

Fig. 8-19. A modern type windmill in a pasture (photo by Paul F. Long).

was a necessity and only limited amounts were available through natural means. In the East, dug wells were used and the water lifted by hand; perhaps a windlass was utilized. On the plains the depth of the water table necessitated the drilling of wells, and some machine was then needed to raise the water to the surface. The windmill was the answer. Whirling in the unceasing clean prairie breezes, the wind catchers devised and constructed by the pioneers made western settlement possible.

Almost everyone who has spent a portion of his lifetime in a rural setting has some remembrance of windmills. The greening of the grasslands, the call of the meadowlark, and the repairing of the pasture windmill were infallible signs of spring which were recognized by all rural inhabitants. One of the spring pleasures of a farmboy was to accompany Dad to the pastures for the annual maintenance of the old mill.

The windmill is of uncertain origin. Certainly the first windmills were crude and much different from our modern concept of these machines. As early as the 10th century a primitive horizontal mill was used in Persia; perhaps it had come into use as much as three centuries earlier. The mill we commonly associate with the Dutch, the typical European mill, was an invention of the peoples of Northern Europe. Historically these great machines date from 1185, and by the end of the 12th century the windmill was widely employed across Northern Europe. The use of windmills was accepted less readily in Southern Europe, but by the 14th century the windmill had become firmly established in Italy.

The first European wind machines were used for the milling of grain. Later, especially in the low countries of the North, the mills were utilized to pump water. Probably the pumping windmill—modeled on the gristmill—was developed in the 14th century.

Some 200 years later, with the invention of the rotating mill cap, the sails of the mill could be turned into the wind. With this improvement, mills became larger, better constructed, and were used for pumping until the end of the 18th century.

When they came to America, the peoples of Europe brought the art of windmill construction. From the eastern seaboard across America out on to the Great Plains, great Dutch or Holland windmills were built which caught the wind with their huge sails. Often the mills were highly modified as a result of needs and the building materials at hand. For the most part, the role of the great Dutch mills was to grind the grain of the pioneer farmers and townsmen (Figs. 8-21 and 8-22). Near the end of the 19th century, though, a number of these great structures were built to provide power for machinery used in manufacturing farm implements.

The greatest popularity of the windmill on the prairies of the Great Plains occurred following the Civil War. While windmills were introduced to the plains by settlers and stockmen who could not possibly have existed without them, the wind catchers were first used extensively by the transcontinental railroads. The Union Pacific was one of the first American railroads to put windmills to use, and many other railroads soon adopted these machines. Generally, mills utilized by railroads were of a type known as the "railroad pattern" and sold under the trade name of "Eclipse." These mills were patented in 1867 by an Indian missionary named L.H. Wheeler

Fig. 8-20. The machine which made western settlement possible—and still working (photo by Paul F. Long).

Fig. 8-21. This Dutch style smock windmill built at Lawrence, Kansas, in 1863, was used for grinding grain, and later furnished power for manufacturing farm implements (photo by Kenneth Spencer Research Library Kansas Collection, University of Kansas).

and manufactured by the Eclipse Wind Engine Company. As the iron tracks were extended westward, great mills with their 22½′ diameter wheels sprouted up along the route. Spinning in the western wind, mills provided the great volume of water needed by steam locomotives.

Early windmills on the prairies were not the steel mills we might envision. Rather, the early machines were constructed largely of wood— scraps or any timbers available—and built as cheaply as possible. In a bulletin he prepared on homemade mills in 1899, Erwin Barbour, of the United States Agricultural Experiment Station of Nebraska, told of his observations. He traveled from the Dakotas down through Nebraska, Kansas, and Oklahoma. The backbone of mills, according to Barbour, appeared to be the Plate Valley from Omaha to Denver. From this backbone, the ribs of homemade windmills extended northward and south and off on all sides along watercourses where settlers battled arid plains.

Homemade wind machines were classified into seven types by Barbour, the names being descriptive of the mills. Windmills built by settlers were known as jumbos, merry-go-rounds, battle-ax, holland mills, mock turbines, reconstructed turbines, and shop made turbines (Fig. 8-23). The names and designs for homemade mills quickly spread over the frontier.

The windmill as we know it today was an American invention. Early manufactured mills—like their homemade counterparts—were built of wood rather than steel. About 1854, Daniel Halladay devised a mill with many vanes or sails which made a smaller diameter wheel possible—most windmills from that time commonly used a wheel 8' in diameter. Halladay also worked out the principle of self-governing, an innovation enabling mills

Fig. 8-22. This Old Holland mill was built in 1885 at Milbank, South Dakota, and operated as a grist mill (photo by South Dakota State Historical Society).

Fig. 8-23. An old battle-ax windmill built by a Nebraska settler (photo by Nebraska Historical Society).

to maintain a uniform speed regardless of wind speed. Soon many types of mills were being manufactured, and many modifications and improvements were made on wind catchers. Fanless mills, multi-wheeled mills, and, in the 1930s and 1940s, the highly modified windchargers which produced electricity, were some variations.

Following World War II windmill sales drastically declined. Small gasoline engines and electric motors, especially with the advent of rural electrification, pumped water for thirsty livestock on prairie grasslands. Of the 150 companies that had once built windmills in the United States, only two survived into this decade. The Aermotor Company, formerly located in Chicago and Broken Arrow, Oklahoma, today builds its mills in Argentina. Dempster Industries, Inc. of Beatrice, Nebraska, is the only other surviving manufacturer of wind catchers (Fig. 8-24).

Today a good deal of research is being conducted in the United States regarding the potential of gigantic windmills to produce electricity for cities and factories. Meanwhile, windmills still spin away the years, pumping water as they have for centuries. It appears likely more mills will spring up each year, and old empty towers may again be fitted with wheels to catch the clean, free winds. As down through the past, when the grass is new and the lark calls, many a farm boy and his Dad will go about the pleasurable chore of repairing the old windmill.

WIND-POWERED HEAT PUMP

A novel way of using wind power to help American farmers beat the energy crunch is being explored. Rather than using wind to generate electricity, pump irrigation water, or grind grains, Cornell University researchers are trying to run heat pumps directly with wind power.

The objective is to determine the feasibility of connecting a wind turbine mechanically to the heat pump and operating the device without using electrical energy (Fig. 8-25). A *heat pump* is a "device that works much like a refrigerator for cooling," according to Wesley Gunkel, a Cornell agricultural engineer. "It also is being used as a space heater for homes and office buildings."

A refrigerator removes heat from the air inside it, thus cooling food or making ice. It does not run in reverse to raise the temperature inside the refrigerator.

The heat pump, on the other hand, works both ways. It can heat a home by extracting heat from outside air in areas where the winter is not too harsh. Well water also can be used as a source of energy for space heating.

Fig. 8-24. Vaneless type Dempster mill, with counter-balance (photo by Paul F. Long).

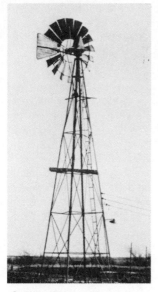

Fig. 8-25. Old-time water pumping windmills like this one may be replaced by wind turbines.

Operated in reverse, the heat pump works as an air conditioner by expelling heat from inside the house.

By driving such a device directly with wind energy, Cornell researchers hope to cool milk and at the same time to produce hot water with heat extracted from warm milk "to meet the hot water needs for dairy farms and for space heating for farm homes and buildings," Gunkel said.

Hot water is needed daily for cleaning and sanitizing milk handling equipment. That translates into 1½ gallons of hot water for each cow every day. In terms of energy requirements, about one-quarter of the electrical energy needed in dairy operations is used to heat water.

When a heat pump is operated directly by a wind turbine, Cornell researchers figured that a high percentage of available wind energy intercepted by a wind turbine could be put to work.

What if the wind doesn't blow for a day or two? With heat pumps, Gunkel said, a series of ice banks could be maintained to cool milk when there is no wind. A few days of hot water supply, created by heat pumps during windy days, also could be kept in a heavily insulated storage tank for use during calm periods.

There is one possible hitch, Gunkel added. The wind may have to blow at about 10 miles per hour on a yearly average. In Ithaca and nearby areas where the Cornell researchers studied wind speeds, the average was clocked at about nine mph in summer and about 12 mph in winter.

ENERGY COST ANSWERS WRITTEN IN THE WIND

The answers to rising home energy costs may be partly written in the wind. A number of small wind energy conversion systems—windchargers or wind turbines—have come on the commercial market in recent years in response to sharply rising home energy costs. While none of the wind turbines is likely to generate enough electricity to make the average home owner energy independent, the energy conversion systems are worth considering, according to Dr. P.M. Moretti, Oklahoma State University engineer.

Some government agencies are figuring annual energy inflation rates of 12 to 16 percent, meaning electricity which now costs about a nickel could cost as much as 9.5 cents per kilowatt hour in 1985 and almost 20 cents by 1990.

Moretti noted, however, that a small wind energy conversion system may cost several thousand dollars, but provide only enough direct energy to operate a hair dryer or a bathroom heater. He added, though, that a "system which is twice as large will not cost twice as much, so that the larger sizes tend to be more cost-effective."

Most manufacturers, Moretti said, make wind turbines with electric generators and put together a complete package for the customer, including the rotor, electric generator, controls, tower, foundation and installation. Prices will vary according to generating capacity and the manufacturer, he said.

As an example of a small wind energy conversion system's cost, Bergey Windpower Co. of Oklahoma said cost for installation of a complete electrical-generating hookup system with an 80' tower is about $5,300. For a complete system with a 60' tower, including installation and setup, the cost is around $4,900. The firm's BWC 1000-S model for connecting into a home's electrical system will generate about 2,500 kilowatt hours of energy per year in most areas of Oklahoma. The state's average yearly windspeed is 13 mph. The payback period on investment for most homeowners is about five to 12 years. The machine has a life expectancy of 30 years.

The site of the wind generator is important, Moretti said. He recommended a tall tower of at least 50 to 60' but preferably higher, well clear of trees and other obstructions. The tower should never be on the roof of a house because of structure-borne noise; nor should it be between a tv antenna and the main direction of tv signals, he said.

What size small wind energy conversion system is most appropriate? Moretti said that ideally it would be one that generated as much electricity as you used. Since many residential electricity bills show more than 730 kilowatt hours per month, requiring a machine rated at about 4 KW—double or more the size of most small wind energy conversion systems—that is probably not practical, he added. With good wind, annual savings can be 20 percent or more of the initial investment, Moretti said.

FARMERS' ALCOHOL

Of all the alternative sources of energy that have popped up like mushrooms since the advent of the fuel crisis, perhaps none is quite as fascinating as *farmers' alcohol*. Surely, none is nearly as controversial.

Farmers' alcohol is alcohol. There are two kinds: *ethanol* (the drinking kind) and *methanol* (which is poison). Alcohol is produced by chemical changes in carbohydrates, which means it can be from the moonshiner's standbys like corn and barley, but it can also be coaxed from potatoes and Jerusalem artichokes, sugar cane, and even sawdust. No doubt the term "farmers' alcohol" is meant to distinguish alcohol produced on or near the farm, from farm products, for energy.

Like the other "new" forms of alternative energy, farmers' alcohol is nothing new. The knowledge and basic technology has been in use for a long time, and alcohol has been used as a fuel since the 1800s. The *Bunsen burner* and alcohol stoves were among the first uses, but with the rise of the internal combustion engine there was interest in using alcohol to replace gasoline. Early studies indicated that alcohol gave greater horsepower, higher compression, similar mileage but lower thermal efficiency than gasoline. The lower cost of petroleum effectively stifled competition.

During World War I countries facing shortages of petroleum took another look at alcohol. After the war, war-surplus alcohol mixed with gasoline in a 20/80 blend was sold in the United States.

In the 1930s, a variety of forces combined to renew interest in farmers' alcohol. The Nebraska legislature passed a law that returned 2 cents a gallon to users of alcohol-gasoline blends in an attempt to bolster grain prices, but a petroleum industry campaign kept the effort from gathering any momentum.

During World War II, alcohol was widely used as a fuel for everything from tractors and ships to B-29s. Its industrial uses included the manufacture of synthetic rubber, munitions, antifreeze and cosmetics.

Since the 1950s, alcohol, which is still widely used in industry, is mainly derived from petroleum rather than from renewable resources like plant matter.

Not until the mid-1970s did widespread interest in alcohol as an energy source revive. Even then, technicians involved in research displayed little knowledge of what had gone before. An article in *Industrial Research* (February, 1974) hailed methanol as "a promising new additive." Propulsion specialist Roberta Nichols, of Aerospace Corp. in El Segundo, California, said that while her study began because of the need for lead-free high-octane gasoline, the energy crisis increased the importance of the results.

She told the magazine: "Gasoline-methanol blends can help ease the fuel shortage in three ways: first of all, 10 percent of the gasoline could be replaced by methanol through direct volume substitution. Also, engine manufacturers can again build high compression ratio engines, which have better thermal efficiencies. These engines consume about six percent less fuel and cost the consumer less money to operate. In addition, fewer barrels of crude oil would be required to produce the same volume of fuel if it did not have to be so highly cracked and reformed in order to obtain a minimal octane number without lead, because every time it goes through another fractionation, there is another volumetric loss."

Two professors at Massachusetts Institute of Technology have run a beat-up Toyota for more than 22,000 miles on gasoline mixed with 10 to 15 percent methanol with no engine damage and increased performance. No modifications to the engine are required with that proportion of methanol, they claim.

The San Diego, California, post office has been using a methanol mix in mail trucks and reports 25 percent better mileage. Professors Reed and Lerner of MIT report 7 to 8 percent better mileage, and 5 percent better acceleration, with no knocking even when using low test gasoline. So alcohol is usable as a fuel for internal combustion engines.

One firm (Waag Western Enterprises, P.O. Box 977, Danville, CA 94526) sells a "Power-Jector" which it claims is a unique development that permits water-alcohol to be injected into an operating engine for more efficient fuel use. In addition to making use of farmers' alcohol, the device is said to give better mileage, result in a cleaner engine due to absence of carbon, eliminate knocking, prolong spark plug life, and greatly decrease emissions of nitrogen dioxide, hydrocarbons, and carbon monoxide.

No doubt similar devices would appear on the market if farmers' alcohol became more readily available. Will it? If not, it won't be because of the lack of technology for producing it.

Alcohol produced by simple fermentation was known perhaps 8,000 years ago. Distilled alcohol is believed to have originated in China about 800 B.C., being distilled from fermented rice. If they could do it, you'd think a homesteader of today could do it, and you'd be right.

The basic information needed can be found in any good library or encyclopedia, or for more detailed and pertinent information, read *Moonshiner's Manual* by Michael Barleycorn. (Available from Countryside General Store, Waterloo, WI 53594, $3.95.) This book is about mountain dew, but that's exactly what farmer's alcohol is. It also makes very interesting reading.

A still basically consists of a pot where the fermented mash is heated, a cap and connecting tube for carrying off the vapor, and a condenser for converting the alcohol vapor back into a liquid. There are other niceties for making whiskey, and a few technical details to consider to avoid going blind or belly up, but for farmer's alcohol these are the basics.

A mash for whiskey might contain 50 gallons of warm water (90-100°F.), 25 pounds of ground yellow corn, 30 pounds of pure cane sugar, 1 to 2 quarts of unsulphured molasses, and 1 pound of baker's yeast.

The corn is soaked in warm water for three days. Then it is put into a mash box or barrel with the other ingredients where, depending on the weather and other factors, it will ferment in anywhere from two days to a week. The resulting mash is poured into the still pot and heated to 172.8°F. The principle is that since water boils at 212°F and alcohol boils at 172.8°F, the alcohol is separated from the water and other ingredients by being boiled off first.

To recover this vapor in usable form, it runs through the condenser, which is a coiled tube surrounded by cold running water. The vapor in the tube is cooled down and returns to a liquid state.

While this is just a basic description and isn't meant as a how-to guide, it serves to demonstrate just how simple the process really is. Depending upon the efficiency of the operation, the proceeding ingredients should produce anywhere from 1 to 3 gallons of ethanol.

This is a simple distillation process suitable for use with materials containing sugars, which are simple carbohydrates. The more complex carbohydrates, starches, and cellulose must first be converted into sugar to make alcohol because the yeast of fermentation works only on sugars. The more complex the carbohydrate, the more difficult the distillation process. While making alcohol from sawdust and other crude wastes is possible, it demands technology that probably is not practical for small operations. Acid hydrolysis and similar methods are necessary with some materials.

It should be pointed out here for the serious homestead experimenter that it *is* possible to make ethanol without sugar. The grain is first malted—sprouted, dried, and ground—to convert the insoluble starches into soluble sugar. While this entails additional labor and also decreases the alcohol yield, it has the decided advantage of not using an expensive, nonhomestead product.

Sugar cane and sugar beets would be logical materials for ethanol production, theoretically yielding 623 and 420 gallons of ethanol per acre. Potatoes would yield 263 gallons per acre if 11.5 tons of potatoes per acre were harvested, and Jerusalem artichokes would produce 180 gallons per acre with a harvest of 9 tons per acre. (According to some sources, yields of Jerusalem artichokes have reached 20 tons per acre, and the average potato yield fluctuates so there are obviously finagle factors in these statistics. In addition, the major carbohydrate in Jerusalem artichokes is inulin, which is easily broken down into fermentable sugars, thus making it attractive for ethanol production.)

The gallon per acre yield of alcohol from some common grain crops is estimated as follows: corn, 168; barley, 71; wheat, 77; and oats, 51. Again, these obviously depend upon yields and still efficiency.

In addition to the fermentable material, the other major ingredient in ethanol production is heat, for the process of distillation takes place at 172.8°F. This was no problem for the ancients or for moonshiners, because wood was readily available. That may not be the case in the future, for there is growing concern that even in wooded areas, if everyone turned to wood for heating, ample supplies of that form of energy would be inadequate. While some advocate the burning of Jerusalem artichoke stalks and other "field trash," the destruction of such cellulose seems untenable from an agricultural standpoint when soil fertility is an even greater problem than fuel availability. The alcohol produced could conceivably be used to heat the mash to produce more alcohol, although that seems very much like feeding the milk back to the cow.

Actually 172.8°F really isn't very hot, and is well within the capabilities of even simple solar heating systems. So far as we can determine, no research is being done in this field. It would seem to have possibilities.

Whatever the heat source, the raw material that remains after the distillation process has feed value. In fact, wastes from distilleries are valuable supplemental feedstuffs even today. If these wastes were available from farmers' alcohol plants, as well as liquor distilleries, even greater quantities would be available.

Today, distillery by-products are classified as distillers dried grains, and distillers dried solubles. The grains are the coarser particles of the spent mash which can be strained out. The solubles are what's left in the water.

Distiller's dried grains average 26 percent protein or more and are also rich in fat, with an average of 8 percent, which makes them valuable and popular as dairy feeds. For beef cattle, 1.5 pounds of distillers' grains are worth as much as 1 pound of soybean oil meal and will supply more total digestible nutrients. These dried grains have limitations as swine or poultry feeds, but mainly because of their bulkiness. Tests have shown that distillers' grains can replace up to one-half of the tankage or meat scrap in a swine ration and up to 10 percent of the ration for laying hens.

Distillers' dried solubles are used in mixed feeds for swine, poultry, and dairy calves because of their high content of B-complex vitamins. (Ruminants synthesize vitamin B and therefore would not make efficient use of additional amounts.) They are also rich in niacin and choline and have a good content of riboflavin, panotothenic acid, and thiamine, but they don't have much vitamin B_{12}. Distillers solubles have as much protein as distillers' dried grains, but the protein is not of high quality for poultry and swine, although it is a satisfactory protein supplement for cattle, sheep and goats.

Technically, then, there is nothing wrong with ethanol. Unlike fossil fuels, it's a renewable resource. Unlike solar energy and wind energy and, to some extent, methane, it's storable and transportable. It's usable in currently available engines. Its by-products or "waste" are potentially valuable and recyclable. Ethanol faces seemingly insurmountable roadblocks nevertheless—not technical problems, but people problems.

A major one is the idea that home production of alcohol is classed as a step or two worse than sabotage. It's interesting to speculate on how we, as a nation, got into this state of mind, and as we delve into history it becomes unnervingly easy to suspect that it was not entirely due to the spector of demon rum. If alcohol taxes of $10.50 per gallon provide 5 percent of the federal revenue in this nation, it seems not unlikely that some force other than temperance is at work in the restrictions placed on home production of spirits. Again, *Moonshiner's Manual* throws some fascinating light on the inequities of the laws governing alcohol production (Fig. 8-26).

Fig. 8-26. Michael Barleycorn, author of *Moonshiners Manual*, relaxes with a jug of his favorite potable (photo by Sandra Buehler).

CHECKLIST OF ENERGY SAVERS

As shorter days and cooler nights force the lights on and the thermostat up, it's time once again to think twice about energy. Since last winter, the crunch has not lessened its bite. Chilly bones and heating bills will return more certainly than snow.

While some of us warm ourselves by chopping wood for the woodstove, others less ambitious will get into the energy-saving act in less conspicuous ways. Listed here are a variety of ideas and reminders. For the items that apply to you, check off the ones that you need to do or would like to remember. See Table 8-3.

Household Heating

☐ Get the right size furnace and waterheater for your needs. A unit larger than necessary merely wastes fuel.

☐ Make sure your thermostat is away from heat or cold sources like windows, heating ducts, televisions, lamps.

☐ Clean your thermostat yearly by removing the cover and carefully blowing away any dust.

☐ Keep all air filters clean to make it easier for your furnace to do its job. Check them every 60 days when in operation.

☐ Insulated windows and doors (combination or thermal pane) help prevent heat loss.

☐ Installing insulation in the walls and ceiling of your home will also greatly reduce the energy needed to heat (and cool) your home. An R-11 is

228

the minimum federal recommendation for walls, and an R-19 for roof or ceiling area.

☐ Don't rely upon portable electric heaters to do full-time heating jobs. They are too expensive to operate.

☐ Be sure your basement windows are well sealed and have storms for winter.

☐ Check that all outer doors close properly. Aluminum doors especially have a tendency to close slowly if not lubricated or adjusted properly.

Kitchen Appliances

☐ Is yours an older refrigerator? Defrost the freezer often to increase its efficiency, and check the door gaskets for any escaping cold air.

☐ Dust or vacuum the condenser coils on the back or bottom of your refrigerator periodically.

Table 8-3. Power, Current, and Monthly Kw-hr Consumption of Various Home Appliances.

appliances	power in watts	current required in amps at 12V	at 115V	time used per mo. n hrs.	total Kw-hrs. her mo.
Air Conditioner	1,566	130.0	13.7	74.0	116.0
Blanket, electric	177	14.5	1.5	73.0	13.0
Blender	350	29.2	3.0	1.5	0.5
Broiler	1,436	120.0	12.5	6.0	8.5
Clothes Dryer	4,856	405.0	42.0	18.0	86.0
Coffee Pot	894	75.0	7.8	10.0	9.0
Dishwasher	1,200	100.0	10.4	25.0	30.0
Drill (¼-in. Elec.)	250	20.8	2.2	2.0	0.5
Fan (attic)	370	30.8	3.2	65.0	24.0
Freezer (15 cu. ft.)	341	28.4	3.0	29.0	10.0
Freezer (15 cu. ft.) frostless	440	36.6	3.8	33.0	14.7
Frying Pan	1,196	99.6	10.4	12.0	15.0
Garbage Disposal	445	36.0	3.9	6.0	3.0
Heat, electric baseboard, Average size home	10,000	832.0	87.0	160.0	1600.0
Iron	1,088	90.5	9.5	11.0	12.0
Lightbulb, 75 watt	75	6.25	.65	320.0	2.4
Lightbult, 40 watt	40	3.3	.35	320.0	1.3
Lightbulb, 25 watt	25	2.1	0.2	320.0	0.8
Oil burner, ⅛ HP	250	20.8	.22	64.0	16.0
Range	12,207	1020.0	106.0	8.0	98.0
Record Player (tube)	150	12.5	1.3	50.0	7.5
Record Player (solid state)	60	5.0	0.52	50.0	3.0
Refrigerator-Freezer (14 cu. ft.)	326	27.2	2.8	29.0	9.5
Refrigerator-Freezer (14 cu. ft.) frostless	615	51.3	5.35	25.0	15.2
Skill saw	1,000	83.5	8.7	6.0	6.0
Sun lamp	279	23.2	2.4	5.4	1.5
Television / B&W	237	19.8	2.1	110.0	25.0
Television / Color	332	27.6	2.9	125.0	42.0
Toaster	1,146	95.5	10.0	2.6	3.0
Typewriter	30	2.5	.26	15.0	.45
Vacuum Cleaner	630	52.2	5.5	6.4	4.0
Washing Machine (automatic)	512	42.5	4.5	17.6	9.0
Washing Machine (wringer)	275	23.0	2.4	15.0	4.0
Water Heater	474	37.2	3.9	89.0	40.0
Water Pump	460	38.3	4.0	44.0	20.0

□ Don't overfill the refrigerator. Keep enough space around each food container to allow for good circulation. Keep air vents clear.

□ Make sure the pilot light on your gas range is properly adjusted. It could be using more fuels than it needs to.

□ By turning your electric range off just before your cooking is over, you can use residual heat to finish the job and keep food warm before serving.

□ When possible, cook several things in your oven at once by taking the average of the heat needed and setting the temperature control accordingly.

□ Electric skillets, toasters, waffle irons, popcorn poppers, electric fondue pots, slow cookers, coffee pots and other small appliances generally use less electricity than a range.

□ Read your appliance manual to find the optimum temperature for your refrigerator and freezer. It's common to keep the setting too high, which wastes electricity.

Laundry Appliances

□ Get the right size applicance for your needs. A 20-pound washer may allow you to do a week's wash, thus using less power than several loads in a smaller machine.

□ Oversudsing and overloading make your machine work harder than it needs to.

□ Clean the lint filter on your washer after each load to keep your machine running efficiently.

□ The sun and wind is still your best clothes dryer, cutting down on ironing and leaving your clothes smelling fresh. If you do buy a dryer, check the voltage tags on the back to find one that is economical in its power usage.

Lighting Ideas and Hints

□ For areas of infrequent use, install a 25 or 50 watt light bulb.

□ Night lights can be phosphorescent and not require any voltage.

□ Battery-operated clocks and radios are extremely efficient, and real power savers if the batteries are rechargeable.

Chapter 9

Tools, Machines, and Vehicles

Tools, machines, and vehicles play an important role in successful home-steading. This chapter has information on hammers, handsaws, a sed planter, a cream separator, tractors, and other items.

HAMMERS

A hammer uses the principle of the lever and releases stored energy when it makes contact with a surface. It is a descendant of the hand-held heavy rock, probably one of man's earliest tools.

Hammers are identified by type and weight. The most used weights or sizes are 10, 12 and 16-ounce. Handles come in the same general shape, with a length and taper that balances that size head, although the substances they are made of will vary.

You'll save yourself some frustration, time and energy by coordinating proper nail size, wood hardness, and hammer size and weight. The most common is the *nail (claw) hammer*, designed to drive nails and brads into wood or soft materials (Fig. 9-1). The claw end is used to pull them out. The curve of the claw varies; steep curves allow maximum swinging space in small areas and give good leverage on large nails firmly held. A straighter claw pulls out small nails easily.

The standard weight for this type is 16 ounces. Never use a nail hammer to work metal, pound a cold chisel, or drive or set rivets: it's not designed for those jobs.

Several face shapes are available. If the face is flat and hits the nail slightly at an angle, the nail bends, If the face is too round, the hammer head slips off the nail. The bell-faced version allows you to whack the nail flush to the surface of the wood, with less chance of making dents around the nail, and also helps you to be accurate while allowing for a bit of human error.

A *rough framing hammer* is a great boon for big jobs (Fig. 9-2). It's used for large (8 to 16 penny) nails. At about 20 ounces, with a long handle, it's

Fig. 9-1. Claw hammer.

great weight and size make for fewer strokes than with a smaller, lighter hammer.

As the longer handle decreases its accuracy, a checkered face helps to increase friction between nail and hammer head. For this reason this tool is to be used only for "rough framing;" a glancing blow will leave a mark. The other end is a straight claw, for ripping out sections.

Machinist's hammers (also called *ballpeens*) have hemispherical-shaped heads which are used for shaping metal, peening rivets, and striking in limited areas like corners (Fig. 9-3). The flat part drives wedges, sets bolts and pins, fits babbitts into bearings, and drives cold chisels and punches.

Soft-faced hammers, or *mallets*, have heads of material softer than the surface being worked on. They are often made of wood, leather, lead, brass, rubber, or plastic.

A mallet is used for loosening stuck screens, windows, setting in dowels, forming sheet metal, and other jobs where a metal hammer would dent or mar the surface. They are also good for driving wood chisels and gouges.

Take care—mallets are damaged easily by uses other than what they are intended for. Usually a 1½ pound and a 12-ounce one will do the most work, although very light work would make a 4- to 6-ouncer necessary.

You can shoot nails with a *whammer*, or *stud gun* (Fig. 9-4). It is sort of a staple gun used mainly for installing plywood paneling. Though its uses are not very extensive, it is very good for that.

A *hand-drilling sledge hammer* (also called a *spiking sledge*) is short-handled and heavy for heavy blows within a small range (Fig. 9-5). It is double-faced. Use it for hardened masonry nails, cold chisels, star drills, and driving stakes, spikes and small posts. Be sure to wear protective goggles if you do hardened metal work.

Fig. 9-2. Rough framing hammer.

The *shingling hatchet* is necessary for shakes and shingles. Its face is checkered and beveled—fatter, to lessen the chance of missing. The other end is a cutting blade (Fig. 9-6).

The *dry wall hammer* is a lightweight tool which avoids awkward swinging positions because of the head's slanted shape (Fig. 9-7). The opposite end has a blade, useful in cutting around electric outlets and has an indentation for pulling nails.

The *tack-hammer*, also called a shoemaker's hammer, has a large flat face with slightly rounded rim (Fig. 9-8). One end is magnetized for holding tacks. The other end is for stronger whacks after positioning.

A *finishing hammer* is for small jobs around the house such as installing picture hooks—anything involving nails up to the 8 penny size.

Hammer Handles

Handles come in fiber glass, solid steel, tubular steel, and wood. These materials vary in terms of shock absorbancy and durability. Here is

Fig. 9-3. Machinist's or ball peen hammer.

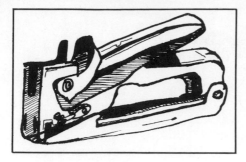

Fig. 9-4. Whammer or stud gun.

how they compare, from greatest to least: shock absorbency: wood, tubular steel, solid steel, fiber glass; durability: solid steel, fiber glass, tubular steel, if used properly, and wood.

Tightening the Hammerhead

If your hammer has a wobbly head because its handle has shrunk, take pliers, remove the wedges from the end of the handle, and carefully drive out the handle from the head. Then wrap a piece of waterproof, fine-grain sandpaper about halfway around that part of the handle which fits into the head with the grit side of the paper next to wood.

The sandpaper provides a secure grip. With the wedges driven back in, you have a hammer good for several more years of service. Note the textured heads in Fig. 9-9.

HANGING AN AXE

There comes a time in the life of every homesteader when an axe handle becomes too splintery and weak for safe use. A new handle is the answer, but for a novice "hanging an axe" can be a rather difficult job. Here are a few tips on procedure.

First, consider the axe handle. The handle is removed by cutting off all protuding wood with a hacksaw. Place the axe head in the oven of your wood

Fig. 9-5. Spiking sledge.

Fig. 9-6. Shingling hatchet.

stove and let it "bake" for several hours, until the wood is slightly charred and shrunk. A light tap with a hammer and the old wood will drop out.

Next you must select the new handle. A skilled old-timer can whittle his own handle from seasoned hardwood. Most persons buy their axe handles at the local hardware store.

Do not buy the first handle you see on the rack. There are several things to keep in mind. The two main types of axes are *single-bit* and *double-bit* (Fig. 9-10). A single-bit has only one cutting edge—something like a big hatchet—with a handle which is curved at the extreme end where your hand grips the handle when splitting wood. A double-bit has two cutting edges and a straight handle.

Select the type needed and also the length you think sufficient. Be sure to check for straight-grained wood, running the length of the handle. Cross or slanted-grain wood will soon split with use, and you will be back at the hardware store, buying another handle. The saw-cut in the wedge end should be fairly well centered.

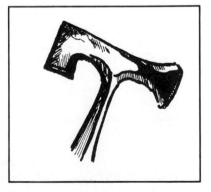

Fig. 9-7. Drywall hammer.

235

Fig. 9-8. Shoemaker's or tack hammer.

You must also have a wooden wedge and two or three metal wedges. The wooden wedges should be from slightly softer wood than your handle, for example, a birch wedge for an ash handle. The metal wedges are a standard size but sometimes are hard to find. Metal screws can be used or even old iron washers.

Back home again with your new handle and old axe head, you now begin to shape the wedge end of the handle to fit the "eye" of the head. Since no two "eyes" are the same, this is a one-of-a-kind job. Use a wood rasp and sandpaper and try to get the handle to fit smoothly and snugly into the eye. Be sure the axe handle is dry, as damp wood is slightly swelled and a supposedly tight-fitting handle can come out when dry. Try to fit the axe head as close to the shoulder as possible—in other words, as far down from the wedge end as the shape of the handle will allow. An axe hung out on the very tip of the wedge end of the handle is derisively known as "hung for scattered timber," and it is not a desirable setting.

When shaping the handle, also try to fit the head with the cutting edges parallel with the handle. A head slightly twisted to one side will not strike true when cutting wood. As you fit the head, sight down the length of the handle from the extreme end to the wedge end, flat sides perpendicular to the ground, and you will quickly see whether the cutting edges are in line. Another thing to watch for is to place the curved side of the head toward the shoulder, and the straight side toward the wedge end.

With the head pushed on the handle as far as possible, hold the axe with one hand, the axe head toward the ground. Hit the extreme end a few sharp blows with a hammer. This drives the head on as far as possible. A novice may think the head would be driven off with this method, but just the opposite is true.

You should now have extra wood sticking out the top of the axe head, around 1 or 2". Do not cut this off until you have driven in the wooden wedge. To do this, trim the wedge to fit the length of the eye, place the point end into the saw cut in the handle, and tap it down into the eye. Keep tapping the wedge down until it fits firmly. It is not necessary to have it extremely

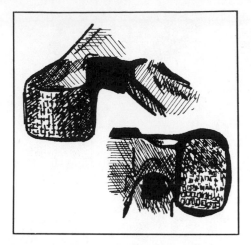

Fig. 9-9. Textured heads.

tight, as it is possible to split the axe head by wedging it too much. This seldom happens.

Cut off the excess handle and wedge protruding from the top of the head. Place metal wedges on the wood at an angle and tap into the head.

Your axe is now ready to be sharpened and put to use. Happy chopping.

A JIG FOR KINDLING

Most people enjoy chopping firewood into kindling, but it can take time and sometimes be a nuisance—especially when those little sticks don't want to stand up straight. By using a jig to hold the kindling while chopping, however, you can turn a chunk of wood into a pile of kindling very neatly and in only one-third the usual time (Fig. 9-11).

The jig described here is simply a chopping block with a "fence" of 2 × 4s around it—something you can put together very quickly, using readily available materials.

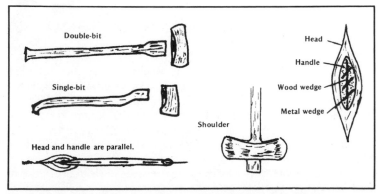

Fig. 9-10. The two main types of axes are single-bit and double-bit.

Fig. 9-11. A jig is useful when chopping wood.

To make a jig, you need to round up: a solid 12″ long chunk of wood (most any kind will do) with straight edges (no knot bumps). The diameter of it should be somewhere around 10″, depending on the general size of wood you'll be splitting. You also need eight or nine 22″ lengths of scrap 2 × 4, a strip of tough rubber from an old tire or similar heavy material long enough to cover the top perimeter of the jig (about 2′), and a few nails (Fig. 9-12).

Nail the 2 × 4s to the wood chunk, making sure the bottom comes out level. Two nails per 2 × 4 is sufficient. Then fasten the strip of rubber to the top of the 2 × 4s, and you are done. (The purpose of this rubber strip is to protect the 2 × 4s from being split or whacked out of place. The nails for the strip should be put in places where the axe can't hit them should you accidently strike the rubber.)

To use the jig, simply drop in a piece of wood and chop it up, being careful not to hit the rubber guard. You might hit the guard a few times a first, but you'll soon get the feel of it and it won't be much of a problem.

The kindling jig saves time in that the sticks won't forever be tipping over; they will always be up and ready. With the usual way of making kindling—leaning the pieces against a log—it takes well over a minute to whack a cob into inch kindling and another half-minute to gather them up. With the jig, you spend only 20 or 30 seconds splitting and almost no time gathering. Also, the kindling won't come in contact with snow, if you're working on snow-covered ground.

If you chop a lot of cobwood into kindling, give this jig a try. Good splitting!

SHARPENING HANDSAWS

Are you and your chain saw compatible? B.J. Deilke has owned two chain saws. One was of a spirit that refused to start. Whenever Deilke

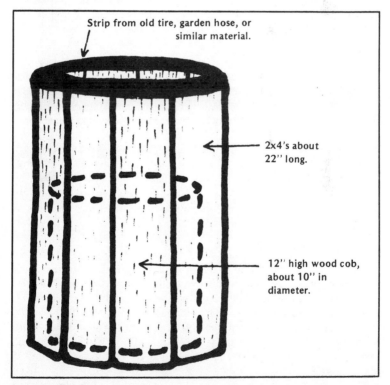

Fig. 9-12. The jig.

wanted to saw wood, he would take this used saw to town and have the dealer start it. Then he would rush home and saw wood the remainder of the day.

Several years ago he bought a new chain saw of a different make. It starts beautifully. It is a small size saw, 12″ blade, and works great for the first half hour. After the first half hour, it gets heat stroke, and has to be shut off—that is, if it doesn't do this on its own—to be cooled down for about a half hour.

Deilke had a dump truck load of slabs to saw this past winter, for firewood, and started in with the chain saw. Years ago, he did all of his sawing with a little handsaw, a tubular steel bow saw, or what he was informed was a Swedish bow saw. When the saw was new, the work was easy. After about two months the saw cut crooked, or bound in every cut.

No way was Deilke going to saw that slab pile with that old handsaw. He detested handsaws to start with. He did buy a new blade—just in case something happened to the chain saw.

The one day Deilke sawed with the power saw, it took him 2½ hours to saw six slabs. The day he "tried out" the bow saw, 14 slabs were cut in about 70 minutes.

A neighbor got the same size load of slabs, at the same time Deilke did, and sawed his with a power saw. Deilke finished sawing his slabs in half the time it took his neighbor. The neighbor had a 14″ blade power saw.

Jointing the Blade

Before any handsaw can be properly filed, it is necessary to see that the teeth are uniform in height. This is known as *jointing* a saw and is done by running a file, held perfectly parallel, across the tips of the teeth. If, when filing, the file is not held perfectly flat on the teeth, the points will become rounded.

The amount of jointing must be judged. If the saw has been properly filed, and the teeth are uniform in shape and height, jointing, or evening, may be unnecessary. If, however, the teeth are in bad shape, it may be necessary to reshape them often, at short intervals of use, to restore their quality. It is best, though, to joint the teeth, lightly, each time the blade is sharpened (Fig. 9-13).

Setting the Teeth

Setting the teeth may be done before or after jointing. Some experts prefer doing it before. Here, again, the width of the set will vary with the condition of the blade, and the type of wood being sawed. The set should be deeper for softwoods, and less for hardwoods.

Special tools may be purchased to set the teeth. The purpose of setting the teeth is to insure that each alternate tooth will cut its own groove, or kerf, wider than the saw blade, so there will be no troublesome binding of the blade. Deilke has never set the teeth on his bow saw more than 1/16 to 1/8″. This seems ample.

240

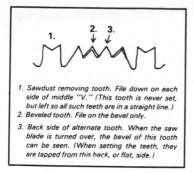

1. Sawdust removing tooth. File down on each side of middle "V." (This tooth is never set, but left so all such teeth are in a straight line.)
2. Beveled tooth. File on the bevel only.
3. Back side of alternate tooth. When the saw blade is turned over, the bevel of this tooth can be seen. (When setting the teeth, they are tapped from this back, or flat, side.)

Fig. 9-13. Consult this diagram when filing the handsaw.

Study your saw blade when new, and see which teeth are set in which direction. Usually, the teeth near the handle retain the direction of their set, as well as the angle to file. Following this, bend one tooth one way, the next tooth in the opposite direction. This "spreads" your teeth to give a wider cut. Perhaps to simplify, or complicate matters, all teeth should be set from the back, or flat side, so each beveled tooth is "shoved" forward (Fig. 9-14).

One way to set the teeth, and the most common method, is to set the first tooth, skip the next, and do every other one of the teeth in one direction. Reverse your blade, and do all of the remaining teeth in the other direction. The trick to setting saw teeth is to put equal pressure on all of the teeth so they keep on an even line (Fig. 9-15).

Filing the Teeth

In filing, or sharpening the teeth, again, it helps to study your new blade before being used, or study the teeth close to the handle of the saw, on worn blades. (These teeth don't get much use and remain somewhat as they were when new.) You will see that each side of the tooth is beveled. Each tooth has the bevels only on one side, the opposite side being perfectly flat. Hold the file perfectly parallel to this bevel, and file away from you. Lift the file at the end of each stroke and repeat, pushing the file away from you. Preferably, use the same number of strokes to each tooth, which keeps the teeth even. When one side has been filed (alternate teeth), turn the blade and file the other side. When each tooth has been filed to a point, on very dull saws, or has had the point sharpened, on saws in better condition, the work is done.

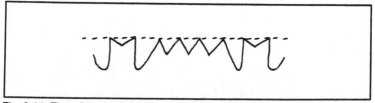

Fig. 9-14. Tips of the teeth-jointing line. All tips should be even.

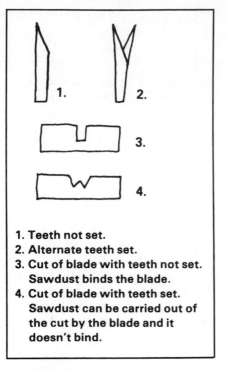

Fig. 9-15. Exaggerated views of the saw's teeth.

1. **Teeth not set.**
2. **Alternate teeth set.**
3. **Cut of blade with teeth not set. Sawdust binds the blade.**
4. **Cut of blade with teeth set. Sawdust can be carried out of the cut by the blade and it doesn't bind.**

Some filers, at this point, lay the saw flat and very lightly file or pass an emery stone across the length of the teeth, on both sides, to remove any rough burrs that may have formed in sharpening the saw. Deilke touches up his saw once a week, if time permits, but at least every other week. It does take a few minutes, but think how often you have to clean and sharpen your power saw.

CHOOSING A CHAIN SAW

A tree in the place where the new shed must go? Branches from the last storm hanging precariously over the porch? Logs too large for manageability?

Sooner or later almost every active countrysider has need of a chain saw (Fig. 9-16). Considering that annual chain saw sales almost tripled from 1971 to 1974, it's fair to bet former renters are discovering long-term economy by purchasing their own.

If you need a large chain for a short time, it's still best to rent. For a smaller saw or longer time, consider rental plus cost of fuel, oil, driving to the place to pick it up and again to return it (along with the prospect of getting only a mediocre machine, complete with worn chains). Often this can add up to a large fraction of the price of your own chain saw, especially if you need it for several days.

Although electric models are available, most chain saws have a small, high-speed, two-cycle engine which drives a continuous toothed chain around a guide bar, and is fueled by a mixture of regular gas and a special nondetergent oil. Chain saws are used mostly for overhead pruning, tree felling, and log bucking.

Ready to buy? There are many to choose from. Subtle differences in looks can indicate much greater differences in function.

Evaluate Your Workload

How much work is to be done? How large a diameter are the trees you will be cutting?

As a general rule, chain saws will cut diameters twice their bar length. If the majority of your work involves, say, trees of about a 20″ diameter, a 10″ bar length would force you to make two cuts each time. Do you have the time and energy, or would perhaps a larger size bar and chain suit your needs better? (For most nonprofessional use, a 16 or 17″ bar is adequate.)

Your own physical strength should be taken into account when choosing among the various weights of saws. The heavy saws (14 to 16 pounds) can do everything. If you don't mind trading some of that speed for easier handling, the medium weight (11 to 12 pounds) is for you. The lightweights (10 pounds or less) have their own individual drawbacks, but offer dividends in easy maneuverability.

A small chain saw is safer than a handheld circular saw, and cuts more cleanly than larger chains, which tend to chew and falter.

Electrics are the least expensive and have definite advantages and disadvantages. While you won't be able to take an electric chain saw out to your back 40 to fell trees, you'll have no starting problem in cold weather and considerably less noise. They're great for jobs on rooftops or in trees where it's difficult to pull a starter rope (although your reach is limited to

Fig. 9-16. A chain saw is a useful machine on the homestead.

the length of your cord). As there is no fuel storage and no exhaust fumes, "plug-ins" are much safer for indoor work.

Some chain saws are more economical (and ecological) than others. A large tankful of fuel will not necessarily last longer than a smaller tank. Even greater variations exist in how much cutting is accomplished for each ounce of fuel.

The price and power of the gas-fueled saw are determined by engine displacement (measured in cubic inches), and length of bar and chain. After that, many special features are available which will up the price still more.

The Trimmings

Every chain saw has an oil reservoir and dispensing system, because the chain and bar guide need to be lubricated every five minutes or so. Some models have a button to push which dispenses the oil; others are automatic, but include the thumb button for added squirts when cutting green or dense wood. Still others are fully automatic. Which version you decide on depends upon several factors. The automatic costs considerably more; however, it will probably help your machine stay in adjustment and last longer, and eliminate fear of forgetting to push that button every few minutes. It saves oil, too.

For about $20 you can get a breakerless electronic ignition. Its value to you depends on your climate. Frost, fog, and other moisture will not foul the points.

Extended use can cause buildup around exhaust ports, which may create sparks —a hazard if working about dry brush. For this reason, some chain saws have spark arrester screens in their mufflers.

Another option is the spiker bumper. Teeth extend above and below the chain at the front of the housing. They allow you to take a firmer bite into the wood. Two kinds are available; the bolted-on steel type with large, sharp teeth are much better than the kind with rows of bumps cast into the engine housing.

Some models have a compression release—a small hole in the cylinder wall that opens to reduce pressure buildup when the starter cord is pulled, making cord pulling smoother. Usually this is not very important. In cold weather or as your saw gets older, though it could make a difference.

Some versions have two triggers—a rear trigger for situations like reaching up to a high limb, and a front one useful when working close to a piece.

The safest machines are equipped with a kick-back guard which protects your left hand, and a chain brake that stops the chain automatically if the kick-back guard is pushed forward. This is especially needed during limbing. The top part of the guide bar tip is most dangerous; kick-back occurs when this area hits a branch.

There are other little pluses to consider:

☐ It is possible to extend the life of your chain saw somewhat by getting the roller nose attachment.

244

☐ A safety lock will prevent the throttle trigger from being accidently activated, as by a twig; you must be grasping the rear handle.

☐ The actuating lever, which cocks a spring that snaps against the clutch drum, is a saving addition if you fall or trip, if you have mishandled a drop start, or your hand slips forward.

☐ Still more extras: a hand shield, trigger interlock for carrying an idling engine, sprocket-nose chain bar, a chromed saw chain, power-tipped guide bar, vibration isolation, and reversed starter cord positions for lefties.

Some Care and Safety Tips

The proper stance for starting is usually with the saw placed on the ground and your right foot through the rear handle as you hold down the front handle with your left hand. Pull the cord sharply with your right.

As soon as the engine starts, check to see that oil is getting to the chain. Make sure the chain does not rotate when the engine idles.

New chains stretch some. When breaking a new one in, readjust the tension after a little while. A chain can be ruined in five minutes of cutting if it's too loose. Do this two or three times.

Whenever there's a need to remove the chain—it's easily enough done, and takes only minutes—check the sprocket. If it's worn, as it will be if you've done much cutting, replace both sprocket and chain. These are relatively expandable pieces compared to the motor.

Don't inconvenience yourself with a half-done job and a broken chain. A spare chain makes as much good sense as a spare tire in your car trunk. Some chain sawers find it wise to keep an "everyday" chain and a "Sunday" chain, too—one for risky, irregular work where a chain might more easily snap, and another for clearcut things such as bucking logs.

Engine repairs are costly, but they may be necessary if you use car oil. Even "two-cycle" oils are a gamble, having been designed for water-cooled outboards. It is best to stick with oil marketed by any major chain saw maker.

It's fairly easy to foul a spark plug; just try to start the engine with the ignition switch off. Always keep spare spark plugs handy, too.

Your saw is dull when it begins to throw sawdust instead of chips. Don't delay in sharpening it! Touch-up filing is not too difficult to do yourself, although it is time consuming. Refiling, a more involved and professional-type sharpening, is done less frequently and is best left to an expert.

If a hot engine balks when you try to restart it, check the fuel tank to make certain that the air filter is not clogged. Remove the spark plug and wipe off any fuel that may have coated it. Try starting the engine with the choke in various positions.

Most chain saws have one large safety drawback—the noise. Some saws create enough furor to cause permanent hearing damage after just 15 minutes. Ear protectors are extremely wise.

Running the fuel system dry before storage will reduce gumming. Pull the chain drive cover off and brush out the accumulated gunk, then flush parts with solvent or kerosene. If you're not intending to use the saw for some time, the chain is best removed and stored in a can of oil.

TRACTOR-POWERED LOG SPLITTER

Because hydraulic wood splitters can considerably ease the labor involved in splitting firewood, they have become quite popular in the past several years (Figs. 9-17 and 9-18). The commercially manufactured models are priced from $150 to $1,500.

Here is a tractor-powered splitter which was built in November, 1976 for less than $35 for materials, using a few new parts along with recycled items (Fig. 9-19).

Here's what you'll need:

Tools

- ☐ Welding equipment.
- ☐ Oxyacetylene cutting torch.
- ☐ Drill.

Pipe

- ☐ 2   2½″ rounds × 5′0″ (threaded both ends).
- ☐ 2   3″ rounds × 1′0″—slide.
- ☐ 2   3″ rounds × 0′4″—wedge mount.
- ☐ 4   2½″ pipe couplings.
- ☐ 1″ rounds × 4″ spacers.
- ☐ 1   2½″ rounds × 2½″ long hydraulic ram mount.

Iron Plate—⅜″

- ☐ 2   4½ × 3½″ triangles ⎫
- ☐ 1   5 × 7″ square.   ⎬ slide
- ☐ 1   3½ × 5½″ base.   ⎭
- ☐ 1   6 × 5½″ upright.   ⎫ fixed end
- ☐ 2   3 × 6″ triangles.   ⎭
- ☐ 3   5 × 4 × ½″—for wedge.
- ☐ 1   ⅜ × 4 × 5″—back of wedge.
- ☐ 1   ½ × 2 × 2″—lower wedge.
- ☐ 2 spacers.

Angle Iron

- ☐ 1½ × 1½ × 5″ × ⅛″ triangles—wedge spreaders.

Channel Iron

- ☐ 2   2 × 5 × ⅛″ without one leg
- ☐ 2 × 2 × 5 × ⅛″—support each end

Other Materials

Leaf spring: 2 1½ × ⅛ × 1'4"
1 hydraulic cylinder
1 hydraulic control
1 set hydraulic hoses

Construction

Lay rails and couplings on a flat surface (Fig. 9-20). Place blocks on edge between the rails to assure that they are parallel. Clamp rails or fasten with wire. It is very important to keep the rails parallel. Lay a 1" pipe between the couplings and weld securely. Proceed by welding the rest of the pieces for the fixed end in place (Figs. 9-21 and 9-22).

Next, construct the wedge (Fig. 9-23). Remove the loose couplings from the rails and slide first a 12" piece then a 4" piece of 3" pipe onto each rail. Replace couplings; check again to assure the rails are parallel.

Fig. 9-17. Steve Schmidt's hydraulic splitter could have saved this fellow hours of work (photo by Jean Martin).

Fig. 9-18. This most reassuring woodpile needn't take days if you use a hydraulic splitter.

Slide 4″ long pipes up against the couplings and weld the ½″ plate wedge sections in place as spacers. Add the ⅜ × 4 × 5″ plate (attach only to the slides; the couplings remain removable). Next the one-legged channel is attached to the ½″ plate sections and the ⅜ × 4 × 5″ plate. Add the angle (1½ × 1½ × 5″), the support channel, and the leaf spring foot (Fig. 9-24).

Now the slide. Weld the triangle brace in place on each 12″ by 3″ round. Stay back ½″ from the end to allow the bottom edge of the 5 × 7″ plate to rest on the 3″ round pieces.

Shim each slide with cardboard to assure it is centered on the rail. Position and weld the 5 × 7″ plate in place. Attach the 2½″ round × 2½″ pipe for the hydraulic cylinder ram (Fig. 9-25).

During construction, make sure that the rails are parallel and that the hydraulic cylinder ram travels parallel to the rails. Light angle irons are used to mount the hydraulic control. A piece of ½″ round was used to extend the control handle.

Fig. 9-19. Here's the homemade hydraulic wedge splitting a chunk of wood. Note the one-legged channels, angles and removable couplings.

248

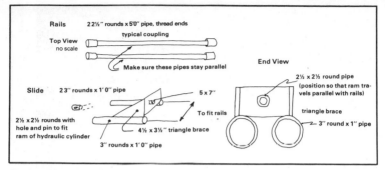

Fig. 9-20. Install the 3″ pipe pieces on the rails before welding this part to assure that they will slide easily.

Once the cylinder and control are mounted, the necessary length for the hydraulic hoses can be determined. Equip the supply. Return hoses with quick attach couplers, and your're in business. See Figs. 9-26 and 9-27.

BUMPER JACK BALER

You can build a strong, simple, inexpensive one from a packing case and a bumper jack. It takes under two hours.

The inside dimensions of the box are 15″ × 28″, but any size rectangular box will do. It must be strong.

Cut a square hole in the middle of one end of the box. Make it a little larger than the shaft of the jack. The shaft will slide through this hole. Drill a hole through the blade of the jack (the part that slips under the bumper) at its lowest point. The hole should be ¼″ or ⅜″. Bolt the blade to the end of the box so that when the shaft is assembled to it, the shaft will ride easily through the square hole you cut for it in the box. The shaft will be supported and moved by the blade—the opposite to their functions as a car jack. Use the largest washer you can find on the inside of the box to spread out the force and retard splitting the box.

Drill a few ¼″ holes through the base of the stand of the jack, and bolt it to a piece of ½″ plywood cut to fit very loosely inside the box. This is the piston.

Fig. 9-21. Here is the back side view of the fixed end.

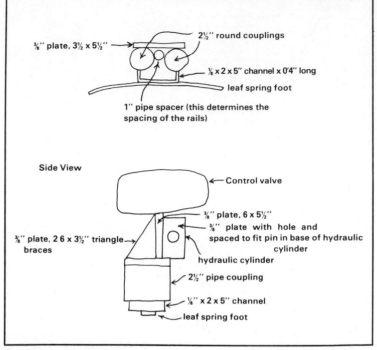

Fig. 9-22. Light angle iron was positioned on top of the fixed end to fasten the control valve to wedge.

Assemble as shown in Fig. 9-28. To operate, push the shaft as far out of the box as possible, snap on the piston, and set the jack for "raise." Lay two pieces of twine in the box with their ends hanging over the notches. Toss in the material and compress it. Pull the ends of the string occasionally. When the bale is well pressed, tie the ends of the string around the top. Set the jack for "lower," and pull the shaft away from the bale. That's it.

HOMEMADE HAY CHOPPER

The price of a large hay chopper is far beyond Winnell Callahan's budget or needs, so he has fixed one up with his electric rotary lawnmower. Once the chopping box and retainer bin are made, the actual work is very little. Callahan has found it usually takes between 30 and 45 minutes to chop one month's supply of hay for each doe.

In the fall he sharpens the cutting blade and removes the wheels and handle of the lawnmower. Then he hangs the base by a pulley on a joist. This enables him to raise and lower the machine into a box built of scrap lumber, which holds the uncut hay. This box is a little larger than the lawnmower, about 24" wide, 30" long, and 20" deep. One side is open for the exit of the chopped hay into the retainer bin. The box is built on 8" legs.

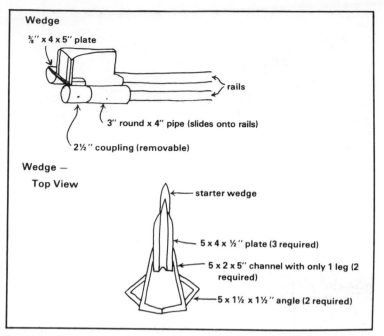

Fig. 9-23. The entire wedge assembly is removable to allow for extension or replacement of the rails.

When it comes time to chop hay, a big flake is shaken apart into the box and the mower is lowered, with the funnel mouth toward the open side of the box. When the electricity is switched on, the blade quickly chops the hay and throws it into the retainer bin. When the box is empty, switch off the motor. Wait until the blade stops turning, then lift up the lawnmower and put in another flake. Keep this up until you have the required amount of chopped hay.

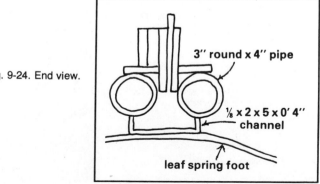

Fig. 9-24. End view.

Fig. 9-25. The slide from the back side, showing 2½" round by 2½" pipe attachment for the ram.

SEED PLANTER

This seed planter is really a very simple mechanism to build and operate. The main section or heart of the planter is the part labled E (Fig. 9-29). This is the container which holds the seed. It is two circular pieces of wood with a metal band around them to make a hollow wheel. On one side there should be about a 1" hole which is used to fill the container with seed. This hole should be plugged with an ordinary cork. The size of the holes around the metal band will determine what kinds of seeds can be planted, and spacing of those holes will set the spacing of the seeds (Tables 9-1 and 9-2).

More than one seed container will be necessary for a full variety of seeds. If the greater number of holes is used for close spacing, then some of them can be covered with tape to provide a greater spacing between seeds. To change seed containers, the keeper pin on the side of the cover plate should be removed along with the pin next to the seed container. The axle then slides out freeing the seed container. To hold the container close to the wheel so that the two pins engage the two holes on the seed container, you can use a washer and keeper pin. This makes the seed container rotate with the wheel.

You can make an on/off mechanism for controlling the flow of seeds. This is done by drilling an oversized recessed hole into the spacer which is connected to the wheel. In this recess place a compression spring which will fit around the axle. This will require pressure on the opposite side of

Fig. 9-26. Note the adaptor for the longer control handle.

Fig. 9-27. The assembled splitter is shown with the ram extended.

the seed container to keep the container engaged with the wheel. To do this, you can use a simple throttle type cable which runs to the handle or a rod or stick which has a linkage. When the container is engaged to the wheel, it will rotate and drop the seeds through the tube. When released, the spring will push it out enough to be out of line with the drill tube. This will save seed by being able to control the flow.

Any size axle may be used from a ½″ solid rod to a piece of water pipe. The drill tube should be about a ¾″ water pipe (Fig. 9-30). The wheel can be made of pieces of plywood laminated together or by using regular boards. Either way, when laying them together the grain on the different layers should be perpendicular to each other. You can cover the furrow by adding a length of heavy chain so it drags behind the drill tube (Fig. 9-31).

HARVESTING EQUIPMENT

How many of you are presently in the market for a new radish combine? How about a cabbage harvester, cucumber picker, or a snap bean picker?

For nearly every crop grown, there is now available or now in development a special machine to harvest it. Most of these special machines

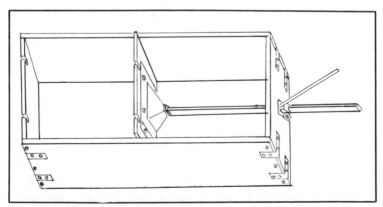

Fig. 9-28. Diagram of the bumper jack baler.

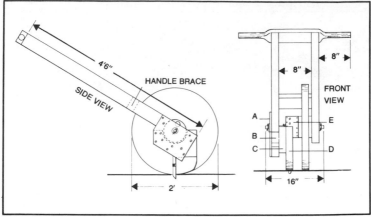

Fig. 9-29. Side and front views of the seed planter.

are completely out of reach for the small or diversified grower. Their existence, and their use by the largest growers, helps determine the market price of produce.

You can harvest enough grain to feed your family with a sickle or a scythe with grain cradle, a homemade flail, and a couple of buckets for winnowing. You cannot harvest enough grain to supply your local co-ops and natural foods stores for a year, using these methods, and expect to support yourself doing so. The stores and co-ops will not want to pay you four or five times the price they presently pay a commercial supplier, so that you can hire enough folks to get the grain harvested, assuming you can find enough people willing to do backbreaking work for minimum wage.

You must use a combine for any commercial quantity of grain. You might choose to purchase an old one, or you might choose to hire the work done by a custom operator. Clearly, there is no economic sense in every small farm having its own combine; it's much better to help a neighbor pay for his by hiring him to harvest your crop. (Have you ever driven through a middle-class subdivision on a Saturday afternoon and speculated on the level of alienation necessary to induce every single family to purchase its own riding lawn mower?)

Beans

Similarly, you cannot justify hand picking and hand shelling dry beans for sale. (Beans sold as "hand picked" are picked over by hand in order to remove trash and imperfect beans; they are not removed from the bush by hand.) Some New England growers have formed a co-op that shunts harvesting equipment from farm to farm as the season progresses. They are fairly well equipped.

If you are not in a traditional bean growing area, though, you may have to improvise. Instead of special bean pulling and windrowing machines, you

Table 9-1. Hole Size and Spacing on Seed Container for Various Seeds.

as a garden seeder	hole size	hole spacing
Beans	(in inches) ½ - 9./16	(in inches) 1
Beets Spinach Swiss Chard	¼	¾
Cabbage	⅛	3 ½ - 6
Lettuce Turnips Carrots Onions	⅛	¾
Peas Okra Corn	½ 5/16 ½	¾ 6 3
As a Grain Drill		
Wheat Oats Rye	5/16	⅛
Milo Sorghum	5/16	½

Table 9-2. Relationship Between Hole Spacing on Seed Container and Spacing in Row.

spacing between holes on seed container	spacing of seed in row
¾"	3"
1"	4"
1 ½"	6"
2 ½"	10"
3"	12"
4 ½"	18"
6"	24"
9"	36"

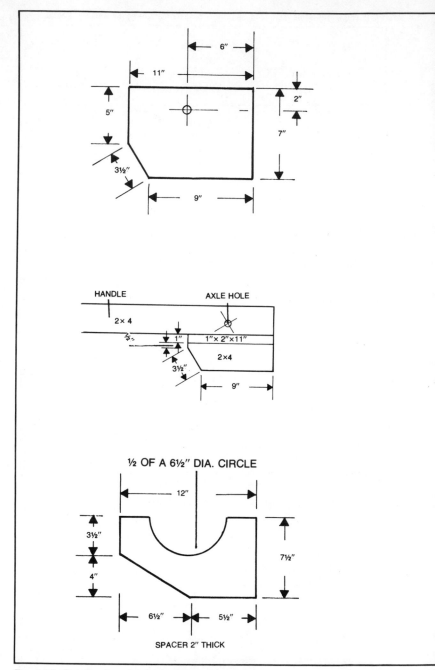

Fig. 9-30. Construction details for the seed planter.

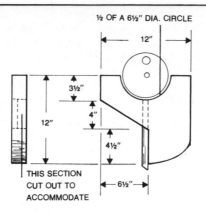

½ OF A 6½" DIA. CIRCLE

12"

3½"

4"

12"

4½"

THIS SECTION
CUT OUT TO
ACCOMMODATE

6½"

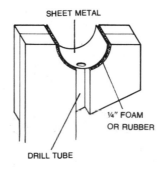

SHEET METAL

¼" FOAM
OR RUBBER

DRILL TUBE

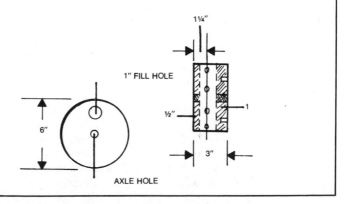

1¼"

1" FILL HOLE

6"

½"

1

3"

AXLE HOLE

can use (with great care) a sickle bar mower to cut the plants and a hay rake to windrow them. After they are sufficiently cured, you will have to get the beans to a thresher or get a thresher to the beans, depending on how old and what type of thresher is available (Fig. 9-32) If none is available, don't grow beans. Soybeans are harvested with a combine.

Corn, Vegetables, and Fruit

Field corn, if it is not chopped for ensilage, is harvested with a picker, or a picker-husker, or a picker-husker-sheller, depending on what's available in the neighborhood and what you want to use the corn for. If you need to remove the grain from the ear (in order to make cornmeal, for instance), you can run it through a hand-cranked sheller. Small quantities can be picked, husked, and shelled entirely by hand. Corn can also be cut and bound into shocks, by hand or with a cornbinder. The stalks are used as fodder.

Sweet corn for fresh market (as opposed to processing) is always picked by hand. The only mechanical advantage to be had is in a well-designed picking sack that permits the worker to pick with both hands.

The tool of choice for digging a small plot of potatoes is a *potato hook*. (It has four blunt tines and looks like a pitchfork that got put together upside down.) If your yield is good and you are selling retail at high prices, a potato hook is fast enough. For large quantities at wholesale prices, though, you need some kind of digger. A one-bottom plow is all right; a shovel plow or disc hiller (reversed for digging) is better. An old two-row harvester is better still.

For most other vegetable crops, harvesting tools are in the category of aids rather than automatic harvesters. Judicious choices of wagons, containers, packing materials, and so on make a tremendous difference in ease of picking. Human beings still do the work, though large growers who are not big enough to use automatic harvesting machines like carrot combines or tomato harvesters do use mobile conveyor systems so the pickers can spend all their time picking instead of carrying. For small growers, even these machines are not really needed. Most of the harvesting equipment on Dick Margulis's farm consists of a few sharp knives and a large collection of 5-gallon plastic buckets. They serve as picking containers, washing tubs, and chairs; one, with the bottom removed, is a funnel for packing sacks.

Fruit, similarly, is nearly all picked by hand. Professional apple picking crews still use ladders and canvas bags that open at the bottom to unload. A medium-sized orchard in Margulis's neighborhood has abandoned that system in favor of one that amateur pickers can work with more easily: they have a truck with a hydraulically raised platform on top. Pickers stand on the platform and pick with both hands into containers at their feet.

Both vegetable growers and fruit growers generally have some sort of washing and grading equipment. Margulis has a low-sided table and a hose. A bottomless bucket funnel is suspended on one end of the table. Simple automatic washers start at around $500 or $600. Grading tables with conveyors add hundreds more.

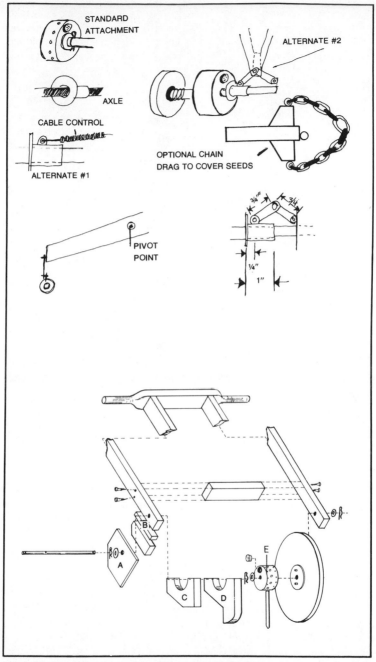

STANDARD ATTACHMENT

AXLE

CABLE CONTROL

ALTERNATE #1

ALTERNATE #2

OPTIONAL CHAIN DRAG TO COVER SEEDS

PIVOT POINT

3/4" 3/4"

1/4"

1"

A
B
C
D
E

Fig. 9-31. Cover the furrow by adding a length of chain.

259

Fig. 9-32. Brooks Mills of Brewer, Maine, uses this machine to thresh and clean his beans right on the farm and thus commands premium prices for them.

PEA SHELLER

Leo M. Lawlor took an old idea and redesigned it into a practical pea sheller for his own needs. It took several months of part-time planning, sketching and laying out his design on paper. Once all the necessary materials were assembled, he put it together in about two days.

It takes about two minutes shelling time to complete a drumload of peas (Figs. 9-33 through 9-39). The peas are not damaged. Anyone with average mechanical ability and a strong desire can build this pea sheller.

Materials should run about $60 depending on how much you have to buy new and how much you may have on hand. The motor you can borrow from your table saw, bench grinder or chicken plucker. Lawlor will send a complete set of plans for $5. Mail your requests to him at Michael's Enterprise, Box 1681, Ames, IA 50010.

260

Fig. 9-33. Freshly picked peas shell the best (photo by Leo M. Lawlor).

CREAM SEPARATOR

Assembling a cream separator is like working a puzzle at first. After a while, though, putting the separator together is a logical, simple procedure.

Bonnie Bahn took a picture of the pieces of her separator (Fig. 9-40). They are numbered in the order in which they go together.

Fig. 9-34. The front door of the main frame is opened to reveal the shelling drum. (photo by Leo M. Lawlor).

☐ **The Tubular or Central Feed Shaft and Base.** This piece fits over a spindle which connects the milk circulating parts of the separator with the strictly mechanical parts (Fig. 9-41).

☐ **Rubber Ring.** This fits in a groove on the bottom of the central feed shaft and will seal the unit tightly when it is all assembled (2 in Fig. 9-41).

☐ **Distributor.** This piece fits over the central feed shaft and makes it impossible to turn the discs in the wrong direction (3 in Fig. 9-41).

☐ **Discs.** The discs fit over the distributor and will slide down the appropriate grooves. Bahn's separator has 17 discs. She removed a disc when she was having trouble with the separator clogging up, and it seemed to help. It was a temporary measure though, and she replaced it when she knew more about how to regulate the separator. If the discs must be in sequence, they will probably be numbered. The discs on Bahn's separator have a special hanger for them where they can be hung to dry, or if need be, washed without getting them out of sequence (4 in Fig. 9-41).

☐ **Cream Screw Disc.** The cream screw disc is shaped like the other discs, but has a neck piece. At the top of the neck is the cream screw. The cream screw is a hollow screw that must be turned by a key. One

262

usually comes with a separator, but an appropriate hex key might work (5 in Fig. 9-41).

☐ **Bowl Shell.** This piece covers and encloses all of the discs and connects with the central feed shaft and rubber ring to seal the bottom. It will probably only fit one way, so you won't have to worry if you have it on right (6 in Fig. 9-41).

☐ **Bowl Nut.** The bowl nut holds all these parts tightly together when it is screwed on the top of them. This total unit is sometimes called the separator bowl, and it is inside the separator bowl that the actual process of separation takes place. As you turn the crank, the separator bowl spins. This spinning creates centrifugal force inside the bowl which in turn increases the specific gravity of the milk by about 1000 times. When standing, the specific gravity of cream is about 0.9 grams, and skim milk is about 1.036, a difference of 0.136.

In a spinning separator bowl, cream is about 900 grams and skim milk is 1036, a difference of 136 grams. This considerable difference in specific gravity causes the cream to separate instantly, and the design of a separator is such that the cream and skim milk are caught in separate containers. Skim milk collects in the outer portion of the bowl and is directed to the skim milk

Fig. 9-35. The access door to the shelling drum is removed, exposing rotor paddles (photo by Leo M. Lawlor).

Fig. 9-36. About four pounds of fresh peas are loaded into the drum (photo by Leo M. Lawlor).

outlet. Cream collects in the center of the bowl and is directed up the central feed shaft to the cream outlet (7 in Fig. 9-41).

   ☐ **Bowl Nut Tightener.** The bowl nut has two holes on top and a mark on it that when it is tightened corresponds to a mark on the tubular feed shaft. This tool has prongs that fit into the two holes to tighten the bowl nut (8 in Fig. 9-41).

   ☐ **Skim Milk Cover and Outlet.** This piece directs the flow of skim milk, and below it you will have to sit a container big enough to hold the

Fig. 9-37. The access door to the drum is replaced and latched. Anticipation accelerates (photo by Leo M. Lawlor).

skim milk. On Bahn's separator this piece has a bigger hole in the center than the one that is the cream outlet, because it must sit further down on the separator bowl (9 in Fig. 9-41).

☐ **Cream Cover and Outlet.** The bowl below this outlet won't need to be as large as the one under the skim milk one (10 in Fig. 9-41).

☐ **Regulating Cover.** This piece sits on top of the cream cover and outlet and must contain a float (11 in Fig. 9-41).

☐ **Float.** The purpose of the regulating cover and float is to regulate the inflow of milk (12 in Fig. 9-41).

☐ **Supply Can.** The supply can on Bahn's separator sits directly on top of the regulating cover. On many separators it is to one side of it and is connected by a tube with a shut off faucet. Make sure the faucet is closed before you pour the whole milk into the supply can. Start turning the crank, and when you have established the right speed open the faucet (13 in Fig. 9-41).

Fig. 9-38. The rotor begins to spin, gearing up for its job (photo by Leo M. Lawlor).

Fig. 9-39. The rotor slaps the pods open. The peas fall through the drum screen (photo by Leo M. Lawlor).

☐ **Shutoff Valve.** Instead of a faucet in the milk line, the separator uses this device inside the supply can. When the separator is going at the right speed, rotating this slightly will allow the milk to flow (14 in Fig. 9-41).

Once the Bahn's had washed and reassembled their new separator, they were discouraged to discover that it must be bolted to a sturdy, level table. They built a special table for it.

Fig. 9-40. The assembled cream separator (photo by Bonnie Bahn).

The Bahn's built the little table with two thoughts in mind. It had to be suitable for separating milk, and it had to fit in the space they had planned for it. For the top they bought a 2½' piece of 2 × 12 for $1.25. They used scrap 2 × 4s, but used about the equivalent of four 8' ones. For a small table, three 2 × 4s would be quite enough. Normally, 2 × 4s would cost $3.50 to $5. They used 25 cents to 50 cents worth of nails and paid $1.80 for a can of Gloss White Enamel paint to give it a dairy look and make it easy to clean. All this would make a similar table cost between $6.80 and $8.55.

The top of the table is sort of L-shaped. The Bahns sit the bowl for cream on the table and the skim milk container on a chair beside it. They plan to build a drop leaf for the skim milk container. There is no doubt, though, that their separator is conveniently located and easy to keep clean.

FOOT-POWERED SEWING MACHINE

You want to buy a second-hand portable electric sewing machine? Several months ago Bonnie Bahn bought a treadle sewing machine at a second-hand store for $70. She planned to keep her electric machine, but she hasn't used it once since she got the treadle one. Now she's convinced that whoever invented electric sewing machines was wasting his time.

Treadle Machines—New or Used?

Treadle sewing machines can be bought new. The price of a Singer machine starts at $99.95. The cabinet is extra with a starting price of $160. If you are clever at making things fit, an old cabinet can be used.

Perhaps your present machine can be converted to treadle power. If your machine has an outside motor connected to the hand wheel by a belt, it is probably convertible. Finding a cabinet to fit your particular machine may tax your ingenuity, however.

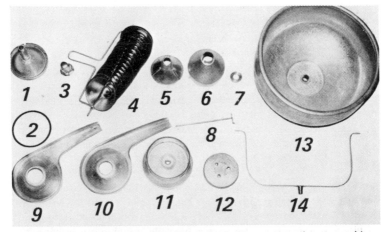

Fig. 9-41. The cream separator disassembled. The numbered parts are identified in the text (photo by Bonnie Bahn).

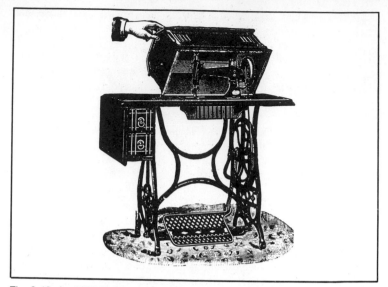

Fig. 9-42. An 1895 high-arm sewing machine.

The advantage of buying a new treadle machine is that you can get a machine, with a built-in zigzag and buttonhole mechanism, conveniences that are lacking on older models. Attachments for buttonholing and using a zigzag stitch can often be found for the old machines. If you use these stitches a lot, the built-in device that moves the needle on new machines is easier and does a better job.

Older machines are usually cheaper and work just as well when it comes to straight stitching (Fig. 9-42). Bahn couldn't affort a new cabinet, and the idea of putting a new machine in a mellow old cabinet didn't appeal to her.

Cheap Machines May Be Repairable

Sam and Sheryl Champie bought a Standard for $25. The plate underneath the needle (throat or needle plate) was broken so they made one. The hardest part was finding a flat piece of chrome. Sam's solution was to use a piece of chrome from the hub cap of his 1949 Ford pickup. It was the right thickness, and part of it was flat. He cut it out with a hacksaw and ground and filed it until it fit perfectly. He then drilled holes in it and filed them until they were the correct shape. The finished throat plate works and looks great.

The only presser-foot on the Champies' machine was a cording foot. This didn't work well for regular sewing, and they wanted to replace it. Their local store, however, didn't have a presser-foot that would fit their machine. Because Singer pieces are universally available, Sam decided to make their machine so it would accommodate a Singer presser-foot, zipper

268

foot, etc. To do this, he had to take out the entire rod that ends with the presser-foot attachment. He was then able to file the end to the correct shape and drill a hole for the screw to attach a Singer foot.

The Easy Way

Bahn wanted to buy a machine that wouldn't require a great amount of fixing before she could start using it. The White that she found was complete. Needles and bobbins for it can be found easily. Check the top of the needles on a prospective purchase. The most common needles are flat on one side and rounded on the other. Be sure you can get the kind the machine needs. A round bobbin can usually be found to fit an old machine, but the long shuttle ones are harder to find (Fig. 9-43). Most old machines come with a collection of assortments but if there is some special attachment you plan to buy, such as a buttonholer, be sure you can get one to fit the machine.

Problems and Solutions

Frequently old machines have no belts connecting the treadle wheel with the hand wheel. Belts are merely a long leather cord and can be easily made. If there is a belt, try the machine, or if there is no belt just turn the top wheel. If it won't turn easily, try to find out why before abandoning the machine.

If the hand wheel won't turn or if the needle won't complete the up-and-down motion without sticking, the machine may be clogged up with dirty oil or with pieces of thread. Lift the head so you can see the bottom of the machine (Fig. 9-44). If the rods are bent or the machine corroded, it's a risky purchase. If it's just covered with dirty oil and stuck with tangled threads, it's probably okay.

To get your machine in working order, first remove all tangled threads. Squirt kerosene into the oil holes and wipe the bottom of the

Fig. 9-43. The pointer indicates the bobbin release lever. Above the bobbin are the throat plate and pressure foot (photo by Alan and Bonnie Bahn).

Fig. 9-44. This is the way the underside of the treadle sewing machine should look. Check here to see if any of the rods are bent or corroded (photo by Alan and Bonnie Bahn).

machine with kerosene. Wipe dry. Oil the machine in the appropriate holes with sewing machine oil. Thread it and see how it sews.

The tension if frequently out of adjustment. If the top thread appears straight, the top tension is tighter than the bottom. If the bottom thread is straight, the bottom tension is tighter. When the tension is correct, the line of stitching looks the same from both the top and bottom. Adjustments are usually made with a dial on top of the machine. If this adjustment isn't adequate, the lower tension can also be adjusted by a screw on the bobbin case. In checking tension always do so with the presser-foot down.

Sometimes when you try to sew the needle will break. This may mean that the needle is loose, or the presser-foot is loose, or the presser-foot is not fully down. Pulling the material too hard may make the needle hit the throat plate and break. Making a throat plate as Sam Champie did is very exacting business. The hole for the needle to go through must be exactly where it should be or the needle will hit it and break.

Sometimes the thread keeps breaking. This could mean that your machine is improperly threaded. The thread may be catching on something or rubbing against the presser-foot. This also may be caused by tension badly out of adjustment.

The machine may skip stitches. This usually indicates that the needle is bent or wrong for the fabric you are using. Sometimes the belt to the treadle wheel slips. If this happens, the belt should be removed and a small piece cut out to tighten the belt.

The material may bunch up behind the presser-foot. This usually indicates that the starting thread is caught around the presser-foot or the material. It can also happen if the tension is badly in need of adjustment.

270

A treadle machine will not sew backwards as an electric does. Either the material must be reversed, or knots will have to be tied to keep the stitching from pulling out.

Treadle machines have many advantages over electric ones. Most importantly, they don't need electricity. You can even sew outside if you want. They excel on sewing through heavy material that cause lesser machines to spin their motors and refuse to proceed.

Motors don't make sewing machines more efficient. Putting a motor on a sewing machine is typical of a bureaucracy that promotes a person one step beyond his most efficient position. Bonnie Bahn's machine is completely efficient just as it is.

SEWING MACHINE TURNS INTO A SPINNING WHEEL

Joan Siegel and Stuart Golder use their treadle sewing machine for spinning. They didn't even sacrifice the sewing part of the machine. It both sews, and spins, and changing from one to the other is quick and easy.

They had been using a drop spindle for spinning, and it was a simple matter to connect it to the treadle drive of the sewing machine. The drop spindle had been made from an old wooden pulley with a hole drilled in the center and a dowel stuck tightly in the hole. They sawed a frame for this spindle out of a 1 × 4 × 6¾″ board. (Fig. 9-45). The hole must be larger than the dowel of the spindle. It was drilled all the way through before the center piece was cut out so that they'd be in line.

Siegel and Golder pulled the dowel out of the *whorl* (the pulley) and put it through the hole in the left end of the frame, through three metal washers, through the pulley, through three more washers, and through the other hole in the frame. The dowel should fit in the pulley tightly enough so it won't turn, and through the holes in the frame just loosely enough so it will turn freely without wobbling.

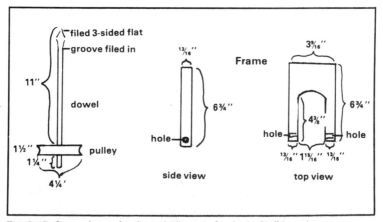

Fig. 9-45. Saw a frame for the spindle out of a 1×4×6¾″ board.

Fig. 9-46. The spindle frame is attached to the top of the treadle sewing machine stand or table with a C-clamp. Washers fill the space on the dowel between the pulley and frame (photo by Stuart Golder).

The dimensions of the frame depend on the size of your whorl. Use the number of washers that works best. You may not even need any.

Now slip the belt off the sewing machine and put it to one side of the cast iron wheel under the table. You don't need to undo it.

Attach to the Machine

Then attach the spindle and holder to the top of your treadle stand, using a C-clamp (Fig. 9-46). Line up the groove in the pulley with the groove in the drive wheel of the sewing machine. (If your machine has a skirt guard, it may have to be removed.) Take a stout piece of cord about the same diameter as the treadle's drive band (nylon works well) and run it around the drive wheel, cross it once, and put it around the pulley. Make it a snug fit, and be sure it doesn't rub on anything. (It does rub against itself where it crosses.) You may have to clamp the spindle assembly further forward so the cord doesn't rub the table.

If you use nylon cord, melt the ends so it doesn't fray, and then staple or sew the ends together. It's easier to do this if you loosen the clamp and slide the assembly back.

Now, with the cord around both wheels, adjust the tension by sliding the assembly forward and clamping it when the cord is snug (Fig. 9-47). You're all set to tie a leader (1½' of yarn) on the dowel, and spin away.

Spinning

It's similar to spinning on a drop spindle, only it's horizontal. Your right hand controls the tension on the wool, while your left pulls out the unspun

272

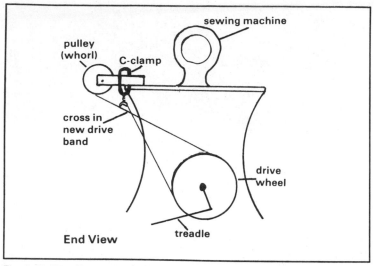

Fig. 9-47. Note the cord around the drive wheel and pulley.

wool (Fig. 9-48). When you're ready to let the twist enter the unspun part, let go with your right hand.

When your left hand is out as far as is comfortable, use your right to direct the spun wool onto the spindle, still holding the unspun part in your left hand. It sounds complicated and is more easily demonstrated than

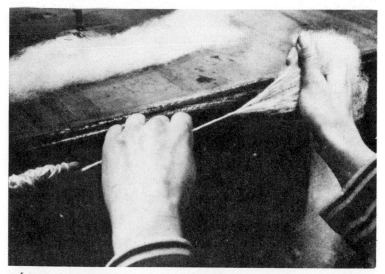

Fig. 9-48. Now for the spinning—the left hand pulls out the unspun wool, while the right hand maintains tension. Let go with the right hand when ready to let the twist enter the unspun part (photo by Stuart Golder).

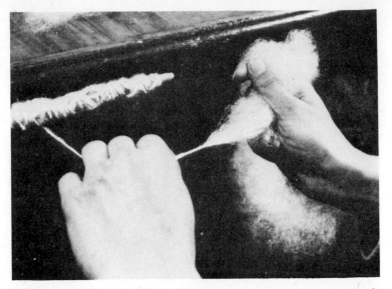

Fig. 9-49. Winding on—the left hand holds the yarn while the right hand guides it with a loose touch. Once you get the rhythm, you can treadle away at a steady pace (photo by Stuart Golder).

described. Once you get the hang of it, it all falls into a rhythm. You can treadle away at a steady pace (Fig. 9-49). When you want to sew, unclamp the spindle assembly, put the sewing machine drive band back in place, and you're ready to sew.

WASHING WITHOUT WATTAGE OR WASHBOARD

There really is a simple and effective way to do the weekly wash without wattage or washboard. Use the hand-operated washing machine known as the James Washer. You can save a lot of water and electrical energy with a small expenditure of personal energy. If you approach it the right way, wash day can be a painless, even pleasant, experience.

At first glance, the James Washer seems to be just a tub supported by braced wooden legs (Fig. 9-50). The real heart of the device is the very effective agitator that can be operated easily with one hand (Fig. 9-51). A cover contains the splashing water while the washing is in progress. A shallow compartment, reinforced with wood, is located at the end of the tub opposite the agitator handle. A wringer (available as an option) can be attached to the outside of the compartment. There is a drain valve at the bottom of the tub for quick emptying when the wash is finished.

Why a James Washer?

In 1971 Gale L. Flagg and her husband were preparing to make their move back to the land. Gale started doing their laundry by hand. She felt

274

that by living as much as possible the way they were planning to live after their move, the transition wouldn't be so abrupt or difficult. Gale asked her mother for her old washboard and got to work. She soon discovered that heavy scrubbing on that antique board wore out collars and socks and heavily soiled areas on work clothes. She began to think there must be a way to wash that would be less lethal to the laundry.

Many Questions

About that time the Flaggs saw the blurb about the James Handwashers in the *Last Whole Earth Catalog*. The person who made that entry wondered if the legs were sturdy enough. That put the Flaggs on guard. They sent a letter to the manufacturer asking what their "guarantee" meant. They replied that the device was "guaranteed to wash clothes clean." That made the Flaggs even more wary, so they asked questions about construction and materials. The replies were not very specific, so they asked for the name of a James Washer owner near them.

Back came the name of a gentleman in Delaware. The Flaggs were living in Vermont. The Flaggs wrote and got a delightful letter in response.

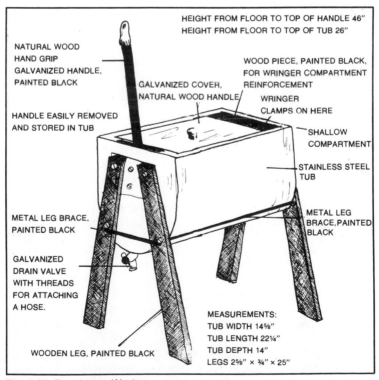

HEIGHT FROM FLOOR TO TOP OF HANDLE 46"
HEIGHT FROM FLOOR TO TOP OF TUB 26"

NATURAL WOOD
HAND GRIP
GALVANIZED HANDLE,
PAINTED BLACK

WOOD PIECE, PAINTED BLACK,
FOR WRINGER COMPARTMENT
REINFORCEMENT

GALVANIZED COVER,
NATURAL WOOD HANDLE

WRINGER
CLAMPS ON HERE

HANDLE EASILY REMOVED
AND STORED IN TUB

SHALLOW
COMPARTMENT

STAINLESS STEEL
TUB

METAL LEG BRACE,
PAINTED BLACK

METAL LEG
BRACE, PAINTED
BLACK

GALVANIZED
DRAIN VALVE
WITH THREADS
FOR ATTACHING
A HOSE.

MEASUREMENTS:
TUB WIDTH 14⅝"
TUB LENGTH 22¼"
TUB DEPTH 14"
LEGS 2⅝" × ¾" × 25"

WOODEN LEG, PAINTED BLACK

Fig. 9-50. The James Washer.

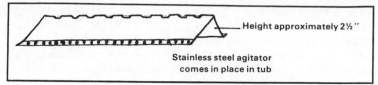

Height approximately 2½″

Stainless steel agitator
comes in place in tub

Fig. 9-51. The agitator can be operated easily with one hand.

The man and his wife had been using James Washers for many years. They had replaced them as they rusted out (that was when they were made of plain galvanized metal). In 1971 the washers were being made with stainless steel tubs and the Delawarians recommended one. The main also happened to be a James Washer dealer.

The Machine Arrives

The Flaggs finally sent off their order with some worry, but hoped for the best. (The last letter from the Eden Metal Company didn't inspire confidence. They refused to answer any more questions, but said if 120,000 satisfied customers weren't good enough for the Flaggs then just forget it!)

When the carton arrived and was unpacked, the Flaggs were dismayed. The legs had been poorly packed in the tub and had dented it. Also, the seams of the tub appeared to be poorly soldered. They assembled the machine (an easy job) and filled it with water, expecting the worst. To their surprise it held water without leaking! It did a good job of washing the clothes. The legs were plenty sturdy, too.

Doing the Weekly Wash

When Gale gets ready to do the weekly wash, she doesn't plug in an electric cord. She just moves the James Washer a couple of yards from its spring-summer-fall home under a big spruce tree (Fig. 9-52). (The legs rest on flat rocks to forestall rotting.) She sets it under the hand pump that brings very cold water from the brook. You can use hot water, if it's available.

She uses Cold Power for a detergent. One cup of detergent is enough for a full tub. She adds about three-quarters of a cup right away for the first couple of loads and adds the rest when she gets to the really dirty stuff. Then she pumps water directly into the wash tub—15 gallons according to the brochure, 100 strokes with the hand pump. If you have only a few items to wash, you need only enough water to float them.

The sheets get done first. Although the brochure claims the machine will take four to six sheets at once, they must mean mini-sheets. Gale finds one king or queen-size sheet is all she wants in there at a time, plus a few smaller articles, such as pillow cases and napkins. Next she does white underwear, followed by other light-colored articles, then colored pieces, and finally work clothes and socks. In most seasons she does all this with one cup of detergent and one load of water.

276

To do the actual washing, she needs only to move the agitator handle back and forth. She sets a timer and begins: four minutes for lightly soiled items; up to 10 minutes for dirty work clothes. If the clothes are very dirty, she may add another one-quarter cup of detergent. As the time goes by, she watches the birds, butterflies, the sky and thoroughly enjoys herself.

You can purchase a wringer with the washer, if you wish. If you already have one, that will do. When the wringer is attached, the handle is a bit low, as are the clothes in the tub. Gale finds it easiest on her back to kneel or sit on a low stool or overturned pail. It also helps to have a forked hardwood stick to fish out the clothes.

When the wash is all done, the water is drained through a valve at the bottom of the tub (the faucet is threaded so a hose can be attached for indoor use). Then the tub is rinsed and refilled with more cold water for the rinsing process. The brochure says a few strokes on the handle and the clothes are rinsed clean. Gales finds that about 30 strokes on the handle are most effective. Sometimes one tub of water rinses the whole wash. In mud season and after plowing with the horse, more rinses are needed.

Saving Energy

The James Washer saves energy. It doesn't use a speck of electricity and doesn't tire out the laundress either. It takes Gale two to two and a half hours from start to finish for a week's wash, including sorting and hanging out.

When cold weather and snow come early in November, the washer comes back into the house. It has its own special corner. On wash day Gale moves it to the center of the room (easy to do—it weighs less than 25 pounds, maybe 35 pounds with the wringer). Then it takes four pails of water for washing and another four for rinsing. That's about 25 to 30 gallons in all. (A week's wash for two uses about 100 gallons in an electric washing machine.) While she operates the agitator handle with one hand, she reads a book or magazine placed on a high stool.

The washer does as good a job as the laundromat and maybe better. You can keep an eye on spots and stains and rub a little detergent into them if they aren't coming out.

Fig. 9-52. Gayle Flagg does the laundry in her outdoor washroom.

Problems

The machine's agitator had some rough rivets that caught a few threads on more delicate clothing. If you find rough edges on your agitator, smooth them with a file. It did the trick for Gale.

The plastic handle for regulating the wringer pressure cracked and broke off. Gale hasn't solved that problem yet.

The handle of the agitator moves back and forth in a slot cut in the metal. If you go too far, the handle will hit the metal and cause a dent that might develop into a tear. Gale has gone too far many times when her attention has been caught by a soaring hawk or a butterfly landing on her arm. No dire thing has happened, but she means to add some wooden or rubber stops someday. You might do that first if the new galvanized fiberglassed tubs appear to have that weakness.

The James Washer is available for $86.45 and its optional wringer for $32.90 from Countryside, Highway 19 East, Waterloo, WI 53594. Wisconsin residents should add 4 percent sales tax.

MAKE A HAND-OPERATED WASHING MACHINE

After eight years of hauling clothes to the laundromat and spending $5 or $6 once there, Herbert Huff's wife decided it was time to get her own washing machine. The thought of another noisy appliance, which would undoubtedly add several dollars a month to the electric bill, didn't appeal to the Huffs. It seemed that the best choice for the energy-conscious Huffs was a hand-powered washing machine (Fig. 9-53).

They heard about the James Washer, but never managed to save up enough money to buy one. When Huff found a wringer at a barn sale for only $3, he decided right then to build his own washer.

The washer is built from ½" exterior grade plywood (good on one side) coated with fiber glass on the inside (Fig. 9-54). Using all new materials except the agitator and ¼" dowel, the total cost of the washer was $38.84. Not bad considering a James Washer costs around $100, plus another $50 or $60 for the wringer.

Building the Washer

The only problem with using plywood is that it's usually warped. Any warped parts in the tub sides or ends are going to make the whole thing

Fig. 9-53. The hand-powered washing machine (photo by Herbert Huff).

Fig. 9-54. The washer is built from exterior plywood, coated with fiberglass on the inside (photo by Herbert Huff).

deformed, and certain parts won't fit properly. For this reason, top, bottom, and agitator support covers should be "custom cut" rather than cut in advance. Take measurements for each part as you go along, and you'll have tight fitting parts that look good. See Table 9-3.

Start by cutting the sides and ends from ½" plywood. Join them by inserting three triangular-shaped wooden wedges in each corner. Drill two small holes through the plywood and wedge and join all three parts together with #10 wood screws 1" long. Huff made his own wedges each 2" long, by cutting a 2 × 2 diagonally.

Tip the bottom (small side) up, measure 2" from the bottom edge in several places, and draw a line all the way around the inside. Take eight more wedges, line them up on the mark, and attach them with one screw each. These blocks will serve as a support for the bottom.

Make sure the four sides are square and, in several places, measure the area where the bottom will sit. Cut and install the bottom, and attach it with four screws. Don't worry about cracks between the bottom and sides—you can fill them in with fiber glass later.

Next, take the 2 × 4s and cut the legs. Huff used a wood rasp to round off the corners on his. Draw a line down the center of the end panels, and place the legs at the most comfortable height for the operator. Once you

Table 9-3. Materials List for the Hand-Operated Washer.

½", exterior grade plywood-		
	4½×4'	$9.00
1	1⅛" dowel 2½' long	.85
1	8' long 2×2	.99
1	8' long 2×4	1.50
50 wood screws		1.85
1 faucet		2.75
12	¼" bolts, nuts, washers	2.00
1 faucet nut		.20
2 quarts fiber glass resin		10.35
1 package fiber glass cloth		
	(8 square feet)	3.35
1 used wringer		3.00
¼" dowel		——
rubber mud flap		——
scrounged stain and Varithane		——
1	5" long, ¼" bolt	——
		Total $35.84

279

have the legs lined up, trace around them with a pencil, Take one leg at a time and drill three ¼" holes in each one. Stagger the holes so the wood won't split. Attach the legs with ¼" carriage bolts 2¼" long, washers and nuts.

Using Fiber Glass

To waterproof the inside of the tub, you'll need 2 quarts of fiber glass resin which can be bought at auto paint supply stores and one package of fiber glass cloth measuring 8 square feet. The cloth should be used all around the bottom and on all corners. The rest of the tub can be coated with resin alone.

Before you start laying down cloth, fill in all the gaps between the corner blocks and the crack around the bottom. You can buy thick fiber glass mat for this job. Huff had good luck using recycled fiber glass insulation. Just tear off some insulation, thoroughly saturate it with resin, and push it into the crack with your fingers.

This is a good time to tell you how to get fiber glass resin off your hands. Lacquer thinner works great. but go easy with it. Your skin might be sensitive to it. If so, wipe off the excess with a rag you're not fond of and wash with Lava or another abrasive-type soap.

While you're waiting for the fillers to dry, drill a 13/16" hole in the bottom for the drain faucet. Locate the hole dead center and about 2" from the end panel. Once the filler is dry, cut a piece of fiber glass cloth big enough to cover the bottom with an extra 2" all the way around.

Hold the cloth in place with thumbtacks, removing them before the glass sets. Using a razor blade, cut out the cloth covering the drain hole. Mix up a batch of resin and smear some on the threads of the drain spout. Pour some resin around the hole where the nut will set. Push the faucet through the hole, tighten down the nut, and pour resin all around the nut.

Before you coat the rest of the cloth, add a bit of lacquer thinner to the resin. This thinned resin will soak right through the cloth and saturate it completely. Now cut out four 4" wide strips, long enough to run from top to bottom, for the corners. Tack them down and coat them with thinned resin, also.

After the glass has dried, take a piece of window screen 3" square, place it over the drain opening, and tack it down at each corner. Mix up a batch of resin (don't thin it). Pour it over the outer edge of the screen until the screen is covered. Use a piece of cloth to apply the rest of the resin. Put about three coats of resin on the interior and check for water leaks.

The Agitator

Huff made the agitator from a piece of rubber mud flap that he recycled from a school bus. Cut it to measure 9½" wide and 8" high. He used four wood screws and ¼" washers to attach this to a 2½' long, 1⅛" dowel. A plywood agitator coated with resin could be used, but a rubber one will bend when it hits a wad of clothes.

The agitator supports were made from 2 × 2s. First, Huff cut one piece

16½" long for the cross piece. The ends were cut on a slight angle to fit the tub sides. The other two pieces were cut 5½" long. Huff managed to scrounge up 4" of ⅜" dowel. He drilled holes in it and used it to join the long and short pieces of the supports.

Next, Huff drilled a ¼" hole through the short 2 ×2 s and another one through the 1⅛" dowel. After reaming out the dowel hole a little, he coated the inside of the hole with several coats of fiber glass resin to act as a waterproof bushing. He attached the agitator and support to the tub with four wood screws.

The Cover

A 15½" × 2¼" piece of plywood attached with two wood screws to the inside of the tub serves as a lid and wringer support. Like the agitator support and the rear lid support, it should be ½" from the top edge of the tub so the lid will set evenly. He measured from the front lid support back to half the distance of the agitator cross support so the lid would rest on the first half of the 2 × 2. Then he cut out a lid and made a notch on each side for the wringer.

Next, he measured and cut two plywood squares to cover up the other half of the cross support and the short agitator supports. Each piece was drilled and installed with two wood screws. A scrap of 2 × 2 attached with two wood screws made a handle for the lid.

Finish

To finish off the washer, Huff sanded down the rough spots and applied two coats of Black Walnut stain. Once it was dry, he applied two coats of high gloss Varithane. The wringer also got a coat of paint and Varithane.

Washing Clothes

Washing clothes is an outside job juring the summer months. Huff's wife simply pulls the washer out of the garage, fills it with water, and gives each load 10 to 15 minutes of agitation. Some folks might think that operating a hand-powered washing machine is an awful lot of work, but Huff's wife will tell you otherwise. She's convinced that loading and unloading clothes, fighting her way through traffic, and spending two hours in a laundromat with a humidity factor not unlike a tropical rain forest is much more strenuous than staying at home and washing by hand (Fig. 9-55).

USEFUL WAGON

You can pull this wagon with a small Cadet type tractor or the Ford 8N. It's larger than the small metal carts you buy for a suburban lawn, but smaller than a hay wagon. Use it to haul hay, firewood, grass, leaves and logs. Lambs and pigs can be moved to different areas. Fertilizer, seed and the ever necessary tools can be taken down to the field being planted. Even large items can be moved by taking out any one or all of the sides. With all sides in place and the four hooks and eyes closed, it's even good to take a group of small children for a ride.

Fig. 9-55. Washing is an outside job done on the porch in the summer. It's not a lot of work—easier than going to the laundromat, these home-steaders say.

This wagon is not heavy and is easy to unhitch and maneuver. The wheels are sturdy enough for heavy loads and for stability. They use 4.80-4.00 tires (available at Sears) supported by a ½" metal rod (Fig. 9-56).

NEW LOW PROFILE 18 HP POWER KING TRACTOR

Power King 18 hp garden tractors are now offered with 16" rear wheels to provide lower center of gravity and greater stability on earth and snow removal work (Fig. 9-57). Previously offered only with 24" wheels, the new model 1618 may be equipped with 7.50-16 or 9.50-16 lug-type tires, or with 8.00-16 lawn tires. Model 1618 is ideal for use with Power King 1/3-ton front loader, with dozer, snowplow, lawn mowers, and all other attachments and implements when a 16" frame clearance is adequate. Power King's model 2418 provides a whopping 19" cultivating clearance; 12 hp and 14 hp high-clearance models are also offered.

The new model employs Power King's standard all-gear drive, reported to deliver near 100 percent of engine horsepower to the wheels. This is said to be an energy-conserving drive train since more work can be done with each gallon of gasoline. All Power King models are available with manual or hydraulic lift, and three-point hitch for rear implements. Over 20 attachments include 48" and 60" rotary mowers, rotary tiller, 42" and 48" snow blowers, and log splitter.

For additional information, contact William F. Reeder, Sales Manager, Engineering Products Company, P.O. Box 1510 E. Ellis St., Waukesha, WI 53187.

"SIAMESE" FARMALL IS NOT A HOAX

Clyde Wishart's "Siamese" Farmall "D" tractor is a hard-working curiosity. It is not a toy or a hoax, but has advantages that cannot be found in factory-built tractors (Fig. 9-58).

The Farmall "D" is built from a Farmall "A" and a "B". The "A" is built offset for cultivating purposes and is called a one-row tractor. The "B" is a two-row machine. A Farmall "D" can be made from these two machines in most average home shops.

282

By removing the right final drive from the "A" and placing the complete transmission, center housing and engine from the "B," the tractor becomes 8½" wider than normal. By modifying the drawbar from the "B" and building connective supports at the bell housing and from the axle area, you form the Siamese tractor. Wishart has modified the differential so the "D" can be run on both engines or one.

Why run two engines? When haying, the left engine is used to propel the Hesston PT-7 mower conditioner and the baler. The right engine is used for the exact ground speed needed during haying. Total, these engines give us up to 34 horsepower.

When picking up hay, raking or doing other similar chores, Wishart uses only the right engine for minimum power and fuel use. On the manure spreader he uses both combinations, depending on the weight of the load.

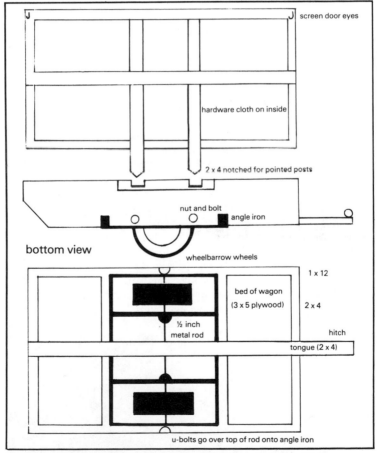

Fig. 9-56. The wagon is used to haul hay, firewood, and other items.

Fig. 9-57. The Power King 18 hp garden tractor.

One nice thing about the Farmall "D" is that Wishart only has about $1300 invested in it. He bought the "A" in 1954 for $800. The othe tractor and the machine shop work cost about $500. In about 3 hours, he can remove the Siamese section and restore the "A" to its original form.

CARE OF THE HOMESTEAD TRACTOR

This is a section about keeping after old tractors. Don't expect something that's going to read like a page from a John Deere service manual.

Most countrysiders are pushing tractors that look like they were made before Gutenberg's first press, and that makes finding service manuals difficult. In addition, the idea of a step-by-step book telling us how to care for machines is a bit alien to our total lifestyle. We know the old tractor needs attention once in awhile, but our approach to this fact of life gets somewhat philosophical.

That old tractor in the barn is just another inhabitant of the farm, sharing space with the goats and the pony. Like the livestock, it needs and gets shelter, feeding, grooming and love—enough of each to keep it going, and the best of each that can be given at a reasonable cost (Fig. 9-59 and 9-60). What we plan on doing here is to show you how to disperse just the right amount of such attention. Because springtime is coming up, we'll concentrate on warm weather care right now.

Like any animal on your farm, that mechanical animal can use a good bath towards the end of winter. This is particularly true if you've been using it to plow the driveway and haul firewood. A stored tractor collects dirt, too.

Dirt is as much the tractor's enemy as it is to man or beast. Grease and grime can make the machine overheat, with a clogged radiator being the biggest problem. The dirt can also act like an insulator, keeping too much

Fig. 9-58. Clyde Wishart, of Burnham, Maine, built this "Siamese" tractor.

Fig. 9-59. Small, old tractors can serve the homestead well, with proper "care and feeding," as Dave Belanger demonstrates.

heat inside the motor block. Dirty electrical wires can cause carbon tracking and short circuits (Fig. 9-61). This will rob power, waste fuel, and even cause fires.

Hand cleaning is the cheapest way to get rid of chunky dirt. Use a paint scraper or wire brush to do the scraping. In the old days a lot of farmers used rags soaked in gasoline or kerosene for breaking up stubborn grime. This is very dangerous and is not a good way to go today. Besides, gasoline is pretty expensive. A spray-on auto engine cleaner will do the job better and faster. Just apply such a solvent per can label instructions and allow it to

Fig. 9-60. Most homesteaders use older, smaller machines, and home maintenance is a necessary skill. John Gunnell took this picture of a retired Eagle tractor.

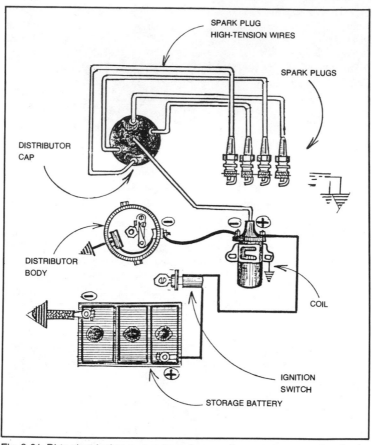

Fig. 9-61. Dirty electrical components and connections can cause carbon tracking, short circuits or even a fire. All items shown in sketch should be thoroughly cleaned.

soak into the dirt. While it's soaking in, use some plastic wrap to cover the wires and electrical connections. Now hose the tractor down real good.

Final grooming will include painting bare metal spots so that surface rust won't form. Heavy-duty enamels will do a good job. Even better are the new polyurethane paints used by manufacturers of trucks and tractors. A repaint with such finishes will last as long as the tractor does, but there are dangers involved in their use. Stick to enamels for now. Using the modern "super paints" is another story.

So much for grooming. Food and drink come next. Tractors eat gasoline (or other fuels) and drink oil and water (antifreeze in winter). Your animals probably get fed and watered twice a day. Once a day will do for a tractor that sees regular use. Tractors are less fussy than the goats or rabbits, but more so than your pickup or family car.

To ready the machine for springtime use, there are feeding considerations. The tractor should have been stored for the winter with a full tank of gas to prevent the icing up of condensation in the tank. This fuel should still be good, but top it off with a can of dry gas or "heet." Inspect the water level in the radiator and the battery. Both should be filled to within sight of the filler rims, but not quite to the top. You should drain your old oil or storage oil out of the crankcase. Install a new oil filter and add fresh lubricant until the dipstick reads close to full. Next, place a few drops of lightweight 3-in-1 oil in the reservoir on the generator to keep the bearings lubricated.

After the weather breaks and you get the tractor out in the fields, you should keep a feeding record for it. Jot down the number of hours that it is operated each day. The level of oil in the crankcase should be checked by a dipstick reading after every 10 hours of use. The water levels for the radiator and battery bear inspection every 20-60 hours, on the average. Oil should be changed after 200 hours of operation, or sooner if it gets real dirty.

A tractor has to breathe right, too, especially in the spring when it sees heavy use. If your goats aren't breathing right, you'd sure look for the reason and the same should go for the tractor, too. The internal combustion engine is basically a pump that sucks in air at the carburetor and passes it out the oil breather tube. This means the carburetor must be adjusted to admit the right amount of air, while the breather tube cap must be clean enough to let the old air out.

Luckily, the carburetor on most old tractors is a simple device to mess around with. This is done by twisting two screws either in or out (Fig. 9-62). One controls the amount of incoming air, and the other regulates the speed at which the engine spins. You can test to see if you already have a good adjustment by taking the tractor out in the field and suddenly pulling the hand throttle (speed control) wide open while driving up a grade. If the engine picks up speed quickly and smoothly, everything is okay. If you feel or hear skipping and coughing, back off the air control screw just a fraction of a turn. Keep testing the tractor and adjusting the screw until things seem just right.

When the carburetor is set just right, you should remove the cap on the oil breather tube for cleaning. There will be a filter element inside the cap. It can be cleaned by dipping the entire cap in a container filled with clean paint thinner. Do not bring heat, flame, or a cigarette near the container, as the thinner will be flammable.

With this kind of basic care and feeding, plus a bit of fresh grease in the transmission case, the majority of old tractors used by small farmers will give years of trouble-free service. Even such things as tuneups, carbon-and-valve jobs, clutch installations, and electrical repairs can be handled on the small farm, without professional help.

To keep an old-fashioned tractor running right, a lot of regular feeding and care is required. Such attention should be dispensed on a regular schedule. Tractors need more care than your truck or car. Your service

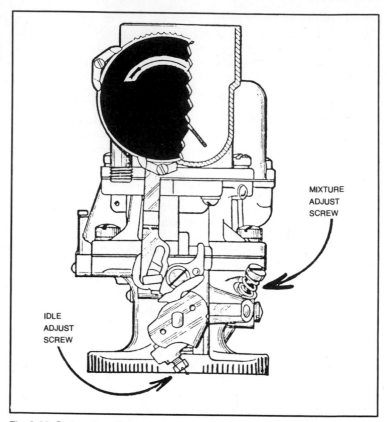

Fig. 9-62. Carburetor adjustments on your tractor are similar to those on your car or pickup. Adjust mixture screw first, idle speed later.

schedule should be set up on an hours of operation basis, much like airline mechanics use.

After every 10 hours of operation, wash the air cleaner, and top screen filling the reservoir with fresh oil (Fig. 9-63). Apply grease to all fittings. Check the dipstick oil level. Inspect the radiator water level. Clean the oil breather tube cap. Check the operation of the fuel filter, and check tire inflation pressures with a tire gauge.

After every 30 hours of operation, clean the battery and check its water level. Grease the front wheel bearings. Examine the tractor for loose nuts and bolts. Clean the radiator tubing.

After every 100 hours of operation, check transmission and gear oil (change very 600 hours).Change the oil. Install a new oil filter. Put light oil into generator filler—a few drops. Drain and flush the radiator and cooling system (Fig. 9-64). Clean and regap spark plugs. Dress ignition points and thoroughly inspect tires for cuts.

SPRING TRACTOR TUNEUP

The success of any small-scale farming operation is directly related to how well the tractor is maintained. If you're planning to kick up some dust this spring, you may want to give some attention to your ancient machine's powerplant. Tractors should be serviced in the spring, whether or not they are used throughout winter.

We're sure that most tractor owners can see the logic behind tuning the motor of a machine that's seen wintertime use. The cold weather takes its toll on man, machine, and beast alike. With mechanical things critical parts that turn, twist, or move in any way need adjusting or tuning up. In

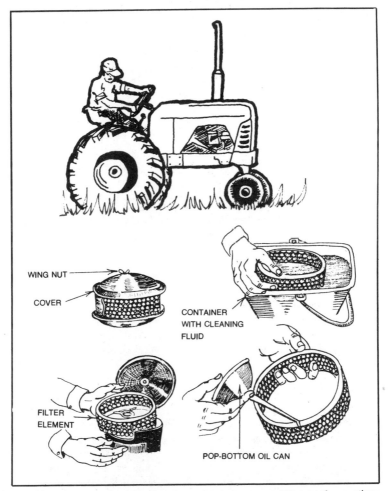

WING NUT

COVER

CONTAINER
WITH CLEANING
FLUID

FILTER
ELEMENT

POP-BOTTOM OIL CAN

Fig. 9-63. The air cleaner on a tractor needs service every 10 hours of operation: That could easily mean 4-5 times a week in the spring.

Fig. 9-64. The radiator on your tractor should be flushed frequently, after 100-250 hours of operation. Low cost plastic flushing guns are available for this purpose at most automotive jobber outlets.

addition, various components in the cooling or electrical system will be wearing thin and needing replacement. Machine designers make allowances for this by making such parts relatively simple and cheap to replace. Why should a tractor that's been stored inside need fixing, too?

It won't if you've had it in a heated barn that's totally dustfree and humidity-controlled. This, however, isn't the common case. A tractor that's simply setting in a normal storage area can collect condensation in the gas tank, dust and dirt around electrical parts, a light trace of rust here and there and some moisture where none should be. In addition, the cold can cause chemicals in the oil and antifreeze to undergo some strange reactions. Rubber parts, like hoses and wires, may freeze, dry out, or start to fall apart.

Any motor that runs on volatile fuels is basically a pump. Your tractor motor pumps in air which is passed to cylinders (usually four) where the air gets mixed with gasoline and compressed by a piston. The compacted air/gas mixture takes an electric spark from the spark plugs. This causes an explosive reaction which is used to spin a crankshaft. The spinning action goes back through the gearbox, where it's multiplied and passed to a differential (split gear) that converts it into movement of the rear wheels.

The whole operation is kind of simple, except that a good deal of proper coordination is needed to put the forces to work. For example, the air is admitted to the cylinders by valves which work much the same way as the damper on your airtight wood stove. If you don't use your stove damper properly, some smoke is going to leak out of the stove. If the valves in the motor don't open and close correctly, the air/gas mixture will leak past the piston. You waste energy in both cases. With the stove you'll lose heat and waste a good chunk of black oak. With the tractor you'll waste gas and lose lots of power. If the leakage is bad enough, the motor won't even run.

This kind of coordination is required from other systems in the power train, too. For example, the electrical contact points are really a type of switch designed to control the strength of the spark that gets things popping. A little moisture on the points will result in a weakened spark and a small explosion. Power and gas will be wasted. Dirty electrical wires, leaky pistons, contaminated fuel, improperly adjusted carburetors, and dirty spark plugs can all throw your tractor off kilter.

Everything we've covered so far is the same with your car or truck, as it is with the tractor. So why not just take the old farm machine to the village service station and pay to have it tuned up there? We can give you a few reasons:

- ☐ It may be a long way to go in a tractor.
- ☐ It will be cheaper to do it yourself.
- ☐ The tractor will need repeated service.
- ☐ Obsolete parts and specifications may be hard to get.
- ☐ It's totally against the concept of the self-sufficient farm.

Tractors are easy to service at home. Repairs on cars and trucks are sometimes best left to the professional mechanic because he has special tools that can help him reach where you can't with common hand tools. It's cheaper to have him do the job than to buy all the tools you would need.

This is not the case with an old tractor. Since the motor sits practically out in the open and high up off the ground, you can reach almost every nut and bolt with normal wrenches and screwdrivers. Also, you won't need a $200 hydraulic jack to get beneath the tractor motor. Tractors were designed to be cared for right on the farm. It's almost natural to do things yourself in this case.

Basic springtime tractor motor service will include:

- ☐ Dressing or replacing the contact points.
- ☐ Greasing the magneto or distributor.
- ☐ Cleaning all battery and electrical connections.
- ☐ Checking the condition of spark plug wires.
- ☐ Regapping and cleaning or replacing spark plugs.
- ☐ Cleaning the fuel filter sediment bowl.
- ☐ Draining and renewing antifreeze or coolant.
- ☐ Checking all hoses.
- ☐ Adjusting drive belt tensions.
- ☐ Cleaning distributor cap towers.

All 10 steps are clearly illustrated in Figs. 9-65 through 9-73 and Table 9-4. We have also provided a list of the recommended spark plug applica-

model	spark plug	gap
ALLIS-CHALMERS		
TRACTORS		
Gasoline		
B, C, CA, D-14, G, 1B	J8 /UJ8	.030
RC, S, WC, WD, WF, WS, D17 (⅜" Reach)	J8 /UJ8	.030
D-10, D-15, H-3	J7	.025
D-12, D-15 Series II	J10Y	.025
D-17 (¾" Reach)	N11Y	0.25
D-19	N8	.025
H-4 Crawler, 170, 180, 190, 190 XT	N6	.025
A, E(20-35), E(25-40), 1U, K, L, M, U	W10	.030
WK, WM: Monarch 35 and 40	W10	.030
Grader 42 and 54, UC	W10	.30
UC (14mm Heads)	J11	.030
WD-45	J12Y	.025
GT-25, GT-30	D16 /UD16	.025
CASE		
TRACTORS		
Gasoline		
D Series, LA Series, (18mm Heads)	D15Y	.025
430, 431, 435, 440, 441, 445, 470	D16 /UD16	.025
530, 531, 535, 540, 541, 545, 570, 610	D16 /UD16	.025
730, 731, 732, 733, 734, 740	D16	.025
741, 742, 743, 744, 770	D16	.025
830, 831, 832, 833, 840, 841	D16	.025
842, 843, 870, 910, 930, 970	D16	.025
Series C, D, L, LA, R (⅞" Heads)	W14	.030
LH and LAH Diesel	K97F	.025
JOHN DEERE		
TRACTORS		
Gasoline (18mm Heads)		
A, AR-AO, B, G, H	D16 /UD16	.030
50, 60, 70, 520, 530	D16	.030
620, 630, 720, 730	D16	.030
3010, 3020, 4000, 4010	D14	.025
4020, 4230	D14	.025
Gasoline (14mm Heads)		
L, LA-LI, M, 40, 320, 330	H10	.025
420, 430, 440, 1010, 2010	H10	.025
1020, 1520, 2020, 2030, 2510, 2520	N11Y	.025
4030	N11Y	.025
FE-1	N12Y	.025
Gasoline (⅞" Heads)		
A, AR-AO, B, BR-BO, D, G	W18	.030
L Series	W14	.025
FORD		
TRACTORS		
1975-78 104 CID	RN10Y	.035
1975-78 158, 175, 201, 256 CID	N8	.035

Table 9-4. Chart Shows Champion Spark Plug Applications and Electrode Gap Measurements for Popular Farm Tractors (courtesy Champion Spark Plug Co., Toledo, Ohio).

model	spark plug	gap
1965-77 (3&4 Cyl.).....................................N8		.025
1961-67 6-Cyl. Gasoline............................F9Y		.030
1961-67 6-Cyl. LP-gas...............................F10		.020
1952-64 4-Cyl. Gasoline.............................H11		.030
1952-64 4-Cyl. LP-gas................................H8		.020
1958-62 Diesel Models AG3		— —

INTERNATIONAL
WHEEL TRACTORS
Gasoline and LP-gas (See Note Below)

model	spark plug	gap
Cub, Cub Lo-Boy, 154, 184, 185 Lo-Boy..............D15Y		.025
Series A, A-1, AV, AV-1, B, BN, C D15Y		.025
H, HV, M, M-TA, M-TAV, MV, O-4..........................D15Y		.025
OS-4, O-6, OS-6, W4, W6, W6TA.......................D15Y		.025
100, 130, 140, 140HC, 200, 230, 240 ....D15Y		.025
300, 330, 340, 350, 400, 404, 424....................D15Y		.025
444, 450, 453, 454, 460, 464, 504....................D15Y		.025
544, 560, 574, 606, 656, 660, 674....................D15Y		.025
706, 756, 766, 806, 826, 856........................D15Y		.025
2400, 2405, 2410, 2412, 2424, 2444...................D15Y		.025
2500, 2504, 2510, 2514, 2544 ....D15Y		.025
2606, 2656, 2707, 2756, 2806, 2856..................D15Y		.025
3400, 3500, 3514, 3616, 3800, 3850..................D15Y		.025
I-666, I-666 Hydro D15Y		.025
I-686, I-686 Hydro D15Y		.025
284...N12Y		.025

MASSEY-FERGUSON
TRACTORS

model	spark plug	gap
MF180, MF175, MF265 w /Perkins AG4-236...J8 /UJ8		.025
MF165, MF255 w /Perkins AG4-212 ....J8 /UJ8		.025
MF135, MF150 w /Perkins AG3-152 (⅜″ Rch.) J8 /UJ8		.025
MF135, MF150 w /Perkins AG3-152 (¾″ Rch.) ...N12Y		.025
MF230, MF235, MF245 w /Cont. Z145 ....RD14		.025
MF175-180 w /Cont. G-206.....................................D16		.025
MF175-180 w /Cont. GB-206 ....D14		.025
MF165 w /Cont. G-176...D16		.025
MF165 w /Cont. GB-176 (LP-gas) D14		.025
MF135 Special w /Cont. Z-134 ....D16		.025
MF135 Deluxe & Vineyard, w /Cont. Z-145............D16		.025
MF1100 w /Wauk. F-320G......................................D14		.025
MF1100 w /Wauk. F-320G (LP-gas)................D10 /D9		.020
11 Pony, 16 Pacer, 21 Colt, 22, 22K, 23 ....D16		.025
23K, 30, 30K, 33, TE20, TO35, F35, MF35...........D16		.025
F40, 44 Special, 333, 444, 555 ....D16		.025
44, 55, MF50, MF65, MF85, MF88, MF90.............D16		.025
TO20, TO30, 203, 101 Jr., 102 Jr........................D16		.025
PA, CH, 25...W14		.025
44 Special, 333, 444, 555 (LP-gas)......................D14		.020
97 (LP-gas) D9		.020
TEA20...L10		.025

**After Eng. 152UA15061A

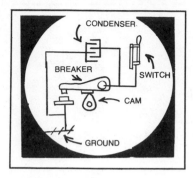

Fig. 9-65. Contact breaker points are actually an electrical switch and must be kept clean with a file made for the purpose.

tions for older model tractors. All 10 operations should be considered in addition to the cleaning procedures.

FACTORS THAT DETERMINE USED EQUIPMENT PRICES

Here are the 10 factors that determine market prices for used tractors and farm equipment, according to *Marshall's Farm Equipment Guide.*

Age

The age of a given tractor or other farm machine is by far the main consideration in establishing the market price. An older unit is obviously less valuable than a newer machine of the same make and model. The difference is not always as great (or as small) as one might expect. In many cases improvements are made by the manufacturer during the course of a model run without changing the model designation, and machines which incorporate the change or improvement may be considerably higher priced on the used market than models of the immediately preceding year which do not have it. Also, a certain amount of deterioration takes place in the condition of a machine strictly on account of age, whether it is operated or not. Deterioration in rubber tires, belts, hoses and even presealed bearings are examples.

Mechanical Condition

The basic mechanical condition of a machine is often the major consideration, especially in the case of older models which may or may not be

Fig. 9-66. Tractor drive belts should not be worn or weathered and should be tight enough that normal pressure induces no more than ¾" deflection from straight dotted line.

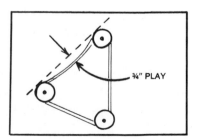

¾" PLAY

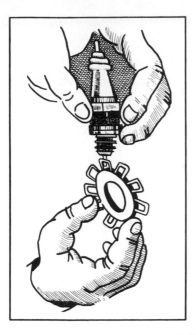

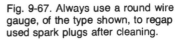

Fig. 9-67. Always use a round wire gauge, of the type shown, to regap used spark plugs after cleaning.

economical to repair and overhaul. Determining mechanical condition is sometimes difficult. The buyer should take all the time needed to satisfy himself as to the unit's overall mechanical shape. In the same way, a recent major overhaul can add considerably to the market value of a used tractor or other machine, especially if the extent and cost of the work can be readily and accurately established, and the work was performed by a reputable shop.

Hours of Use

Most motorized farm machines and virtually all farm tractors built in the last 10 to 15 years are factory-equipped with hour meters which record

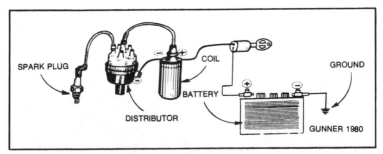

Fig. 9-68. All electrical connections shown must be shiny clean. Wire brushes, sandpaper, or file can be used.

Fig. 9-69. Distributor cap towers can be cleaned by clamping small pieces of steel wool into a cotter pin with a nail through eye.

the elapsed time during which the engine has been operated. Unless such meters have been tampered with, the hour meter reading is an excellent indication of the amount of useful service life left in the machine. Basically, the buyer of a piece of used farm equipment or a tractor is actually buying the unused service life remaining.

Maintenance

For any experienced tractor or farm machine owner-operator, it is usually not difficult to determine how well (or how poorly) a used farm machine has been maintained by its previous owner or owners. Under good maintenance and with careful operation, the useful service life of any farm machine is greatly extended. Equipment that has obviously been well looked after and carefully operated always commands a premium price. Another important consideration is the storage of the machine during the off seasons. Equipment that has been stored under cover when not in use is generally in better condition and has a better appearance, and thus usually sells for a better price.

Size and Capacity

Since the late 1960s there has been a definite and steady increase in the size, power, and capacity of most farm machines. This has been the

Fig. 9-70. Homemade battery cleaner can be fashioned by inserting broken file blades deep into a rubber bottle stop. Commercial tools for battery cleaning are also cheap and available.

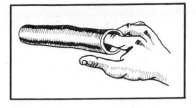

Fig. 9-71. Check the inside of rubber hoses, as well as inspecting the outside. If any deterioration is noted, replace the hose.

response of tractor and equipment manufacturers to the steady growth in farm size and the shortage of farm labor. Thus, it is often found that used machines in the largest size and model categories have retained more of their original value and are in greater demand by buyers than smaller models of similar age. Premium prices especially are paid for the largest combine models, even those as old as 15 years, and their larger size and capacity is the main reason. The same effect sometimes works in reverse: in most parts of the country the demand for small utility tractors exceeds the supply. Their prices hold up extremely well over time.

New Machine Prices

The current list price for new equipment is an important factor in the value of used machines, especially late model units. It is not at all uncommon for current model used units to actually rise in market value as the price of comparable new units increases. This is, a less prominent factor in the case of older units (about five years old and older).

Fuel Type

Diesel-powered tractors and equipment such as self-propelled combines appear to be rising in market value as fuel prices increase, because of the obvious operating-cost advantages. It is also possible that with increases in on-farm fuel alcohol production the value of spark ignition-engined used equipment will stabilize, or might even increase in some

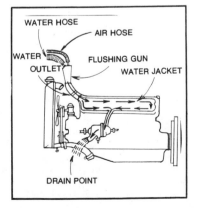

Fig. 9-72. Cooling system must be flushed and refilled with new coolant during spring service. Tractors see long use on hot summer days, so the cooling system must be in top condition.

cases. There have been cases also where premium prices have been paid for LP-gas powered tractors and combines in parts of the country where LP supplies are plentiful.

Optional Equipment and Attachments

Well-equipped used tractors and other equipment have always been more in demand than simpler, "stripped" units of the same make, age, model, and condition. This is especially true in the case of such features (formerly options but now more or less standard equipment) as air-conditioned operator cabs, power-shift transmissions and hydrostatic traction drive for harvester combines.

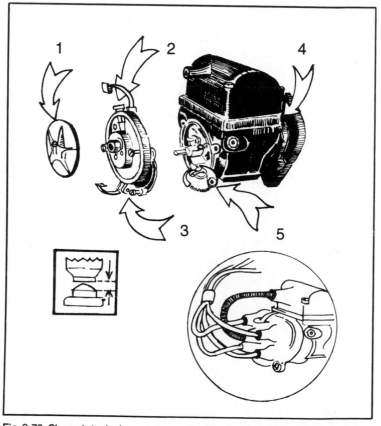

Fig. 9-73. Shown is typical magneto construction on circa-1955 tractor. Parts are (1) distributor rotor, (2) oil cup, (3) distributor body, (4) oil cup, and (5) breaker points. Oil goes in both cups, light grease on breaker pivot. Square insert shows how to dress contact points with one contact crowned. The primary wire (shaded) in round insert must be tight in distributor nipple and magneto nipple. Tape plug wires together as shown.

Popularity

Not all tractors and machines depreciate at the same rate relative to new price: some makes are simply more popular than others, both in the new and used markets. Brand popularity varies in different parts of the nation, but in general machines of the most popular makes are in greater demand and tend to get consistently higher prices than less popular makes.

Changing Farm Practices

Occasionally used equipment values are affected by changes in basic form practices, such as the conversion from corn picker husking to combining. New techniques sometimes do not "catch on" the way they were expected to, and equipment for these may depreciate rapidly in value. Major changes may be coming in planting and tillage practices because of fuel and energy costs and may affect used equipment values in the future.

Chapter 10

Wood

Trees are a valuable and versatile resource for the homestead. Find out how to make your own lumber, use waste driftwood, cure green wood, utilize cull trees, manage a woodlot, and cut and sell firewood.

MAKING LUMBER

Do you have a tree that you'd like someone to make into lumber? It's sad when a tall, straight pine or a lovely maple must be cut to make room for a garden or a building. If this tree can be turned into lumber and the waste part into firewood, it can be rewarding as well. If you live near Baker, Oregon, the thing to do is to have Sam Champie and his chain sawmill make the transformation (Figs. 10-1 and 10-2).

Rugged lumberman, skilled craftsman, carpenter, and home-steader—Sam has found the perfect tool to combine his many roles. A Swedish Husqvarna chain saw with an Alaskan Jr. chain sawmill attachment enables him to provide his own lumber, his own wood for making gun stocks, guitars, and *dulcimers* and a sizable income as well. For Sam, this portable chain sawmill is the perfect solution.

How to Buy a Chain Saw Mill

Sam's chain saw and sawmill is one of a variety of combinations that will do the same job. His does an excellent job, however, and he recommends it.

The saw he uses is a Husqvarna 6.8 cubic inch saw with an rpm of 8400. The cost of the saw without the mill attachment was $589.95. A smaller chain saw could be used, but with fewer rpm's the cutting time would be slower and the saw would wear out faster. Chain saws with roller tips on the bar have higher rpm's than those with plain bars.

The Alaskan lumber-making chain saw attachment is fastened onto the bar of the chain saw and enables Sam to make smooth, precise lumber. This attachment costs $119.50. There are other attachments on the market which will serve the same purpose—to make a portable, efficient, accurate, one-man sawmill.

How to Find and Evaluate Trees

The big advantage of these chain sawmills is that they can be taken right to the tree you want made into lumber. Sam often sells lumber to people from trees on their own property. He loads his chain sawmill rail, wedges, files, axe, fuel, and a chain saw into his pickup and the lumber mill comes to the buyer. He uses the smaller chain saw to fall the tree. The chain sawmill could be used for this, but it would be impractical to keep taking the mill off and putting it on again. Besides, a second saw is handy to remove branches and help out if the chain sawmill becomes wedged in—which seldom happens.

"Evaluate the tree before you cut it down to be sure it meets your needs," says Sam. The tree selected needs to be considerably larger in diameter at the bottom if long boards are wanted. You have to make allowances for the slabs that must be cut off and also for the taper of the tree.

A pine tree needs to be about 22″ at the bottom to provide a timber 12″ × 12″ × 16′. This varies considerably from tree to tree. If the tree is not perfectly straight, there will be even more waste.

The tree you select should be suited to the purpose for which it will be used. Sam uses pine and fir for lumber and available hardwoods such as mountain mahogany for craftwood. He says that it's better if the tree is somewhat green as dry wood creates more wear on the saw. Sometimes construction techniques can compensate for lumber that isn't completely dry.

Sam is paneling the inside of his owner-built house with 1 × 12″ boards he cuts. After they have had ample time to become thoroughly dry, he will put batten strips over the cracks. In this way some shrinkage can be tolerated.

Fig. 10-1. The chain sawmill is ideal for turning a tree into lumber.

Fig. 10-2. Sam Champie makes lumber with a chain saw.

After the tree has been cut down and the limbs removed, a smooth, flat surface is needed to support the mill for its first cut. This can be a plank nailed to the tree you intend to make into lumber or a more elaborate and efficient support rail. Sam made his rail by using two 2 × 4s held together ladder fashion with angle braces. The rail needs to be 2′ longer than the longest board you intend to cut. The width between the 2 × 4s will be determined by the size of tree most of the lumber will be made from. It will

302

have to sit firmly over the curve of the tree to provide a stable support for the mill. An average width is about 12″, but one rail won't fit all trees.

The rail is placed on the log. The roller guides on the mill are adjusted to run along the rail with the saw blade deep enough to remove the top slab from the tree. The mill can be set for cuts from ½″ to 12¾″ deep and has ⅛″ adjustments.

After the top slab is removed, the newly sawn surface is used as a guide for the rollers of the mill. It is then set to remove the bottom slab.

When the top and bottom slabs have been removed, the log is turned so the cut edges are at right angles to the ground. The rail or plank is placed on the third side and squared up with the sawn sides. These slabs can be used for firewood or for fences, stairs, bridges, or rough buildings.

From this point on, the cut surface on top will be the guide for the mill. The mill is adjusted for the size of wood that is needed and in short order there is a pile of finished boards. Sam says, "Removing slabs is the hardest part. Cutting the lumber is much easier, especially if thicker than 1″ lumber is wanted."

Sam particularly likes making heavier lumber. The house he is building for his family utilizes logs and heavy beams. There is a special market in the area, as thick lumber and beams are expensive and hard to come by commercially.

Sometimes nails, wire, or other metal are embedded in trees. This would keep them from being usable at a commercial mill. With Sam's chain sawmill, valuable trees need not be wasted for this reason. The saw handler has complete control of this sawmill. Hitting metal will probably only cause him to have to sharpen his chain.

The chain of the saw will need frequent sharpening. Sam says that he sharpens his after about every 100 linear feet of 12″ wide wood that he cuts. A ripper chain or chisel chain can be used. Sam prefers the latter. The teeth may have angles from 10°-35°. Sam files his to 35° because it makes for faster sawing. Although the lumber is rougher with the teeth at this angle, it is still remarkably smooth.

In an eight hour working day Sam cuts about 300 board feet of 1″ × 12″ lumber or 500 board feet of 2″ × 12″ lumber. During this period the sawmill burns about 5 gallons of gas, and 3½ gallons of oil are needed for chain lubricant.

About 50 percent of what Sam makes in his lumber cutting goes for expenses and the rest is profit. Although the chain sawmill is a good money-making tool, Sam and those who buy lumber from him find it is also a way to avoid mass produced, shoddy lumber.

Have you ever bought lumber and decided to settle for 2″ × 6″ board because 2″ × 12″ boards weren't available or if they were you'd have to mortgage your place to buy one? Sam Champie doesn't have to face that problem. You won't either if your neighborhood has a traveling sawmill.

If you own the sawmill you'll also get paid for cutting down your neighbor's trees. That's not a bad way to solve a problem!

MAKING USE OF WASTE DRIFTWOOD

Helen Blanchard lives in Ward Cove, Alaska. After a storm with gale winds on a high tide, logs that have lain on the edge of the high tide mark begin moving, drifting out into Tongass Narrows to drift back to the beach when the tide turns, gently settling on the beach in criss-cross fashion to block the steps leading up to the front gate. The quickest way to rid the beach of these logs is to saw them into lumber, cooking and heating stove lengths (Fig. 10-3). The large cedars are sawed into shakes and picket bolts for fence posts.

The homesteader's handiest tools are the chain saw, the axe, and the froe. Helen's husband could drag a crosscut saw, but the fuel he would save is minimal, counting the energy he would use healthwise that he could use to an advantage in other ways about the homestead. The Blanchards will go back to the crosscut saw when the necessity arises.

Their house is covered with cedar shakes as are the barn, the chicken coop, and the smokehouse. Good stoves are a must when the homesteader is depending on wood for fuel. The Blanchards have an airtight woodburning heater that is never allowed to grow cold. Even in 80° summer weather during the day, their nights are cool and damp, so a small round log smolders for 24 hours before another is laid on, keeping the house dry and comfortable. Helen dries her herbs and vegetables in baskets set over the slow warmth. Her cookstove is an Olympic wood range with a solid cast frame. The Blanchards took out the original firebox back and front to replace the cast iron with firebrick. In cold weather a filling of water-soaked knotty hemlock will keep the kitchen warm overnight. There will be coals

Fig. 10-3. Blanchard cutting a driftlog on his Alaska homestead.

to start the fire going to prepare breakfast.

With the addition of an "Alaska sawmill" to the chain saw, the homesteader can saw all sizes of lumber for building and planks for raised garden and greenhouse beds. The lumber, firewood, shakes, pickets, and fence posts are not the only materials salvaged from driftlogs. The Blanchards save all the sawdust to use for animal bedding and litter, which eventually ends up in the garden via the compost heap, to keep their garden soil friable and easy to till.

Most of these logs have been set adrift because of decay and knots. The decay can be heaped into a pile for later garden mulches, the knots used for firewood, and the clear lengths for building materials.

Waste driftlogs to the Alaskan homesteader replace oil, electricity, fertilizer and expensive building materials which cost the consumer more and more each day as energy from fossil fuels becomes scarce and the price skyrockets. So if you live on the beaches or where waste logs or lumber is available, put this wonderful natural resource to use, and save energy the practical way.

CURING GREEN WOOD

When Mike Goc was a boy, his *Golden Picture Book* always showed beehives to be rounded conical mounds. Not knowing a hive from a hummock, Goc always assumed that's where bees were kept. When he moved to the country, he learned that his picturesque notion was nothing but a pavement pipedream. He did see rows of stovewood stacked like his imaginary beehive. When he started stacking wood that way himself, he automatically christened the pile "the beehive." For those without a woodshed, it is the best way to store green wood so that the sap will dry out of it and rain water won't flood it.

First of all, there should always be a legitimate reason for killing a live tree. Anyone who would cut down an antique tree just because he doesn't like to rake its leaves in the fall should be exiled to the farthest, most barren desert. In addition most woodlots, especially if they've been neglected for some years, have plenty of deadwood, standing or no, so that live trees don't have to be killed.

Sometimes it is necessary to fell a green tree; a diseased or damaged tree that will soon become diseased is best cut. For example, on Goc's forest homestead he is currently engaged in a sad struggle with oak leaf wilt. Beautiful old red and black oaks whose strength had kept them thriving for close to a century are dying, choked by a disease that literally strangles their circulatory system. There is no cure. The only acceptable method of control, and that not a very effective one, is prompt removal. A lot of stove logs come out of an 80 ft oak that is 30″ at its base. That's where the beehive woodpile comes in handy.

Although those oaks are dead or dying, they still aren't good firewood. Green wood simply doesn't heat. It smolders, hisses and smokes, but produces few Btus.

Fig. 10-4. Start a beehive with a round that's large and difficult to split. Lean other logs, splits and rounds, firmly against it.

Also, green wood is dangerous. While it's smoldering in the stove, it fills the chimney with highly flammable creosote. This gunk adheres to chimney walls and eventually ignites into a roaring fire, sometimes taking the whole house with it. Then there is the simple matter of waste. Burning green wood is like picking onions in June. You'll get a little something. If you wait a while longer, you'll get a whole lot more. The same wood that doesn't heat anything when green will burn like a collier's dream if properly stored for a while. A carefully built beehive woodpile is the ideal way to store green wood.

Making a Beehive

A carefully built beehive woodpile is the ideal way to store green wood. To make a beehive start with the largest, heaviest chunk of wood available (Fig. 10-4). When splitting up large trees, there often is a fork or a heavy knot that just won't cleave. Rather than struggle with it, use this rock-hard hunk as the perfect starter log. After it dries, it will split with ease. Stand it firmly on end, making sure it won't topple. This will be the center starting point. Then simply start leaning other splits and logs around it. At this point, the straighter they're stacked the better. Don't stand flat edges against each other—they'll take until pension day to dry out.

Splits from the trunk of the tree should not be placed one against the other. Break up these blocky sections with a round log from the branches. All pieces should be solidly placed. If they wiggle or wobble, replace them. A weak bottom course could mean the whole pile will later tumble.

Roughly speaking, the base of a beehive should be as wide as the pile is high. Since most men can reach somewhere between 7' and 8' high, the diameter of the first layer of logs should be about the same.

The second course of the beehive is made slightly different than the first. Start again with a center chunk that stands firmly on its own. Now start stacking logs around it. Gradually increase the angle at which the logs lean as the edge of the pile is approached. That is, logs near the ends should lean more than those near the center.

This serves three purposes. Leaning logs are less likely to roll or shift, making the pile more steady. Second, increased lean means more air space between the logs for quicker drying. Third, a beehive has to taper as it rises. Increasing the lean shapes the taper. The outside bottom edge of the

306

rim log on each course should slightly overlap the top edge of the log below it. This allows rain to run down the side of the lower course instead of into its top.

Any succeeding courses are laid up the same way with an eye to increasing lean and taper. The final course should consist of only a few logs that are practically horizontal. After the last log is in place, step back, straighten your aching back, and admire what you've built. While doing that, observe what will happen when it rains next week. Most of the wood will stay dry because it is covered by the outer layer. That outer layer itself will remain drier than you'd first expect. Most of the rain will slide down those sloped sides before it can soak in (Fig. 10-5). That's how a beehive is supposed to work. It allows some air circulation to dry green wood but prevents rain from wetting the stack.

We have described a relatively small woodpile, about the size of one cord. A beehive can be made as large as a little mountain, provided enough wood and ambition is available. In order to build a taller stack with a wider base, more than one course has to be stacked at a time. Then one works with a steadily increasing mound of wood rather than succeeding courses.

Let It Sit

The next question is how long should the wood dry? The problem is not so much with the wood but with its owner. The longer hard firewood sits, the better. Therefore, the best way to handle a beehive is to build it and forget it, if you can. For the last five years Goc has been heating solely with oak that has been dead longer than he has been alive. So sitting around for 30 years won't hurt the wood. A stack of good wood can be sorely tempting in mid-January.

Generally speaking, summer cut wood should have at least one hot summer to dry out. Winter cut wood, with less sap, could be burned the following winter. The longer firewood sits, the more heat it produces. Probably the greatest amount of heat comes out of a log that the sap has thoroughly dried out of, has never been rained on, and is just a year away from starting to rot.

It isn't easy to find wood that is in such an ideal state. By stacking up a beehive and letting it sit, it's possible to approach that ideal. That's about as close as most of us will ever get.

Fig. 10-5. In a completed beehive the sap dries out and the rain runs off.

Fig. 10-6. Build a log cabin from cull trees.

USING CULL TREES

To a homesteader, all trees are valuable. The Bahns of Baker, Oregon own about 40 acres of trees—mostly pine. The tall straight trees are for lumber—their own and their investment in the future. The crooked trees, the insect or fire damaged trees, the downed trees, and the small diameter trees that are thinned out so that their neighbors can develop better are the Bahns' continuous and much valued harvest.

One of their most plentiful sources of cull trees is from an area damaged by fire. The fire killed the trees but left them standing. From these trees, the Bahns built a small log cabin which is used as a goat shed (Fig. 10-6). They make excellent, solid logs even though they are messy to handle. The charred bark soon turns anyone who handles them an interesting shade of black.

The Bahns used some of these fire damaged logs and some poles to build another pen for housing bucks. They made this one a two story pen to house two bucks separately, so that there would be less fighting and using them for breeding would be easier. A platform is built halfway up on the inside of this shelter. One buck has the lower portion, and the other buck has the upper portion. The buck that was put in the pen with the second story enclosure had a tendency to weak pasterns. All that jumping up and down from his high shelter actually seemed to strengthen his pasterns.

Two people can handle logs that are 12″ or less in diameter. The Bahns seldom use trees larger than that for their small buildings. If you have very many trees of large diameter that must be culled, they recommend a portable chain sawmill that will allow you to make lumber of the tree right where it falls.

The Bahns have used both their half-ton pickup and a one ton stock truck to haul logs to where they planned on using them. This means they must move the logs when it is neither too muddy or too snowy for the rigs to

308

maneuver safely. Their neighbor tells how, many years ago, he skidded logs out using horses. This was done in the winter when skidding was easier, the damage to the skid trail was less, and the other chores were less pressing.

From time to time the Bahns have supplemented the cull trees on their property with poles from Forest Service land. In eastern Oregon it is possible at certain times of the year in certain locations to get a 'pole permit' from the Forest Service. These permits allow them to take a specific number of poles from a specific area. The permits describe in detail exactly what kind of trees may be taken.

Fences are an obvious use for poles. Poles are almost essential for corrals where cattle will be held for branding, vaccinating, etc (Fig. 10-7). When held in close confinement, cattle will easily run right through a wire fence.

To make a strong corral of poles, many straight poles must be gathered to form the horizontal part of the fence. This kind of tree is often the by-product of a thinning operation. Vertical posts must be extremely sturdy and durable. The Bahns use the often scorned juniper tree for vertical posts. They are extremely sturdy and unbelievably heavy. The Bahns don't mind the extra muscle they require because they outlast any other wood post available locally that isn't treated with a preservative.

Posts from juniper trees are gnarled and beautiful. The Bahns used to cut fence posts to 8′ lengths. Now they deliberately select tall, crooked posts for corners and gates. In this way the tree's spirit and individuality isn't completely lost.

Poles also make excellent hay feeders. A hay feeder for cattle must be large and strong. The feeder has a sturdy base made of small logs and a V-shaped hay feeder made of many poles. The goats have a hay feeder made from a panel of poles. The bottom of the panel is fastened to the wall of their shed and the top is slanted outward and held by strong wires.

Sometimes the cull log itself suggests how you might use it. A few years ago they cut down a couple of willow trees that were shading the

Fig. 10-7. A cattle corral.

garden and a danger to the house. They fell across the creek. With a little pushing and shoving, the Bahns got them into position. Their new footbridge was nearly made.

Cull trees are also a good source of firewood. The Bahns favorite trees for this are large diameter trees that have been on the ground for a while and are just starting to decay. In addition there are scrap pieces left over from sheds, fences, feeders, bridges, etc., that make good firewood.

MANAGING YOUR WOODLOT

Woodland management consists of three basic steps; thin, cull, and harvest. Management of the homestead woodlot can be somewhat different from that of the large commercial acreages. Clear cutting, as is done on many commercial forests, would be defeating the purpose on the homestead.

Who can manage a woodlot? Anyone who knows the different species of trees, how they grow and best utilization of the different species. With a little common sense, he can manage his own woodlot. There is a lot more to proper management than the three basic steps.

Let's take a recently purchased homestead that has a section of woodland whether it is only a few trees or several acres. The only difference size makes is that you do more of everything on the larger acreage. Possibly you would need different equipment if the acreage is large enough.

First, establish boundaries. Many people have gotten into trouble by cutting trees that did not belong to them. If your property boundaries are not well defined, talk to your neighbor and maybe you can establish boundaries by mutual consent. If your neighbor knows no more than you, maybe you can find an old-timer in the area who can help. Stay away from an official survey, if possible. They are very expensive.

Now that you have an established boundary, mark it. The best way is to blaze and paint. Trees standing directly on the line should have two blazes, one on each side towards the line. It isn't necessary to mark every tree, just enough to enable a person to follow the line.

All lines eventually have corners. They are marked to show the direction the property line takes from that tree. If only your property corners at the point the tree will have two blazes. If two properties corner, there would be three blazes and four properties would have four blazes. All corners should have witness trees. They are three or four trees circling the corner with three small blazes on each tree facing the corner. This tells a person to look for a corner and not continue on in a straight line.

Now that the line is blazed, paint the blazes. Any good paint will do, but regular tree paint or bright fluorescent paint is best.

Next, cruise the timber stand which is simply walking through the trees and making plans. It can be as simple as just taking mental notes as you walk or as elaborate as marking each tree to be cut and putting down on paper the species, diameter, estimated volume, and planned utilization of each tree.

Now that you know what trees belong to you and the condition of those trees, you are ready for the real management. In the established woodlot this would be a combination of all three basic management practices; thinning, culling, and harvesting done at the same time.

Thinning is done to let light in so that seedlings can sprout, and the remaining trees can get enough food and water for good growth. Keep in mind that tall, fast-growing trees reaching for the sunlight make straight, limb-free stems, so do not open up the tops too much.

Cull trees are those not good enough to save for future timber. They could be diseased trees, crooked trees, or trees that will never make good quality timber. Cull trees usually make good firewood.

Harvesting is simply the cutting of any usable trees, whether for firewood, saw logs, or any other use that gives them value (Fig. 10-8). Some usable material can usually be gotten from all three basic steps. Usually the thinning, culling, and harvesting is done on a continuous basis on the homestead in comparison to a 10 year or more basis on the commercial forest.

While you have been going through this whole process, you should have had one thing on your mind that would control the whole process. That is, what do you as an individual want out of your woodlot, and what can it give you? Those decisions should govern your choice of trees to leave for future growth.

Now you can see why each woodlot will be handled slightly differently from any other woodlot. If you know your trees, how they grow, their best

Fig. 10-8. The harvesting of trees on a homestead is usually done on a continuous basis (photo by Jean Martin).

uses, and your desires and use a little common sense, you can manage your own woodlot.

CUTTING WOOD

Many of us have vowed never to be caught unprepared and dependent on the public utilities for our very lives. The independent's likely fuel will be wood—hopefully self-cut. If you are inexperienced in this ancient art of fuel gathering, read this section carefully.

Your first attention will be to your tools. Make sure your saw is fully gassed and oiled, the breather and oiler unobstructed, and the chain sharp and properly tightened. Proper tension will vary with the type of saw. Make sure the chain does not hang, but can be easily pulled around the bar. Always carry your T-wrench or "duty tool" in your back pocket when cutting, as a chain will loosen after use and need readjustment. Running out of gas halfway through a tree necessitates the folly of leaving the tree hanging while you make the long walk back to the gas can or tools. A dull saw that is spitting sawdust rather than chips is dangerous, too. A chain not getting oil will tighten and stall the engine eventually, but may damage itself and the bar in the meantime.

Now you must choose a tree. The first tree in a stand is very important. Walk around a bit before beginning to cut and choose a tree inclined to fall into an opening. Hanging a tree up in a neighboring tree necessitates a perilous and time-consuming extrication. You're way ahead of the game if you avoid the situation. By and large, the small-time woodcutter must drop a tree according to its own inclination. Give careful attention to determining this inclination; it can be tricky. Though the trunk may lean one way, the greater weight is given to the upper limbs and leaves, especially in the spring and summer when incredible volumes of water are coursing through. The wind can play havoc with you, too, tossing the treetop to and fro, always changing the tree's inclination.

The wind's direction and velocity are the most variable factors in cutting wood. It is the fickle wind that causes most of the accidents among experienced loggers. Do not cut if the winds are high and gusty. A tree may lean obviously to the right but rock back to the left as a gust passes, inviting disaster. Also present on windy days, lurking unseen above, are the "widow makers"—dead limbs and tree tops waiting only to be dislodged and come crashing down to add to their already ominous legend.

Once you've determined which way the tree wants to fall, cut away vines, brush, and lower branches to give yourself plenty of room to move while cutting. Pay special attention to the route you need to take should you need to escape quickly. Inspect and clean the tree of sand, stones, or other foreign matter which will dull your chain. If dealing with a large tree, it may be necessary to remove the larger buttresses (the flared root tops at the base of the tree) to get evenly high cutting faces.

The direction of the fall is controlled by the notch, or face-cut. The reason for the face is to remove a surface for the tree to jam on or pry against

312

as it begins to fall. For the trees with obvious inclinations, make the cut to the side you wish the tree to fall. The notch should be about one-fifth to one-third of the tree's diameter and should never be higher than its depth. The danger of eliminating or undercutting the face, even on trees that may be growing near horizontal, is the prospect of splitting.

Some trees are notorious splitters, alder being the champion in our area, the Pacific Northwest. A tree may split because it is hollow inside, or from grains, internal twists, and stresses that may not be apparent unless the wind shifts or the face is cut improperly. Stand to the side as you cut the face, usually on the side to which you expect the tree to come as it falls. This protects you from splits. Cut as low as possible on the trunk. This will give you more wood and is a standard good logging practice since the lower the stump, the less danger it presents as obstruction. Also, by bending to make the cut, you give yourself time to straighten up and avoid a murderous split. It takes longer to fall backwards than to straighten up.

On high-risk splitters (those with obvious weaknesses or acute inclination) you may make a *small* notch first, on the back side of the tree, slightly above the expected back-cut level to give the trunk a chance to snap off rather than split (Fig. 10-9).

On trees without too much inclination, you may influence the line of fall by "hinging." This hinge, about one-tenth of the tree's diameter, is the last piece of wood still holding the tree as it begins to fall. It will continue to pull the tree towards the hinge until the last bond breaks. In this situation, the face is cut at a right angle to the direction of fall. Undercutting the depth of the face can cause splitting on the back-cut. The danger in overcutting is the tree falling, in *any* direction, before you can even make the back-cut. Make the horizontal cut first, then take out the notch, generally from the top down, endeavoring to make the cuts meet neatly. In some situations, upcutting the notch may be in order, but it's easier to go with gravity whenever you can.

As you make the back-cut, or felling cut, generally position yourself on the side of the hinge to protect you from splits. Make the cut exactly horizontal and higher than the base of the notch. On a small tree put the bumper of the saw to the log directly behind the hinge and move the bar in an arc around this fulcrum to get a fanlike cut (Fig. 10-10). Never cut through to the notch or you lose your control altogether. As the tree begins to fall, the hinge twists the tree on the stump and pulls it towards you. Step around to the rear of the tree so that it falls away from you. Don't commit yourself until you know for sure the direction it is going.

Should a tree ever begin to fall towards you, never succumb to the irrational urge to outrun it. Panic seems to make this a natural human reaction, but with foreknowledge, you need only step around the tree, behind the line of fall.

To fell trees with a diameter exceeding the bar length of your saw, you must make a series of fanlike cuts. Stand behind the notch and start the first cut with the tip of the bar cutting into the tree just behind the hinge (Fig.

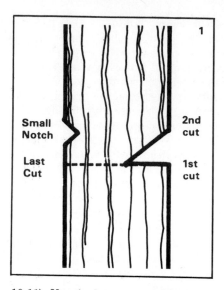

Small
Notch

2nd
cut

Last
Cut

1st
cut

1

Fig. 10-9. Note the small notch.

10-11). Use the bumper as a fulcrum and change the fulcrum as little as possible. Leave the bar in the cut to move the saw to the next fulcrum, or the cutting direction could be changed too easily.

The final cut is made with the bar engaging (180° opposite) the hinge. Move the bar in an arc leaving an equal amount of wood as a hinge. It is very important to always hold the bar in a horizontal position when cutting.

When felling very big trees, it may be that the center of the tree is not cut through when you have finished the series of fanlike cuts. This can be avoided by boring into the center of the notch *before* making the back-cuts (Fig. 10-12). This boring cut can sometimes be used when cutting soft leaf wood to relieve tension in the trunk and avoid splinters being torn out of the log in the middle of the hinge.

When cutting coniferous trees in the summer, it may be desirable to make splint cuts at either side of the tree. These cuts should be at right angles to the notch and in the same plane as the back-cut will be. Without these cuts, the splint wood may split when the tree falls. Make the depth of the cut about equal to the width of the bar.

Sometimes, just as it seems the tree must topple, the wind or a miscalculation may rock the tree back on the stump, pinning your saw and/or jamming it tight against the narrow back-cut. If you cannot snatch the saw out of the bind, don't linger; shut the saw off, step back and with one eye out for stumbling blocks and brush, carefully choose the safest line and back off. Once safely away, you may analyze the situation and choose one of several courses.

The safest course is to let the wind blow the tree over. The problem here is the wind's unpredictability. You cannot go off and leave a potentially murderous situation poised indefinitely; it can come down seconds later or

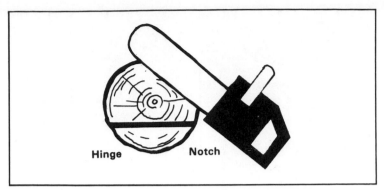

Fig. 10-10. Put the bumper of the saw to the log directly behind the hinge.

months later. You are responsible for the tree. It must fall before your responsibility ends.

The best tool in this situation is the wedge. For all its simplicity, the wedge is, pound for pound, the most powerful tool you may own. Big-time loggers, dealing with die-straight firs or redwoods 150′ tall, can bring them down on a dime by wedging in the back-cut. You, too, can apply wedging principles to influence the fall of most trees, but many trees you may be cutting for firewood will not grow as straight and balanced as the big-money trees and may not be as susceptible to wedge manipulation.

In any case, if your saw is not pinched in the back-cut, the wedge is inserted and driven in with a small sledge or mall. Many trees, especially alder, are likely to pinch back and spit the wedge out by rocking back in reaction to the first one or two blows. So, once the wedge has been tapped in place, hit it a good lick, then as the tree rocks forward, quickly set the wedge by hitting it again, before the tree rocks back. Whenever driving

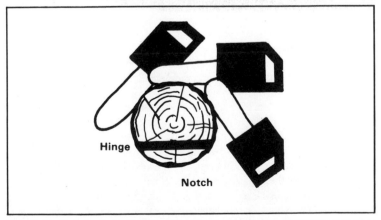

Fig. 10-11. Start the first cut with the tip of the bar cutting into the tree just behind the hinge.

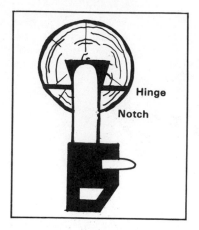

Fig. 10-12. Bore into the center of the notch before making the back-cuts.

wedges, be aware that sharp metal splinters may fly into your, or an observer's, eye and cause severe injury—out in the woods, perhaps far from medical attention. Wedges should be kept trimmed of burrs and chipped edges. Also, there are plastic wedges available that eliminate this problem. You can make wedges out of hardwood with the grain going into the tree. Safety goggles are the best insurance against eye injury when using any tools. It is best to carry two wedges, as most jobs will require more than one.

If the fully driven wedges do not influence the tree enough to tip it back along its intended line, if your saw is still stuck in the way, if the tree can be dropped back in the direction it wants to go, and if you have another saw (cutting with an axe at this point is quite hazardous, but it is a way), make a new cut below the first attempt, reversing the face and back-cut (Fig. 10-13). Be sure you have room to move because this tree could go anywhere at this point.

If the wedges haven't worked, or if the tree is looking down on your barn or the neighbor's fence, and you can't drop it back where it wants to go, a long, stout rope or cable and block are in order. Try to anticipate problems such as nearby buildings, etc., beforehand, and attach your block and line before beginning to cut. Hooking onto a delicately balanced, wind-sensitive toppler is an adventure of rushing peril. The block should be chained to a solid base; the line is run through it and set around the trunk or a stout limb as high as possible to gain maximum leverage. How to set the line is up to you, but it is foolhardy to climb the tree. If there is absolutely no other way, add your weight to the situation on the side of greatest balance. Before you even consider climbing, tie a light rope to the heavier rope or cable, weight it with a rock, toss the rock over a limb, and haul the cable up and around the tree. Listen for cracking and groaning. Watch the treetop. Have partners well clear and watching for you. Once the line is set, if sufficient pull-power can be applied by truck, tractor, partners or neighbors, the tree will fall towards the block.

If you do not have a block, the line can be run around a nearby tree or stump and pulled too; this affords greater friction than a block, a less efficient return for your labors, and causes greater wear on the line. In the absence of a suitable tree or stump, you may pull directly towards the power source, but be sure your line is long enough to take you beyond the falling tree.

A tree may begin to fall only to get caught in adjacent trees. This may happen often until you learn to fell the trees in a stand with a mind always to open a path for the next tree to fall. Don't jump into the biggest tree or the one nearest the truck. Walk around a bit. A whole logical order may be suggested, and hangers may be avoided.

Sometimes that tree's going to catch and stay cradled in a neighbor's boughs. When that happens, you have a dangerous situation with great tension exerted throughout. First, watch out for the tree's butt. It may still be in contact with the stump, and at any time, may slip off and jump back, battering ram style. Don't be behind the stump. As the tree begins to fall and the problem is developing, back off and keep eyes up for dislodged "widow makers." If possible, pull the tree free with cable and truck. Be alert. It may take many minutes for stress to wear down a supporting limb, but with a loud snap, the tree may suddenly shift, roll free, and fall to either side. Usually you can perceive the direction of the stress and with cautious circling, approach the hanger from behind to set the choker.

If you cannot pull the tree free, you may be able to free the bind by upcutting with your saw. This hand-to-hand exposure confronts you with unimaginable energy—great massed weight, pulled by gravity, levered and twisted, coiled to explode with a speed and suddenness to which you could never react. Your upcut will be made from the stressed side, but do not stand on the side your saw will cut from (Fig. 10-14).

Fig. 10-13. Make a new cut below the first attempt, reversing the face and back-cut.

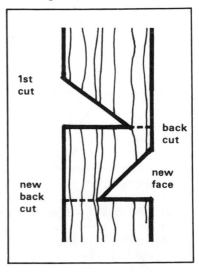

1st cut

back cut

new face

new back cut

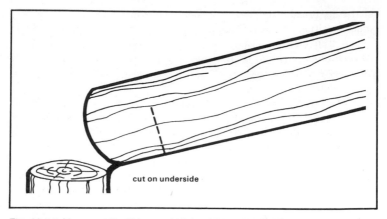

cut on underside

Fig. 10-14. Your upcut will be made from the stressed side.

It may take several cuts to finally loosen the entangled top, and each cut is very perilous. Again, always make yourself plenty of room to move. Movement is your principle advantage in this encounter. Be prepared to simply release the saw if it should be wrenched by a great shift. In fact, anytime a tree wants to take your saw, let the saw go. Do not resist the irresistible force, and it is likely the tough bar and chain will be undamaged. Even if the saw is totaled it can be replaced. Do not wrestle with a tree; step back and keep yourself intact.

A friend of ours was making an up-cut on a leaning tree and the bind exploded, throwing him back 20', still gripping his wildly screaming saw. Fortunately, he was unhurt. Fortunate, too, was the fellow he was cutting with—he was standing behind our friend, but far enough back to escape the horror of the chain saw. If your temperament allows it, it is safer to have company in the woods, but whenever cutting with others, only one saw should be running in the same area. Everyone should focus his attention on the same tree. The cutter should never begin until he knows everyone is well out of the way.

Resist the temptation to "jackpot" by felling the good neighbor tree with the helping hands. Probably, you'll wind up with two leaners, domino fashion. This can go on indefinitely, until the variables geometrically multiply beyond your ability to consider them all. A few trees all leaning, swaying, and twisting can become an instantaneous accident. If you find yourself confronted with a growing jackpot situation, walk away for awhile and think your next move through. Calmly prepare yourself and make the next cut pay off.

If you've got the tree on the way down, here are a few more things to consider. A tree falling uphill may kickback off the stump just as if it had caught in nearby trees. The limbs break the fall, and gravity pulls the butt back downhill (Fig. 10-15). A tree falling downhill will jump out and down the hill, sometimes for many feet. The larger the tree and the greater the slope, the broader the jump. Consider this effect in determining cutting order, positioning yourself and equipment, and avoiding obstructions.

A tree may fall across something—a fallen tree, stump, or land configuration—and the resultant lever action will flip the butt about with a big whoosh (Fig. 10-16). An old-timer told us how such a butt caught him not so gently under the chin and set him dazed and blinking, 12' up and back atop an old first-growth cedar stump.

Even when the tree is down you may not be through. It may be the tree has fallen over tough, pliant brush or smaller trees. Sometimes these will be unbroken and pinned, and when severed as you clear brush, will spring up, slapping and ripping like some jungle trap. Stand aside and be alert. As you limb, be aware that the trunk may shift as supporting limbs are cut out. Also, cut limbs from the stress side, as when upcutting, to avoid binds and the jungle trap effect.

By entering the woods forearmed and forewarned, you should be able to face winter well-stocked with your own fuel and a measure of independence from the all too fallible (not to mention expensive) public utilities—and with all your own limbs, too, to warm by the fire.

FIREWOOD

If you own a woodlot or have access to one, you can make extra money cutting and selling firewood. That's what John McDowell and his father-in-law found out a few years ago when they advertised firewood for sale. Even though they didn't start cutting the wood until the fall season and despite the fact that heavy snows later in the winter effectively locked them outside the woods, they still managed to sell several hundred dollars worth of wood.

That was three years ago. The energy crisis and high fuel prices have made the use of firewood even more attractive today. Wood stoves, furnaces, and fireplaces are selling like hotcakes, and they all need firewood to fuel them. Harvesting firewood is fast becoming a cash crop which few

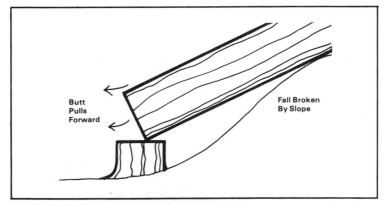

Butt
Pulls
Forward

Fall Broken
By Slope

Fig. 10-15. Gravity pulls the butt back downhill.

319

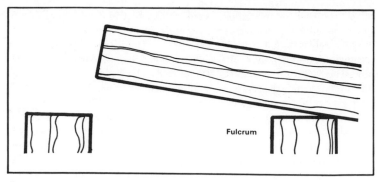

Fig. 10-16. Note the fulcrum.

homesteaders can afford to ignore (Fig. 10-17). Firewood advertisements in one fair-sized Iowa city are currently asking an average of about $80 a cord for mixed hardwoods. Nationwide, the average is considerably higher.

Sources of Wood

The ideal source of firewood is a fully mature woodlot with plenty of standing dead trees. These dead upright trees are excellent because they are already dry and seasoned, for the most part, and they haven't become wet or rotten by prolonged contact with the ground.

Thinning out the dead trees from your woodlot does more than just provide you with firewood. It allows more sunlight into the woods and gives young trees a chance to thrive.

As for cutting living trees, keep in mind that these generally need at least six months seasoning—including a summer—before they are ready for firewood. It's always good woodlot management, however, to remove diseased and damaged trees, those which are very crooked in shape or crowded, or those which are *wolf trees*. A wolf is a very large tree with a wide, spreading crown that's taking up lots of growing space. A wolf's trunk may be too branchy and poorly formed to sell for sawlogs, but the entire tree will yield a great deal of firewood.

If, however, you don't have a woodlot of your own, you can approach those who do for permission to cut in their timber. This method is what McDowell usually did, as his father-in-law knew many farmers who didn't mind them cutting on their land. Situations such as these, however, soon may be a thing of the past with the value of standing timber going higher and higher.

In some parts of the country, particularly in the west, the government may issue firewood-cutting permits from public land. Sometimes, too, the big lumber companies will let firewooders come in on their land after the lumberjacks and cedar savages have done their work. Around sawmills, you often can find large wood chunks and heavy slabs at reasonable prices which could be resold as firewood, with a little help from you.

If the owner of a woodlot has previously sold some of his bigger trees, such as walnuts, oaks and maples, to a sawmill, he often has the large tops of these trees littering the ground, waiting for someone to saw them up for firewood. A small advertisement in a local paper or farm publication might put you in contact with such an owner, or you can just scout along the farm roads until you spot some. If all else fails and you still haven't found a source of firewood, offering to pay a woodlot owner $3 to $5 a pickup load of wood may win their approval.

Once you have your source, the best types of trees to cut are those which give a high amount of heat and are easy to burn and split. Ash, birch, hard maple, hickory, pecan, and oak fall into this category. Trees which will produce a medium amount of heat but still burn and split easily are cherry, soft maple, and walnut. Elm and sycamore are next in quality, but these two should always be quite dry and seasoned before being sold. Dry red elm is a good burner. Aspen, basswood, and cottonwood produce a low amount of heat, and few people will want to buy them.

Equipment Needed

If you're already cutting firewood for your own use, you probably have most of the needed firewood cutting equipment. A truck or a trailer is essential. So is a gas-powered chain saw. The very small, 10" cut saws should be avoided if possible; they rarely seem to be able to hold up under a heavy cutting schedule. A medium- or large-sized saw with at least a 14 to 16" cut is best. It will give you the power and dependability you need. There are few things more frustrating and unprofitable than tinkering with a balky chain saw all day when you should be cutting wood.

A splitting maul and wedges will certainly be needed. These can be used to wedge up leaning trees you're cutting, as well as for splitting wood. Someone just starting in selling firewood will probably do okay the first

Fig. 10-17. Harvesting firewood is fast becoming a cash crop.

year or two splitting wood by this method. The power-driven hydraulic splitters do make splitting easier and faster, but they are costly, easily running $400 to $800 or more. Such splitters may not be needed for a small operation. Don't sell the old maul and wedge short; you can still split a good-sized pile of wood with these time-tested implements.

Wearing a hard hat while felling timber is a good practice. A dead branch falling silently from high up on a tree is not called a "widow maker" for laughs. Likewise, wood chips and sawdust flying in your eyes while using a chain saw is irritating, and downright dangerous, unless you wear safety goggles. As for steel-toed boots, they'll be worth every cent you paid for them the first time you drop an 80 pound chunk of wood on your toenails.

Cutting and Hauling

The real work, and time-consuming factor, in selling firewood is not the cutting but the handling. The ideal situation would be loading the wood onto your truck, only once, in the woodlot, and offloading only once—at the customer's house. Most times, however, you must store, split, and season the wood between the woodlot and the customer's door, and this means more handling and moving. The next best thing, then, is to *minimize* the number of times you have to handle the wood.

The person who is only cutting firewood for his own use can afford to be fussy, stacking everything up in neat little piles and maybe moving it around two or three or more times in the process. When you're selling 10, 20 or 30 cords of wood a year, you could be working with up to 105,000 pounds, you're wasting time, energy and, possibly, profit.

Working with trees that are already dead and dry will often save you some handling. In most cases, you don't really need to stack this wood carefully to dry or season, as you do with green wood. It can simply be dumped in a large pile in a shed or in the open with a tarp covering it. The larger chunks of wood (eight inches or more wide) can be placed in a separate pile for later splitting.

Green wood requires more time and care; for one thing, it must be reduced in moisture to about 20 percent, which is considered thoroughly air-dried. Sometimes woodcutters leave stacks of green wood corded up right in the woodlot where it was cut. They stack it in a criss-cross, open-crib pattern with plenty of air space between the pieces. A year later, it's ready for market.

What? A whole year? You really need the heat of summer to season green wood. In Iowa, for example, there are about 180 effective air-drying days between April 1 and October 31, but only 35 such days in the other five months of the year. Properly seasoned firewood has more heat value per pound than green wood, is easier to ignite, and less likely to build up creosote in a chimney. Most customers will not appreciate your selling them green wood, to say the least.

How to Keep Customers

You won't have to sell firewood long before you learn there are two basic types of buyers: those who want long wood (18 to 24") for fireplaces and wood furnaces, and those who want short wood (12 to 15") for stoves. It's a good idea to stock both lengths of wood and even custom cut to your customer's specifications.

There seems to be more fireplace-size wood buyers at present than those who want woodstove sizes, probably because stove owners are most serious about wood as a fuel and often cut their own. This ratio is probably even now changing. Also, if you get a woodstove owner who buys *all* his fuel instead of cutting it, he'll likely make a most steady customer—if you treat him right.

McDowell got most of his customers by advertising in local and shopper papers. Sometimes he used the swap shop program on a nearby radio station. When things began to lag, he had some advertisements printed up at one of these "quick print" places. He mailed them to potential customers in an affluent suburban neighborhood. He obtained their addresses by simply driving along the streets and noting which houses sported chimneys or stovepipes. This campaign brought additional sales.

Some of the things he mentioned in his ads were: the type of wood he was offering, whether it was dry or seasoned and split, price, as well as a statement that he would deliver promptly. Sometimes McDowell had specials where two loads of wood could be had for $5 less than the standard combined price. A number of folks took him up on that offer.

Other than being friendly or courteous, the best way to please customers is to give them a little more than usual at a little less price. The half-ton pickup truck McDowell used normally would carry a half cord of wood (also called a rick). McDowell also tried to deliver promptly and, if the customers wanted him to stack the wood for them, he did.

More Than a Business

Selling firewood is a business and a method of self-employment and, as such, it means come tax time, filling out a "profit or loss from a business" form and also a "computation of social security self-employment tax" form. It also means you can deduct from your gross sales total such things as supplies, vehicle mileage, advertising, etc. Bigger expenses like trucks, chain saws and splitters, must be capitalized over a period of several years. With self-employment tax alone running over 8 cents on the dollar, it behooves one to keep a close record of all deductible expenses.

Selling firewood is not really for "armchair enthusiasts." It's more a "get up and do it" job with lots of manual labor. In the course of a day's time, for instance, if you've managed to cut, load and deliver two pickup loads of wood, you've lifted, lugged, and tossed about 7,000 pounds of wood. Most likely, you also have a little sawdust and dirt down your neck, a little sweat on your forehead, and a little tiredness in your bones.

On the other hand, there are few finer things than being out in the autumn woods cutting firewood on a brisk, blue-skied October day. You feel great. You're working for yourself; and you're more in tune with the woods, and seasons and the weather, and even the forest creatures, than you ever could be working in a factory. The fact that you get paid for doing it makes it just that much better.

Chapter 11

Workshop Projects

This chapter begins with a short course in mechanical drawing. Then read about some useful items you can make in your workshop.

MECHANICAL DRAWING SHORT COURSE

Most homesteaders have read hundreds of "how-to" articles and books illustrated with photographs, and sketches. As readers, we may have misunderstood the meaning of the sketch, and the intended directions to build. In other words, what is clear to the person holding the pencil is not always clear to the person holding the hammer. Photos accompanying text may be of poor quality or taken from detail-hiding angle. The illustrator may be working from a verbal description, and may not even know what it is that is being drawn.

Check through a few *Countrysides, Popular Mechanics,* or some other "how-to" magazines. Are you able to read the drawing. Would you be able to build the project using the drawing as a guide? If your answer is yes, then grab your hammer. If not, put down your hammer and concentrate on the rest of this section.

The materials needed for sketching are few and simple: paper, pencil, and an eraser. No T-squares, triangles, scales, or any other fancy items are required. Graph paper is helpful in sketching straighter lines and in counting off the inches (centimeters). You can use ¼" squares, which are large enough to show detail. The scale depends on the actual project size. A ¼" square could equal 3", or 12", whichever has better detail.

The most used types of sketches are *orthographic* and *pictorial*, but we won't go into any explanation of the pictorial. Orthographic, or right angle drawing, means that the viewer is perpendicular to the object. You don't get much detail from one side of the object, so there are three perpendicular views to give us the needed information: the top, front, and right side views.

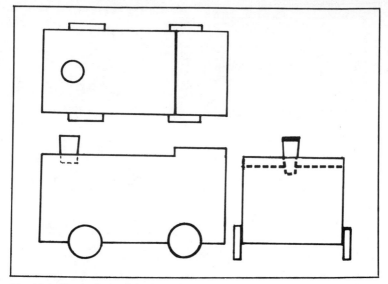

Fig. 11-1. Three views of the toy train.

The toy train (Fig. 11-1) illustrates three views and their proper placement on the paper. Notice the dotted lines under the smokestack. These indicate hidden lines, or "x-ray vision" on the part of the viewer. It shows detail which can't be seen otherwise. In this case, it tells us that there is a hole drilled into the locomotive, and the smoke stack dowel is placed in the hole.

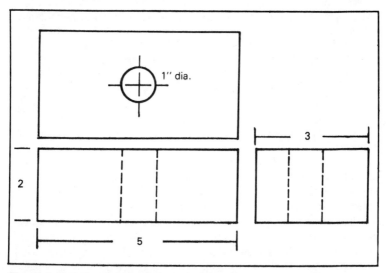

Fig. 11-2. Note the size dimensions.

326

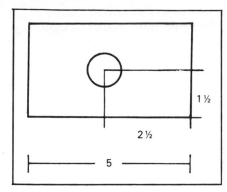

Fig. 11-3. Location dimensions.

The next step is to add dimensions to the sketch, which gives us specific information about the project. Sometimes a sketch doesn't seem to belong with the dimensions. The object in the sketch looks square, but the dimensions are, say 3″ by 5″. This discrepancy in proportion can throw you off, but is easily corrected. If the dimensions are 3 by 5, make it 3 units by 5 units on the paper.

Here, again, is where graph paper helps. First, size dimensions (Fig. 11-2) tell us the length, width, and thickness of the block, and the size of the drilled holes. Second, location dimensions (Fig. 11-3) tell us where to drill the hole, or where to put the dado joint. Notice that it is possible to dimension the length in four places, but for clarity and efficiency it is not done. There are several rules for dimensioning, but they can all be broken *if* the drawing is better understood by doing so. Clarity is the key, and a jumble of numbers, crossed lines, and arrowheads is most unclear.

In a way, this is a restatement of how to make a dimensioned sketch, so it is not difficult. We need to know the length, width, and thickness of each part of the project, how many of that part are needed, where holes and angles are to be, and how it is fastened to the next part. We can fill in the blanks of a project parts chart (Table 11-1) shown here to answer many of the questions. Following this order will simplify buying lumber, too, because the folks at the lumberyard think in terms of 2 × 4 × 8′, or 1 × 6 × 12′. The part is usually an upright, brace, shelf, top or something similar, but if you are thinking of writing down "whatchamacallit," use part 'A' and part 'B' instead.

The garden tray (Fig. 11-4) is a handy project for holding berry boxes, peat pots, or garden tools. It has eight parts as shown in the three-view sketch. The dimensions in the top view tell us that the bottom of the tray is

Table 11-1. A Project Parts Chart.

# Pcs.	Part	T	W	L
1	Block	1	3	6

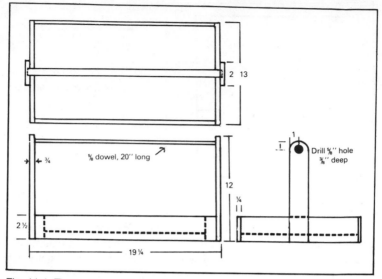

Fig. 11-4. Three views of the garden tray.

¾" thick, 13" wide, and 17¾" long. In the top view we also see that the sides are 19¼" long, and in the right side view the thickness of ¼" and width of 2½" are shown. The side view shows the thickness of the uprights, ¾", and the right side shows the width and length of 2" and 12". The side view has two location dimensions for the ⅝" holes for the handle. You should be able to locate and write down the three dimensions (Table 11-2) for the ends. The handle is dimensioned using a note, which is probably less confusing than dimensioning in the conventional way. The entire project could be dimensioned in this way, provided it is clear to the builder. It is still necessary to add the location dimensions in the conventional way.

There is more than one method for this type of communication, but rather than argue over their merits, it has been the intent of this section to develop some skills in making and reading sketches. For practice, take a drawing from a magazine and see if you can make a parts chart. Don't forget

Table 11-2. Garden Tray Parts Chart.

# Pcs.	Part	T	W	L	# Pcs.	Part	T	W	L
1	Bottom	¾	13	17¾	2	Ends			
2	Sides	¼	2½	19¼	1	Handle			
2	Uprights	¾	2	12					

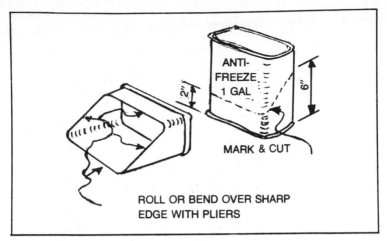

ANTI-
FREEZE
1 GAL

6"

2"

MARK & CUT

ROLL OR BEND OVER SHARP
EDGE WITH PLIERS

Fig. 11-5. Use an antifreeze can to make a scoop.

to double check your paper work. Remember, a mistake on a sheet of paper is cheaper than one on a sheet of plywood. When practicing your sketching, ask yourself, "Is it clear?" or better still, hand it to someone else for some constructive criticism. If all is clear, you will want to get out the hammer and saw.

"SCOOP" FROM RECYCLED CANS

One can always find use for a large scoop on the homestead, whether it be scooping feed grains, dirt, compost, or lime for spreading on the garden. So save your antifreeze cans or similar containers and rework them (Fig. 11-5). Use tin snips or scissors for cutting and roll the edges with pliers.

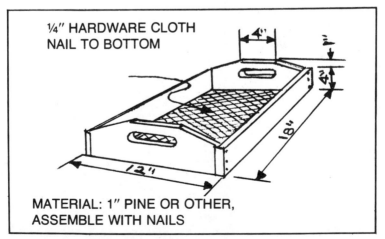

¼" HARDWARE CLOTH
NAIL TO BOTTOM

4"

1"

4"

18"

12"

MATERIAL: 1" PINE OR OTHER,
ASSEMBLE WITH NAILS

Fig. 11-6. Construction details for the soil sifter.

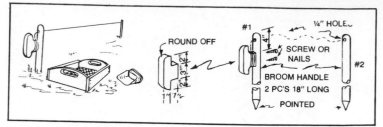

Fig. 11-7. An aid for planting straight rows.

HOMEMADE SOIL SIFTER

A soil sifter is an asset throughout the year. This one is light in weight and is small enough to be handled easily. Use it to sift soil or compost when potting plants. It can double as a carry-all, being suitable for transporting bulbs, plants, etc., when planting. It can also be used to gather and hose the dirt off beets, turnips, radishes, lettuce, etc (Fig. 11-6).

PLANTING STRAIGHT ROWS

Every gardener enjoys a well-planned garden with long, straight rows of plants. One way to insure this is to construct this simple aid. See Fig. 11-7.

Cut two 18″ pieces from a discarded broom handle or ¾″ dowel rod. Whittle a point on one ends of the stick and drill a ¼″ hole through the other

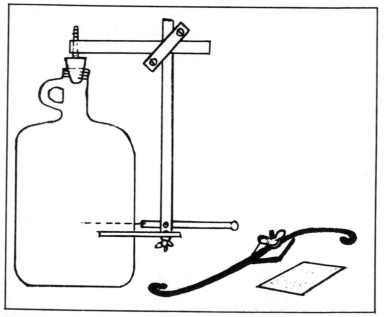

Fig. 11-8. A bottle cutter.

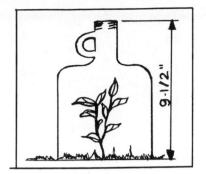

Fig. 11-9. The top portion of the bottle makes a mini-greenhouse.

end, near the top. Mount a cleat to one stick so the string may be rolled or wrapped to prevent tangling. Thread the string through the hole of the No. 1 piece, through the No. 2 piece and tie. To use, press No. 2 piece about 10" into the ground at one end of the garden row. Unwinding the string from the cleat, move down the row and press No. 1 piece in the ground at the other end of the row. Tighten the string till taut.

GLASS JUGS HAVE MANY USES

Save those gallon vinegar, cider, and dinner wine jugs for making many useful and inexpensive items. A bottle cutter will be required, but it is easy to use (Fig. 11-8). Bottle cutters are available at most hobby shops and hardware stores for $3 to $10.

The top portion of the bottle makes a very good mini-greenhouse or hot cap and will maintain 15° above the outside temperature (Fig. 11-9).

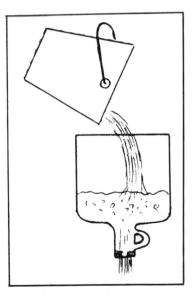

Fig. 11-10. The top portion can be used wherever a large funnel is required.

331

Fig. 11-11. The bottom portion can be used to feed and water rabits.

The open top provides the necessary oxygen for plants. There is no danger from frost and no need for removing and replacing them each night and morning. The top portion can also be used wherever a large funnel is required (Fig. 11-10).

The bottom portion can be used to feed and water small stock such as rabbits and chickens (Fig. 11-11). The edges of the bottom portion should be sanded lightly with carbide paper, which should be provided in the bottle cutter kit. It is also available at hobby and hardware stores.

TIRES CAN FEED AND WATER LIVESTOCK

Figures 11-12 and 11-13 show a couple ways to put worn out tires to practical use on the farm or homestead. They are especially useful where small numbers of sheep or goats are kept, and where pen space is none too plentiful.

The watering system consists of simply setting a water pail or tub inside a tire of suitable size. A 13″ tire is about right for the common 20-quart tubs which are often used to water small penfuls of animals. It will eliminate most of the contamination problem, as it keeps them from standing with their hind feet next to the pail. Part of the tire may be cut away to fit it more compactly into a corner or against a wall.

The feeder is made from half a tire, cut around the center of the tread. If a large, heavy tire is used, some difficulty may be experienced in cutting around it. Pry the edge, or bead sections, apart and go around the inside with a sharp knife. On a 20″ truck tire, this was soon accomplished, and each half made a feeder for about 10 sheep or goats.

Fig. 11-12. A feeder made from half of a discarded tire.

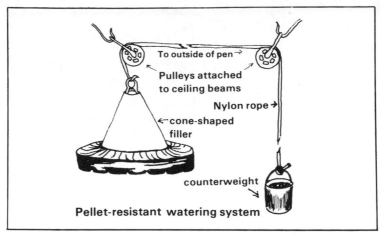

Fig. 11-13. A pellet-resistant watering system.

The cone shaped center filler can be made of sheet metal on a wooden frame, or improvised from other material. It must be sturdy enough to prevent risk of the unit dropping and perhaps injuring animals.

Two pulleys are needed, one directly over the spot where the feeder is to be used, and the other one outside of the pen, located where it won't cause inconvenience or be disturbed by animals. They are fastened securely to the ceiling, preferably at least 7' or 8' above the floor. Clothesline pulleys are suitable.

A nylon rope in good, strong condition is fastened to the top of the filler cone, passed through the first pulley, then through the outside one, and attached to a counterweight. This can be a leaky but sturdy pail, with enough scrap iron or other material in it to be just able to lift the feeder up against its pulley, when empty. A scoopful or so of feed should hold it down to the floor. As the feed is being eaten, the animals will hold the feeder

Fig. 11-14. An inexpensive flood-light.

333

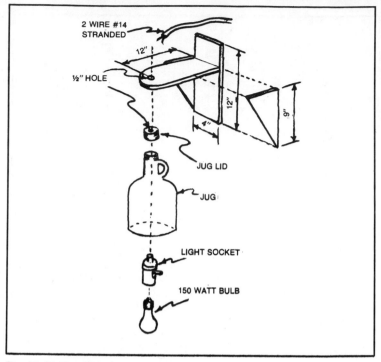

Fig. 11-15. Floodlight assembly diagram.

down with their noses until it is empty. It will then be pulled up several feet by the counterweight, and thus take up no pen space when not in use, as well as collect no pellets.

These half-a-tire feeders aren't very satisfactory unless suspended this way, as otherwise, they take up too much room, and fill up with pellets.

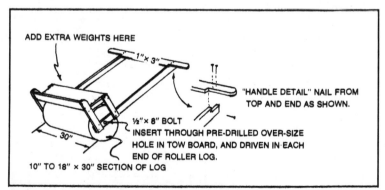

Fig. 11-16. A place is provided for extra weights.

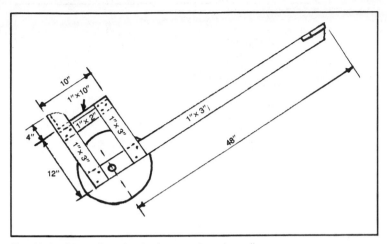

Fig. 11-17. Dimensions for the lawn and garden roller.

It is quite probable that the overhead pulley system described can be adapted to some other style feeders.

FLOODLIGHT

Most outside floodlights cost $39.95 or more. The light in Fig. 11-14 cost $1.35 plus a few pieces of scrap wood.

Construct a light bracket from scrap wood (Fig. 11-15). Later you nail this to your light pole or to the corner of the building near the area to be lighted.

With a glass or bottle cutter, remove the lower portion of a 1-gallon vinegar or clear wine jug. Assemble as shown in Fig. 11-15. After assembly, tape and seal the top of the jug and lid. The glass jug serves two purposes: light refraction and amplification, and it protects the bulb from the elements.

Fig. 11-18. A useful handy-cart.

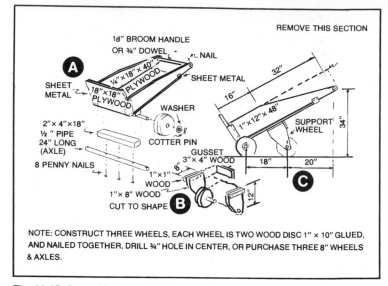

Fig. 11-19. Assembly details for the handi-cart.

LAWN AND GARDEN ROLLER

You can build your own garden and lawn roller with a few pieces of scrap lumber and a 30″ section of a log 10″ to 18″ in diameter. The one in Fig. 11-16 has a place provided for additional weight if needed, such as a couple of concrete blocks, bricks, or rocks. Any change in design is okay, as long as the end result is a roller with a tow bar for pulling. See Fig. 11-17.

HANDI-CART

If you need something to move those heavy sacks of feed or bales of hay around the barn when feeding, build this handi-cart (Fig. 11-18). The support wheel doesn't pivot; raise the handle just enough for turning corners.

Cut and shape two pieces of 1″ × 12″ × 48″ pine. Drill ¾″ holes for the handle. Cut one piece of ¼″ × 18″ × 40″ plywood for the bottom, and one piece ¼″ × 18″ × 18″ for the end. Assemble with glue and nails as shown in Fig. 11-19A. Reinforce the areas shown with sheet metal.

Cut ½″ × 24″ pipe. Drill a ⅛″ hole at each end for the cotter pin, and three holes so the pipe axle may be nailed to 2″ × 4″ × 18″ wood. Glue and nail it to the bottom, locating the center of the axle 4″ back from the end. Drive nails down through the ¼″ plywood bottom into 2″ × 4″ × 18″ piece.

Cut out and assemble all details shown in Fig. 11-19B for the support wheel. Then glue the wheel to the center of the bottom panel, locating it 18″ from the front wheels (Fig. 11-19C). After the glue is dry, install six 1″ wood screws down through the bottom into the assembly.

HOMEMADE GARDEN CART

Michael Barlett's gardening and harvesting are a lot easier since he built a sturdy cart—for about one-third the cost of a similar size and style of store-bought cart (Fig. 11-20). Here's how you can duplicate the cart.

Using scrap materials, make an angle iron frame to the size of the cart you want, perhaps 48 by 32". Weld the corners, making sure they are square. To give added strength for heavier loads, reinforce the bottom by welding a couple of pieces of angle iron across the bottom from side to side.

Fashion the handle from small diameter scrap pipe or from conduit. Then weld it to the underside of the frame. The handle extends out from the frame about 16".

The bottom is made from plywood ½" or ⅝" thick, bolted to the frame. Cut out and bolt on plywood pieces for the front and sides. Make the sides about 6" shorter than the frame, and angle the top corner for easy loading. A strip of flat iron ¼" thick was bolted on the top edge of the plywood on the front and sides as a protector of the edge and also as an extra attachment point for the stand.

The stand, also made from small diameter pipe, attaches to the top edge of the sides at the frame and extends down half the diameter of the wheel. Then attaches at the frame corner.

Now for the hardest part—the wheels and axle. Use old bicycle rims. First, remove all of the spokes and the hub. Cut a circle of ¾" plywood with a jigsaw to fit tightly inside the rim. Then put a wood screw into each former spoke hole. Get a round piece of ¼" plate metal about 10" in diameter; bore a 1" diameter hole in the center.

Push a 6" piece of tubing through the hole and weld it, leaving about 3" on both sides. Then bore a hole in the center of the plywood just large enough to accept the tubing, which is then pushed through. Bolt a thinner metal piece, approximately ⅛" thick on the other side. This serves as a

Fig. 11-20. Michael Bartlett made this inexpensive, but sturdy garden cart.

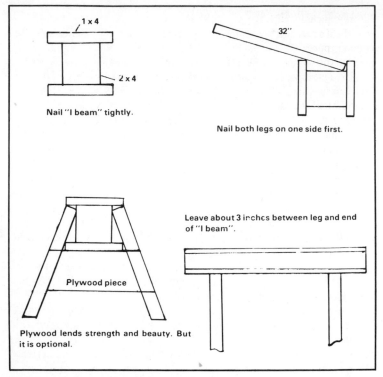

1 x 4

2 x 4

Nail "I beam" tightly.

32"

Nail both legs on one side first.

Leave about 3 inches between leg and end of "I beam".

Plywood piece

Plywood lends strength and beauty. But it is optional.

Fig. 11-21. Construction details for the sawhorse.

bearing. Put a grease fitting in the tubing as close to the wheel as possible on the outside to further the life of the bearing. This makes for a very sturdy wheel.

For the axle, use a piece of round shaft the same diameter as the inside dimension of the tube through the wheel. The length is determined by the width of the cart frame, plus 12". The axle is then welded to the bottom of the angle iron frame about one-third of the way back from the front to allow for good balance. The wheels are held in place by drilling a hole in the end of each side of the axle so a cotter key can be inserted. Paint the cart with a rugged enamel.

SAWHORSE

A good sawhorse is the foundation of most homestead building chores. Most sawhorse designs require complex, mitered cuts which are nearly impossible to duplicate without sophisticated equipment or jigs. These cuts are frustrating and time consuming. A wobbly sawhorse is useless.

The sawhorse described here is quick and easy to build with only a few hand tools. The tools include a saw, a hammer, a measure, and a pencil.

Materials include one 3′ 2 × 4, two 3′ 1 × 4s, four 32″ 1 × 4s, and some nails 2½ to 4″. If a really finished product is what you're after, you need a piece of plywood approximately 16 × 30.

Nail the two 36″ 1 × 4s to the 2″ sides of the two by (Fig. 11-21). This will give a wooden "I" beam. Nail it securely: this "I" beam is the working surface. It is wide and has a good "lip" on which to use clamps. It is ideal.

Now for the legs of the sawhorse. Turn the "I" beam on its side and nail one of the 32″ pieces onto it. Nail the other leg on this side before turning it over. Stand it up, and you have a sawhorse.

At this time, you may wish to mark and cut the plywood so that it fits to support both the "I" beam and the legs. This addition lends strength and beauty, but is optional.

This sawhorse is simple and long lasting. The design is flawless. It is one indispensable homestead tool which can be built cheaply and easily.

SAWBUCK

Build a sawbuck with a wood hold-down arm. The weighted arm holds the logs tightly in place so they can be sawn without need of further

Fig. 11-22. A sawbuck like this one makes it easier, and safer, to cut firewood—including those pieces that are just a few inches too long for the stove.

Fig. 11-23. Herbert Huff uses a sawbuck he devised to cut small pieces safely and easily.

assistance. Build the sawbuck long enough (4′) so it will hold logs up to 8′ in length.

With the exception of the concrete weight which takes a few days to cure, you need about two hours to build the sawbuck. The buck is made of four crosspieces nailed to three side braces. Overall length is determined by the length of the side braces. The first two crosspieces are spaced at 12″, (to support the short logs), while the last two are spaced at 15″. If you'd like to make a cheaper, lighter sawbuck, use three crosspieces (or two if you don't want a hold-down arm) instead of four.

Each crosspiece is made from the following 2 × 4 inch lumber parts: two 4′ long cross arms, one 12″ long spacer block, and one 18″ long brace. Use 16d nails for added strength.

Start by measuring 18″ from one end of a 4′ cross arm. Next, line up the spacer block on that mark and nail it with one nail at each end. Take the other cross arm and mark it with a dot right in the center of the board at the 2′ (halfway) mark. Lay the second cross arm on top of the first, line it up so the ends and sides are flush with each other, and put one nail through the halfway mark.

Now spread the cross arm apart until you reach the proper working height for you, and mark the angle of the cross arm onto the spacer block. While you're hammering three or four nails into the cross arm, keep your eye on the angle mark so the cross arms stay in proper alignment.

Slip the brace between the cross arms so it will cover as much of the cross arm as possible, and nail it down, also. Make the other crosspieces the same way, using the first one as a template for obtaining the correct angle. Cut the side braces to the desired length, and nail them to the crosspieces as shown in Fig. 11-22.

Hold-down Arm

Make the log hold-down arm from a scrap piece of 2 × 4 (length depends on the angle of the cross arm). Hammer several nails into one end to help grip the wood and mount a door hinge onto the other end. The other half of the door hinge is screwed to the upper side brace.

The weight is made by filling a 3 pound coffee can with ready-mix concrete. A ⅜″ anchor bolt, 6″ long, is inserted into the wet concrete. After it has cured for a few days, drill a ⅜″ hole in the arm and fasten the weight with a nut and washer on both sides of the arm.

Arm Block

To hold the arm out of the way when it's not in use, build an arm block. Fasten a door hinge onto a short piece of 2 × 4, then screw the other side of the hinge into the cross arm (running perpendicular to the weighted arm). Swung into the closed position, the block lies flush against both cross arms.

To help hold the weight of the heavy arm, nail another piece of scrap lumber to the second cross arm. The bottom edge of the arm block rests on this scrap when it is in the closed position. The sawbuck helps you cut small pieces safely and easily. (Fig. 11-23).

Chapter 12

Crafts

The lady of the homestead will enjoy making a jacket, sock dolls, a denim satchel, woolen pillows, rugs, and quilts. Ways to recycle baling twine and tin cans are detailed.

WASHCLOTHS

At first thought it may seem not worth bothering to make washcloths out of the corners of old bath towels. Upon looking at a catalog and finding washcloths priced from 79 cents to $1.59, it wouldn't take long to save a number of dollars.

Towels usually wear out in the middle, so you can cut a washcloth from each corner. If the hemmed or selvage edges of the towel are still in good condition, only two sides of the washcloth are left to finish. You can do this in a few minutes by hemming, overcasing, zigzagging, or perhaps just pinking. Likewise, dish towels or pillowcases can be made from the corners of a sheet which still have strong material though the middle is worn to shreds.

USES FOR OLD SOCKS

The tops of old socks with worn out heels and toes can be handy as cuffs in making or repairing children and adult clothing. Tops of heavyweight synthetic or wool socks make warm cuffs to keep the snow and wind off wrists and ankles in snowsuits, jackets, and snowpants. Children can get more wear from coats by adding cuffs to lengthen sleeves as children grow. Similarly, lighter weight sock tops can be used as cuffs on knit shirts and pajamas.

Some old socks make good dishcloths. Cotton is especially absorbent and suitable for this purpose. Sew two together, if a larger dishcloth is preferred. Yarn can be raveled from badly worn socks to match others that can be repaired with only a little darning.

A THREE-CUT JACKET

This jacket requires cutting only three slits in a square of fabric. There is very little sewing and almost no waste of material.

Figures 12-1A through 12-1C show how to make a medium-sized adult jacket from a 42″ square of fabric. Dimensions can be changed to accommodate any member of the family. For narrow widths of hand-woven fabric, two pieces can be used, with a seam at the center back.

Cut along the solid lines in Fig. 12-1A. Then fold along the dotted lines as shown in Fig. 12-1B. Stitch the under arm and front yoke seams by hand or machine. With the selvage sides of the fabric forming the ends of the sleeve, no finishing is needed there. You may hem the neckline and front edges, bind them with bias tape or decorative braid, or face them with same or contrasting fabric. The bottom edge is fringed and tied in tassels or held with a row of stitching to prevent further raveling. The front can be left open, or closures such as buttons and loops or a zipper could be used. Figure 12-1C shows the finished jacket.

INFANTS' FOOTWEAR

The idea is prevalent that small children should have the support of high topped shoes when starting to walk. Many pediatricians are now recommending that children go barefoot or stockingfoot as much as possible. This leaves them free to exercise and strengthen their arches and ankles by curling their toes, walking on tiptoes, and moving their feet freely. Shoes are not necessary for normal foot development but for protection from weather and injury.

If floors are cold and more warmth is needed, slipper socks may be the answer. Those with leather soles help prevent falls if floors are slippery.

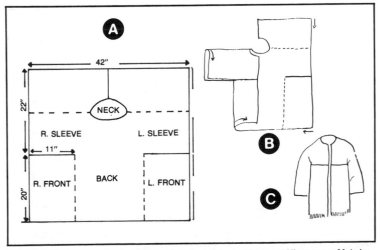

Fig. 12-1. You can make a medium-sized adult jacket from a 42″ square of fabric.

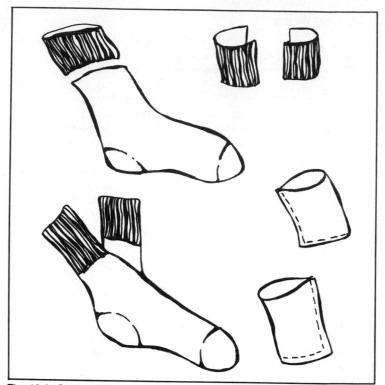

Fig. 12-2. Cotton socks are needed for each doll's body (drawing by Margot Mayr).

Homespun yarn can make very warm booties, slippers, or socks. The flexibility of soft shoes such as tennis shoes is desirable, but rubber soles cause excessive sweating for some individuals.

Whatever your children wear on their feet, make sure they are properly fitted. Socks, slippers, or footed sleepwear that is too small can be just as damaging as tight shoes. Many foot problems that can affect people for life start in childhood with continued use of footwear that has become too small with rapid foot growth.

SOCK DOLLS

With relatively few materials and little time, you can create a charming sock doll that will delight any child. These dolls also make lovely gifts.

For each doll's body, you will need a cotton sock (Fig. 12-2). Use men's size 11-13. Cut 2½″ off the ribbing. You will be left with a tubular piece of ribbing. For the two arms, cut this piece in two along the folds. Fold each piece lengthwise and sew along the raw edges, leaving an opening for the stuffing.

To form the legs, first cut 2½" into the folds on the remaining piece of sock. Turn the sock inside out and stitch along the raw edges. Leave an opening in the crotch for stuffing. Turn the sock right side out and stuff until it's firm. Use quilt batting for stuffing. Then sew the crotch closed.

The head is made by wrapping heavy thread around the sock about 3" from the top. Wrap tightly and secure the thread with a knot in the back of the neck.

Stuff the arms and sew them onto the body about 1¼" below the neck and slightly forward. To make the hands and feet, wrap some thread around the arms and legs about ¾" from the end (Fig. 12-3).

The hair is made by wrapping yarn around part of a bent coat hanger. Wrap evenly 120 times and then sew down the center of the yarn with a machine. Slip the yarn off the hanger and make additional strands of hair. Make five or six strips for each doll.

Begin sewing the hair on a girl doll about 1" up from the neckline. Place the yarn strips so the end is 1½" from the center of the doll's face. Hand sew the yarn strips to the head, sewing the next row of hair directly above the first strip, and so on.

For the boy doll, make a hairpiece long enough to reach around his head. Sew evenly around the head along the reinforcing line of the sock (Fig. 12-4).

Carefully mark the doll's face with a pencil and then embroider on the features. Use red for the mouth, pink for the nose, and brown or black for the eyes.

A piece of cloth 10" × 24" is needed for the dress. Sew narrow hems on top and bottom edges. Then fold the piece in half, and in half again. Make the

Fig. 12-3. The legs and arms are formed (drawing by Margot Mayr).

Fig. 12-4. Hair is made for the dolls (drawing by Margot Mayr).

armhole by cutting an L-shaped 1¼″ deep and ¾″ wide cut along the folded
edge. Turn the raw edges to the inside and machine stitch. Connect the
armholes by placing the right sides together and sewing a few machine
stitches at the neckline. Sew the back seam of the dress (Fig. 12-5).

Gather the neckline of the dress together using a hand gathering stitch.
Slip the dress on the doll and pull the gathering thread snug.

Use your imagination to make each dress unique. Decorate the bottom
of the dress with ric rac, a piece of ribbon, or some lace. A 24″ length of
ribbon can be tied into a bow around the doll's neck, with a matching bow
sewn into her hair (Fig. 12-6).

The boy's clothes are made from a sock the same size as the sock used
to make the body. Cut 2¼″ off the toe of the sock for the hat. Turn the raw
edge under the hem by hand. Stuff the hat full and sew on the head. Fold the

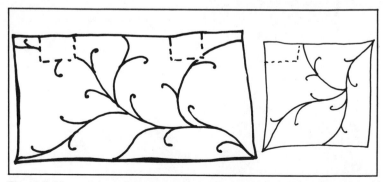

Fig. 12-5. You need a 10″×24″ piece of cloth for the dress (drawing by Margot
Mayr).

346

Fig. 12-6. A doll for the girls (drawing by Margot Mayr).

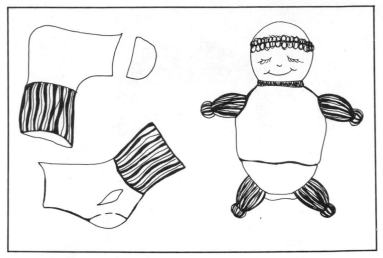

Fig. 12-7. A doll for the boys (drawing by Margot Mayr).

curls down toward the face in order to get the stitching as close to the hairline as possible.

The boy's suit is made from the remaining piece of the sock. Cut armholes by making a vertical slit just below the ribbing and about 1⅛" from the center fold. Stitch down raw edges. Do not make the slits too large as they stretch a great deal when you dress the doll.

Place the suit on the doll. Fold the top of the ribbing to form a turtleneck. Fold the bottom raw edges of the sock under two or three times up to the crotch and sew together (Fig. 12-7).

Fig. 12-8. The durability and volume of the satchel will depend on the size and strength of your jeans.

DENIM SATCHEL

While fitting right into the fashionable "faded" look, this type of purse is easy to make and uses few materials. Its durability and volume will depend on the size and strength of your jeans (Fig. 12-8).

Here are the simple directions to make your own "recycled" satchel at an affordable price. Cut two matching pieces from the seat of the pants, so that the pockets are centered (1 in Fig. 12-9). Cut two 1" pieces of material on a bias, making them as long as the width of the top of the purse (2 in Fig. 12-9). These are the facings. Attach them (right sides together) to the top of the front and back sections of the purse (Fig. 2-10). Press the facings toward the insides.

Cut two matching strips from the remaining material, about 3" wide and a length that equals twice the distance from the hip to the shoulder plus 8" (3 in Fig. 12-9). The extra is for the knot at the top of the shoulder. These pieces join the front and back of the purse and extend to become the shoulder strap.

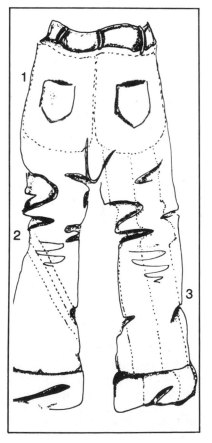

Fig. 12-9. Cut material from the pants for the satchel.

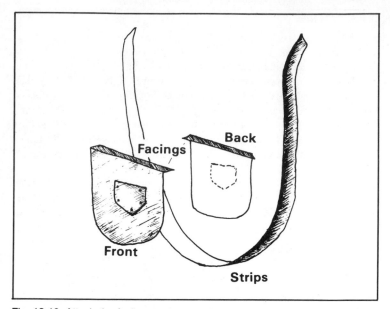

Fig. 12-10. Attach the facings to the top of the front and back sections of the purse.

With the right sides together, baste one strip to the front half of the purse body so that the free ends of the strip extend an equal distance from the top edges of the purse body. Baste the back half of the purse, right sides together, to the same strip. Stitch both seams on your machine. Remove the basting stitches.

Press a hem on both sides of the second strip, making the hems the same width as the seams you have just stitched. Now baste this strip, wrong sides together, against the first one that you have already stitched to the purse. Be sure to fold the raw edges toward each other. This covers the raw edges inside and gives a more finished look to your purse. Be sure that the second strip matches the first in length and positioning.

Machine stitch on the outside of the purse using either a straight or zigzag stitch. Press a hem at the end of the straps and stitch. Tie a simple overhand knot to make the purse hang as a shoulder bag. You may sew a snap at the top of the purse if desired. To make a purse even more personal, embroider the person's name on one of the pockets.

PILLOWS FROM RAW WOOL

Many homesteaders may be wondering if there isn't some way to make use of wool, rather than selling it for practically nothing. Wool can be spun into yarn, of course, but many people don't have the time or skill to spin the wool. You can use the wool to make many useful items such as pillows and small rugs, with very little work (Fig. 12-11).

Fig. 12-11. Make these pillows from raw wool.

First, spread the fleece out and cut off any pieces of wool having manure on them. Throw these pieces away. Separate the fleece into pieces about 18" square. The next step is to wash the wool in Woolite and cool water. It will take three or four washings to get the wool clean. It will also

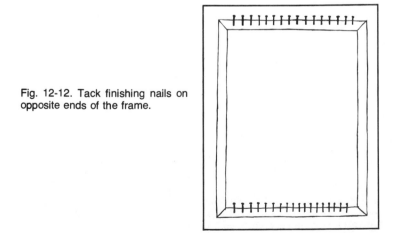

Fig. 12-12. Tack finishing nails on opposite ends of the frame.

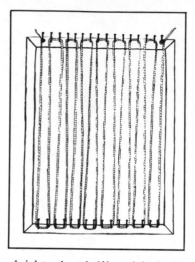

Fig. 12-13. Wind the yarn back and forth across the frame and around the nails.

shrink to about half its original volume. After the wool is washed, spread it out on a towel to dry.

To make a pillow or rug, you'll need a frame. An old picture frame or any other rectangular frame will do. Tack some finishing nails, about 1″ apart, on opposite ends of the frame (Fig. 12-12). Now you need some yarn, cord, or twine. Starting at one corner, wind the yarn back and forth across the frame and around the nails. (Fig. 12-13).

Now you're ready for the fun part—using the wool. Take a handful of wool and gently pull it into a roll about 8″ long and 1″ thick (Fig. 12-14). Start weaving the roll of wool over and under the strands of yarn (Fig. 12-15). With another handful of wool, repeat the process. As you finish each row of weaving, push it down against the previous row to make the weave sturdy. The weaving goes very quickly—you're weaving about 1″ at a time. For contrast, you can weave rows of yarn, and even beads, into your work.

When you've woven all but about 4″ of the space in the frame, stop weaving. Cut the yarn between the nails and tie every two strands of yarn

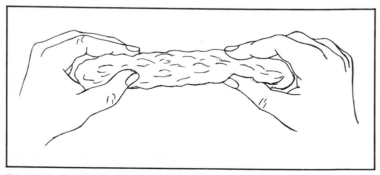

Fig. 12-14. Pull the wool into a roll.

352

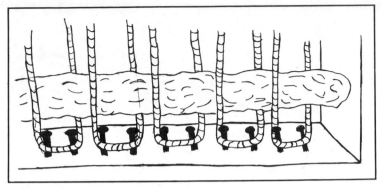

Fig. 12-15. Weave the roll of wool over and under the strands of yarn.

together (Fig. 12-16). This will hold the weave tight. You can leave the ends for fringe or cut them off. If you're making a rug, you're finished. If making a pillow, fold the weaving in half. Sew up two sides, stuff with wool or cloth scraps, and sew up the opening. The pillow is finished.

Once you've mastered this simple method of using raw wool, you can use your imagination to create many other useful and decorative items for your home and family.

RAG RUGS

There are a number of ways of making rag rugs with little or no equipment. Cumbersome and costly looms with expensive carpet warp are not needed for crocheted, hooked, or braided rugs. These traditional

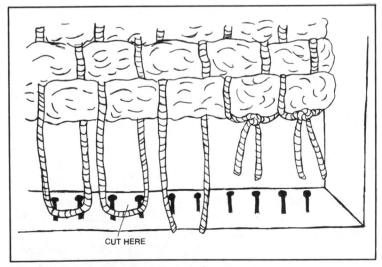

Fig. 12-16. Tie every two strands of yarn together.

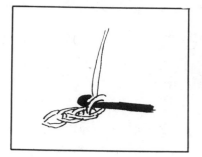

Fig. 12-17. Chain stitch—make a loop by catching the thread around the crochet hook and pulling through previous loop.

methods have been used for generations to make useful and attractive rugs from discarded clothing and other textiles. These methods are also used in making yarn rugs, but they are expensive that way.

Rags are torn in strips and sewn together the same way for any of the rag rugs. Strips may be wider for braided rugs than for hooked or crocheted rugs. Less sewing is involved with long strips from large items such as sheets or curtains rather than from small garments. It is advisable to use cotton rags for one rug and wool for another rather than combine them.

CROCHETED RUGS

Crocheted rugs are usually oval-shaped. To start, take a large crochet hook and chain 6″ to 8″ (Fig. 12-17). Then hooking into this beginning chain, single crochet as shown in Fig. 12-18. Continue to single crochet around and around hooking into the previous round until your rug is the desired size. Along the straighter sides single crochet once in each stitch from the previous round. Going around the sharper curves on the ends of the oval, crochet twice in some of the stitches to increase so that each round has more stitches than the previous round, and the rug will lay flat. If you don't increase enough, the rug will curl up. If you increase too much, the edge will be ruffled.

HOOKED RUGS

Hooked rugs are made on a backing fabric such as burlap. Although there are a variety of special latches and gadgets for various types of hooked rugs, a large crochet hook is all that is needed.

With the strip of fabric held below the backing fabric in your left hand, work from above with the hook in your right hand. Push the hook down

Fig. 12-18. Single crochet. Insert a hook through a stitch, catch a thread around the hook, draw back through the stitch, catch thread again, and draw through the two loops.

Fig. 12-19. Making a hooked rug.

through the burlap and hook it around the rag strip. Then pull the loop to the top of the burlap as shown in Fig. 12-19. Unhook the hook and leave the loop on the surface of the burlap. Repeat by pushing the hook down and pulling up loops of a consistent length. These rugs are surprisingly durable and don't easily become unraveled during use.

BRAIDED RUGS

A simple three strand braid is sufficient for making braided rugs (Fig. 12-20). There will be fewer problems with tangling if relatively short strands are braided. More strips can be sewed on as you go rather than starting with a big ball of sewed together rag strips.

After you have a length of braid started, you can start sewing the braid together. Coil the braid in a round or oval. Stitch by hand with a needle and strong thread as inconspicuously as possible. Stitch each round onto the next. You can stop with a small area rug or continue until you have a room sized rug.

QUILTING

Quilt making has finally come out of the past and into the now, and with quite a bit of fanfare. What used to be considered a slightly "odd" gift is now the hit of the entire party (Fig. 12-21). Maybe it's because we are beginning to see our world in a different light—not a collection of throwaways, but investments in the future.

Fig. 12-20. This braided rug was made of uncut nylon stockings.

Fig. 12-21. A quilt is not really difficult to make.

Aren't quilts hard to make? Don't you need all those quilt frames that take up a whole room and 20 friends to finish it? Not really. Just like anything else, as the years go by, quilt making gets easier and more efficient. With the invention of the sewing machine, hundreds of hours have been taken off quilt making time.

Basically, a quilt consists of a front, a back, and a filler. Our Amish friends call a quilt anything with a thin middle, and anything with heavy batting is "comfort." That just goes to show that a quilt can be suited to any need by the weight of batting.

Whatever the style, though, there are several important rules to follow. Most important is the material used. Make sure the pretty prints you buy are washable over a long period of time. There's nothing more discouraging than to make a quilt, wash it several times, and have certain squares fade. It takes away from the entire design.

There's a lot to be said about using old material, material that has been worn as clothes in some way. You know it won't fade because it's already been washed many times. There's always material on every garment that's less worn than other parts. For instance, the material on the bottom back of a shirt or blouse is usually in pretty good shape. If you're using new cloth, wash it in hot water first to check its durability.

Use generous seam allowances on your quilt. Often quilts have been sewn, washed, and then had to be repaired because not enough seam allowance was given. The squares pulled apart. It wouldn't be much of a task to repair a large block quilt, but a quilt that incorporated hundreds of small squares could be a disaster if it should pull apart.

The next suggestion is very basic, but often not considered until it's too late. It's the batting, or filler.

Old blankets are a dream, but watch their fiber content. Wool blankets inside children's quilts could make an interesting problem on wash day—an even more interesting problem after it's taken from the dryer all hopelessly pulled together.

A synthetic blanket, on the other hand, lends itself very well to just about any type of quilt. A soft, lightweight store batting is the usual choice for a baby's first quilt. It's warm without the weight.

As long as you don't mix your materials, like knits and cottons, and you select your batting carefully, there's no reason why anyone can't turn out a nice quilt on the first try. How do you start? Design and sew the top. Measure the bed top to get the desired size, and sew with that goal in mind. By quilting on a floor or bed, it's easier to visualize the design as it's being sewn. Long extra strips can be run down each side and across the top and bottom for added length and width. It also gives the quilt a "framed" look.

When you've finally decided on the batting, the backing (a bed sheet works wonderfully well) and the design you'd like for the top, find a large clean floor space and lay down the sheet. Next lay the batting on top and the finished top piece on last. Either invite several friends over to hold, or find several large volumes of books and place some on each corner.

The idea behind the friends or the books is to get all three layers even and tight. When this is done, take some large safety pins or a needle and thread. Insert them here and there to secure the three layers. When this is done, yarn and a large eyed needle can be used to "tie" the layers together. Usually the ties are no further than 12″ apart. Using a colored yarn that will enhance the pattern is pretty. Make sure you make the double tie on the top piece and not the sheet.

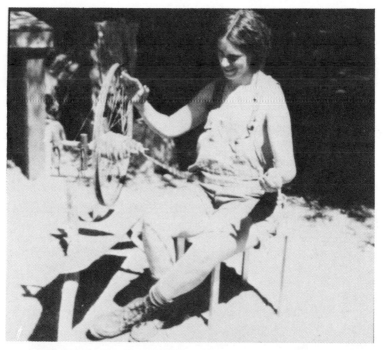

Fig. 12-22. It doesn't have to be fancy to do the job, as you can tell by the smile on Barbara's face.

Fig. 12-23. From the junk pile to a work of art, and all it took was a little imagination.

When the entire quilt is tied, the edges can be bound with blanket binding or in the same material used in the quilt. The edges can also be turned in and sewn under instead.

To applique a quilt square, use the zigzag on your machine, and make the stitch length close. There's no need to "finish" the outside of your appliques when this method is used; the zigzag stitch stops any raveling.

There are many books that give quilt designs and patterns, but the ones we treasure most are the ones we've thought of ourselves. Use your imagination and a little common sense. Produce something you can be proud of for many years.

SPINNING WHEEL

Making a spinning wheel just occurred to Bernie Lichtenstein and his friend Barbara one day. They have a black sheep and white woolie who have been given them about 10 pounds of wool each. Barbara had been handspinning the wool on a drop spindle, but it took a long time to produce just a two or three ounce skein using that method. Barbara loves it, but that sort of goes without saying. Looking at her finished balls of naturally dyed wool, some of them incorporating camel hair, Alpaca, or human hair, is pretty exciting. Nevertheless, the idea of a spinning wheel to help things along in a beautiful way was intriguing.

Bernie and Barbara looked at their *Foxfire Two* book. It had diagrams, pictures, and even measurements for handmade wheels. It all looked possible, maybe even simple.

358

In between caring for their livestock, the garden and themselves, Bernie and Barbara rummaged around their 10 acres in search of materials for the wheel. They found a couple of ½″ and 1″ dowels in the junk which they used for the spindle and holder. A 4″ long piece of rough, split oak was used for the bench. Some solid, green oak sticks were retrieved from the firewood pile to be used as legs. There was an abandoned and lonely bicycle wheel in the junkyard—providing a ready-made wheel. It was 24″ in diameter, not quite as large as most of the wheels in *Foxfire Two*, but it looked as if it would do the job. It did.

Bernie and Barbara stripped the tube and tire off the wheel, cut a long strip from the tube, and glued it all along the circumference of the wheel where the original tire used to lay. They figured that would make a nice straight runway (and a smooth one) for the string that runs, like a fan belt, around the wheel and spindle, thus keeping the machinery in motion.

Following the diagrams in *Foxfire Two*, Bernie scaled the other measurements to coincide with our smaller wheel. It worked and still does, much to Bernie's amazement.

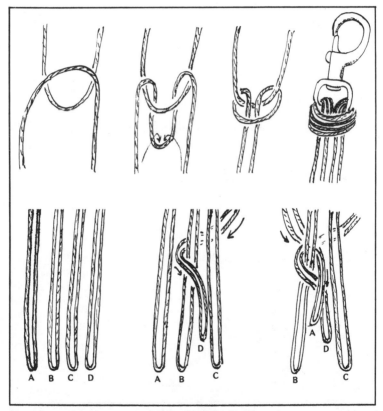

Fig. 12-24. Using uncut twine and making the braid.

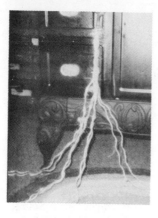

Fig. 12-25. On a cold winter's night, braiding next to the woodstove would be a delightful pasttime.

A professionally crafted or factory produced spinning wheel costs in the neighborhood of $100. Barbara's wheel is rough hewn and finished and certainly is not as well-balanced and polished as the costlier product, but it works and works well (Fig. 12-22). The total outlay for the wheel was approximately $2.50 for some epoxy type glue (Fig. 12-23).

RECYCLING BALING TWINE INTO ROPE

It seems like a shame to pile up and burn used baling twine, especially when considering its high price. Through the years there have been gadgets and machines invented for the purpose of making twine into rope. The results often were not as good as expected.

Nancy Ellison has made many ropes from used baling twine, with a four strand round braid. No equipment is needed. It doesn't take long to make a good sized rope, as 20′ can easily be braided in half an hour.

Fig. 12-26. Make a log carrier out of baling twine.

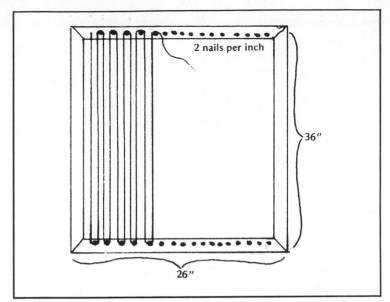

Fig. 12-27. Space the nails every ½″ so there are four threads per 1″.

Although not very refined in appearance, braided ropes are strong. Nancy's horses have broken posts, halters and snaps, but they've never broken any of the braided ropes.

Twine ropes can take a year or two of use tethering animals to graze before weakening due to rotting. Indoors they last longer.

Nancy uses uncut twine slipped from bales and looped together as shown in 1, 2 and 3 of Fig. 12-24. This makes use of the sturdy knots made

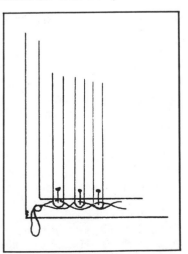

Fig. 12-28. Scrap yarn is twined at both ends on the outside of the nails.

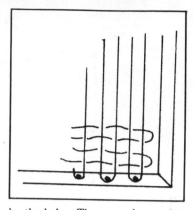

Fig. 12-29. Tuck the end of the beginning piece of twine into the second row.

by the baler. There aren't very long strands of twine to be tangled while braiding and additional twine is looped on as needed. The knots can be turned to the inside of the braid as you come to them. If you cut your twine to open your bales, you will need to make additional knots.

If a snap is desired on the rope for attaching to horse halters or goat collars, the twine can be looped onto the snap as shown in 4 of Fig. 12-24, before starting to braid.

Nancy uses a four strand round braid, which actually is eight strands thick, as a loop of twine is used as one strand. Fasten the beginning end to something sturdy, such as a wall, door, or piece of furniture. Make the braid as shown in 5, 6, and 7 of Fig. 12-24. It will save some confusion if you have the system thoroughly in mind. As you braid, alternately pick up the strand to the far left or right. Then bring it under and around the middle of the remaining three strands (Fig. 12-25). That's all there is to it. For thicker ropes more loops of twine can be used together as one.

WEAVING A LOG CARRIER OUT OF BALING TWINE

After thinking of various items to weave with baling twine, Judy Haas decided a log carrier would be a useful project (Fig. 12-26).

Her log carriers are made on a Navaho-type loom. To avoid getting too involved in discussing Navaho weaving, we will describe weaving log carriers on a simple frame loom.

A 36" × 24" log carrier is adequate for our purposes. Larger sizes will hold more logs, but they are difficult to carry into the house. For the warp threads (the threads to be wound back and forth around the nails of the frame loom), Judy uses either crochet thread or rug warp. Space the nails every ½" so there are four threads per 1" (Fig. 12-27). For the top and bottom finished edges, a cord of scrap yarn should be twined at both ends on the outside of the nails (Fig. 12-28).

Those familiar with weaving might want to set up heddles. Basically, the piece of baling twine is woven over and under the threads, alternating threads each row. (Haas puts masking tape over the end of twine to make a

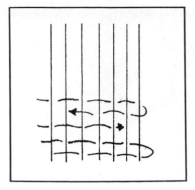

Fig. 12-30. Overlay the next piece of twine and continue.

point.) Tuck the end of the beginning piece of twine into the second row (Fig. 12-29). With a fork or Afro pick, push the twine down firmly after each row is woven. When the first piece of baling twine is used up, overlay the next piece and continue (Fig. 12-30). These splices will stay firm.

As you near the last 10″ of weaving space, begin at the top and work down, tucking in the loose beginning thread as before. Weaving is difficult for the last few rows, but keep squeezing the twine until no more rows can be done.

A strap can be made by braiding the baling twine (or yarn), making a belt on an inkle loom, or by using scraps of leather. Judy uses a sewing machine to sew it into position (Fig. 12-31).

RECYCLINQ BALER TWINE TO DECORATE THE HOME

Once the hay bales are cut open, baler twine is considered to have served its purpose. Its lifespan can be lengthened with a little ingenuity, thread, and a needle. Recycle baler twine into hotpads, coasters, and doormats that are durable as well as attractive (Figs. 12-32 and 12-33).

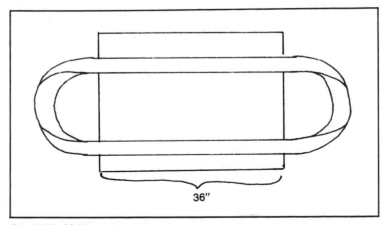

36″

Fig. 12-31. Making a strap.

Fig. 12-32. Recycle baler twine into attractive items.

To begin, gather the discarded baler twine and sort it according to length. If you want to add a little color to your project, the twine can be dyed. Before dyeing, tie the strands together loosely in bundles of 10. Follow the instructions on the package for mixing the dye. Leave the twine in the dye bath for a couple days to allow it to absorb as much color as possible. After dyeing, the twine must be braided.

To braid, tie three strands together at one end. Braid 2″ or 3″ before anchoring the braided end under a table leg or something heavy that will anchor your work as you braid. When you come to the end, tie a string around the strands several times to keep the braid secure.

To lace the braids together, you will need a rug needle and strong thread such as carpet warp or jute. If you have dyed your twine, the lacing thread should be dyed along with it. The finished product will have a better appearance if the lacing thread is the same color as the twine.

Thread the rug needle with lacing twine and knot the end. With your braided twine, make a tight coil measuring 1″ in diameter. Using a rug needle, pull the needle and thread through the coil. Coil one more row and secure it to the main coil in three or four places. Try to keep your stitches hidden as you work. Repeat this procedure of coiling and attaching until the circle is the diameter you wish (Fig. 12-34).

Before joining a new braid to the coil, untie the knotted end. Then

364

overlap the new braid with the braided coil about ½". As you lace, make sure the ends of the braid get tucked in neatly.

When your project is as large as you want, secure the end of the final row by wrapping the lacing thread twice around it and the row before it. Cut off any extra thread and braid.

RECYCLING CANS INTO ART

We overlook the obvious when we throw away trash that needs only a little imagination in order to become useful. Take tin cans, for example.

What once was a can that contained cherries or lard could be transformed into decorative containers that hold magazines or fireplace logs. Soup cans could become lanterns, and large tuna fish cans could blossom into hanging plant baskets. The process is simple, but the result is stunning and has the look of a complicated technique. So get out your cutting torch and your imagination, and get to work.

Tools

A cutting torch performs two functions: making the designs, and changing the can's surface from a gleaming shine to a dull blackish hue (Fig. 12-35). Besides a cutting torch, the only other tools you'll need are holding clamps to help grasp the hot cans while you work.

Fig. 12-33. More durable items that have been recycled from baler twine.

Fig. 12-34. Working on a project made with twine (photo by Karen Hiembue).

Materials

The cans used should be clean and free of labels or any surface printing. Except for cans used to make lanterns, there should be no surface grooves.

Hanging planters are best made from a 54-ounce institutional tuna fish can (Fig. 12-36). Good sources for these cans are schools, restaurants or hospitals. You'll also need four small 's' hooks and 54" of small link chain.

Lanterns are made from two #5 soup cans (Fig. 12-36). To join them, you'll need flux and brazing rods. You'll also need two small 's' hooks or 6" of brass wire and 36" of decorative chain. Large baskets are made from a 50 pound lard can or a 30 pound frozen fruit can.

Construction Steps

Clean the empty cans and remove labels. Draw a design on the surface of the can using a permanent marking pen or experiment with freehand cutting.

Cut the border design first and then cut the body of your design. Do your shaping last by carefully bending the cans into shape. Torching will cause the cans to take on a blackish tone, which is the result you want. Rust can be prevented from eventually occurring by giving the finished product a coat of spray satin varnish.

Planters

Cut your design. To hang the basket, you'll need an 's' hook inserted in each of three small holes spaced equally apart cut near the top of the can. Cut the 54" chain into three 18" pieces and slip them onto the 's' hooks. Use pliers to close up the hooks, securing the chain. Join the three loose ends of chain with the fourth 's' hook. The basket is ready to hang.

Fig. 12-35. Recycling tin cans into useful objects is easily accomplished with a cutting torch.

Fig. 12-36. Soup and tuna fish cans become lanterns and hanging plant baskets.

367

Fig. 12-37. An attractive basket.

Lanterns

Cut designs in two #5 soup cans and cut both ends off one of the cans. Shape the two cans by pushing outward from the inside to form a slight bulge. Braze the two cans together, connecting the two open ends.

To hang the lantern, you'll need 's' hooks inserted in two small holes cut in the top can and opposite each other. Cut two pieces of heavy brass wire, each about 3" long, and bend them into an 's' shape. Braze them onto the lantern.

Attach the ends of the 36" decorative chain to two 's' hooks, squeezing with pliers to secure the chain. If you have used brass wire hooks, simply slip the ends of the chain onto the hooks.

A candle is most safely burned in the lantern if it is inside a candle glass. When the candle burns, its light casts the designs of the lantern onto the walls, making a very pleasant effect.

Baskets

After cutting your design, push the can carefully outward from the inside to form roundish sides. Nothing more needs to be done, unless you wish to spray it with satin varnish (Fig. 12-37).

368

Chapter 13

Fencing

Homesteaders often have trouble deciding what types of fencing to erect on their property. This chapter contains some helpful information about fences.

ALL-ELECTRIC FENCE

One of the most unusual and functional fencing ideas we have ever seen was the all-electric fence the late L. H. and Helen Wells had around their goat pasture in Springfield, Il (Fig. 13-1). The place was in the country when the Wells built their house during the 1930s. By the time the last goats were sold in the late 1960s, it was side-by-side city houses all over the place. Right on a corner, black Nubian goats grazed peacefully in their pasture! The fence around the pasture helped keep things peaceful.

Wells fenced the pasture with woven wire stock fence, and electrified it. The fencing was hung on metal insulators on steel posts. A wooden top rail kept the posts rigid and the fencing tight. The bottom of the fence was about 4″ off the ground. Then he hooked it all up to an electric fence charger which ran off house current.

The result was a fence which kept everyone out of trouble. The goats stayed away from it—no problems with goats climbing on the fencing or reaching for greener grass on the other side and stretching the fence. No neighborhood children put their little hands through the fence to pet the goats and feed them things goats shouldn't eat.

Actually, once everyone got used to the fence Wells didn't turn on the electricity very often—at night, maybe, or during the day if they were gone. After the first experience with the fence, no one ever came back to check to see if it was still "hot."

Fig. 13-1. An all-electric fence around a goat pasture.

TYPES OF FENCES

For many homesteaders fencing, in the broader sense, may not be necessary. Pasture fencing obviously involves greater expanse and expense.

What are you going to pasture? It's a rare goat who will get much nourishment from a pasture. It takes quite an area to keep a couple of goats happy and well-fed, and they'll have a small area cleaned out and dead in a year. It might be better, and it will certainly be cheaper, to keep the goats in an exercise yard and bring their food to them. You can cut hay or weeds off that pasture, bring their food to them, and they'll eat it. If left to roam, they'll trample more than they'll eat.

Cows and sheep are grazers, unlike goats, and make better use of the limited pasture areas most homesteaders have. A cow that is trained to electric fencing will be kept in by a single strand. (Sheep are something else—their wool insulates them from the shock, and nothing less than stout field fencing will contain them.)

It is possible to tether a homestead cow, changing the location daily or more often as growing conditions demand. Tethering goats is frowned on, not only because they won't eat grass unless starved to it, but because they're much more active and therefore are good candidates for strangulation. They will also be more vulnerable to dogs and other predators.

Hogs can easily be pastured by using hot barbed wire about 3″ off the ground. Like other animals (except sheep), after they get zapped a few times they won't go near the boundary. Most people frown on barbed wire as the devil's own invention, but it does have some merits where hogs are concerned. Cows are usually pretty thoughtful about where they go and aren't likely to be harmed by barbs, but goats and horses are better off without it (Fig. 13-2).

370

Fig. 13-2. Barbed wire, though cheap and effective fencing for some classes of livestock, has limited use on a homestead. The fence is good for cows, but would probably be ineffective—even dangerous—for goats.

Woven wire is expensive. If you're in a fairly permanent situation and have the money, good woven wire is probably the best bet.

Electric fencing will work for most classes of livestock except sheep. It's a lot easier to stretch and it's cheaper, but you do have the cost of a fencer and juice.

The cash-poor time-rich homesteader will want to consider pens large enough for exercise, made either of wire, stock panels (welded steel rods), or wood. The stock panels, incidentally, while expensive, are strong, look good, will last a long time, and for a small area should be considered (Fig. 13-3). A good job done now will save not only money but time and frustration over the long haul.

For some people, the choice will be wood. New lumber is expensive, but fencing panels can be constructed from demolished buildings and scrap from other sources (Fig. 13-4).

A 45" high, 330' long roll of medium weight field fencing will cost in the neighborhood of $60 (Fig. 13-5). Barbed wire sold in 80 rod spools (four times as much) will be about 50 percent the price, and smooth wire about 25 percent of the cost of field fencing. With these prices, it will cost about $167 to enclose an acre with field fencing, about $60 for barbed wire (single strand), and only about $30 for smooth electric fencing, exclusive of posts and insulators (Fig. 13-6).

Fencing is expensive (Fig. 13-7). For many homesteaders, the best idea may be to confine the animals in relatively small (and cheap) enclosures and to bring the fodder to them, which is what a lot of big-time

Fig. 13-3. Stock panels, made of welded rods, come in a variety of lengths and heights. Some have closer spacing of rods near the bottom to prevent baby pigs from escaping. They are ideal for goats and can be fastened to wood or metal fence posts.

371

Fig. 13-4. A board fence, especially one as sturdy as this one, will hold in just about anything. Wood is expensive and requires proper care and treatment to provide long service.

livestock raisers are doing these days (not because of the cost of fencing, but because of the forage animals waste by trampling and close grazing).

A 5' or 6' fence of good woven wire should protect your goats. Use livestock or "poultry and garden" fencing or 2 × 4" wire mesh, 11 or 12 gauge weight. Stretch the fence tightly on sturdy posts. Be sure the fence is tight against the ground. Dogs may try to crawl or dig under.

An exercise yard 20' by 30' would probably be enough for two goats, if it has shade and is well-drained with sand on it to avoid mudholes. For the sake of running room, it is nice if the exercise yard is 50' long in one direction. We've seen healthy goats living comfortably with less space.

Consider fencing all of your farmstead with woven wire. It would cost some money, but possibly less than you think. It would keep neighbor children and dogs out of your garden and away from your livestock and poultry. Plus, it would help keep your animals home where they belong, too.

Wood fencing is strong and long-lasting, but it costs a lot and is more than you really need. A 12-gauge wire fence is strong enough for goats, dogs and for larger livestock, too.

A *Border Collie* is a great dog for heading livestock, but you don't need a "herd" dog. You need a "watch" dog who feels like the place belongs to him and barks at strange noises and other dogs, chasing after them if they intrude on his turf.

PRESERVING FENCE POSTS

The best way to preserve fence posts is with creosote. Though using creosote is initially a lot of work, it is a real time and money saver in the

Fig. 13-5. Field fencing is fine for cows and sheep, but it will quickly be torn down by goats standing on it to peer out at the world. Note the construction of the bracing to keep the fence tight and the posts straight.

Fig. 13-6. This fence seems to be in a class by itself: it incorporates two sizes of poultry mesh, field fencing and barbed wire! Many homestead fences don't fit textbook descriptions.

long run. Not only are material costs reduced if you can make a fence last twice as long, but the actual fence building is a real chore, one you will want to avoid redoing.

To creosote posts, you'll need two containers of creosote. Place one over a hot fire and bring it up to 170-180°F. Avoid extreme heat. First, soak the posts in the hot cresote for four hours and then soak in the cold creosote for two or more hours. Painting the posts two or three times with hot creosote and an old broom is the next best way of accomplishing this task.

It is also possible to preserve fence posts by boring out a center cavity and filling it with a preservative solution. The hole is bored from the bottom up, just far enough so the top of the cavity is about 4″ above ground level. Then, starting from one side of the post, bore another hole at a slightly downward angle till it joins the center cavity. Plug the hole in the bottom of the post—a 1″ or 2″ long wooden peg will do the trick. The plug is to keep the liquid from escaping out the bottom.

After the posts are set in the ground, fill the center cavity with a wood preservative. Creosote would probably be your best bet. The easiest way to do this is to put the preservative into a container having a long spout, as this facilitates pouring it into the hole on the side. When the cavity is filled, plug the side hole to prevent evaporation and keep out dirt and insects. The preservative will gradually be absorbed by the wood, completely saturating the area adjoining the central cavity. When the solution is completely absorbed, simple remove the plug on the side and add more preservative (Fig. 13-8 and Table 13-1).

Fig. 13-7. Chain link fences aren't too common on farms and are probably less common on working homesteads. Their main disadvantage, high cost, is outweighed for many people by their long life, low upkeep and appearance.

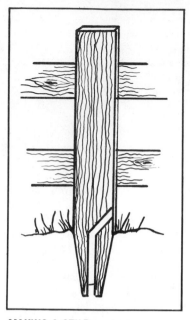

Fig. 13-8. One way to preserve fence posts is to bore a cavity in the lower portion of the post and fill with creosote. The post then gets saturated from the inside out.

MAKING A STILE

A *stile* is a handy thing that will save wear and tear on your fencing. A stile is used to assist a person in climbing over a fence. Some stiles are fancy stairstep things. That's too fancy for goats—they can climb stairs, too.

This simple stile does the job nicely. Set two posts about 2′ apart. One post should be extra long for an easy hand hold. Nail a "ladder" of boards across the posts (Fig. 13-9).

HEDGES ARE LIVING FENCES

In the eastern United States, trees were plentiful enough that early settlers had no need to devise enclosures out of anything but wood. As land was settled further to the west in the wide, treeless prairies, the living fence became a necessity. Pioneers with English backgrounds began using hedging techniques that were popular in their homeland. The use of living fences slowly dwindled though, as both wire fencing and lumber became widely available at a small cost. Now that the cost of wire and lumber for fencing is so high due to shortages and increasing production costs, hedges and living fences once again have practical as well as aesthetic application. The modern homesteader will want to take another look at this method of creating privacy and security as he lays out his homestead for maximum security and ecological soundness.

There are a number of things to consider regarding the use of a hedge in place of a wire, stone, or wood fence. What are you trying to accomplish?

If beauty and privacy are your main concern, you can achieve these quite easily by planting with low growing shrubs or hedge plants popular for your locale. You'll gain the added benefits of a windbreak and, if you choose a variety that has flowers for the bees and berries for the birds, you'll all be happier.

Do you intend to keep something in or out with your living fence? If so, things get a little more complex. Keeping elephants out of an orchard will require an entirely different approach than keeping your goats in their pasture, the rabbits out of your garden, or the dogs away from your sheep. Cows, horses, and other large animals will not require as dense or foreboding a wall of live thorns and branches as will sheep or goats. Goats, especially, will find most shrubs or hedge plants very much to their liking. Remember, goats are not grazers. They won't keep your grass trimmed. They are browsers, animals that like to eat things that grow above the level of the grasses—in other words, your young trees, shrubs and hedge plants. Only the most thorny, thickly growing plants could stop a goat from eating its way through, but with proper planting and pruning, even goats can be contained by a living hedge.

Table 13-1. Life Expectancy of Post Below Ground.

kind of wood	not treated (years)	treated creosote (years)
Osage Orange	45	46
Red Mulberry	35	40
Red Cedar	30	37
Black Locust	30	36
White Oak	17	30
Catalpa	17	28
White Cedar	14	30
Honey Locust	11	30
Burr Oak	17	26
Black Walnut	10	27
European Larch	8	20
Red Elm	7	25
Ash	6	25
Butter Nut	6	2
Red Oak	6	20
Willow	4	27
Basswood	4	27
Soft Maple	4	26
Hard Maple	4	26
Box Elder	4	26
White Elm	4	25
Hickory	4	20
Aspen	3	27
Cottonwood	2	26

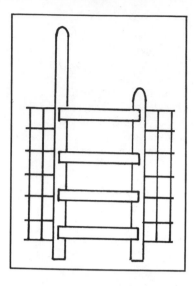

Fig. 13-9. This stile helps you climb over a fence.

Do you need the enclosure soon? You might as well forget a living fence. It takes most plants about three years or more to grow heavily enough to keep anything in or out. If a hole develops in your living fence, it takes nature's time and your careful planting and pruning to close it up again.

Will you want to change the arrangement of your enclosure? Again, a hedge isn't recommended as they're heck to move around. Only the most permanent places can use a living fence to best advantage—like your orchard, garden, berry patch, the grape arbor, or permanent pasture.

Just how does one go about planting and caring for a hedge or a living fence? First, if at all possible, talk with a local nurseryman to see what grows well in your area; what's winter hardy; what will bear a good cushion of thorns or heavy, twiggy growth; and, most importantly, what will stand a good deal of cutting back and pruning. Most plants which best adapt to a hedge situation are those able to withstand being cut clear back to the ground after the first season of growth, and which retaliate by sending forth scads of lateral sprouts to create a really dense base for your hedge.

For most hedge plants, dig a double trench and plant along the trench according to the distance recommended for a rapid closing of gaps. Space the small plants so that each plant in one trench falls between two plants in the parallel trench. Make sure the soil is well worked and supplied with a good dose of organic matter to ensure the fence gets off to a good start.

A plant that easily adapts to all but the most northern parts of the United States is the Osage orange (Fig. 13-10). This treelike shrub can be planted and cut back severely, forcing heavy side shoot development. This creates a thick, wide base for the hedge, without having to plant so many young shrub plants.

Using the Osage orange as an example let the plants grow undisturbed for the first year. Then, in the spring, cut the double row right down to ground level. This forces side shoots to develop. In mid-summer and again in September, cut the hedge back about 4″. Do this again in the third year, too, but this time cut the hedge back to 4″ to 6″ above ground level, instead of to ground level, as you did the first year. You can see why the plant used must be able to withstand heavy pruning.

Now comes the secret of a thick, healthy, impenetrable hedge. Never let the top part of the hedge get wider than the base (Figs. 13-11 and 13-12). If you allow this to happen, rain and light can't reach the shoots or base branches, and the thing will start to die off down there where you need it to be the thickest. The best way to prune a hedge that's intended as a fence is to have the sides slope slightly inward and the top sheared to be either slightly rounded or rooflike.

Even *Rosa multiflora*, a commonly used living fence that's hardy as far north as southern Wisconsin, must be pruned back occasionally to allow light to get to its base. Many multiflora fences are left unpruned as they send out long thorny canes rather than twiggy branches. Occasional cutting back will help to encourage heavier base growth.

Some possibilities to check into for living fences are: multiflora, *Rosa multiflora*; Osage orange, *Maclura aurantiaca*; Japanese quince, *Cydonia Japonica*; Honey locust, *Gleditsia triacanthos*; Black locust, *Robinia*

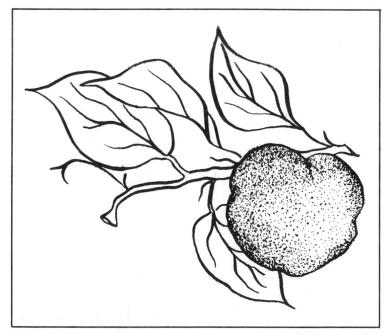

Fig. 13-10. The Osage orange plant.

Fig. 13-11. Trim and prune so a central leader type of growth is maintained. Base is wider than the top and sides slant for maximum sun exposure.

pseudoacacia; Spanish bayonet, *Yucca gloriosa*; Barberry, *Berberis vulgaris*; Buffalo berry, *Sheperdia argentea*; and Russian olive, *Elaeagnus angustifolia*.

FENCE AND GATE

This is an all-purpose fence which is suited for the barnyard or garden. It is high enough for horses, cows, and chickens. It makes a good hog fence (Fig. 13-13).

Fig. 13-12. Never trim hedges or bushes so the top is wider than the bottom. Light and air can't penetrate dense growth.

378

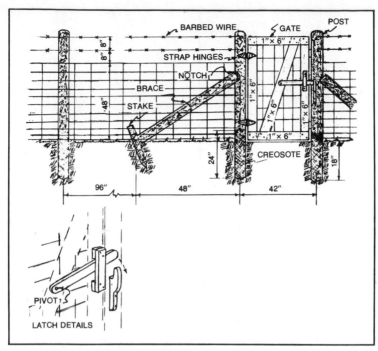

Fig. 13-13. An all-purpose fence and gate.

All wood posts should be coated with creosote to reduce rot and decay. Braces should be placed at all corner posts and the gate post.

GATE AND DOOR LATCHES

One of the oldest and most simple methods of securing a door or gate is shown in Fig. 13-14. It is nothing more than a piece of wood with a nail driven through the center into the post or door facing, jam, or trim.

Fig. 13-14. An old method of securing a door or gate.

379

Fig. 13-15. This method was used on the doors of pioneer cabins.

The method shown in Fig. 13-15 was used on the doors of pioneer cabins. A latch was located on the inside of the door. It could be operated from outside by pulling a string. At night the string was pulled inside for security.

The sliding latch in Fig. 13-16 was used on cabin doors and farm gates. It was the original sliding bolt latch as we know it today.

The chickenyard and garden gates on early American farms were held closed or shut by the use of a weight (Fig. 13-17). Another simple gate was constructed with four pieces of barbed wire tied to a small pole and held in closed position with two wire loops (Fig. 13-18). Farmers referred to this as the gap.

STUMP FENCE AND HEDGEROW

If you asked most of today's homesteaders what they need the most and what they have the least of, their answer probably would be good fences and money, respectively. Good fences not only make good neighbors, but keep your livestock home and separated from your crops (Fig. 13-19). As you are probably well aware, good wire and wood fencing is terribly expensive. Even if you provide all of the labor, the materials alone can cost thousands of dollars, depending on how much land you have to enclose.

Expense can be avoided. Let's look at how the old-time homesteaders used their ingenuity and readily available materials to construct their fences.

Fig. 13-16. The sliding latch.

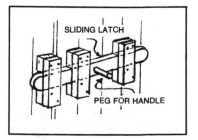

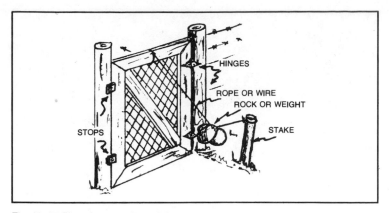

Fig. 13-17. Note the use of a weight.

One of the simplest methods of fencing in livestock was the *stump fence*. When the land was being cleared, early homesteaders would pull the stumps out of the ground and haul them to the fence line. The stumps were placed on their sides, close enough together so the roots would entwine to form an impenetrable barrier. You might not have enough stumps to surround your entire field, but perhaps you could fence one side using this method.

Hedgerows, or living fences, have long been in use in Europe, but have not been used extensively in the United States. An established hedgerow can be a very strong barrier. During World War II, tanks in France were unable to knock them down. They do require growing time before they become useful, but if you're planning to stay put, they provide inexpensive and practical fencing.

In extremely cold climates, hedgerows are a good wind screen and can lower the wind-chill factor by as much as 40°. In the summer, they will

Fig. 13-18. A simple gate known as the gap.

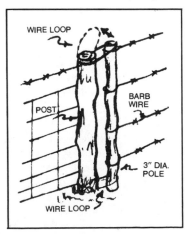

Fig. 13-19. This type of fencing can do a good job of keeping your livestock at home if you live in a rocky, rugged area.

provide shade for the livestock, although the shade will cause a loss of some pasture around the perimeter of the field.

When you start a hedgerow, you must be patient. It will take time for it to grow tall. It must be pruned severely for the first five years to make it bushy and wide on the bottom. As it grows, you can entwine the lower branches so they will grow together and prevent large gaps. These hedges will also provide excellent cover and food for birds and other small wildlife.

Some plants that are suitable for hedges are Osage orange, hawthorne, beech, red cedar (animals will not nibble on this), honey locust, and multiflora rose. If you are interested in starting a hedgerow fence, talk to someone at a local nursery who can help you pick out a plant that will do well in your area. If you can find someone that already has a hedge of the plant of your choice, you can probably get starts free or at minimal cost.

One of the bonuses of these "old time" fences is their natural look. They will blend in with the environment much better than a woven wire or electric fence.

382

Chapter 14

Animals

No homestead is complete without animals. Horses, goats, sheep, and dogs are among the animals featured in this chapter.

THE HOMESTEAD HORSE

In this first installment of Jackie Spaulding's new book, you can learn what to look for in an animal to make owning a pleasure or work horse an enjoyable and rewarding experience.

Introduction

Today the book market features many titles on horses: quarter horses, Arabians, Morgans, Saddlebreds, ponies, Western riding, English riding, jumping, dressage, cattle cutting, roping, racing and more. All horsey subjects to be sure, but all lack much vital information for the first time horse owner, especially the person who is a new small farmer or homesteader, and wants to use the horse for more than show riding.

Many people cannot afford to spend several hundred dollars for the horse, the same for a show saddle, clothes, a horse trailer, to hire a groom and trainer, and put up thousands of dollars worth of perfect fencing. They just want a horse to ride, perhaps drive, and enjoy.

There are a few do's and don'ts that will make this ambition much more realistic and safer. Each year an alarming number of people are injured by horses. Over 80 percent of these injuries could have easily been avoided with some knowledge of horses. There are few "accidents" that occur around horses. Most injuries happen because someone made a mistake.

It stands to reason that the fewer mistakes that are made, the fewer injuries and unpleasant experiences will arise. It has been said "Physician, heal thyself!," which can be interpreted by horse people as "Horseman, teach thyself!" Learn all you can every day. It isn't painful, and it will definitely add to your everyday pleasure.

Heavy Harness

Very few horses are actually used in this country today for heavy harness work. Under this classification would fall drawing heavy loads with a wagon, heavy field work, such as plowing large acreage, mowing hay, hauling manure, raking and stacking hay, cultivating, and hauling logs from the woods.

As tractors became more common and "in style," horsepower with the real thing, became old fashioned. Horse-drawn farm implements became "junk" and then "antiques." Large teams soon all but disappeared from the family farm with people now scorning the old, slow ways.

Again, the times have changed. With the fuel shortage cutting deeply into the pockets of all people, a power source that operates on homegrown "fuel" (hay and grain) and adds to the environment, instead of polluting it, is becoming once again in demand.

It is quite different for a large farmer to farm with horses and compete with farmers that are using super-sized tractors and other equipment, but for the small farmer bent on self-sufficiency, the horse makes sense (Fig. 14-1).

Even if a tractor is used for some of the faster, heavier work, a draft horse can certainly help out. For instance, bale your hay if you must, but how about using a team to pick up the bales? It is a lot easier to call "get up" and "whoa" to a team than climb up and down from a tractor, while working alone.

If a person intends to farm solely with horses, he or she will be in definite need of at least one team of heavy draft horses, such as Belgians, Percherons, or Clydesdales. The horses weigh from 1,500 pounds to over a ton each. This weight also carries with it some gentle power. Where a light horse team would have to really pull to draw a plow through heavy soil and sod, these giants only need to lean into their collars to keep the plow moving. Keep in mind though, that these heavy horses are not only strong, due to their weight, but also have large appetites in order to maintain this weight and have energy left over to apply to daily work. Therefore, they are not practical for use on small homesteads.

Light Harness

Although the term "light harness" refers primarily to driving horses (buggy, cart or coach), it can pertain to horses doing lighter work in work harness. This means a horse that can be driven on a buggy to town for groceries, but can also do a lot of little chores around the farm, such as cultivating the garden or small corn field, hauling small amounts of manure daily, plowing the garden or small fields of light soil, or pulling firewood or a stoneboat.

It is this type of horse, often weighing between 900 and 1,200 pounds, that was the most common on small farms before the machine age struck the farm. A horse of this size is easily maintained on a small acreage, but can also do its share of the work.

384

Saddle

There are many time that a good saddle horse is not a luxury but a necessity. In many areas roads are either nonexistent or seasonally impassable by conventional means. Travel is still often necessary, for needed supplies or any emergency.

When a saddle horse is used for weekend trail rides or shows, a person can be a little less picky on the kind of ride he or she gets, and pay more attention to the looks or color of the horse. When the horse is a needed mode of travel, the smoothness of gait and common sense it possesses are of utmost importance. A superior gaited ugly horse that will not shy and buck when a grouse flies up in front of it will be choice over a beautiful horse with choppy gaits and a nervous temperament.

Stock Work

Where cattle are kept, especially beef cattle on range or semirange conditions, a horse that is good at working stock can easily replace ten hired men on foot.

Fences need to be periodically checked, many of which run through brush and trees and are not accessible by truck or even jeep. Cows need to be watched at calving time and checked for such things as fly-strike, pinkeye, or injuries. Cattle are easily driven and sorted by one or two people who are mounted on good cow horses.

Even dairy cattle owners often have need for a good cow horse. Cattle do get out of the fences, into the corn field, or through a gate that has been accidently left open. It is a lot easier to bring them home gently by a good horse than to try to chase them down on foot, especially when they are excited by their newfound freedom.

Fig. 14-1. Horses for harness work make sense for self-sufficiency.

385

Packing

In many inaccessible areas, especially mountainous terrain, the only practical means of carrying people and supplies in and out of a homestead is by saddle and pack horses. Packing by horses can be slow work, but one person mounted on a good horse can lead several trained pack horses, each loaded with several hundred pounds of supplies. In most cases, packing is much more economical than having a bush pilot drop supplies off by plane and often much more dependable than trying to haul freight by water. Rivers have a way of becoming too fast following a storm or in spring runoff, or becoming too low in the summer months.

There are many uses for horses even in today's world. It quickly becomes obvious that one cannot have a heavy work team, a light harness horse, a saddle horse, a stock horse, and a pack horse on 40 acres. One must choose the type of horse that best suits the work needed most often. There are several breeds of horses that are noted for their versatility, able to do all but perhaps steady heavy harness work.

The Morgan

This breed is best known for its versatility. It is the first American breed, originating just after the Revolutionary War. The *Morgan* began with one stallion named Figure, and was later called after his owner, Justin Morgan. Today, 150 years after the breed was established, the Morgan type remains unchanged. The Morgan is a medium-sized horse with terrific muscling in the hindquarters, neck and shoulders, but fine bone and supreme disposition. The Morgan has excelled in general farm work, in running and trotting races, and in pulling contests, often against heavier horses. The Morgan is no "plowhorse" in looks or spirit. He moves with animation and gayness, even when pulling a manure spreader. This gay spirit makes him a "Sunday" horse or show horse. The Morgan is usually black, chestnut or bay (Fig. 14-2).

The Quarter Horse

The *quarter horse* is best known for its ability to work with cattle and steadiness as a Western mount. It is heavily muscled in the hindquarters, usually balanced with a long neck and wide chest for endurance while running or working at speed.

The quarter horse is being seen more and more in driving harness and work harness, as its strength, combined with quietness, makes a good candidate for an all-around homestead horse. Another plus factor for the quarter horse is his availability, as it is now a very popular breed in the show ring.

The quarter horse is usually 1,000 to 1,200 pounds, and often stands about 14.3 to 15.3 hands (a hand is 4″). Common colors are chestnut, bay, dun, and palomino (Fig. 14-3).

386

The Appaloosa

When endurance is desired, the *Appaloosa* ranks with the best. He was bred by the Nez Perce Indians as both a daily mount and a war horse. Sensibility, nimbleness, and stamina were musts. Horses not possessing these traits were quickly culled. The Appaloosa has today been crossed with other breeds, such as the thoroughbred and quarter horse, but often the old, stock type is seen. This horse may not win a beauty contest with its thin "rat tail," slightly Roman nose and heavy neck, but beauty comes last when looking for a "using" horse. Look instead at the muscling in the rear quarters, strength of neck and solid, sound bone.

The Appaloosa comes in a very wide range of colors, from black, with a few flecks of white over the rump, through the leopard markings, often white with distinct liver or black spots, to white with a few dark hairs sprinkled in. The eye rim looks pink, and the nose is often pinkish and "freckled." The hooves are striped, dark and light, with the stripes running up and down (Fig. 14-4).

Grade Horses and Crossbreds

Although there are several advantages to choosing a purebred, such as the value of the foals produced and stability of type, there are many good grade horses that will fill the bill equally well as a versatile homestead horse. If you need a working horse, you will most often have to choose a mature horse, as many colts and fillies do not mature with enough bone or muscle to be able to stand steady work. You will want a grade or purebred with strong, slightly heavy hindquarters, a long, sloping shoulder, muscular

Fig. 14-2. Morgan.

Fig. 14-3. Quarterhorse.

neck, and fairly heavy bone, especially in the legs. Also, few horses under 900 pounds can be called true working horses. True, many small horses and ponies can do their share of work, but there is much more that can be realistically expected of the medium-sized or larger horses in the way of constant strength and stamina, day in and day out, year after year.

Choosing the Right Horse

The first thing to consider when thinking of buying a horse to help out on the farm is to decide what jobs you will be doing with the horse. Will it be strickly heavy work—plowing large fields, cultivating 40 acres or more of corn, or hauling large amounts of manure? Here you will want one of the heavier type draft horses, weighing at least 1,200 pounds. You wouldn't be awfully comfortable working cattle or riding long distances on a very wide-backed heavy horse, so the type of horse you choose would be a medium-sized horse with comfortable gaits, agile feet, and an alert, sensible mind.

For all but the heavy draft work, it is possible to find an all-around horse that can, with training and a little natural ability, do nearly all the jobs around the farm where true "horsepower" is able to function. Choosing this versatile athlete involves more than picking a pretty and inexpensive horse.

Very few people should start out by buying a young horse with little or no training behind it. A horse is just too big and powerful to fool around with when neither you nor the horse are educated. The young horses do not mean to hurt a person, but they are easily excited—especially by mistakes of a novice trainer, and can panic in a second. True, a young horse is usually cheaper. Many people have bad experiences with them, usually due to their own lack of knowledge and experience, making the people forever against horses, which is a shame.

It only takes a couple of 10-second mistakes with these young, impressionable horses to ruin them for life, so for a first horse, it is wise to choose a trained, middle-aged horse (seven to 14 years old). Many young horses, even though fully trained, are a little full of play at times, requiring a good rider or driver to keep the situation constantly under control.

By six or seven, most horses have settled down from that coltish age of play and are ready for work. They have hopefully been ridden and/or driven for several years, and have seen a lot of different sights that they have learned are harmless.

Many times an older horse (15 to 25 years old) will be cheap and still sound and able to work. These older horses can be a bargain, but keep in mind that they can die or become unworkable at any time, be sure to have the prospect checked by a veterinarian, with special regard to teeth (they do wear out or get sharp edges that need to be filed off), heart, lungs, and soundness of legs. These older horses have an advantage over many younger horses in that they have usually worked longer and will make fewer mistakes, provided they have been driven or ridden by fairly experienced people. They will often know more about the job they are doing than a new horseperson.

It is best to choose either a mare or a gelding, no matter how tempting buying a stallion is. There are many other things to consider than the possibility of collecting breeding fees every spring. Very few people have a barn and pasture set up that is anywhere near safe for a stallion. No matter how gentle, a stallion is a breeding animal by nature. There are instances,

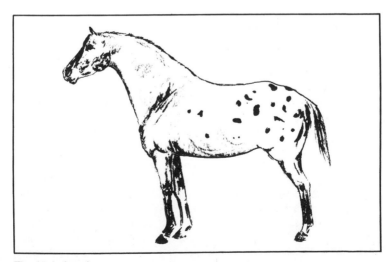

Fig. 14-4. Appaloosa.

389

no matter how well trained he is, that the stallion's breeding urge takes over, maybe only for a second. In this second he can kick or strike out, jump a fence, shove a person down or dance around. Any of these actions could cause injury to the rider, driver, or another person. To be happy, the stallion must be with other horses, but few pasture fences are good enough to hold a stallion in should another horse pass by on the road or other side of the fence. It is true that many stallions have been and are ridden and worked, but the only time this is successful is when the rider or driver is an experienced horseman and is working a well-trained stallion.

The mare may have a few while she is in heat that she is a little untractable, but if she is bred each year there is little to worry about from this. The mare should not be worked hard the last two months of pregnancy, but she can do light work. And quite soon after the foal is born, she can resume the normal duties with the foal at her side or temporarily shut in a box stall.

While the gelding may have a slight advantage over a mare because she must take off for her foal, the mare does have the advantage of producing that foal, and thus providing replacements or salable animals.

The gelding is in most cases the steadiest working horse. Since he is castrated he has no breeding urges to distract him from the job, nor are there the sometimes upsetting hormonal changes at heat that the mare has. Well trained, he is all business, and will stick to it all day. One word about a gelding—be sure he is a gelding. Sometimes a stallion has one or both testicles in the abdominal cavity. They do not descend into the scrotum as do those of the normal stallion, and thus the stallion appears to be a gelding. These horses are dangerous, being of a worse temperament than a stallion. They can be castrated, but it is a dangerous operation and usually costly. These horses are known by several names, and it is wise to be aware of them, as some sellers will mention in passing the fact that the horse is a *ridgling* gelding, "partly entire," or a *monorchid* (having one testicle) or *cryptorchid* (having both testicles).

These "stallions" usually have undependable dispositions, being calm one minute, and flaring up the next with no apparent warning. They will usually look like a stallion, having more crest than many geldings, and act more like a stallion around mares. Beware of any gelding that is untractable. It may only be excitability or lack of training, but you don't want that either.

Good and Bad Habits

Just like people, horses have many personal and work habits which can be either good or bad. Some bad habits are less significant and can be lived with. Others are bad habits and are dangerous or impossible to put up with. A horse is very much a creature of habit, so it is very important that any and all of its habits are as good as possible. Bad habits are very hard, if not impossible, to change. It is said that horse training consists of encouraging the horse by punishment and reward to form acceptable habits. When a horse is improperly trained, it has very little going for it in the way of good habits, but is instead like a spoiled or frightened child.

When you look for these good and bad habits, you will usually be able to spot them quite quickly. You will be able to spot things that owners do to try to cover up some of the bad habits.

The most important habit to look for in a horse to be used by a newcomer is steadiness—the ease of going about its work with no fuss and bother. There should be no jerky movements, head tossing, dancing, or tail switching. The owner should not have to be pulling the horse back all the time or nagging it to move forward. Do not base your decision on the use of spurs, crop or whip, even when used sensibly. These are aids, meant to convey gentle commands, not punishment, or something to make the horse "go." It is better for the newcomer to have a horse that is a bit slow to start than one that leaps forward at the slightest cue. Sometimes a cue can accidently be given by mistake, and an accident could result if the horse is not steady.

Refusal to work, called *balking*, is evidenced in several ways. They can include complete refusal to move away from the barn or other horses and to start a loaded wagon or buggy; rearing; dashing back to the pasture gate or barn; and kicking out and bucking. A tie-down on a high-headed horse may just be a decoration, but often it indicates a horse that is prone to rear (Fig. 14-5). (Don't think for a minute that a tie-down will keep a horse from rearing if it really wants to! Some people believe that it will, and it does discourage some half-hearted rearers.)

Always insist that the horse be worked alone, as many balkers will go along nicely if worked with another horse. When worked alone, they "stick" badly.

A horse that is overly "hot," which is a horseman's term for one that wants to go fast or is "speed crazy" is no working horse (Fig. 14-6). Horses

Fig. 14-5. A tie down may indicate a horse that rears.

Fig. 14-6. A "hot" horse is no working horse.

that are run a lot, raced by inexperienced people, shown in games or in pulling contests tend to get "hot." (The term "hot" here does not mean sweating up, although these horses certainly do get sweated up into a lather.) You can tell such a horse by its dancing and fretting when worked a minute at any speed, or with the pulling horse, when he is about to be hooked up. Many pulling horses leap forward as they hear the load hooked, knowing that it is time to give it their all. This is not a trait you'd want in your cultivating horse.

In some areas, buggy horses are raced, as well as sulky horses. These buggy horses get excited when they hear another horse about to pass or come up on them from the rear, expecting a race. You will feel such a horse tighten up, and he will usually begin snorthing and pulling on the lines. Some buggy horses have enough sense to be worked down to the point where they are safe for a novice driver, but ofters remain "hot" for life.

The horse should stand quietly when asked to during its work, not trying to turn around, back up, or go forward. This is especially important for both light and heavy harness horses, as it is easy to have an accident if the horse steps over the traces or shoves against the shafts. Remember though, if the horse in light harness is wearing an overcheck, it should be taken off when the horse is to stand for any length of time because it is uncomfortable when standing. Many horses get excited, trying to get away from this uncomfortable feeling. (The overcheck is fine while moving as the horse usually carries its head higher then. It is easy to hook up the check rein before starting out again.)

The horse should stand when tied. This sounds basic, but many horses will not. Some will simply dance around or paw the ground, which can quickly become annoying. Many horses have never been trained to stand tied and will yank back on the halter, usually breaking either the halter or the lead rope. These horses will not stand in a tie stall, horse trailer, or simply at a tree or hitching rail. Beware of the horse that is tied with a neck rope or a rope behind its hind quarters. Many horses are tied this way, as it is the safest way to tie a horse, make sure the horse will stand without these. The horse that is a halter puller will often be all right if the owner keeps the butt rope tight behind the horse while going up to untie the horse, but if he does not, the horse will yank back. Most people will unhook the butt rope on entering the stall, and fasten it up to keep it clean, then go to the horse's head. If the owner doesn't do this and carries the end of the butt rope into the stall, not letting go of it until the horse is untied, remind yourself to see if this horse will stand tied elsewhere (Fig. 14-7). After all, some people do form habits, like horses, and a person can automatically do something even though the situation does not warrant it.

The horse should accept its tack (bridle, saddle or harness) gently. No head tossing, kicking, shying, or biting should be evident. Keep in mind the actions of the owner. Some people can bring out the worst in a horse. Many horses toss their heads or shy and kick due to the ignorance or insensitivity on the part of the person who is tacking them up. A bit should not be jammed against the teeth, a crupper yanked under the tail with the tail wadded up, or a saddle plopped in place and a knee jammed into the horse's side, "to make him let out the air he's holding in."

Reject immediately any horse with very bad stall habits. These include kicking, biting, striking (kicking with the front feet), swinging against a person trying to get into the stall with him, cribbing or chewing on wood (does the stall have scalloped edges, or does the horse wear a collar?), or pacing around and around in the box stall. These habits are very hard, if not impossible to get modified or changed, especially for the novice horseman.

Fig. 14-7. While taking the butt rope into the stall is a good practice, it may indicate that the animal will not stand without it.

Will the horse pick up all four of its feet? Many owners show how nicely the horse yields his forefeet, but never quite gets around to the hind. Is there a reason for this?

Perhaps most important is to find out if *you* get along with the horse. Horses and some people just have conflicting personalities and nothing can be done to alleviate the discord that arises. How do you find out if you get along with your prospective new horse? Try him out. You cannot just watch the owner work the horse and assume that he will do as much for you. Perhaps the owner has had more experience with horses than you have. It is very easy for an experienced horseman to get the most out of any horse, but another thing for the horse to work well for a novice. Admit to both yourself and the owner of the horse you are looking at that you are a novice if you are a little inexperienced. This goes for all people, even if you are very experienced in one phase of horsemanship, say Western riding, and are looking to buy a good driving horse. If you have had no experience with this type of horse or tack, say so and learn. Your ignorance will soon become obvious anyway. Most leople enjoy helping someone else learn, but are extremely irritated with a know-it-all.

What is the best way to try out the horse you are interested in? First of all, check his personal habits. This can be quietly done while the horse is in his stall, in the pasture, or on the lead rope, while talking to the owner. Do not give the owner the impression you are giving him the third degree. Use some tact, as no owner likes to feel that the buyer thinks he's trying to sell him a lemon.

Watch the horse as he stands and is lead. Check his legs for soundness. Especially watch for:

☐ *Ringbone,* which looks like a bony ridge running around the leg, usually in the fetlock. If close to a joint, it can be a definite unsoundness (Fig. 14-8).

☐ *Splints or bone spavins,* which are calcium deposits that have been laid down at the site of an injury of severe strain. Many spavins and splints are considered a blemish rather than an unsoundness, depending on the amount of interference they cause. You will notice them as hard bumps, usually on the long bones of the legs (cannon bones) or near the hocks. Don't confuse them with bumps arising from old wire scratches and cuts. This is scar tissue in the skin and muscle, and is seldom serious (Fig. 14-8).

☐ *Founder,* which is a condition of the feet coming from toxins (sometimes after a mare foals with a slight uterine infection), overeating, being watered while hot, or being too heavily grained.

The horse that has foundered will usually be very sensitive on the toes, walking more on the heel. The toes may tend to grow out too long, before the heel does. The heel may be contracted and the sole of the foot dropped down, making the foot look too long even when trimmed. There may be ridges around the foot, but there are many foundered horses that do not have founder rings, and many horses with rings that have not been foundered.

☐ *Thrush,* which is a condition usually arising from dampness in which the horse spends a lot of time in a dirty stall or barnyard. It is characterized by a very foul odor, especially after the foot is cleaned. In bad cases, you will see a blackish or pussy discharge in the frog and heal areas. Thrush can be cleared up in most cases, with few aftereffects, but it can lead to infection, sometimes running into the bone. You should not buy such a horse unless it is agreed that if the thrush cannot be cleared up, the owner will refund your money. Get it in writing (Fig. 14-8).

☐ *Bowed tendons* are usually caused by overexertion. Pulling too heavy a load, running too fast, especially on hard surfaces and in muck are all frequent cases. From the side, you will notice that there is a definite bowing of the tendon running from the back of the knee or hock to the back of the fetlock. Many horses that have bowed a tendon in past years can still work, but they are not as sound as they could be, and are set up for more trouble in later years (Fig. 14-8).

Any other halting or restricted gait should be questioned. The horse should walk freely on all four legs, swinging his head evenly. If there is any lameness present, the head will bob when that leg hits the ground. If you have any doubts as to the soundness of the legs, be sure to mention it to your veterinarian before he comes to check the horse.

Be sure to check the horse's wind. That is, be sure the horse is not heavy (a term commonly used in place of wind-broken). Heaves are a condition similar to emphysema in people. When the horse is worked very hard, he will be unable to breathe normally. You can tell a heavy horse by the "double" movement of the flank area as the horse breathes, especially after he's trotted a bit. Instead of a simple in-out-in-out movement, it will be in-out-out-in-out-out-in. A heavy horse will usually have flaring nostrils because he is trying to gain more air. Many heavy horses are useful, but they are not up to weighty or fast work, and are definitely not sound.

You have looked the horse over carefully while visiting with his owners. You get along well with him on the ground, so ask the owners if they would ride (or drive) him for you.

Watch now how he responds to tacking. He should remain calm, take the bit well, and not appear crabby.

Have the owner demonstrate how the horse works for him, doing the work you are buying him for. If you plan to haul logs for the most part, see the horse work in the woods if at all possible. With every type of job there are special obstacles that the horse must work around with no excitement. With the logging horse, there are trees, stumps, and ruts. For trail horses, there are spooky looking rocks, pieces of paper, grouse, deer, machinery, and so on. If the horse is supposed to work cattle well, see him do it. Some horses charge and bite cattle, and others do not pay enough attention to either the ground or the cattle. A buggy horse should be able to turn tightly, without becoming afraid of the pressure of the shafts on his sides or the noise of the wheels rubbing on the metal rubbers. He must not be afraid of oncoming traffic, or vehicles coming up from behind. The heavy draft horse

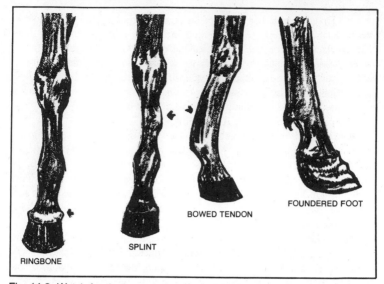

Fig. 14-8. Watch for ringbone, splint, bowed tendon, and foundered foot.

RINGBONE

SPLINT

BOWED TENDON

FOUNDERED FOOT

must not balk or become excited if the plow or other implement should strike an immovable object such as a rock. He should accept strange noises, both from the machinery he is drawing and from outside sources.

After the owner has demonstrated the horse's abilities, and the horse has done well, it is time for you to try him out. One word here. If the horse does poorly, just politely tell the owner that he isn't just what you were looking for and thank him for showing you the horse. Don't go on and try the horse unless you feel that you are a better rider or driver than the owner (be honest) just for a free ride or drive. Don't tell the owner he has a crummy horse or some such remark. People are sensitive about their horses, about like they are with their children, and it doesn't take much to get an owner to really bristle.

When you try out the horse, some of the most important things can be learned before you get far from the barn. Does the horse start off willingly? Will he go a few yards, then stop at your command and then start off again quietly? This is one of the hardest tests for many horses. If he will do this, he has a lot going for him, as the lazy horse will not want to start once, let alone twice, especially near the barn. The overly ambitious horse will not want to stop and stand.

The horse should not be lugging on the reins continually or trying to snatch them from your grip by tossing his head. Neither should he plod along, ears flopping, not paying any attention to what is going on around him.

Turns should be executed smoothly with no hesitation, fighting, or resistance. You will be able to tell the horse is resisting when he stiffens his neck and raises his head to avoid the action of the bit. A horse that is being driven should not speed up at turns.

It is not a good idea to work the horse at any speed, unless it is necessary that he does work at speed, such as a cutting horse (used to sort cattle), as the horse is not familiar with your riding and you are not familiar with the way the horse responds to commands. There is no sense upsetting a good horse just to show off your ability. If he works well at a canter, he will work just as well at a gallop.

Ride the horse, drive him 15 or 20 minutes. In this length of time you should be able to tell if you like the horse, get along with him, and make the decision whether or not you will be buying him. An hour's ride or drive is not necessary.

If you are buying a horse that is supposed to ride and drive, be sure you do both, as many people figure that if a horse can be ridden, he can be driven. This is not so.

Try to drive the horse first, because some horses enjoy the freedom of riding so much that they become somewhat excited when brought in and "restricted" into harness. It might be just enough to give you the wrong impression that the horse is nervous in harness.

PLEASURE HORSES

It's time that we rediscover the usefulness of the horse. For if we don't find more economical ways of feeding our horses, and more economical ways of using our horses, the 20th century may once again witness the decline of the equine. We're not talking about the draft horse, now. He is making a comeback that is heartwarming and apparently perfectly timed. The draft horse farmer is justified in a great guffaw at the expense of the tractor farmer who sits idle for lack of diesel fuel. That cycle has come full circle.

If the budget can stand it, the pleasure horse is often one of the first animals to appear on a homestead. The horse touches the romantic in a homesteader. As the homesteader gets wrapped up in more vital things like food production and income, old Bess quickly gets retired to the back pasture because she's a pleasure horse—picturesque but not practical.

What can you do with your homestead pleasure horse? First, bring her in from pasture. Put her right in the center of all the activity. If this means feeding her hay all day, even in the summer, and turning her out to pasture only at night, do it. You aren't going to use her for all the little chores that she's good for if you have to spend half an hour to catch her. Any of the equipment that you need to use her—brush, hoof pick, saddle, bridle, harness, whatever—have within arm's reach. It's best to keep leather in a dry warm place, like the house, but if it means foregoing the horse for a more convenient energy source, haul it all out to the barn. Keep it out where it's easy to get to. Keep it close to the horse and handy for use.

Now that the horse is ready, what can you do with her? Well, as a start, if you have other animals as well as your saddle horse, you no doubt have fences. They need constant checking and repair. Saddlebags are a help here to carry hammer, nails, pliers, etc., and they can easily be made out of a burlap bag. More elaborate ones can be made out of canvas or nylon, or, if you're lucky enough to have some tanned hides, leather.

If you have errands or visit friends within a 5-mile radius (or further if you and your horse are in good shape), ride old Bess (Fig. 14-9). If you have to cross private property, get permission first. If you think someone might complain about manure, take an extra minute to disperse it. The day will no doubt come when people will run out to gather the manure for their precious compost piles, but it isn't here yet, so don't push people to the point of complaining.

If you have a ways to go to catch a bus, or not so far to a rural school, scout around for someone with a stall or paddock where you could keep your horse during the day. You supply the hay and water. You maintain the fence or stall. You clean up after the horse. You might want to get a pair of big coveralls to go over school clothes, or change once you get there if your friends don't think old Bess is the best perfume (Fig. 14-10).

Then there's vacation time. Go camping with old Bess. Map out a route, maybe only as far as your back woodlot, maybe to a friend's farm. Practice tying or hobbling your horse at home first. If you have only one horse and lots of potential campers, you can use the horse to tote the tents while you hike. It's a good time to practice the diamond hitch and other bits of esoteric knowledge. Be sure to plan for your horse's food and water as well as your own. Camping within hiking distance of home will not only broaden your homestead eyes, but might help decentralize vacation pressure, and may be a way of the future. After a summer, our national campsites look like inner city vacant lots anyway.

Fig. 14-9. Pleasure horses can be used for many small homestead tasks and short trips.

Fig. 14-10. This horse is popular with the kids (drawing by Barbara Francis).

All of this can be done with the minimum of equipment. Get a harness, and a whole new world opens up. The collar and the hames that fit that collar are the most important part of a harness. They must fit properly. If you don't know how to fit a collar, find someone who does. That's best. If that rare someone can guide you and your horse in the art of driving, that's ideal. Short of that, dive into anything you can find on the subject. The *Draft Horse Primer* by Maurice Telleen is a good place to start. There are several draft horse magazines as well as occasional articles in magazines like *Countryside* where you can glean useful information and ideas. There's no way to beat learning from a real teamster.

The rest of your harness doesn't need to be studded leather. Many other cultures make good use of rope and chain. If you go this route, be sure to check the horse frequently for rub marks. Adjust the rope or chain, or replace those parts with softer, less irritating leather before sores develop.

Once you have the horse familiar with the rudiments of driving, and you've digested all you can find about logging with horses, head out to the woods, hitch her to a light log, and be ready for anything. Be prepared to do a lot of sweating and running yourself to begin with. It may take you half a day or maybe two half days to get into the rhythm of working with each other. Stick with it. With plenty of rest periods, you and your horse might develop new heights of respect for each other while you're collecting the winter's heating supply.

You might want to build a skid sled or a go devil that the horse can pull. It can help when hauling wood, collecting maple sap in the spring, or toting fence posts out to the pasture. If you and your horse really get into driving and if you have a rough riding horse, you may find that you prefer to drive. Besides, it's a nice way to share one horse.

You'll find many things that the horse does as well or better than a tractor or truck. When anything requires lots of stop and go, like collecting sap, the horse is better for the job. For clearing small trees and brush from a neglected pasture, the horse is at least as good.

You can put sides on your sled and use it to haul manure, unless you're milking 50 cows. The horse can at least haul her own manure to the compost or field.

One horse plowing can certainly be done. If you can dig up a service-able plow (and they *are* around), save it until you and the horse are pros. Even then, you might want someone to lead the horse while you figure out the ways of a walking plow.

Winter plowing is something else. A crude but effective plow can be made by joining two boards in a V, weight it with a large stone, attach a singletree and the horse, and try it. It may be the best labor saver and easiest way to keep a path open from the barn to the house. Get at it before the snow's too deep, and the horse should have no trouble.

As for winter fun, try skijoring. Put on the collar, hames, and tugs (in fact, you will want to add another length of rope to the tugs so that the skiier is well behind the horse). Bridle the horse, and have one person ride and guide while the other is pulled. Down hill or cross country skis both work. You can also try this with a toboggan. If you have a cutter or sleigh, you're all set for winter fun.

There are many things you'll notice the more you do with your horse. In fact, sitting on the back of a horse is one of the best ways to get an excellent view of your crops, pastured livestock, woods, wildlife, and maybe a whole field of Indian paintbrush or wild strawberries. You also may notice that with all this work, the horse needs more good food. If she's working for you, don't skimp on her feed. If she doubles as a show horse on weekends, you may find her in better shape (though probably too lean and fit for today's fat halter classes), more responsive to you because of the extra time you spend together, and, finally, not tail swishing ring sour.

Horse owners, and pony owners, at this time of short energy and short money, have to look at their equine friends with new, and some very old, eyes and ideas. Ponies can do almost everything a horse can do, and they eat less. In fact, take that fat pony that the kids have outgrown out of pasture and put him into harness. You'll all have a ball.

If old Bess is still young and rather frisky, don't despair. A more hot blooded horse will take more time and more patience, but it can be done. In fact, with daily handling and some honest sweat work, you may find that the horse isn't so high strung, just too full of hot feed. Occasionally you'll come upon a real screwball that's too unpredictable to learn anything. Avoid him like the plague.

If you haven't yet bought your homestead horse, good temperament, good health, and good training should be foremost. Good horses can be found in any breed or color. Keep an open mind and a sharp eye.

THE NORWEGIAN FJORD PONY

How would you like to have a horse with a pleasant disposition and good temper who is a surefooted hard worker and is seldom afflicted by common equine sickness? This same horse can serve as a riding horse, a pack horse, a cart horse, a children's pony, or a light draft horse.

This is not some new breed of horse developed by frantic scientists working day and night. This horse has been selectively bred for possibly 2000 years (Fig. 14-11). The *Norwegian Fjord* pony has been part of the Scandanavian scene for centuries. Traders used the Fjord to pack their loads between remote towns and settlements. Farmers used them for all phases of farm work. The legendary Vikings were fond of horses and used the Fjord in their travels and ventures.

These light dun-colored ponies developed in the rugged farmlands of what is now Norway. In this sector of northern Europe, the small farm holdings demanded a light, durable and versatile draft animal which was economic to keep. The Fjord filled these requirements admirably, and its popularity soon spread into neighboring countries.

Around the turn of the century, Denmark, a country less than one-third the size of Wisconsin, began to import Fjord ponies for use on small farms. Since then, over 16,000 ponies have been brought into Denmark—almost one for every square mile. In many parts of Scandanavia and northern Europe, the Fjord is used to haul produce to the market place in addition to its work on the farm.

In the western United States, the Fjord has established a reputation for being a surefooted pack animal. Many outfitters have switched to this horse over much harder to handle mules.

The Fjord pony is not a large animal. Males will have an average height of about 14 hands. The mares are somewhat shorter, averaging about 13 hands high.

One striking feature of the Fjord is its close resemblance to its ancient ancestor, the wild horse of Eurasia (Fig. 14-12). The horse, known as the

Przewalski's horse, is the only true wild horse in existence. The wild horse of the American West is a feral version of a domestic horse. The Przewalski's horse is one of the extremely rare, endangered animals of the world. No authority knows for certain if any of these Ice Age horses still roam in a natural environment. There is a possibility that some small bands still remain in the Atila mountains of Mongolia. All known Przewalski's are in zoos or other protected reserves (Fig. 14-13).

The two breeds share several features which have caused some zoologists to feel that there is a relationship between them. Both are about the same height and general size. They both have a dark dorsal stripe and often have dark bands on the legs. They both have erect manes.

It is somewhat ironic that the Norwegian Fjord pony, a direct descendant of the prehistoric Ice Age horse, may be the perfect horse for those who are trying a new style of living on today's homesteads.

SIX BREEDS OF GOATS

There are six popular breeds of goats in North America, but most goats probably are mixtures of one or more. While most homesteaders only want a goat, regardless of breed, sooner or later they want to trace the roots of their milk provider and pet. Here are a few simple rules for identification.

Fig. 14-11. The Norwegian Fjord pony is a result of 2000 years of selective breeding (photo by John Tobias).

Fig. 14-12. Two Fjord ponies graze in Colorado. The breed's dorsal stripe and stocky neck show their close relationship to Przewalski's horse.

The most popular breed in America is the *Nubian.* Purebred Nubians are easily distinguished by their long flowing ears and Roman noses. Nubians can be any color, and they're noted for the high butterfat content of their milk. Originating in the semi-tropics, Nubians are short-haired goats, and they are the breed most likely to ignore the September-to-January breeding season.

Saanens are white, with dished faces and erect ears. These are the Holsteins of the goat world and are popular because of their high milk production. A good animal of any breed is preferable to a poor animal of the "best" breed.

Toggenburgs are erect-eared brown animals with distinctive white markings on the face, rump, and legs. Toggs have the distinction of having the oldest registry of any domesticated animal.

Alpines attract many people because of their markings. There are a number of color patterns on these erect-eared animals that make them distinctive and beautiful.

LaManchas are easily identified by their "gopher" ears. They can be any color or color pattern. Technically, they aren't really a pure breed. They are good milkers and exhibit a wonderful dairy disposition.

The sixth breed is the *Angora,* which is not a dairy goat since it is bred for its fine hair or wool, and meat. They do give milk, but the homesteader interested in milk rather than fleece would be advised to consider another breed.

Which breed is best? There is no best breed, as there are great variations among strains and families. For the family interested solely in milk production, there is nothing wrong with a cross-bred goat (one of mixed parentage) provided it has the genetic potential for milk production. Some people luck out on their first goat. Others get taken, and unfortunately, lose interest in goats as a result. That's part of the art of homesteading.

SHEEP

It all started with clover. As R.G. Lau and his wife walked along their lane, she commented what a shame it was to waste all the lush clover growing in the meadow by the stream. Over the years Lau has come to know what these casual offhand comments really mean, and he automati-

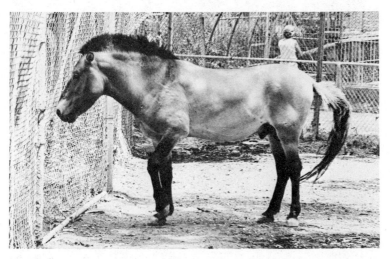

Fig. 14-13. Przewalski's horse, the only true wild horse, is now probably found only in zoos (photo by John Tobias).

404

cally resigned himself to the fact that they were soon going to take the big step from chickens to four-legged livestock.

Sheep were crossed from the potential list of animals the Laus might raise on their 7-acre homestead. Each of the other farm species were given careful consideration. Volumes of literature were avidly consumed on horses, hogs, cows, steers, and goats. Occasionally comments on sheep would be included in this literature, and they would find themselves paying more and more attention to it as their objections to other livestock developed. Through the process of elimination—horses too expensive, hogs too smelly, steers too big, cows too demanding—the Laus found their choice narrowed down to one—*sheep* (Fig. 14-14).

Lau's biggest mistake was calling sheep worthless. Nothing could be further from the truth. The benefits of sheep are legion, especially for the organic homesteader striving for a certain degree of self-sufficiency. For years Lau would drool over the lamb chops at the supermarket, but the price was always prohibitive. Now the Laus dine quite frequently on leg of lamb, rolled shoulder roasts, lamburger, and the like. This enjoyment of lamb meats is increased by the knowledge that they are controlling the quality and are consuming healthy and tasty meat. In fact, lambs can be brought to market weight (about 100 pounds) without any artificial stimulants. All they need is their mother's milk and some pasture. It is not even necessary to have an expensive grain feeding program. Lamb is one of the most easily digested meats and is advocated by the American Heart Association which says "Live longer with lamb."

The Laus presently have a flock of 10 ewes and one ram, producing as many as 15 lambs a year. Excess lambs are sold directly to individual buyers, and the Laus have found this freezer trade to be advantageous for them and their customers. They can command a premium, yet fair price while the customers get quality lamb much cheaper than at the supermarket.

Putting primary emphasis on food comes naturally to people with hearty homestead appetites, but the advantages of sheep go far beyond pleasing the palate. You can't write about sheep without covering the topic of wool. It is hard to beat a natural fiber like wool. In this day and age of shortages, it is nice to have available a renewable resource like wool. Sheep are sheared once a year in the spring and produce anywhere from 5 to 15 pounds or more of wool per head, depending on the breed. A common rule of thumb is that the wool clip (harvest) pays the feed bill. This is basically true, but the Laus have found selling directly to consumers to be more profitable. There is currently a tremendous interest in handicrafts in this country and among them is the art of handspinning. These spinners provide a ready market for the annual wool crop. In fact, there are some owners of small flocks of sheep who started off being spinners and took up shepherding to have a ready supply of wool on hand.

Fig. 14-14. Sheep are not worthless animals (photo by Jean Martin).

Though the Laus arc too busy to do their own spinning, they do make use of the lamb hides. "Sheer luxury" best describes the softness and comfort of properly tanned lamb skins. They take the sting out of sitting on a cold car seat on a winter morning, and surprisingly enough, provide equal comfort for summer driving as well. Their beauty and practicality result in their having many uses around the house and make them valuable sales items.

In addition to producing meat and fiber, without making great demands on the grain and oil supplies of the world, sheep produce the best natural fertilizer an organic gardener could want. Sheep manure is a valuable source of potash, containing about 20 pounds per ton, more than any other manure. It is also high in nitrogen content, providing 19 pounds per ton. It is second only to chicken manure and contains 7 pounds of phosphorus per ton. It is dryer than cow or hog manure and thus, easier to handle, and less offensive to the olfactory senses of the squeamish.

The traditional pastoral scene of grazing livestock is indeed a beautiful one. Taking a break from digging potatoes or weeding the sweet corn and just watching the sheep grazing contentedly is truly the pause that refreshes. It really isn't time wasted when the entire family goes out to the barn on a cold winter's eve to watch the lambs go through their antics. They climb up one side of their mother's back and slide down the other, trying to steal swigs of milk from each other's indignant mother, until finally they are exhausted and curl up next to mom to rest.

For all they have to offer, sheep demand very little in return. In south central Pennsylvania, they are on pasture from April through November. These are the busy months for planting, tending, harvesting and preserving crops, but lazy months for shepherding. The main job is just enjoying the sheep efficiently converting grass into meat and wool. This makes them the perfect complement for the avid gardener. Grass and clover make the best pasture for sheep, but they also devour weeds such as poison ivy and burdock. They also help the Laus keep up with their lawnmowing in the spring. Unfortunately, their tastes also run to apple trees and peonies, resulting in the need for some protective fencing. Sheep can not be neglected during the summer months. There are summer chores, such as looking for any developing health problems, but these can be done at the convenience of the shepherd.

During the winter months, sheep demands and sheep chores increase, but are still minimal compared to other livestock. Sheep do best in a well-ventilated, but draft-free shelter. This can be a simple three-sided shed or part of a big barn. Add some clean bedding material and you're set for sheep.

Hopefully, by winter the ewes are pregnant and, consequently, they will require sustenance for their own health needs as well as the developing lambs. The Laus feed their sheep clover hay and some mixed hay, as well as a whole grain mix, grown right on the homestead. Dairy-fresh water, a salt block, and weather permitting, a little exercise outing in the yard, round out the Laus' sheep program.

The Laus have also found sheep to be of a convenient size for hauling and handling. They transport the sheep in a crate made to fit in the back of the station wagon. Most lambs and some adults can be trained to be led and stand for a handler without too much trouble.

Finally, if you decide to take up sheep raising, start small. Sheep have a flocking instinct and are very unhappy alone. It is best to start with one ewe and one ram or with a pair of bred ewes. You'll soon discover for yourself that sheep are economical and enjoyable livestock with which to work.

WORKING STOCK DOGS

If a man's dog is his best friend, then a stockman's dog is his best hired hand. If you're contemplating investing in a canine helper, remember that all stock dogs are very active and require supervision. Their training demands patience and can be frustrating. It takes a long time to see any results, but the finished product is worth every bit of it.

That cherished and lovable family mutt just won't do for a working stock dog. Start with an animal that is apt to have the inherited traits and instincts for herding. A farmstead is no place for stray or untrained dogs, or dogs that the former owner couldn't keep in town because they needed a "place to run.

You might have to pay a tidy sum for a purebred pup from working parents, but don't overlook a cross between two working breeds. These pups are not as expensive and can develop into excellent workers. The most important thing is the right dog for the job and the right dog for you. You will not be happy with less.

Here is a short description of the working breeds that are still used on farms and ranches. (Very few of the "working breeds" currently registered with the *American Kennel Club* (AKC) have any stock working ability left in them.)

Border Collie

This dog is small, long-haired, usually black and white with a long bushy tail. An excellent worker, it has been used for ages as a sheep dog in Scotland. Some strains work cattle, but most are better suited for sheep and small stock. This breed is very active, and if you are the nervous type, it might not be the best dog for you.

Shetland Sheep Dog

This dog is a Collie in miniature, AKC registered. Some have no working ability left and are timid. If you find a good one, you will be doubly rewarded. Shelties eat very little, their coats do not require much work, and they are fierce guards of your stock and property. Breeders sometimes will sell or give away "oversized" ones, and these are the best workers of the breed. Remember, you are gambling with a Sheltie. They have been show dogs for too long.

Pulik or Puli

This dog looks like a medium-sized, unkempt poodle. The coat is black with some variations, long corded and waterproof if ungroomed. This breed has not been too popular in the show ring, so most of the working ability is still intact. They have been used mostly for sheep but will work other stock.

Australian Shepherd

These dogs are of Spanish origin, and come in many colors: blue merle, red, black with tan markings or without. Some have one blue eye or green eyes. Spanish priests in California used these dogs to protect large herds of sheep from predators. The breed is aggressive, especially the males, and work cattle, horses or sheep equally well. They are good with children and make excellent guard dogs.

Australian Cattle Dog (Queensland Blue Heeler)

The dog is a true Australian, small with blue-mottled coat, some tan markings, standup ears and a long tail. The dog is a true heeler, used mostly to drive cattle. The dogs are good for stock work in pens or where a lot of loading and shipping is done. They can be taught to gather cattle, but will heel instead of going around to the head and bringing the stock to you. They make good cattle dogs but have to be trained differently than other breeds.

Kelpie and McNab

This is another Australian breed used mostly for sheep. They are slender black and tan or red dogs, working about the same as a Border Collie. They make good all-around dogs. They have not been bred for show and are not very uniform in bone, size or coat length.

English Shepherd

Somewhat larger than other herding breeds, the dog is mostly black and tan. Some are red, and a few with white markings. They are not too well-known in the United States outside of Texas. Outstanding watchdogs and workers, they are good with children and easy to train.

Crossbreds

If the cross is between two working stock dogs, the results can be fantastic. In cases where one parent is unknown or not of a working breed, you will be taking a chance.

The heading sheep dog breeds are best for most farmsteads. They will save you many steps and are not likely to run your stock through a fence as a heeler might. If you are going to be driving a lot of stock, a heeler might be best. To bring your stock to the barn, you need a herding dog that will get around the stock and bring it to you. By the way, this is the first lesson for a young stock dog after basic obedience.

Puppy or an Older Dog

An older dog should be considered first, depending on how he has been handled. Most likely he has already had some basic obedience training and is large enough and wise enough to start working. If the dog has been worked before, he might have some problems, but usually they can be overcome with time and patience. A young dog, up to 18 months, usually has not yet become too attached to any one person thereby making a change difficult.

It takes a puppy from three months to over one year to start showing interest in stock. Just because a small puppy will not chase everything in sight does not mean that he will not work. Some of the best stock dogs have not shown interest in stock till they were well over a year old. Then comes a year of training and about another year of actual working experience to handle stock well. So, if you start with a puppy, it will be about three years before you have the finished product. He will also need all his shots. If your mind is set on a puppy, by all means get one and enjoy it.

Your working dog also becomes your partner and should be treated as such. Most people who have outstanding working dogs take them everywhere they go and treat them as members of their family.

Male or Female

You will run into a lot of controversy. Usually a male is more aggressive, somewhat harder to train (there are exceptions), will roam more readily, will establish a territory, and get in fights with other dogs over it. A male should not be taken inside of your dog-owning friends' houses even if invited. Most males just can not resist the urge to mark things that have the scent of other dogs.

Chapter 15

Livestock Feed

You can greatly reduce the cost of feeding your animals through careful planning and planting. Your garden can provide livestock with plenty of nourishment.

A GARDEN FOR GOATS

Why not plant a garden for your goats? It will help cut feed costs and increase milk production. If it's planted along with your regular garden, it won't even be much more work. Just plant things that goats like and will benefit by milk-wise. Most of these are things you like, too.

Green beans and *soybeans* are goat delicacies that will increase milk production. Green beans should be picked just as they reach the bean stage. Plan on using 50' to 100' of row for each goat. After the main harvest, beans will continue to produce, or you can cut the plants and feed them to the goats and replant the ground. Soybeans can be fed either as beans or as a whole plant. Cut the plant 2" above the ground just as the beans are beginning to form for highest protein content. The plants will continue to grow, and two to five cuttings can be taken depending on where you live. If you have the room and want to give your goats a real treat, plant ⅛ to ¼ of an acre to soy beans for them.

Squash and *pumpkin* are another good treat for your goats. *Zucchini* and *butternut* are fine for goats. The zucchini is fed during the summer, the butternut is saved for winter use. Zucchini is so prolific that about eight bush plants will feed one goat 3 pounds a day all summer. Let the zucchinis get large, about 18" long and 4" to 6" thick. They are easy to grow and will produce till frost.

For pumpkins, plant a variety that matures large, like the Big Max. Butternut squash is better than pumpkin because of its solid meat. It has a sweeter, finer flesh than pumpkins. Squash and pumpkin must be chopped for the goats. Quarter them lengthwise and slice them.

Kale is a good crop for winter feeding and can be planted after some of your regular vegetables are taken off. If you can locate the variety that grows 5' tall, that is what to plant. It is available in Great Britain. If winters are not too severe where you live, the kale will stay green all winter. In Morrison's *Feeds and Feeding* it states that dairy animals should be fed as though it were summer the year round. So succulents are very important to milking goats. Kale should be planted to mature before the steady winter cold sets in for good. In mild climates or mild winters, it may continue to grow some all winter.

Mangels are one of the best crops to grow for your goats. They grow 2' long and will yield 20 to 40 tons per acre. Mangels can replace half your grain requirements. As they grow two-thirds out of the ground, they are easily harvested. While providing the nutrition of grain, they also provide succulence, thereby doing a two-fold job.

Harvest and put mangels in a root cellar, or pile leaves or straw around them in the rows. Mangels should not be fed until after they have been stored a few weeks. Freshly harvested roots can cause scours. Mangels should be fed sparingly to bucks and wethers, as they can cause urinary calculi if fed over a long period. Mangels are as good or better than corn silage as a winter feed. Tests have shown that cows milk slightly higher when fed mangels than when fed corn silage. Anyone who has tried it, will tell you that it is not an easy thing to get goats started on silage. There is also some controversy as to whether it is safe to feed corn silage to goats. There have been some cases of death when corn silage was fed in sufficient amounts to increase milk production.

The variety you can choose is a cross between a mangel and a sugar beet. The yield is as great as with the mangel, but they are more nutritious. An eighth of an acre planted to mangels will produce enough roots for a herd of 11 milkers for three months. It is a good idea to have enough mangels to feed the goats when they come fresh in March.

Comfrey is one of the highest protein foods you can feed your goat. It ranges between 20 and 30 percent protein. It is easy to grow, but requires a very alkaline soil. This is easy enough to do by adding ground limestone to bring the pH up to at least 7. Comfrey is started by root cuttings. It has huge leaves and spreads but is easily contained. It grows well in all types of soil. Goats often won't eat the fresh cut leaves but will eat comfrey that has been allowed to wilt in the sun for a few hours. Comfrey can also be made into hay, but it difficult to cure in large amounts. At least a dozen plants per goat should be planted. They do take up a lot of room, requiring spacing 3' apart in rows 3' apart.

Most people who grow gardens will have sweet corn. Goats love the stalks which, if you have a shredder, can be chopped so they will eat the whole thing. They will do a pretty good job if you just toss them the stalks. For the best feed value, cut the stalks as soon as you finish harvesting the sweet corn and before they turn brown. If you let them dry, they can be chopped and fed as fodder, but a lot of food value will be lost.

412

Table 15-1. Crops to Grow for Goats.

plant	approx. yield 100 row	seed required for 10 row	comments
Carrots	125 lbs.	½ oz.	low in protein; high in copper, manganese, vitamins A and C
Comfrey	(see comments)	16 roots	high in protein, grown for curative reasons; an attractive and easily raised perennial; established plant can be cut four times during growing season
Green beans	50 lbs.	1 lb.	high in digestible protein, digestible energy, calcium, and phosphorus
Kale	2 bu.	½ oz.	high in digestible protein when dried
Mangel beets	100 lbs.	2 oz.	low in digestible energy, minerals, and vitamins; good winter feed because of succulence and bulk; feeding to bucks may cause urinary calculi
Potatoes	3 bu.	½ peck seed potatoes	low in digestible protein; high in digestible energy, copper, manganese, niacin, and vitamin C
Pumpkins	100 fruits	¼ oz.	low in digestible protein and energy; high in vitamins C and A
Soy beans	50 lbs.	½ lb.	high in digestible protein and energy, especially when dried, also high in calcium, magnesium, and potassium; plant can be fed whole when green; plant can be cut and dried as hay before beans mature; dried seeds can be fed
Sugar beets	100 lbs.	2 oz.	low in digestible protein; very high in digestible energy
Sunflower seeds	100 plants	¼ oz.	high in protein and digestible energy, potassium, phosphorus and manganese; entire plant may be fed
Sweet corn, whole plant w / o ears	(100 ear)	4 oz.	low in digestible protein; high in digestible energy
Tomatoes	200 lbs.	50 plants	low in digestible energy and digestible protein; high in vitamins C and A, especially when dried
Wheat, hard red winter	25 bu / acre	1½-2 bu / acre	high in digestible energy, carotene, niacin, and vitamin A

413

As you finish up your garden for the year, plan to sow winter wheat. It will do your soil good by preventing erosion. If you have only one or two goats, you can stake them out on the wheat during the winter to some fresh succulence. If you have too many goats to tie out, they will appreciate it if the wheat is cut and brought to them. Your reward will be in the milk pail.

During the summer the goat garden "goodies" are fed as an evening meal when the goats come in at sundown. Since they won't graze at night as cattle do, they benefit greatly by this extra feeding.

Now is the time to plan ahead for next year. Goats like variety, so plant a goat garden of several different vegetables for them (Table 15-1).

A GARDEN FOR RABBITS

Have you considered plantings that will improve your rabbitry and rabbits? You know how good rabbit manure is for flowers and vegetables. Rabbits can do a lot for a garden. A garden can also do something for rabbits. Now's the time to think about it.

Bob Bennett is a stickler when it comes to feeding pellets, but he's not averse to supplementing the pellets with the root, green, grain, and seed crops a garden can produce.

Sunflower seeds are an excellent fur conditioner. All rabbits love them, but they are especially good for those you plan to show. Sunflowers are a cinch to grow at the back of the garden, perhaps among the corn where they won't shade lower growing vegetables, or along the hutches where their shade will be welcome. Corn is great for rabbits if you can spare them some. Rabbits like the dried corn stalks and shucks and the dried ears. A few green shucks won't hurt adults if you don't give too many.

Mangel beets have been grown in Europe for years as a stock feed. Bennett lets them stay in the ground in late fall into winter, covering them with leaves to prevent alternate freezing and thawing. Then he slices them up for the rabbits. Most of them really go for mangels. Rutabagas go over big, too. You might even save space to plant a few carrots for the rabbits. Bennett seems to have room for a few for newly kindled does and favorite old bucks. He dries the tops like hay and feed to one and all. When he thins young carrots, he dries the whole business. The same goes for lettuce thinnings. If you have room, grow your own alfalfa, clover and hay, and even soybeans. Can you grow oats? If so, you've got grain and straw.

The thing to remember is that these items are only supplements. If you want to put meat on your rabbits, you've got to feed grain mainly, and for Bennett that means pellets. Roots, greens, and seeds won't take the place of pellets in Bennett's rabbitry, but they are welcome supplements.

Pumpkin and squash vines can be grown and trained over the tops of outside hutches or sheds containing rabbits. Their shade will be welcome in summer, and their greenery might improve the looks of the rabbitry. Even the most handsome buildings in the world are improved by the addition of some ivy vines for shade and eye appeal.

414

Wire fencing, even string, will support vines. Consider the merits of morning glories, Dutchman's britches, cathedral bells, moonflowers, gourds, or clematis. Don't use too much manure on morning glories or you'll get all vine and few flowers. Dutchman's britches have great big flowers and are perennial. Cathedral bells grow up to 20'.

How about a plant screen? It's cheaper than a fence. A combination frame and vine screen, plus vines going over your hutches, can really cool things off and hide or beautify your hutches. How about a hedge, such as privet, or a row of evergreens? Get out the seed catalogs now and see what ideas you might get to improve your rabbitry and your rabbits (Figs. 15-1 and 15-2).

FOOD FOR CHICKENS

Chickens usually do share their keeper's food. Janet Karsok wouldn't know what to do with her kitchen scraps without them, and they usually appreciate any surplus from the garden. To add to this, though, there are two crops that she grows specifically for them to share. They are kale and Indian corn.

The first year Janet grew kale, she planted a 100' double row of dwarf Siberian kale. It was the first thing up in the garden, and it soon grew into a luxuriant hedge. She could go out and cut a bucketful and it would look as if it

Fig. 15-1. A garden can do alot for rabbits (photo by Jean Martin).

415

Fig. 15-2. The shade provided by these vines is welcomed by the rabbits in the summer (photo by John Martin).

hadn't been touched. Once the chickens got a taste of kale, though, she had no regrets about planting so much. When they see a bucket of the green stuff coming, they come running to meet her.

She cut the vitamin-filled leaves for the chickens from spring well into the winter and then again in early spring before the new planting takes over. The egg yolks are a darker orange than before she began feeding kale, and the broilers seem to be more tender and flavorful.

Last year Janet put out 10 to 12, 100' rows of Indian corn and had a good crop of beautiful ears (Fig. 15-3). Th Karsoks sold a few bunches for decorations and used some for "confetti corn meal." They ground the kernels in an old electric coffee grinder, and the meal made very tasty corn bread and muffins.

They gave the rest to the chickens. Janet believes it is as good for them as field corn.

The Karsoks also had enough corn to give the chickens several ears a day throughout the winter. They really appreciated those extra calories to keep them warm during the cold months.

Indian corn can be planted at the same time as field corn. The Karsoks plant theirs the last week or two of May. Be sure to plant at least four rows for proper pollination, and don't plant it near sweet corn or popcorn. Corn can use plenty of nitrogen, so the Karsoks plow down lots of chicken manure in the fall.

To store corn over the winter, it should be picked when the husks turn light brown and the kernels are hard. Pick out the biggest, most beautiful ears for next year's seed. The Karsoks hang up their seed corn for decoration until they're ready to plant. Remove the husks from any ears you are not going to hang up. Spread out the ears to dry thoroughly. If you pile it up before it is completely dry, it will get moldy.

ROOT CROPS FOR HOMESTEAD LIVESTOCK

Roots are perhaps the easiet of feeds for the small-time live-stock raiser to both produce and utilize. They are vitamin-laden, store without processing, can be regularly harvested for months, and take up less precious ground than feed grains or hay. They can be tilled and handled by hand or with small machinery. For the person whose stock consists of only several dozen chickens, rabbits, or ducks, only several hogs, goats, or cattle, roots are the perfect feed.

The most common feed roots are also the most common food roots. Carrots, red beets, turnips, and rutabagas appear in most gardens and at most tables. Lesser known roots such as those two cousins of the red beet, the mangel and the sugar beet, are unpalatable to most humans but very popular with most livestock.

We have added the kohlrabi to the list of feed roots although it bears its fleshy bulb above ground—it is not really a root crop. It is just as prolific as the others, as popular with the stock, and more nutritious than many of the real roots.

If feeding roots are new to us, it is because we don't know what kinds of feeds our ancestors used. The old-time root cellar often held more feed for animals than humans. Although milk did not necessarily come from man-gels, chopped roots did make up part of many an old-time dairy ration. Any collector of old tools knows of heavy-bladed block knives fastened to large stumps to facilitate the chopping of stock beets. Before Columbus landed in the New World, European farmers raised animals without corn, soy beans or alfalfa. They did it with the help of turnips and beets.

Fig. 15-3. Indian corn.

Perhaps the best reason for growing feed roots is their tremendous productivity. Not only do roots produce a lot, but they keep on producing for a long time. In central Wisconsin Michael Goc plants roots as soon as the ground is workable—around mid-April. By the beginning of June, thinnings are available for feed.

Goc prefers to keep his chickens in a yard. Daily buckets of greens keep them contented, although penned. As the summer wears on and the roots fill out, thinning continues. The hens keep eating greens and roots. They are particularly fond of beets and will carry bits of scarlet to empty corners of the yard as if they were misers hoarding gold. Carrots and turnip roots are not very popular with chickens at this time. Likewise, carrot tops are usually passed up for the more leafy greens.

The chickens don't care for some roots, which is just fine with the hogs. They are quite happy to receive a daily bucket of roots. This time it is the sugar beets, kohlrabies, and mangels that are the most popular. Goc has never seen a hog turn down a mangel.

He does know of one fussy sow who would not touch a white turnip. Only rutabagas would do for her.

One of the assets of root crops is their long growing and harvesting season. Greens and small roots may be harvested in late spring well before the tomatoes see a stake or the corn is ankle high. Months later roots may be harvested until the ground freezes too hard for pulling. Carrots may be left right in the ground, covered with straw and harvested throughout the winter. Animals winter-starved for some fresh vegetables cluck and grunt their pleasures at a bucketful of chopped carrots in January.

Although named after the underground portion of the plant, stock roots actually produce two crops. The greens are the summer crop and the root the winter. Those tops should not be forgotten, for they usually contain much more nutrition than the underground portion. The leaves of all stock roots contain large quantities of vitamin A, a small but important part of all animal rations.

The carrot root is a vitamin storehouse for winter. Packed in sand and fed fresh the carrot brings valuable vitamin A to the stock when they need it most. Beet greens contain a relatively large amount of iron, a mineral essential to swine.

The *kohlrabi* root contains a lot of *ascorbic acid* (vitamin C). All these roots, most especially the sugar beets and mangels, produce food energy. This means that an animal fed beets in the winter will be able to utilize other feed, namely expensive grain, to put on pounds, produce eggs, and not waste it maintaining body heat.

Stock roots provide almost no protein. They do make it possible for an animal to utilize protein from other sources more efficiently. This is probably why old-time stockmen were able to raise meat animals on what we would consider to be a ridiculously low protein diet. You need less if what you've got is utilized efficiently.

Having grown feed roots for several years, Goc has developed a system that he believes utilizes them to their fullest advantage in terms of the animals he feeds. Each April he plants 3,000' of rows to carrots, sugar beets, and mangels. Another 1,500' goes into red beets and kohlrabies. About 100' more is planted to turnips and rutabagas, the least popular of the roots.

As soon as it is possible to do so without damaging those roots left in the ground, thinning begins. Goc's two dozen layers and the three dozen chicks which he raises each summer happily consume a 5-gallon bucketful of greens daily from June to November. As the plants get larger, thinning becomes easier and faster. In the early part of the summer, Goc concentrates his efforts on the quick to sprout and quick to crowd carrots, turnips, kohlrabies, and red beets. Later on, as many of the roots are consumed by either the four-legged or the two-legged animals, Goc switches over to the mangels and sugar beets.

Mangels and sugar beets, in a good year with plenty of water, will grow to the size of quart pop bottles. Such large roots store easily in Goc's damp root cellar. They may be stacked like firewood, which they resemble, until that winter day when they are needed. Roughly chopped and spread out in the yard, a big mangel a day makes fine chicken feed (Figs. 15-4 and 15-5).

To grow such large roots requires extensive thinning. That is just fine. Goc is finishing hogs and maintaining a large sow just at this time of the year. Only humans have a sweeter tooth than a hog. What is sweeter than a sugar beet? By fall the big sugar beets and mangels stand a full foot or more apart in the row. Anyone who has seen how thickly beet seeds sprout knows that it takes a lot of thinning to separate the plants that much. Goc does this without wasting a sprout or even using these feed crops to make compost.

In November all the roots must be either eaten or stored. Turnips and kohlrabies will keep for a short time just stacked in the cellar. Because they don't last without more handling than Goc cares to give them, he doesn't attempt to keep kohlrabies and turnips over the winter. Sugar beets, mangels, and rutabagas will keep longer with much less care, and Goc depends on them to last through the winter.

Carrots deserve special mention for they are handled slightly differently than the other roots. Unlike the others, carrots do not produce much leaf. What they do produce is not very popular. There is plenty of other leafy material around for the animals to eat. It is the carrot root that is valuable. This is because of its great vitamin content. Beets may produce more greenery and bulk, but the root is a nutritional nothing compared to the carrot. Packed in sand or left in the ground under straw, carrots are worth any trouble taken to preserve them. They provide a bundle of vitamins just when those vitamins are most needed. They are the essential ingredient in any scheme using roots for food.

Growing large amounts of feed roots makes it possible for Goc to feed some fresh vegetables to his animals year-round. Goc's experience is

Fig. 15-4. Chopping stock beets.

limited to hogs, ducks, and chickens. When he gets other animals, he intends to feed them roots. They provide home-grown nutrition for the animals.

FEED FOR COWS, PIGS, AND CHICKENS

It is possible to grow the grains and hay that are the basis of most animal diets, but it takes special planting, harvesting, and storage not commonly practiced in the average garden. Gene Logsdon's book, *Small-Scale Grain Raising*, goes into fascinating detail on this. Until or unless you raise sufficient quantities, plan to buy the grain, mixed rations, and hay necessary to feed your stock.

It squeezes a little, especially if you are feeding a meat animal and waiting for rewards. Once you start eating your own meat, you think of feed bills as an investment, like putting your pennies in a live piggy bank.

When the garden is producing, starting with comfrey by the middle of May in Iowa, Monica Brandies stretches that feed dollar considerably with garden produce. Comfrey, high in protein and medicinal value, is a great food and tonic for man and beast. Best of all, it grows like you wish everything would. One plant can be divided by the end of its first season to start 12 to 25 more. Each clump shoots its hairy green leaves 2' in the air and can be cut at least five or six times a season.

Monica has three rows about 50' long. Most animals won't break out of pens to eat this, but if presented first when they are hungry, they clean it up and get their vitamins. It is possible to make "hay" of comfrey, storing it in a dry place. Be sure to dry enough for comfrey tea for sick animals in the winter.

Peapods for Cows and Pigs

Then Monica has bags of peapods for the cows and pigs. From the time canning begins in mid July, she can fill a wheelbarrow a day with garden extras to be divided among the stock.

420

Succulent feeds should be fed in small portions at first so that diarrhea or bloat do not develop. The animals should never be allowed to fill themselves with goodies from the garden to such an extent that they neglect to eat some of the grain and hay which are much higher in food value.

There is something else the gardener must consider with his animals. It is nice to have a cow or goat come to the garden fence to keep you company when you work there. You mustn't let her guess how sweet it is.

So go ahead and load your wheelbarrow with surplus cucumbers or squash, or the spent, but still green, corn plants, or the tail end of the bean or pea vines. Never give an animal a sample across the fence.

You must trundle that load into the darkness of the barn and then piece it out at regular feeding times in the usual place. Pretend you bought it at the feed store. Squelch your pride in your production. Otherwise, your cow will eat it all at once, and that night she will jump the fence, probably tear her udder on the barb wire, and surely eat your remaining garden to instant destruction.

Chickens Love Tomatoes

Chickens cannot be convinced to wait until tomatoes are ripe. If they find them in the garden, you'll never get a crop. So Monica confines as many chickens as she can catch during the vital time and plants her tomatoes at the far corner of the garden and hope they will be safe.

If you carry a special bucket for damaged fruit, you will delight the chickens and add to the control of insects in the garden as well. Monica also gives the poultry sunflower seeds, swiss chard, kale and borage.

Rabbits will eat not only greens but also root crops such as potatoes, mangel beets, Jerusalem artichokes, and the traditional carrots. They like apples and pears, too. Don't ever doubt the value of those old grainy Keiffer pears that produce in such dependable abundance.

Fig. 15-5. Mangel beets are good feed.

Rabbits keep their teeth trimmed on twigs, so share your prunings between them and the goats. They get a lot of protein from comfrey and also sunflower seeds.

The pigs get the corn husks and empty cobs and share with the chickens the spoils of canning. Pigs can get fussy; some won't touch pears.

The only horses that ever whinnied and came running at Monicas approach were bound and determined she'd never have a compost pile in their pasture. They ate everything from pickles to potato skins. She did watch for corn cobs and anything else that could choke them.

Monica sometimes plants a few rows of mangel beets to feed pigs, cows, and chickens. They prefer them chopped. She starts feeding the thinnings in July, and by the time those are gone, she pulls one and leaves one for maximum development. The last ones grow to 5 pounds each and can be left in the garden until hard frost. Then they must be stored in a root cellar, pit, or mound of hay in the warmest corner of the barn or garage. If they freeze, they go to pulp. (Mangel beets can cause sterility in buck goats.)

If you have room, plant extra pumpkins or winter squash. Monica has fed them to cows, goats, pigs, and chickens. Let them spread over the part of the garden that is harvested early, or climb up over the fence and out into the unused road ditches. They can be stored far into the winter, preferrably in a dry place. Pile them in the attic.

Turnips can be planted clear into September when even the second garden has some bare spots. Cows, pigs, and chickens will eat grass clippings, but don't let them heat up in storage or they could cause trouble. Goats and rabbits will eat pine needles and evergreen and fruit tree prunings. Nothing goes to waste on a homestead—not even weeds.

If you have the time, you can haul weeds from the fence rows. most seeds are destroyed in the animal's digestive system. There are only a few weeds that are poisonous: *milkweed, wild cherry, locoweed, jimson*, and other members of the nightshade family. Chances are slim that your stock would eat enough of any of these to hurt them, but check with the county agent for your local offenders and learn to identify and avoid them.

If you don't have animals, you can compost all your garden's waste or excess. You can let it rot on the spot if it is healthy or till it under just to be sure.

If you have room for livestock, plan your garden to feed every hungry mouth on the place. You'll all eat better.

Chapter 16

Butchering

Butchering is the process of transforming livestock into human food. The process isn't pleasant, but it can be less traumatic for both man and beast if the butcher has experience, or at least knowledge.

The best way by far to learn how to butcher is by watching and working with someone with experience. When you're on your own "the first time" is still a major event, but not nearly as unnerving.

The second best way is to read everything you can get your hands on pertaining to butchering, study the diagrams, and have the method down pat in your mind before you begin. Then start on something simple, like a chicken.

We are not going to tell you all about butchering. The subject is far too broad to be covered in this space. Each class of livestock is different, and each butcher seems to have his own little tricks of the trade. Instead, we present some basic information which hopefully will be useful.

THE BASICS

To a homestead butcher, a chicken is pretty much like a pig. The chicken has feathers. The front feet are wings, but beyond that there isn't a whole lot of difference.

This is significant for first-time butchers. There are more similarities than differences in livestock anatomy.

The first step in the butchering process obviously is to kill the animal. Neanderthal man did it with rocks, modern hunters do it with guns, and modern slaughterhouses employ a sophisticated battery of tools, up to and including completely automated chicken killing devices.

On the homestead, the axe is still probably the most common tool for dispatching chickens and other poultry. The diversity of possibilities is almost endless and shows, at the beginning, what a chore it is to discuss "butchering" in a single sitting. Some old-timers still prefer to grasp a fowl by the neck, whip the bird about like a lariat, and, dead bird in hand, proceed from there.

The first time we met Pat Katz, *Countryside's* Betty Crocker, she was telling us how she killed chickens by placing a broomstick over the head, placing one foot on the stick on either side of the neck, and jerking upwards on the legs. Perfectionists prefer to use a thin-bladed knife, inserted through the mount, to pierce the brain of fowl. Properly done, this relaxes the nerves and makes plucking easier, because the feathers are "released."

Similarly, there are several schools of thought concerning rabbit butchering. The most advanced technique is to grasp the animal by the hind legs with one hand, cup the chin in the palm of the other hand with the thumb around the nape, then with a sudden snap render the animal unconscious.

A more common method, perhaps, at least around home abattoirs, is to sharply strike the animal behind the ears with a blunt, stout object. A length of pipe, a hammer, and even a stick will work.

The concussion method works well for other classes of animals, especially goats, sheep, and cattle. Cattle require a sledge.

With this method, you're only rendering the animal unconscious. The immediate next step is to slit the jugular.

Hogs present special problems. Since they cannot be collared or haltered like the ruminants, it's difficult to use a sledge.

The best hog butchering method we've found came from a man who described how an old-time pro went about the process. He merely looped a string around the pig's neck and, speaking softly, led it to the appointed spot. A firm and expert thrust of a blade found the jugular so deftly that the pig acted as if nothing had happened, until it bled to death.

Shooting a pig can be quite efficient or traumatic. Severing the jugular is almost always a necessity to finish the job.

Goats and sheep will shy away from firearms pointed at their brows. Aim from behind, if that's your preferred method. Firearms do have the advantage of being impersonal.

Speaking of firearms, guineas are in a class by themselves, so far as the usual homestead production method of free range is concerned. In 25 years of experience with guineas, we've never tasted one that wasn't shot out of a tree in the woods, just like some wild game bird.

Once the animal is dead, the next step is to remove the outermost coating. In most cases this means fur, which is removed by skinning. Poultry has only the feathers removed. The skin is left intact, and hogs most commonly have the hair scraped off with the skin, again, left on (Fig. 16-1).

With poultry and hogs, the carcass is dipped into hot water—not boiling, but as hot as your hand can tolerate (Fig. 16-2). Dip chickens into hot water, then begin to pluck the feathers from the most difficult areas first: the tail and wings. With the proper water temperature and the proper motion, a chicken can be stripped in a surprisingly short time. The proper motion is actually a rubbing action, against the grain. An experienced chicken plucker can strip a prime fryer in less than a minute.

424

Ducks and geese are handled a bit differently. Sometimes they are picked dry, but this is slower than scalding them first. The feathers and down are valuable and probably easier to salvage if they haven't been soaked. Most people opt for hot water. Waterfowl are rather waterproof, so a bit of detergent in the water helps penetrate the feathers.

The pinfeathers and down left after rough picking are very hard to remove. It is best to dip the plucked birds in melted wax, harden it in cold water, and then strip off the wax and pinfeathers. The wax can be remelted, strained, and reused over and over again.

Another point to remember with poultry is that unless a bird is fully feathered, plucking is a chore. Immature quills just aren't as easy to get out.

For hogs, the usual method is to build a fire under a 55-gallon drum, dunk the carcass in, swish it around to keep it from scalding, and scrape the hair and scruff off with a bell hog scraper. Usually, several applications are necessary.

A handful of wood ashes is said to make the hair easier to remove. We've tried it, and it only seems to make the water gooier, but experiment for yourself.

Other animals—goats, sheep, cattle, etc.—must be skinned. Some people also prefer to skin hogs. There are those who, disgusted with their experiences in plucking ducks and geese, skin them, too.

It's helpful to think of skinning in terms of removing a sweater. There are no buttons or zippers. You skinning knife makes the opening. The procedure is really the same.

Rabbit skins are usually "cased." That is, they are not slit down the belly, but around the head, the front feet, and peeled back like a turtleneck. Larger animals are slit up the belly, out the legs, and around the neck, and the skin is peeled off like a cardigan.

A thin but tough tissue adheres the hide to the body. In most cases this can be worked away by fisting and fingering. Occasionally, however, use of

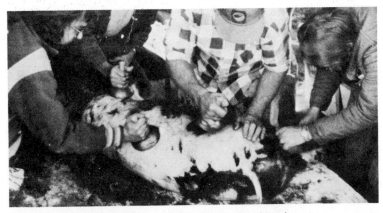

Fig. 16-1. Out of the cauldron and onto the scraping board.

Fig. 16-2. A freshly killed hog is dipped into a tank of steaming hot water to loosen its hair.

the knife is required. With care, neither the hide nor the meat it damaged. It takes practice.

It's important, especially with sheep and goats, not to let the hair touch and taint the meat. The Greeks, who are great fanciers of goat meat, have a method of making a small puncture in the belly, then blowing into it, separating the hide from the meat. More delicate American homesteaders have used tire pumps to achieve the same purpose, and still others have reported success using a garden hose, which not only separates the tissue, but cools the meat more quickly by virtue of the cold water.

Hogs can be skinned, and some people claim it's easier. A curved skinning knife is almost a requisite for this. Most of the lard is lost, and on the self-sufficient homestead, lard is a valuable by-product. Also, skinned hams tend to be less desirable.

After the outer covering is removed, butchering tends to become a matter of utility and scale. Intestines are removed in the same way: a deft slit down the belly exposes the intestines and internal organs, which are removed. After a while hearts, lungs, livers, bladders, kidneys, and more, are all readily identifiable.

Meat cutting is a science in itself. Most homesteaders don't worry about it.

With practice (or if you're a pro), you can produce crown roasts and Canadian bacon and other delicacies. If you're a sausage nut, you'll cut a carcass differently from a steak or chops nut.

The point is, for beginners, it's all edible. It doesn't make a great deal of difference how you cut a carcass, be it a bunny or a beef. You might not

426

come up with a cut recognizable by Messrs. Pride and Price, but once you use a little creative cooking on it, no one will know the difference.

The beginner will certainly want to refer to specific charts to learn the difference between briskets and flanks. The purist will want to perfect his technique on preparing filet mignon and tenderloin.

For most homesteaders, there are no mistakes in meat cutting. If it looks like a steak, broil it. If it looks like a roast, roast it.

BUTCHERING A GOAT

When you butcher a goat, it is very important to quickly cut off the head so the meat isn't tainted by the musk glands under the scalp, according to Jim Henry of Reno, Nevada. Try to keep as much hair as possible off the meat. That flesh is very absorbent and can pick up bad tastes from a few dirty hairs. The way you take off the hide is important here.

Jim kills a goat by cutting the throat and then slicing off the entire head. He lays the goat on the ground and bends the neck around his knee. He cuts the throat and keeps on cutting. He hits the first vertebrae and cuts through the cords and windpipe. All that's left is skin. He pulls the head off right then.

It takes just a few seconds. The head is removed and nothing can go through the bloodstream to flavor that meat. All goats have scent glands just behind the horns—or where the horns would be—and those glands can give the meat a real 'bucky' taste.

Does and wethers don't have the musk odor a breeding buck does, but they have the glands that can affect their meat. Even the immature glands on a kid could taint the meat.

A two-month-old buckling in October may have functioning glands and already smell a bit rank. It probably isn't a problem in kids in spring or early summer. The faster you separate the head from the body, the better off you are in terms of meat flavor.

It is absolutely necessary to have good, sharp knives. Jim really stresses this. You aren't going to have much luck slicing the head off a goat with a dull knife.

The butchering should be done in a clean area with clean tools. Any kind of dirt can cause the meat to taste. Have a pail of water handy to wash off the meat as necessary.

Casing the Carcass

Jim skins a goat by casing it. He takes the hide off in one big round piece. This helps keep hair off the meat.

You start by hanging the carcass up by the rear legs. Punch the hocks and hang the goat by the hocks from a *singletree*.

Make a long cut from one rear pastern to the other. You cut right down through the escutcheon area on the inside of the legs. Skin out the rear legs to loosen the hide. Skin out the tail, since the hide's firmly attached there.

Then you pull the hide down over the body in one piece. It is sort of like pulling off a sweater. Work your arm and fist down between the hide and the flesh to loosen the skin.

If there's an udder, it comes off with the hide. You have to cut through the ligament that attaches udder to body—the *medial suspensory ligament.*

At the bottom of the animal, around the *brisket*, you usually have a little trouble getting the skin away and you may have to use the knife again. Cut the skin inside the front legs and around the hooves, and you pull it off in one piece.

Gutting and Aging

Next the goat is gutted. Jim uses a meat saw to split the breastbone and pelvic bone. A knife is adequate for this on kids. He starts at the top and cuts around the anus area, then pulls the knife straight down the stomach wall. He works his fingers inside around the knife tip to be sure he's not cutting guts.

The intestines fall out easily. You have to cut through ligaments holding vital organs like heart and liver.

Be *careful* not to cut a gut. Jim warns. He admits that he occasionally cuts into an intestine by accident. If that happens, wash the meat with lots of water immediately.

The gutted carcass is hung to age for a few days. Jim points out that there's a biological breakdown of the meat tissues which is part of the quality of good meat.

He ages the meat outdoors even in warm weather. If it's mid-summer, Jim hangs the carcass with a deer sack or something similar around it to keep the flies off. A day or two is plenty of aging when it's hot. The meat glazes and gets sort of a skin on it.

SLAUGHTERING YOUR OWN BEEF

Raising a steer or cow for your own meat supply is almost always economical for the homesteader with a few acres of pasture.

Where some homesteaders incur needless expense is in the slaughtering process. If you aren't squeamish about eating home-grown meat, there's no reason to shy away from doing your own slaughtering and butchering. Having raised and cared for an animal for 1½ to two years, you will be more humane about killing it than any hired butcher. When you load your animal into the butcher's truck and send it off to the slaughterhouse, the animal knows the gig is up. If you do it yourself on your own land, the animal never has a chance to become afraid.

The slaughtering process is basically the same whether you're doing beef, pork or lamb. The major difference is that beef is usually aged five to 10 days between slaughtering and butchering, while the others are not. Some people skip the aging process altogether and maintain that the meat ages well in the freezer.

When your cow or steer has reached its optimum weight, probably fairly close to its second birthday, set aside a full day for slaughtering. Once you gain some skill, the job can be completed in three to four hours, if two people are working together. Plan for this date to arrive in either late fall or early spring when the weather is fairly cold. That way you don't have to worry about spoilage while you work. Butchering is also easier in cold weather because the meat remains firm.

For slaughtering, you'll need skinning knives, a meat saw, and a gun to kill the animal, as well as some means of hoisting the carcass up in the air to skin and gut it out. You can use a .22 caliber rifle and aim for the brain just between the eyes. This is the fastest way to kill any animal except the horned breeds of sheep. Once the animal is down, you must immediately slit the jugular vein in the throat to draw out the blood. This is usually more difficult for people to do than shooting the animal, but it must be done.

If you or your neighbor has a tractor with a front-end loader, you can use it to hoist the carcass in the air. A spreader bar can be made out of a 3' to 4' length of steel pipe, and metal "S" hooks can be bought or fashioned out of scrap steel. One side of the "S" hook is inserted between the tendon and bone of each hind leg near the foot—the equivalent of the Achilles' tendon. The other side of the "S" is inserted into a hole in the spreader bar. Once each leg is attached to the spreader bar, attach the bar to the loader and hoist the carcass into the air until the head just touches the ground.

If you can't borrow a loader, here's an alternative. Locate two large trees that are fairly close together. Place a sturdy beam between the crotches of the trees, and rig up the spreader bar. Then, using a come-along rated for at least 1,500 pounds, hoist the carcass into the air. Remember to be very careful, since you are dealing with 1,000 to 1,500 pounds of beef, and you don't want the carcass to fall midway in the slaughtering process.

The next step is skinning. Skinning a 1,000-pound steer can take up to three hours, if you're inexperienced and working alone. Work progresses much faster if two people are skinning.

Make your first cut from one hind ankle running down the leg across the crotch area and up the other leg to the ankle. Next, start at the center line of the belly and work down the belly and chest from the original crosscut. If you plan to have the hide tanned, work from the belly around the back without making any other cuts in the skin. Otherwise, you can make a center cut down the back to hasten your work.

Depending on the quality of the coat and breed of the animal, you may want to seriously consider having the hide tanned. Work carefully if you plan to have the hide tanned, since you don't want it to look like Swiss cheese.

Once you've worked the skin off down as far as the neck, the step is to cut off the head (Fig. 16-3). You'll need the meat saw to cut through the spinal column just at the base of the skull.

With the head off, the next task is to remove the guts. Your goal is to separate the internal organs from the carcass without cutting into, thereby opening, any of them. This is the trickiest part for beginners. Most particularly, you want to avoid opening either the bile sac, stomach, or intestines. As a precaution, have several buckets of fresh water or a hose handy to wash down the insides if you do break into any of these organs.

Make your first cut with the knife near the anus and cut through to the pelvic bones. Then, with the saw, cut through the pelvic bones. With the knife, carefully work your way down through the muscular wall of the belly until your're halfway to the neck. Next, working from the neck area with the knife, cut through the muscle from the neck up across the breast bone until you meet the cut made previously. With your meat saw, open up the chest cavity using the knife line as your guide. Be careful not to puncture any organs.

Return to the belly area and begin to detach the internal organs from the body cavity, working from the back around each side to the front opening (Fig. 16-4). Once you've detached the organs somewhat, their own weight will cause them to tear away from the cavity and spill out on the ground. Be prepared for this to happen and move out of the way.

Once the organs drop, you'll still need to detach them in certain areas before you can completely remove them. After that job is complete, cut the carcass in half by sawing through the center of the backbone from top to bottom (Fig. 16-5). Then lower the carcass to the ground and quarter it (Fig. 16-6). With your knife, mark a cutting line between the twelfth and thirteenth ribs (counting front to back), and cut through them with your meat saw to quarter each side of the carcass.

The best and safest way to age the meat, if you choose to do so, is to rent a commercial meat locker. It won't cost much and is less risky than hanging the meat yourself. Once you deliver the carcass to the locker company, your work is complete for five to 10 days. During that time, try to

Fig. 16-3. The skinning of the carcass is nearly completed.

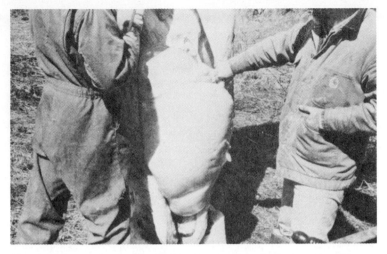

Fig. 16-4. The internal organs should be detached from the body cavity with care.

locate a meat grinder to borrow or arrange with your local butcher to have the meat ground the day you cut it up. Also, supply yourself with a large roll of high quality freezer paper and tape and plastic freezer bags in which to wrap the meat.

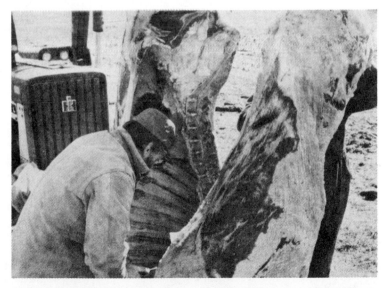

Fig. 16-5. The carcass is cut in half by sawing through the center of the backbone from top to bottom.

431

Fig. 16-6. Some extra fat is trimmed away after halving the carcass.

CUTTING AND PACKAGING THE MEAT

After you've aged the carcass in a rental locker or cooler for five to 10 days, set aside a full day for butchering. Cutting up and packaging the meat takes longer than slaughtering. With two people cutting and one wrapping, it will easily take six to eight hours of hard work to complete the job.

You'll need the following tools: boning knife, butcher knife, the meat saw used in slaughtering, and a grinder to make hamburger. In most rural communities, at least one family owns a grinder that you can probably borrow. If not, the butcher in your local country store will probably grind the hamburger for you at a nominal charge. Other tools which are helpful, but not essential, include a cleaver, meat hook, and block scraper.

A fairly large work area is needed, such as an open shed or garage. You can make two portable table tops out of ¾" plywood, 3 × 5' and covered with Formica, which you can set up on elevated sawhorses. These make a good working surface that easily can be cleaned and stored.

Proper sanitation cannot be overemphasized when handling meat. Your tools, workspace, and hands must be absolutely clean. Bacterial contamination of meat can take place quickly, resulting in spoilage, and possibly illness, to you and your family.

Start with one of the forequarters of the carcass by dividing it between the fifth and sixth ribs (counting from front to back). With the inside up, make a cut through to the back with a knife, then turn the piece over. Using the knife mark as a guide, saw through the breastbone, shoulder blade and backbone. Separate the plate (Fig. 16-7) from the rib by cutting crosswise about 10" from the chine bone.

The rib part can be cut into standing rib roasts, short ribs or steaks. You can bone it by cutting as close to the rib as possible. The meat can be used for rolled roasts and boneless steaks. Much of how you cut up the beef depends on your family's needs and preferences. The plate end can be cut into a few short ribs and the remainder boned for stew meat or hamburger.

From the other half of the forequarter, you'll get chuck and brisket. Separate the foreshank and the brisket from the quarter just above the elbow joint with your meat saw. Then separate these two pieces where the muscles divide them. This line should be obvious when you're actually working with the meat. Bone the brisket and set it aside for corning. (The

432

flavor you can achieve when you do your own corn beef far surpasses anything you can buy in the store, so plan to try it.) The shank portion can be boned for hamburger or cut in sections to be used for soup stock.

Now turn your attention to the arm section (Fig. 16-7). With your knife, make one cut from top to bottom paralleling the cut made to cut off the brisket and shank portion. Then, to separate the arm, make a cut about 5" down and at right angles to the last cut made. Cut out the arm bone, and tie the meat into a rolled roast, if desired. Alternate uses include hamburger or stew meat. The remaining piece of meat can be divided into an English cut and a block cut, or you can use this for stew meat.

The final section of the forequarter is the shoulder area (Fig. 16-7). Separate the chuck blade from the neck and shoulder at the base of the neck with your meat saw. Bone the neck area for stew meat or hamburger, or saw it into appropriate lengths to be used for soup stock. The shoulder piece should be cut into pot roasts. The chuck blade can be divided into either steaks or roasts. Repeat these same steps with the other forequarter. If you started fairly early in the morning, you can plan to take a lunch break when you've finished the other front quarter.

You'll find the hind end less time consuming to cut than the front quarters. The bulk of the meat is located in the hind end, but less boning is needed so the work progresses more quickly. This end also has the more tender cuts of meat, such as sirloin and top round.

With one hind quarter on your table (inside up), trim the fat and save it for either suet or to make soap. (While making soap may sound like a good project to do with children, remember most soap recipes call for lye, so do be careful.) As you trim away the fat, be sure to leave a thin layer on the tenderloin, which is the long, thin muscle just inside the backbone (Fig. 16-8).

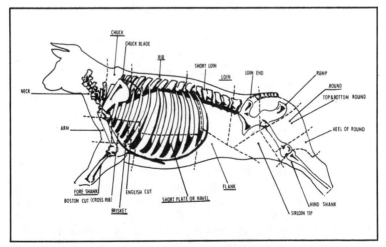

Fig. 16-7. Diagram of a carcass (drawing by Tim Messler).

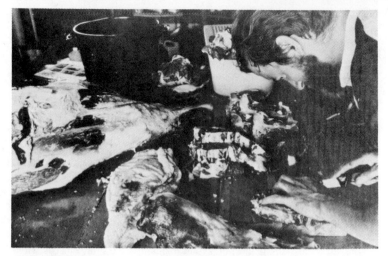
Fig. 16-8. Trimming fat from various steaks and roast.

Separate the flank (Fig. 16-7)) from the rest of the quarter by cutting along the curve of the leg. This meat can be cut up for stew or ground beef. If desired, a flank steak can be separated from the rest of the cut.

Cutting at a right angle to the leg bone, separate the round and the hind shank from the remainder of the quarter. Take the piece containing the round, and separate the tip of the round from it. When viewed in cross section, this is a triangular-shaped piece of meat. To separate the tip, make two cuts, one on each side of the leg bone, and pull the shank portion away from the rest of the piece. Cut away the heel of the round and bone the shank. Use the shank for hamburger or stew meat, and the shank bone for soup stock.

Now turn your attention to the round. The most tender part is the rectangular-shaped piece of meat above the stifle (knee) bone. Make a cut parallel to the end of the round (where your last cut was made), and saw through the bone. Your top round comes from above the bone (the outer side of the carcass), and the bottom round from below. Once you remove the bone from the round, the natural division between the single muscle of the top round and the two muscles of the bottom will be obvious. Cut the round into steaks and roasts of desired size.

Finally, turn your knife to the loin section which will yield choice steaks and rump roasts. First, separate the rump from the loin by sawing parallel to the cut made to separate the hind from the forequarter at a point approximately two vertebrae back from the arch of the backbone. The rump or rear section can be boned and shaped into a large roast by rolling and tying the meat. If you have no need for such a large roast, you can cut this piece up for stew.

Steaks come from the remaining loin end. Cutting from front to back, you'll get club, T-bone, porterhouse, and sirloin steaks. Depending on how thick you make them, you should get from three to five of each kind from each rear quarter. Repeat these same steps with the other hind quarter.

Grinding the hamburger is one of your final tasks. If you haven't been able to borrow a grinder, pack the meat in a cooler and take it to the butcher as soon as possible. Depending on how you cut up the carcass, you could get from 80 to 150 pounds of ground beef from a 1,000-pound steer.

Rather than wrap all this in freezer paper with tape, use plastic freezer bags and seal them with a twist tie. By the time you get to the hamburger, you'll be ready to quit, so use the fastest safe method of packaging available.

When you put the meat in the freezer, spread it around as much as possible. Never stack it right away since that greatly increases the amount of time needed for the inner layers of meat to freeze, increasing the chance of spoilage. Once the meat has frozen solid, you can stack it in an orderly manner.

Assuming someone has been wrapping, labeling, and dating the meat as you go, you're only remaining task is cleanup and disposal of the refuse. Scrub your work area and tools with hot, soapy water and allow to air dry. You can bury the refuse, being sure it's deep enough not to attract dogs. If this isn't feasible, bag it in heavy duty plastic trash bags and get it to the dump as soon as possible.

If you should decide to slaughter and butcher your own meat, be sure to get in touch with your local county extension agent. He or she will have some illustrated pamphlets which will further explain the procedures discussed here.

CUTTING BEEF

Many homesteaders go to all the trouble of raising their own beef, then take it into the packing house and don't have the slightest idea how they want that precious meat cut up. Most packing houses and processing plants take advantage of this customer because they can process their meat in the fastest way possible, saving them time, and time means money to them.

At 18 cents per pound, it's time the small farmer took another look at the way his hard-earned winter meat supply is processed, even if he does it himself. Knowing the various ways to cut up your meat can save you all kinds of money.

Hind Quarter

Round. Have it cut in ½ to even 3″ slices for steak, as well as a round roast. The ½ to 1″ *round* steaks might be tenderized. The 3″ roast might be cut in half, depending on your family size.

If you don't like steak, have your round boned out for eye of round roasts, bottom round roasts, and top round roasts. Depending on your desires, the eye of round, bottom and top might be cut into eye of round steaks, bottom round steaks, and top round steaks. A 1½″ eye of round steak is okay for broiling and Swiss steak. If you would like, part of the round might be steak or roast. Any part of it might be made into cube steaks.

Sirloin Tip. Have it cut in half lengthwise and sliced ¾ to 1" for steaks for broiling. The side containing the most fat and sinew can be boned out for cube steaks or tip kabobs. If you desire, have the sirloin tip cut into roast instead of steaks.

Heel of Round or Pikes Peak Roast. Have it boned, rolled and tied for roast or boned out with sinew-free pieces made into cube steak or stew meat.

Rump Roast. Have it boned out and made into a rolled rump roast or cube steaks. Rumps make excellent roasts, bone in or bone out.

Sirloin Steak. Have then cut ¾" quarters to 1½" thick for broiling or cut 2½ to 3" thick for a sirloin roast.

T-Bone Steak. Have them cut ¾" to 1½" thick for broiling. If you desire, you can have them boned out and sliced ¾" to 1½" for K.C. strip steaks. The tenderloin can be cut into ¾ to 1½" for filet mignon steaks.

Shank. Same as on front quarter.

Front Quarter

Chuck. Have the blade roasts cut 1½" to 3" thick, depending on the size of your family. Then have the 7-bone cut into roasts 1½" to 3" thick or into ¾" to 1" chuck steaks for broiling. If you don't like a lot of roast, have the neck meat cut up for stew meat or put into ground beef. If your family likes roasts, have the neck boned, rolled and tied, then cut it into pieces suitable for your size family.

Arm. Have the arm roasts cut 1½" to 3" thick, depending on the size of your family. For a variety, have several roasts cut off, and then several ¾ to 1" round bone steaks cut for broiling or swissing. Arms can be boned out using the lean, sinew-free pieces for cube steak. If your family enjoys steaks, have the whole arm cut into steaks.

Rib. Have the cap or eye cover removed, and rib steaks cut three-quarters to 1½" for broiling. Have the cap boned out for cube steaks or stew meat. If you want boneless rib eye steaks, have the cap removed and the rib eye cut ¾ to 1½" for broiling. If you would like, have a rib roast cut or any combination of the three, depending on your desires. The back ribs remaining after the eye of the rib has been removed make excellent barbecuing ribs.

Short Ribs or Plate. Have the skirt removed from the inside of the plate and made into skirt steak rolls ¾ to 1½" for broiling. Have the lean cap removed and boned for cube steaks, then have the ribs cut into 1½ to 2" strips for short ribs or for soups or stews. If you don't like short ribs, have them boned *lean* for ground beef.

Shank. Have them cut into 1½ to 2" pieces for soups or boned to be used in ground beef.

Brisket. Have it cut whole for corned beef or cut into ¾ to 1" strips for barbecuing. Some have it boned out for stew meat or cube steaks.

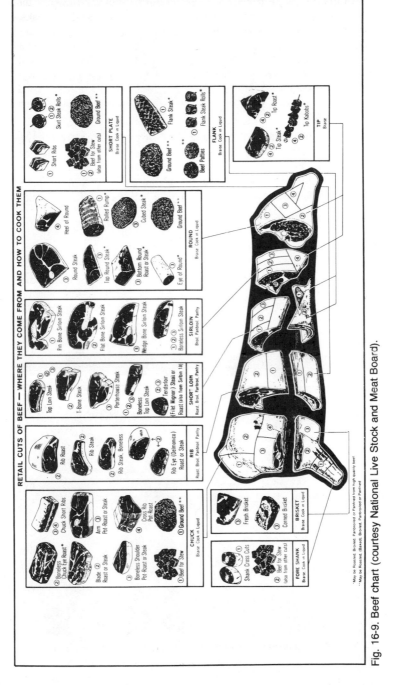

Fig. 16-9. Beef chart (courtesy National Live Stock and Meat Board).

437

Cubed Steak or Minute Steaks. These are often never mentioned because of the time involved in making them. They are excellent eating, as most of you know who have eaten a chicken fried steak, as they are often called.

Ground Beef. Have the trimmings boned *lean* for either patties or bulk. If you desire, have half put into patties and half into bulk for meat loaves and casseroles. See Fig. 16-9.

CUTTING PORK

Because of the initial investment, time, space, and feed required to finish out a beef, the average homesteader chooses to fatten a hog. The hog, unlike the beef, is by far the easiest to butcher yourself and is the easiest to process for either the experienced or the beginner (Fig. 16-10). A half hog consists of four major primal cuts, whereas a half beef consists of nine.

Ham

The most common procedure on a ham is to have it smoked and cured. There are various ways that smoked and fresh hams might be processed.

Smoked Ham. Have the hock removed to be used for seasoning. The whole ham could be sliced completely and packaged in smaller packages to fit your family's needs. It could also be sliced and tied back together for a

Fig. 16-10. A hog is easier to butcher and process than a cow (photo by Jean Martin).

438

RETAIL CUTS OF PORK—WHERE THEY COME FROM AND HOW TO COOK THEM

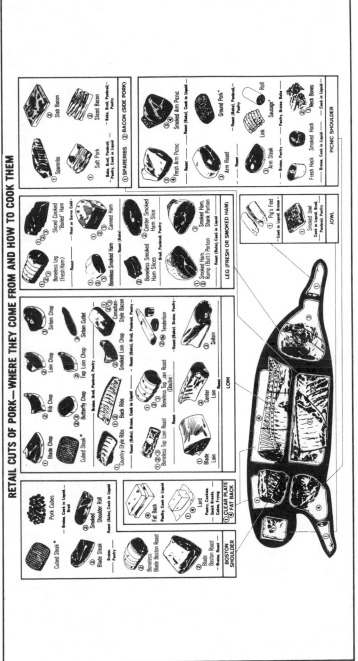

BOSTON SHOULDER

① Cubed Steak *
— Braise, Panbroil —

② Blade Steak
— Braise, Panbroil —

② Smoked Shoulder Roll
— Roast (Bake), Cook in Liquid —

② Pork Cubes
— Braise, Cook in Liquid, Broil —

② Boneless Blade Boston Roast
— Braise, Panbroil —

② Blade Boston Roast
— Braise, Panbroil —

CLEAR PLATE ④ FAT BACK

① Fat Back
— Lard Pastry, Cookies, Quick Breads, Cakes, Frying —

LOIN

① Blade Chop
② Rib Chop
② Loin Chop
② Sirloin Chop
— Braise, Broil, Panbroil, Panfry —

② Butterfly Chop
② Top Loin Chop
② Sirloin Cutlet
② Canadian-Style Bacon
② Smoked Loin Chop
— Roast (Bake), Broil, Panbroil, Panfry —

①②② Country-Style Ribs
①② Back Ribs
— Roast (Bake), Braise, Cook in Liquid —

① Boneless Top Loin Roast
①②② Boneless Top Loin Roast (Double)
② Tenderloin
— Roast —

① Blade Loin
② Center Loin Roast
② Sirloin
— Roast (Bake), Braise, Panfry —

LEG (FRESH OR SMOKED HAM)

①② Boneless Leg (Fresh Ham)
①②②⑩ Sliced Cooked "Boiled" Ham
— Roast — — Heat or Serve Cold —

② Boneless Smoked Ham
② Canned Ham
— Roast (Bake) —

② Boneless Smoked Ham Slices
② Center Smoked Ham Slice
② Smoked Ham, Shank Portion
— Broil, Panbroil, Panfry —

② Smoked Ham, Rump (Butt) Portion
— Roast (Bake), Cook in Liquid —

SPARERIBS

① Spareribs
— Bake, Broil, Panbroil, Panfry, Cook in Liquid —

BACON (SIDE PORK)

① Slab Bacon
① Salt Pork
① Sliced Bacon
— Bake, Broil, Panbroil, Panfry —

PICNIC SHOULDER

④ Smoked Arm Picnic
— Roast (Bake), Cook in Liquid —

④ Fresh Arm Picnic
— Roast —

② Arm Steak
— Braise, Panfry —

Ground Pork *
— Roast (Bake), Broil, Panbroil, Panfry, Cook in Liquid —

Link Sausage *
— Panfry, Braise, Bake —

Roll
② Neck Bones
— Cook in Liquid —

④ Fresh Hock
④ Smoked Hock
— Braise, Cook in Liquid —

JOWL

① Pig's Feet
— Cook in Liquid, Broil, Braise —

① Smoked Jowl
— Cook in Liquid, Bake, Broil, Panbroil, Panfry —

Fig. 16-11. Port chart (courtesy of the National Live Stock and Meat Board).

439

larger dinner. If you desire, have the ham cut in half and the halves left whole, or you can have one half sliced for frying and the other half left whole for baking.

Another procedure you might like is to have the rump portion removed whole then have the center sliced for frying, or have the center removed and left whole for baking. The remaining shank portion can also be left whole or cut into smaller chunks for seasoning. If you prefer boneless ham, have it cured and then have the bones removed and the ham tied back together. Have the bones packaged for seasoning.

Fresh Ham. The fresh ham can be processed in the same manner as the smoked ham. Depending on your preference, if you do not like fresh ham, the fresh ham could be used in sausage or boned out for pork kabobs, pork cutlets, or any combination of the three. Whether fresh or cured, the ham slices can be sliced from ¼" for frying up to 3" from the center for baking.

Belly or Side Meat

If you desire, have the *belly* smoked for bacon or left uncured for fresh side pork. Have it sliced rind off or on and packaged to your family's needs. The ends might be cut into small chunks for seasoning. Have spare ribs cut into 3" to 6" slabs to be used for baking or barbecuing.

Loin

Most people think the pork *loin* is only "bone in" pork chops because the various ways it can be processed are seldom mentioned. You may have it cut into roasts. Depending on your size family, it can be cut into half or smaller roasts. It is also possible to get a combination of roasts and pork chops by having both ends cut for roast and the center and loin sliced for chops. Have them cut ¼" for breakfast chops, ½" for frying, and 1 to 1½" for broiling. If you prefer boneless chops, you might have the center and loin boned out and cut into ½" to 1½" strips or butterflied to be used for stuffed chops. The tenderloin can be butterflied or left whole, depending on what you like. The blade end of the loin can also be cut into 1" strips and cut through, making meaty, country style spare ribs. The sirloin end of the loin can be sliced for sirloin chops or left whole for a roast. You may wish to have your loin cured, and it can be processed in the same manner.

Shoulder

Shoulder. Or fresh picnic as it's often called, can be sliced ½" to 1" thick for steaks, tied back together for roasts or left whole. It can also be cut into two pieces for roasts or boned out for pork cutlets or sausage. You might prefer it to be boned out and tied back together for a boneless roast.

Boston Butt. The Boston butt can be cut the same as the shoulder, and some people have it cured. It makes excellent breakfast meat.

Neck Bones. Use them fresh or have them cured for seasoning.

Jowl. Have it fresh or cured to be used for seasoning or sliced to be used for fresh side or bacon.

Sausage. You can have it seasoned and packaged for your size family.

After you've gone through all the expense and time to prepare your animal for slaughter and used these tips for processing, you'll know you got more meat for your money. See Fig. 16-11.

Chapter 17

Gardening Techniques

Homesteaders garden for self-sufficiency. The single most important reason for the existence of the homestead garden is to feed the family regardless of what happens to any link in the conventional food chain. The homestead gardener must establish goals that are perhaps somewhat different from the goals of most other gardeners and plan carefully in order to reach them. This chapter has plenty of suggestions for homestead gardeners.

GARDENING ORGANICALLY

Anyone who was an organic gardener back in the pre-1960s remembers, without a doubt, the stares, offhand and snide remarks, and chuckles when you admitted to being such. Now that organic gardening and holistic are household words—well, as the cigarette commercial says, "You've come a long way, baby" See Fig. 17-1.

What is it about organics that give such fantastic results? Do the organic vegetables and fruits really taste better? Are plants which are organically grown better able to fend off insects and diseases? What is it about organic material that helps your soil, even though the actual nitrogen, potassium and phosphorus in the material may be very low? Do people and animals really have better health when eating organically grown produce and forage? We are going to examine and, hopefully, answers these and other questions.

A Bit of History

Far from being a recent innovation, organic gardening and farming can stake its claim back into antiquity. Who could forget that interesting piece of information about the Indians and pilgrims burying fish along with the corn seed?

The more modern research, however, was carried on in the 1920s and was reported upon in a book by Sir Albert Howard titled *The Waste Products of Agriculture*. This book was published in 1931 and told about the Indore method of maintaining the fertility of the soil. This method was the forerunner of the compost pile, but was done in an extremely scientific way and tested upon many crops. Sir Albert's work was not widely acclaimed, especially in this country. In the middle 1940s, a foresighted gentleman named J. I. Rodale embarked on a new venture—a magazine called *Organic Gardening*—and the rest is history.

Flavor or Organic Produce

It maybe a pleasant surprise to you when you have company and serve the "strong" flavored vegetables or greens, and the guests take a small serving—just to be polite—and end up having seconds and sometimes thirds. Most folks regard the brassicas (cabbages, broccoli, cauliflower and their kin) as a last-choice vegetable, but they expound at length about the good flavor.

Fig. 17-1. Organic gardening has proven itself in actual practice, and more and more people are taking advantage of its benefits. At the same time, there is less "mystery" and folklore surrounding it than some people used to associate with organic methods. Green manure crops such as rye and buckwheat are becoming common in gardens such as the one shown here.

A lot of people will immediately state that freshness is the secret. That's part of it, but not all. The instant the vegetables are harvested, the difference is apparent. The organic is more succulent, less fibrous, and color-pure. (The oranges are deep, greens deep, and reds a true, bright color, instead of the sickly pale imitations or a dark, rank blue-green which bespeaks of chemical nitrogen.) The "proof of the pudding is in the eating," and this holds so very true with organically grown vegetables.

If you are a nonsmoker and have a keen nose, try this. Buy a bunch of greens at the supermarket or anywhere they have not been grown organically. Simmer in a covered pot. Lift the lid a few times and sniff. They smell like a drugstore. That's all that chemical nitrogen and sprays being liberated by the cooking process. (For an even stiffer test, try simmering a frying chicken bought at the store, then eat it, if you can.) The organically grown vegetable, on the other hand, has an odor indigenous to its variety and cooks, as most of us gardeners and cooks find, in about half the time of store-bought vegetables. They taste marvelous.

Disease and Insect Resistance

Poor soil, devoid of organic material and lacking in nutrients, cannot support healthy plant growth. The organic materials act upon minerals present in the soil and release them for optimum growth, disease resistance, and resistance to insects.

Sir Albert Howard told of an experience when his healthy cattle (fed only on humus-raised feeds) rubbed noses with a neighbor's cattle which were sick with the very contagious hoof-and-mouth disease, but nary a one of his cattle caught the disease. (An interesting account of his work is summed up in a book titled *An Agricultural Testament.*).

The plant world reacts in much the same way to poor soil. Plants will be pale and sickly, as well as host to mildews, rust fungus, and hordes of voracious insects. Judi Blucher has been gardening ever since she could toddle around with a package of seeds, and she has seen this truth proven over and over again. Some of the garden plots were poor, some good, and then there was one excellent one, part of an old alfalfa pasture unused for years, upon which crop after crop of alfalfa matured, was crushed down by snows and rotted, undisturbed.

The humus-rich soil was full of earthworms and beneficial fungi. It needed only a small amount of ground limestone to bring it to perfection. This plot bore enough vegetables for Judi's small family all summer, to can, give away, and store (potatoes, carrots, beets, onions, and cabbage), and this was in a region with a relatively short growing season and on a plot only 30 × 40′. The produce won prizes at local fairs and tasted wonderful. Insect problems were negligible.

The poor plots often yielded little and were constantly attacked by insects and diseases. Also, if the weather turned bad, either too hot and dry or too wet and cold, the plants often yielded almost nothing or gave up and died young and untimely deaths.

444

The good plots were a mixed bag, sometimes good yields and sometimes not, according to the weather, but none approached the quality and ease of culture or flavor of the "alfalfa-ized" plot.

Judi's present garden, which is somewhat over a half an acre, has received leaves and leaf mold; cover crops of all descriptions both winter and summer; shredded organic material of all kinds; plowed-down mulches of hay, straw, alfalfa, barn litter and leaves; manures including chicken, goat, turkey, duck, goose, horse, rabbit and cattle; phosphate rock; kelp meal; cottonseed and blood meal; granite dust and guano-phos (a bat guano and rock phosphate mix); and large amounts of compost.

ORGANIC MATERIAL ACTS AS A BUFFER

Another important aspect of organic gardening is the reaction of the organic material upon the pH of the soil. (pH is simply a scale used to designate the acidity-neutrality-alkalinity of the soil with a scale from zero to 14, with zero being the most acid, seven neutral, and 14 extremely alkaline.) Most of the soils east of the Mississippi River and those lying immediately to the west are acid, and most of the far western soils are alkaline—by rule of thumb, not absolute. Let's see what effect the organic material has upon the soil.

The addition of any kind of organic material to the garden soil "buffers" the soil, helping extremes of acidity and alkalinity, especially by making available nutrients which were tied up by extremes in either direction. For instance, in a soil which is too alkaline, the iron will be tied up and the plants will turn yellow. If not corrected by some means, the plant will turn lighter and lighter yellow, reaching almost white, and then portions of the leaf margins start to turn brown and die.

Naturally, the crops born by such severely chlorosed specimens are minimal or, in some cases, nonexistent. In extremely acid soil, the yield also drops due to a shortage of calcium, and the protein content of grains drops. Legumes, including beans and peas, cannot produce the nitrogen-fixing bacteria so vital to large yields. The cole crops, Swiss chard and beets, dislike acid soil, too.

The addition of organic material also aerates the soil. Many gardeners forget that air is also important to the plant roots, not just water and minerals. If the water remains in too heavy a concentration around the roots, the plant cannot make use of it and will die in seemingly the midst of plenty. The humus acts as a million tiny sponges, absorbing the water in times of plenty and releasing it in times of drought. Then, too, when there is proper aeration of the soil, root crops will form properly, instead of having to force their way through stiff clays and possibly end up misshapen and stunted. Humus will allow for deeper penetration of rains and cut the need for excessive watering during dry periods.

Organically grown produce is highly touted to have superior keeping qualities, and it is easy to comprehend why. Chemically grown vegetables and fruits have weak, sappy cell structures and are more prone to bruising because of this structure. Sometimes the vegetables have been "pumped" near harvest time to make them larger and increase their weight, but, unfortunately, neither keeping quality nor flavor is enhanced by this practice.

Judi Blucher's humus-grown produce has had more or less of an even pattern of growth and has come into maturity naturally. Thus, with normal care, the organically grown vegetables and fruits are better keepers—to say nothing of having superior flavor.

Before land was disturbed by the plow, most of the virgin soils in this country were said to have had about 4 percent humus. Today the "average" soil contains about 1½ percent. It seems ludicrous that a mere 2½ percent could make such a difference, but call to mind the thousands of farmers who "corned out" or "cottoned out" their farm land and left it to erode, while they moved West only to repeat the procedure. Some of these farms were virtually worthless and almost devoid of any topsoil.

The late Louis Bromfield told, in one of his books on farming, of being curious as to why there were small green areas apparent in his seeded pastures. Upon investigation, he found that the gophers were responsible—by bringing to the soil surface the subsoil, which was obviously better than the topsoil left in his eroded pastures. (Bromfield's books, *Pleasant Valley* and *Malabar Farm,* should be read by everyone interested in organics. Although he was not strictly organic, Bromfield leans heavily in that direction. The books tell of rebuilding run-down farms and restoring the land and wildlife.)

Even in percents less than four, organic material helps to put the quietus on many diseases and harmful organisms in the soil. Potatoes, for instance, may be attacked by scab in alkaline soil, especially soils made alkaline by the addition of lime, but organic material incorporated into that same soil will hold scab to a minimum. Club root of cabbage is greatly aggravated by acid soil and is rarely seen on crops grown in neutral or slightly alkaline soil. Nematodes, which live on the roots of many common vegetables and damage yields, may be kept under control by planting a crop of winter rye and tilling it under to rot.

Thus, organic material aids directly by helping healthy plants to grow which resist diseases and insect pests and indirectly by providing inhospitable surroundings for certain types of garden pests.

ORGANIC GARDENING MISTAKES

Barbara Ellen LaConte was humbled last summer. The humbling brought with it lessons that may benefit others who would be better organic gardeners or who are just beginning to tend the land.

The LaContes had remarkably good fortune in their five years in northeast Connecticut (Fig. 17-2). The land they purchased (more for its beauty than for any agricultural potential it had) had been virtually untouched for 15 or more years. It is in a narrow river valley so that, while

Fig. 17-2. The LaContes' Button-wood Farm in northeast Connecticut has a settled, solid feel.

they have fewer hours of sunlight than their higher neighbors, they also have richer, deeper, less rocky soil. They cleared brush and scrub over the years as they expanded the garden from 20 × 40′ to its present 100 × 100′ and found deep, sandy loam, adequately drained, well-balanced and eager.

The setting and, perhaps, the settled, solid feel of the 100-year-old home, surrounding trees and woods attracted dozens of bird varieties, carnivorous insects and ambitious toads and garden snakes. The LaContes had even the few desirable swallows and bats to take the place of insect repellents in June. They had high hopes of learning to grow all their own vegetables and most of their fruit, and they had no experience at all.

Their first garden brought no animal pests, and the second attracted only one rather lazy raccoon (Fig. 17-3). The rabbits munched and multi-

Fig. 17-3. The first garden was a nonorganic postage stamp carved out of sumac, wild blackberries, brush, and rock (photo by Barbara LaConte).

447

Fig. 17-4. The organic transition began with the second garden. This shows late summer sowings of peas and beans with the rows too widely spaced (photo by Barbara LaConte).

plied outside the garden's stock fence. They seemed contented. The LaContes had no droughts or extremes of cold or heat to contend with, neither did they have infestations or plagues of any kind. They did not have to labor long to return soil or environment to health. They were not hampered by lack of time or finances and lived in a gardener's paradise.

With the second garden, the LaContes began organic practices (Fig. 17-4). They became practitioners (of the faith, art, craft, science) by predilection, by magazine articles, and by the book. Predilection moved them to apply manure (trucked from a local stable, mucked from their pig's pen, bucketed from the chicken house), hay mulch, compost, leaves, and winter cover crops. They tilled shallowly in fall and spring, and hoed and weeded during the season. They picked off bean, potato and Japanese beetles when there were enough of them to warrant their attention. The LaContes released praying mantises and lady bugs into the garden, rotated crops, and played with companion planting.

The LaContes had good harvests of clean vegetables and fruit from a thriving soil and environment. They felt organic, talked organic, and bragged organic. They grew smug about the healthiness and rightness of organic methods. They also grew complacent. They did not dream to what extent they were benefiting from the slowness of the environment's response to the changes they had made in it. Organic gardening was not obvious and easy.

The LaContes were humbled in their fifth year. They were fortunate enough to be humbled without losing an entire harvest, but enough went wrong in that season to show them how very much they had still to learn and how much more there was to do than they had done. It might aid someone else who is just beginning to garden organically or who has grown complacent in mastery of organic practices to share what they learned after the fall.

Organic gardening is not merely a process of omission. The magazine articles and books that converted the LaContes to the principles of organic gardening were largely philosohic. Their explanations of the far-reaching implications of agribusiness attitudes and practices for even their small garden were alarming. They could readily see what they had been doing wrong. So they stopped doing it.

One by one, they omitted deep and frequent tillings, stopped leaving the land fallow, and gave up on the applications of artificial fertilizers, pesticides, and herbicides (Fig. 17-5). It was wonderfully quick and, therefore, therapeutic to leave off those and other offensive practices, because it was obvious what the LaContes should no longer do.

It was (and still is) far less obvious what they should do. For four seasons they were haphazard organic gardeners. The LaContes were impulse buyers in a huge market of methodological possibilities. Their fifth garden reflected this confusion of purposes, reflected their failure to choose the activities to which they would commit themselves. See Fig. 17-6.

The methods of postwar farming and gardening are intrinsically repeatable, easily measurable, and, on a small scale, not particularly taxing on energies or intellect. More importantly, big-business-style gardening is impersonal and nearly placeless. By its methods, a garden the same in most

Fig. 17-5. The fourth garden was faulted by too much shade, too many weed seeds left in the rear and too much fallow soil (photo by Barbara LaConte).

Fig. 17-6. Mistakes evident in this shot include too many cabbage plants together in the middle, and at left, the bean plants are too concentrated. They could be enriching other soil areas (photo by Barbara LaConte).

essentials could be grown in Main, Missouri, or Mississippi. By contrast, organic gardening methods are highly personal and unique.

Each gardener must select, combine, adapt and experiment with the methods he will use according to his best understanding of his gardening situation. The decision to practice organic methods is, after all, a beginning, not an end.

No Soil Guessing

The LaContes had their soil laboratory tested for pH, nitrogen, phosphorus and potassium in the first season. It was healthy, well-balanced soil. The extension service recommended 5-10-5 to assure them that whatever the slight deficiencies in the soil, they would not affect the crops.

The garden increased in size. The LaContes, stopped applying chemical fertilizers. In the virtuous enthusiasm of manuring, composting, and cover cropping they made assumptions about how well they were maintaining the health of the soil. They did not have the soil tested or test it themselves. It had been good soil when they began, and they were feeding it great quantities of organic matter.

When, in the fifth season, germination rates declined, peas produced poorly, vine leaves yellowed prematurely, and plants were generally less thrifty, the LaContes grew suspicious. Even a small home test kit revealed (unsurprisingly) locally changed pH, and off the chart deficiencies in potassium and phosphorus.

450

The organic matter content of the LaContes' soil is higher. They were ignorant about the workings of that organic matter and about the availability to plants of the three major foods and of important micronutrients. They knew some of the soil health theories, and they knew that phosphorus and potassium were vital to plant health, but they never decided what they would do, when they omitted applications of chemical fertilizers to make up for the decrease in potassium and phosphorus. They guessed in ignorance. That ignoranced injured the soil they had intended to treat well and cost them an abundant harvest.

Theories about soil functioning and chemical functions in the soil need not necessarily be learned, but your own soil's requirements must be. Those requirements are complex, but they are discoverable by testing. Don't guess. It is simple and inexpensive to do the testing yourself for pH and basic nutrients. Test in the spring with an eye to plant health and in the fall with an eye to soil health. Have professional tests for organic matter and micronutrients done as often as you can afford them. The costs in lost harvests and for soil rebuilding are much greater.

Know Your Compost

No matter how carefully you operate your composting process, the nature of the compost changes with each addition or removal. For most of us, composting is more a handy, virtuous way to recycle wastes from the garden, animals and kitchen than a scientific soil building process. In either case, careful or slipshod, the compost you put on your garden is never the same twice. The changes it will cause in your soil's health and balance are never the same twice.

The LaContes' first seasons of compost were rich with pig manure, chicken litter and droppings, wood ash, grass clippings, leaves, and kitchen and garden waste, which (though they used neither starter nor specific layering techniques) was turned often. By chance, rather than by careful planning and testing, they had a crumbly, odorless, well-cooked compost. Seedlings planted deep took to that compost and crops side-dressed with it flourished.

Last season, also by chance rather than by intent, the LaContes put most of the chicken matter directly into the garden. They had no pig. The sheep grazed the lawn so there were no grass clippings. Out of the lumpier compost that resulted sprung myriad weeds and volunteer vegetables from seeds that ought to have been cooked. The squashes and tomatoes planted in that careless, untested compost set fewer fruits. It required their first application of chemical fertilizer in three years to sustain those few. The neighbor's dog had all she could do to refrain from digging under the garden fence to get at the cause of the ripe aroma on hot days. The LaContes' own dog was not so restrained.

They will now be quite deliberate and painstaking about what goes into and comes out of their compost pile. They will also test the compost's makeup. It matters a great deal.

All New is No Good

Don't change too many things in one season or tackle too many new projects at one time. The LaContes have changed seed varieties, soil management, mulches, weeding styles, irrigation behavior, planting arrangements and methods from season to season and sometimes in mid-season. They have made changes without slow deliberation on their relationships to each other, without consistency and without pausing to carefully reflect on causes and effects before changing again. They have behaved as if "new" were always better and as if they did not depend on the results of the harvest for food. In that regard they played at rather than worked at gardening.

At the same time as they were trying out new methods with wild abandon, they were also adding new projects to the garden. In one season the LaContes planted strawberries, six fruit trees and an herb garden of considerable size and variation. Their enthusiasm and energy were, perhaps, admirable. Their ability to keep up intellectually and physically with the new demands on their time and attention was, as might be expected, less admirable. One new project in a season when most activities and practices are familiar, is sufficient.

It could be said, after all, that through the LaContes helter-skelter enthusiasms they have learned a great deal about different gardening practices in five years. It could also be said that they do not really know first-hand the differences in impact of newspaper or straw or black plastic mulch, or the advantages of pole over bush beans, or of side-dressing with liquid over solid compost. It is certain that their strawberry patch has gone to weed, their fruit trees will not really produce until their sixth year, and in the herb garden the lowest herb plants often compete for light with the tallest.

Patience, planning, and reflection are virtues for the gardener. Lacking those virtues, impatient, experimental gardeners must learn at least to experiment on small patches of garden and restrict the variables in any given season to one or two recordable ones.

Record Keeping

You cannot keep too many records. In the full flush of conversion to organic methods, or under the heady influence of the first open windows in spring, it is exciting to set up charts and lists and plans for recording the events of the coming gardening season. In mid-September when there aren't enough hours in the day for gathering and processing the harvest, and when most of the season's danger periods are past, it seems less important to record the dates of the first full head of cabbage, the largest tomato harvest or the last potato bug. When the steamy days follow each other across the August calendar as if forever, it is perhaps therapeutic to forget to record the daily temperatures.

It may be that detailed records of every aspect of the gardening season—from seed varieties and planting dates through weather and insect reports to the first harvest dates and quantities—are not as vital to the chemical as to the organic gardener. For the first, one season's methods can be pretty much like another's. He can often bale himself out of his mistakes with sprays or quick pick-'em-up fertilizers.

For the organic gardener, anticipation and prevention of problems and repetition of the successful experiences only are keys to his success. Set up (or borrow from magazines or other organic gardeners) thorough and clear charts in the calm of March that can be as easily completed in September as in May. Make entries every day—perhaps at the same time each day to establish a routine. Keep notes and comments short. Lengthy conversational statements rambling across blank pages will quickly become a labyrinth into which records wander and become lost. Review charts, lists, and notes soon after the season is ended while memories are fresh, and put them into an order you will be able to benefit from the following March.

Overplant

Every year the LaContes have had too many green beans, eggplant, greens, and cucumbers. They decided to plant fewer last year. Deficient soil, a late snowfall, a cool June, squash bugs, and a gluttonous bunny-cum-rabbit (with a burrowful of ravenous siblings) gave them cause to rue their decision.

Operate passionately out of the assumption that some quirk or calamity will take half your harvest away. In bad years it will. In worse years it will take both halves. Make insects, drought, the early frost, gallumphing dog, or hurricane work overtime to claim your harvest. In most cases it is not much more expensive or time-consuming to plant at least half again what you think will be enough. If you are blessed with overabundance, you can give it away, market it, or put it by for a less bountiful season.

Get Close to Your Plants

After a winter season of relative inactivity and days on end spent primarily indoors, it is a physical pleasure to plunge into the strenuous first activities of the new garden season. From those first activities—hauling frost-heaved rocks out of the garden and compost in—through the preparation and planting to the tending of seedlings and plants in mid-season, the satisfaction of gardening is both physical and expansive.

Those are nearly all fish-eye, nonspecific activities. They grow out of a wide angle macro-view that encompasses the whole garden or an entire row or an entire crop. Even deliberate attention to these activities would not have been enough to assure a good harvest that last season. Too often the LaContes merely tidied the face of the garden, manicured a section, weeded a row, fed a crop, watered, mulched, raked, hoed without getting down on their knees. They checked under plants for local soil conditions, becoming familiar with as many individual plants as they could—the weak and the strong ones. The large activities filled their time and attention. That failure to get close, to engage in a more microscopic view, in more plant-specific activities in the garden enabled snails, rot, insects, damaged plants, diseases to take hold and undermine the health of rows, of crops—in that last season, of the entire garden.

It takes time to get close. It cannot be done daily in a large garden. It can be done routinely and in rotation so that no plants go too long untended to the detriment of all. In that closeness to individual plants, in that patient familiarity is one key to prevention of large-scale problems. In that specific knowledge of individual plants is the beginning of a personal understanding of the whole ecology of the garden.

Impact on Land

Don't underestimate your impact on the land. With an attitude that was more managerial than stewardlike, and that was crop rather than soil/environment-centered the LaContes made their assault on the piece of land they garden, on its whole environment. They were, after the first year, organic in their thinking, but organic meant to them a series of practices not really connected into a whole view of their relationship to the land.

The LaContes were not organic; their methods sometimes were. They were in wholehearted agreement with the articles they read about the care and tending of agricultural ecological systems; still, they failed to notice, until the system began to break down, that their impact on the ecology of the garden was enormous and in many ways negative. They never fully internalized the notion that the land was not so much for their use as it was a partner with which they could participate in a productive process that would benefit them and should not damage it.

As a result, birds that had come naturally to the site to eat insects were driven further away by the LaContes' clearing of too large an open area around the garden. Earthworms that had made each handful of soil a wriggling, living mass were decimated by careless, intensive applications of highly acid mulches and by too frequency tilling.

Concentrations of certain plant varieties, even though they moved them around the garden, attracted herbivorous insects and animal pests by the fifth season that had not existed in the local ecology before our coming. Vegetation that had not been completely cooked and decomposed in composting had rotted in clumps that caused pockets of unhealthy soil and nurtured undesirable soil microorganisms. Four seasons of untrained tillage and irrigation rearranged soil layers, altered soil-life balances, and broke down the connective films of water that sustain all soil life.

The LaContes recognized with considerable guilt, in the fifth season, that their relationship to the land had been one of a cancer to the body. They had invaded a healthy ecological system, creating massive imbalances, destroying natural defenses and relationships, inviting disease in the form of insects, droughts, predators, dead soil pockets, and had placed that ecology in need of intensive remedial and rehabilitative care.

The chemical gardener might respond to the awareness of his invasion of the ecology of the garden by treating the symptoms of the cancer, by

454

relieving the pain he was causing—by feeding the plants, spraying the insects and weeds, killing the predators, and applying more water. As organic gardeners they could do no less than heal the ailing environment and change their behaviors so that the ecology could accept the changes they were making and adapt healthily to them.

As gardeners, we cannot fail to alter inexorably the ecological systems, the natural patterns and rhythms of the sites we choose to garden. If we were to go away altogether, our garden sites would not revert entirely to their original states. A new, wild ecology would prevail. We can, however, learn to comprehend the enormity of our impact and the irreversibility of it. We can cease to behave as managers, whose sole concern is profitable harvest, or quacks, whose aim is to cure symptoms rather than disease.

SUMMERTIME GARDENING

There are three very important factors to keep in mind to get optimum yields and keep the summer garden bearing into late summer and early fall, if such is possible in your area. The "big three" are thinning, fertilization and watering.

Thinning

Thinning comes hard to most of us. Pull up all those sturdy little seedlings? We have a tendency to sow too many seeds in too little space to avoid any gaps in the rows. (This information is for the regular level bed garden, not for the raised beds or French intensive gardening where plantings are made more closely.) When plants are crowded, they must compete for the same nutrients, sunlight and moisture, to their detriment. Let's see what spacing is needed for most of the common garden vegetables.

Beans, both bush and lima types, should be spaced about 5″ or 6″ apart. If you are expecting or are already experiencing dry weather, later plantings can be 8″ to 10″ apart. The beans will grow very large and bear immense crops; there is usually negligible damage from insects (with the possible exception of the Mexican bean beetle), and the beans can be harvested more easily, with none left to grow overly large thereby cutting future bearing. Then, too, dew and other types of moisture will evaporate rapidly and thus lessen the chance of mildews and rusts. Pole beans need to be 10″ to 12″ apart in the row.

Cabbages should be spaced according to their variety. Midget types can be as close as 10″, but the large Flat Dutch will need about 3′ for insect control and optimum develoment. Err on the side of too much space, rather than too little.

Carrots can stand some crowding especially the thin types, but in summer it's best to allow 3″ between them, especially if the soil is somewhat heavy.

Corn is best sowed in not less than four rows of the same variety, 2½′ to 3′ apart between the rows. It can be grown in hills of three plants 3′ apart in the rows or single plants 1′ apart in the rows or single plants 1′ apart in the row. Corn that is crowded, especially that which lacks nutrients and moisture, will give a poor yield.

Cucumbers which are grown in hills should have no more than three (two are better) plants in each hill. Grown in rows, the cukes should be spaced about 30″ apart. This wide spacing will allow easy access while picking. Melons and squash have the same space needs as cukes.

Eggplants should be spaced about 2′ to 3′ apart, depending on variety and in which section of the country they are grown. In the North, they rarely get above 2′ or 2½′ high, but in the South, with its long warm growing season, a Florida Highbush variety often reaches 4½′ by the time frost comes.

Greens of all kinds need 6″ or so between plants. Chard and collards can stand about 8″ or 10″.

Lettuce, the leaf variety, can stand some crowding, if moisture is ample. (Light shade will also prolong cutting season.) Head lettuce may fail in summer in most localities, no matter how much space you allot it, but if you must, try 15″ with plenty of mulch.

Okra should be grown in rows about 3′ apart and the individual plants about 15″ or 18″ apart in the row. In the South, okra, too, often makes 12′ or 14′ "trees," so be sure they have enough space to stretch out.

New Zealand spinach is a somewhat different green. After soaking the large lumpy seeds for about 24 hours, plant about 1″ deep and thin to about 20″. This heat tolerant green should be grown more widely, for it will provide a large amount of greens all summer if the tips are pinched back and some moisture is provided.

Peas, which generally aren't considered a summer vegetable anyway, can be 2″ or 3″ apart in the row. Plant a double row, preferably on either side of woven wire, spacing them about 4″ apart between the rows. Dwarf peas can lean upon one another and thus do away with the supports.

Sweet potatoes are spaced about 15″ apart in the row, or, if your soil is extremely rich, only about 12″ to avoid stringy potatoes and too lush a top growth. Rows need about 3′ between them.

Tomatoes should have ample space. Depending upon the varieties grown and which cultural method you use, they may be as close as 2′ between plants and rows. Obviously, this spacing is for staked or caged tomatoes or for the small self-topping varieties. Try about 3′ between the tomatoes in cages in the row and about 4′ between rows.

Peppers, hot and mild, are non-demanding, and 18″ apart is about right. This, incidentally, is one garden plant which doesn't seem to need much fertilizer of any kind, although does benefit from loosening of soil by compost and likes adequate moisture.

Root crops such as turnips should have 5″ or 6″ of space in the rows. Small ones can be left for a short while and eaten as you thin.

Fertilizing

Fertilizing may be needed in the summer garden to boost yields or to keep production heavy, especially if your soil is not in top shape or you are just beginning to garden organically. Most plants will benefit from manure or compost water "tea."

The easiest way to make the tea is to get an old sack (burlap sack in the North, tow sack in the South) and put three or four shovelfuls of compost or manure in it. Place the sack in a large container of some kind, and fill the container with water. You will probably have to poke the sack down under the water a couple of minutes, unless the compost or manure is quite damp, as the sack has a tendency to float.

Let this "brew" for two or three days. Then dip out a quantity, mix with plain water until the color of the mixture is about the color of regular fairly strong "drinking" tea, and apply to your plants, but keep the liquid away from the leaves. You can use commercial fish or seaweed (liquid) the same way, simply follow the directions on the bottle. When you are through with the "tea," water the rows thoroughly.

Watering

The one cardinal rule for any kind of irrigation: don't water unless you do it right—and right means deeply. Light sprinkling, which brings plant roots to the surface and encourages them to stay there, is worse than useless, unless you plan to stand the whole summer with a hose in your hand. Water deeply, and then, when the soil is dry a couple of inches down, water again, but don't soak every day. The old rule of 1" per week for optimum vegetable growth and quality is a good one.

The best time for watering in most localities is early in the morning. If you live in a really arid climate. you can "get away" with watering late in the day and not risk foliage diseases. In most sections of the country, you are asking for rust and mildews if you go out and water late in the afternoon, unless you put the hose under the mulches and keep the top surfaces dry.

The best and most hassle-free type of watering is by furrow. Less water is wasted by this method and, if handled well, watering will not need to be repeated for a week or 10 days. Lacking the right setup for furrow irrigation, a sprinkler will do. There are a couple of models for sale which spray in a square pattern and perform well, reaching the often neglected corners of the garden.

Insofar as is possible, try to avoid the extremes of dryness or sogginess. Some vegetables, notably tomatoes and some varieties of melons, will crack open or split when subjected to the yo-yo effect of drying and overwatering. Also, tomatoes are prone to blossom end rot when treated this way. (The rot is sometimes aggravated by a mineral deficiency.) Mulching is a most essential step in conserving the moisture you do have and in avoiding wasting water by evaporation from the soil surface.

WINTER GARDEN IN YOUR KITCHEN

A wonderful thing has happened. For the first time in history, it is now possible for the average home gardener to grow vegetables throughout the winter, right in the house.

We have been leading up to it for a long time. Many experimental-minded gardeners have been working away for several years, testing lights, soils' fertilizers, temperatures and humidities. They have grown lettuce, radishes, onions, and other small salad greens with ease. Now they are stalking bigger game—tomatoes, beans, beets, carrots and chard, among others.

Further, seed and plant breeders are working to develop vegetables varieties especially for this purpose. In a few years, we expect to see an organic vegetable garden in every gardener's kitchen, providing a modest but steady supply of low-cost, fresh, and tasty vegetables for the table, even in the dead of a Minnesota winter.

Not until the relatively recent introduction of special plant-growing fluorescent lights has it been possible to grow vegetable crops indoors with any chance of real success (Fig. 17-7). Annual vegetables require moderate temperatures, good humidity, constant soil moisture, heavy fertilization, and long hours of sunlight. We have been able to provide the first four requirements, only to be stymied by the last. Even in the sunniest south window, the amount of light received during winter's short days is inadequate for the heavy demands of annual vegetables, which must find sufficient energy to germinate, establish strong foliage, flower, then set fruit and bring it to maturity—all in 120 days or less.

With special fluorescent lights that simulate the color spectrum and intensity of the sun's plant-growing rays, we can do much better than ever before, if not so well as we can outdoors during summer. Look at indoor vegetable gardening as a bold adventure, with no guarantee of success. Do your best to simulate outdoor conditions and learn by your experience. You will find some vegetables that do well, and you will grow these again and again, slowly building up your list of annual crops until you have perhaps a dozen different vegetables growing around the house from early autumn right through the outdoor planting days of spring.

The vegetables recommended here for indoor growing need 16 hours of light a day. You can provide this best by setting up your pots and flats in sunny south windows and supplementing the natural window light with fixtures each holding two 40-watt plant-growing tubes, attached to an automatic 24-hour timer. Keep the tubes 4″ above the tops of the growing plants, in order to provide the strong light intensity needed for vigorous growth. Give the plants moderately high humidity—not a steamy hothouse atmosphere, but more than is found in a dry apartment. This suggests an active kitchen, where pots are often simmering, or even a large bathroom, where the door can be kept closed between baths and showers to trap humidity. A more expensive (and energy-consuming) alternative is a portable humidifier.

458

Provide good drainage and water the plants every day, so that the soil is soaked thoroughly but never allowed to puddle. Bring in your best garden loam for this purpose, mixed with a good amount of aged compost and some springy peat moss. Add bone meal or lime to begin with, unless your soil is naturally alkaline to begin with. If you keep an earthworm composting unit in the cellar, work the castings into the vegetable soil regularly.

Fertilize the plants weekly. You can use an all-purpose fish emulsion, mixed according to the bottle directions given for house plants, or a strong compost tea. Manure tea might give your home an unforgettable character all its own—one that you might prefer to avoid.

Spray the plants with water once a day and preferably twice. If you still have problems with maintaining humidity, think about erecting plastic tents over the flats. The kind sold in paint and hardware stores as drop cloths are both inexpensive and large enough for the job.

Keep the temperature at moderate levels—75°F during the day, 60°F at night. Remember that if you keep the flats on top of kitchen cabinets, which is an ideal place, the temperatures up there will be significantly higher than they will be in the middle of the room. Still, most plants will not be injured by temperatures even as high as 80°F provided that the humidity is maintained.

What to Grow?

Almost any vegetable can be grown indoors, as long as its root requirements are not inordinately heavy or its top growth not exceptionally

Fig. 17-7. The pleasures of fresh mid-winter vegetables are possible now even in the far North with the development of sunlight-simulating fluorescent lights (drawing by Gretchen Relanger).

large. Sweet corn, broccoli, asparagus, melons, squash, okra, and similar spreading vegetables are obviously out, unless you are prepared to expend tremendous energy in setting up the proper conditions for them.

Quick-growing salad greens and radishes are relatively easy and should be the first you try. Many other vegetables, with requirements between these two groups, can be grown with moderate success if sufficient care is exercised. Here are some of the likely candidates for indoor vegetable growing:

Carrots. Choose short and dwarf varieties. Thin young seedlings to 1″ apart. Use the plucked seedlings as salads.

Radishes. They are easy to grow. Thin to 1″ apart. Most globe-shaped varieties are ideal for indoor growing.

Beets. Thin plants to 3″ apart after they have become established. Fertilize heavily for quick growth and tender roots.

Chinese cabbage. One plant will fill an 8″ pot. Allow three months to harvest.

Peppers. They are slow to grow, four months to harvest, but the foliage of the plant is so attractive that it is easy to wait. They like warm temperatures and good humidity. When flowers appear, pollinate by transferring pollen from one flower to another, using a soft artist's brush. Without your artificial pollinating efforts, no fruit will form.

Lettuce. Leaf lettuce is the best. It likes cooler temperatures than other vegetables and can be grown well under a cool basement window, with supplemental light. Fertilize heavily for fast and succulent growth.

Tomatoes. Tomatoes are a challenge, but fun to try. Choose dwarf varieties or cherry tomatoes—one plant to a 12″ pot. Give tomatoes the brightest window in the house and add supplemental light for fully 16 hours. Fertilize twice a week. The foliage will feed heavily, perhaps to the detriment of flowering and fruiting, and therefore it's a good idea to prune back foliage when it grows much past the point where flowers emerge. Pollinate as for peppers.

Mushrooms. They are ideal for dim and cool basements, but require high humidity and good ventilation. Buy the specially prepared mushroom growing kits, which contain spawn preplanted in compost, and follow the package directions.

Cress. This is the quickest salad green known. It is ready to harvest in two weeks. Fertilize heavily and give ample soil moisture. Plant every week for a continuous supply over the winter.

Chard. This is a rewarding green, easier to grow than lettuce. It doesn't seem to mind low humidity as much as other greens.

Shallots. These are great for many French recipes. Plant shallots in sandy soil and give them ample moisture and fertilizer. Treat them as you would onions.

Seed Sprouts. If you never sprouted seeds at home, you are in for a treat. They can be used in salads, stews, and many recipes, or can be munched as a refreshing snack. Buy yours untreated, at a health food store,

460

or grow your own outdoors during the summer, and dry them for later sprouting. If this is your first sprouting experience, use this easy method:

Soak the seeds overnight, drain, and spread out in a shallow container. Cover with a double layer of cheesecloth and place in a warm spot. Rinse and drain seeds three times a day. They are ready to eat in three to five days, when they have sprouted. Almost any seeds can be sprouted, although the best include barley, alfalfa, soybeans, lentils, mung beans, rye, millet, and wheat.

Spinach. This is a good indoor crop, but do remember that it likes cool weather. A temperature of 50°F to 65°F is ideal. Grow it in flats or in pots of nearly any size. Spinach in another heavy feeder, of both nutrients and water, so keep it well supplied for fast and succulent growth. It matures in less than two months, and can be harvested before maturity with no loss in quality.

Herbs. A wide variety of herbs may be grown indoors, some in sunny windows with no supplemental light. Most have attractive foliage and make good decorative plants as well. Many are suitable for hanging baskets. All but the largest of herbs, such as dill, caraway and fennel, are indoor candidates. The list includes chives, mint, parsley, rosemary, sage, sweet basil, thyme and winter savory. Many herbs raised outdoors may be potted, cut back, and brought indoors in the autumn.

GIFT PLANTS

Often friends, relatives, and neighbors shower us with gifts, often in the form of potted plants. Especially if you are known as someone who loves plants, your chances of receiving six poinsettas, three chrysanthemums and an azalea are fairly great.

How can you keep these plants looking bright and healthy over holidays? What can you do with them afterward?

It depends on the plant and the conditions you can offer it. Most commercially-produced flowering gift plants should be thrown away, much though it might hurt. Most of these, including chrysanthemums, cyclamen and primroses, are suitable only for outdoor culture. Some can be planted outdoors after they have bloomed, providing that they are varieties hardy in your area. Others, including azalea and poinsettia, make good indoor-outdoor plants which can provide pleasure year after year, given proper care. Here is a quick rundown of some of the more popular flowering gift plants.

Azalea

You may keep potted azaleas blooming for two months or more if you give them cool temperatures, diffused sunlight, and plenty of water. After they have stopped blooming, continue to water the plant frequently and keep it in a bright location. In May, after all danger of frost has passed, transplant the azalea into the open garden, giving it an acid soil. Prune it

461

modereately around June 1. Before the first autumn frost, repot the plant, again giving it acid soil, and keep it in a very cool and light location for at least a month. An unheated sunporch or cold frame is usually ideal for this purpose. Sometime in November, bring the plant indoors. With cool temperatures and diffused sunlight, the plant should bloom in six to 10 weeks.

Chrysanthemum

Most potted chrysanthemums that come from the florist cannot be replanted outdoors in northern areas because they are varieties suited to the south; killing northern frosts will arrive in the autumn before they have had a chance to bloom. In warmer climes, they can be saved for outdoor use.

Even for northern gardeners, potted chrysanthemums can give weeks of indoor pleasure. Keep them in your sunniest window, and give them cool temperatures and plenty of water. A daily misting with cool water will help to maintain the foliage, which often dies down before the flowers do.

If the variety is hardy in your area (your florist can probably advise you), then give it a dormant period after it has finished blooming. Cut it back severely and store it in a light basement or shed, where it is cool but not freezing, and water only enough to keep the roots from drying out completely. (Once a month should do it.) In spring, when danger of frost has passed, replant it in a sunny outdoor location.

As with other plants which have been artificially forced into bloom, the replanting might not take at all. If it does, it might be several seasons before the plant recovers from the trick man has played on its biological time clock. It is often simpler to buy new nursery stock for outdoor planting; still, it is nice to be able to point to a thriving plant that you have rescued from the holiday season—especially if the giver is present.

Cyclamen

There is no practical way to preserve this plant after it has finished flowering indoors. The flowering period can be prolonged greatly if room temperatures are held down to 50°F to 55°F. Admittedly, at temperatures such as these, your cyclamen's pleasure might well be your death of chill. Perhaps, though, you have an unheated sunporch with a window opening at the living room, where the plant could be displayed effectively. At warmer temperatures, the blossoms will last probably for no more than two weeks. In any case, keep the plant in a bright spot. Do not let water stand in the crown of the plant because of the probability of rot.

Easter Lily

These are hardy plants which can be transplanted outdoors after they have bloomed, but with no guarantee of success. After receiving the plant, keep it in bright light, water it liberally every day, and try to keep the night temperatures down to 55°F to 60°F. Although most people simply discard the plant after it has finished blooming, you may try to return it to natural conditions. Keep watering the plant after it has bloomed, until the leaves have turned yellow. After danger of spring frost has passed, plant the bulb in the garden under 6″ to 8″ of soil. New growth should appear by summer, and the plant might even bloom again by autumn. More likely, however, the next flowers will appear during the following summer, which is the normal blooming time for the Easter lily.

Hydrangea

These plants, like azaleas, can be given special treatment to enable their return the following winter. Give your gift plant plenty of water and a bright spot out of direct sun. After it has finished blooming indoors, cut back the stems to within 5″ of the soil line. After danger of frost has passed, sink the pot directly into the garden, in partial shade, and water it often during the season. In late August, repot it in a slightly larger pot, with fresh soil. Just before the first frost (watch the weather forecast), bring the hydrangea inside for its dormant period. Store it in a cool (35°F to 40°F) dark place and give it just enough water to prevent the stem from drying out. Right after New Year's Day, remove any leaves that have not fallen off during dormancy and move the plant to a sunny window. It should then be given cool to moderate temperatures. Start it out at 55°F for the first few weeks, then increase the temperature to 60°F to 65°F range. Give it a good dose of an all-purpose fertilizer at this time.

Some hydrangeas act as litmus paper. Their flowers will be blue if the soil is very acid, and pink if it is only slightly acid.

Jerusalem Cherry

These plants, selling for a dollar or under in thousands of supermarkets during December, are hard to resist. Their bright green leaves, little white blossoms, and orange-red "cherries" make them attractive additions to the holiday table.

Unfortunately, they are basically outdoor plants and generally do poorly under home conditions. Further, they grow less attractive as they grow older. To get the best out of them, keep the newly purchased plant in a cool location (50°F is ideal), away from chills or drafts and give it plenty of water. Despite your loving attention, the fruit will drop after a month or so. The blossoms that were once so promising will probably dry up and fall, also.

When the plant becomes unattractive, it is probably best to throw it away. If you want to give it one more try, cut back the plant moderately after it has lost its fruit, keep it slightly dry and put it outside in the spring, when frost danger is past. It should be repotted at that time, also. Keep it outdoors with some partial shade during summer, keeping it well watered, and bring it in when autumn night temperatures fall to 40°F.

Ornamental Pepper

These are garden annuals, just as other peppers are, and will never make permanent house plants. It is best to keep them in cool temperatures, in full sun, and give them plenty of water and daily sprayings. When they are no longer attractive, throw them away.

If you want to grow your own plants for holiday giving, sow seeds outdoors in spring and treat the plants just as you would other peppers. Pot them up in August and bring them inside before the first frost hits. If they receive enough light (artificial lights will help to lengthen autumn days), they should be in prime condition by December. Again, however, if you do not have a greenhouse, you cannot expect to achieve the same results as experienced, professional greenhouse growers have learned to produce.

Poinsettia

Newly arrived poinsettias, like most other gift plants, should be given plenty of water, a cool room, and full sun. The colored bracts (they are not actually flowers) should last for three weeks at 70°F, up to two months at 55°F to 60°F.

Since the leaves of the poinsettia are attractive, many people simply keep them as foliage plants, making no attempt to induce flowering the following year. They will do perfectly well as such, given ample water and diffused sunlight.

If you want to spend the time to do it right, however, there is a special procedure to follow. After the bracts of the gift plant have fallen, move the plant to a cool basement or sunporch where it will get plenty of light. Withhold water, giving it just enought to prevent complete dryness, and the plant will enter its dormant period. Around May 1, cut the plant back to within 6″ of the soil line and repot it in fresh soil. Resume watering at this time. If night temperatures will not go below 60°F, you may place the pot outdoors for the summer, protecting the plant from very strong sunlight during the day. When night temperatures again drop below 60°F, move the plant indoors in a sunny and well-ventilated location.

If you want the poinsettia to bloom again for Christmas, you must begin special treatment on Oct. 1. At that time, be sure that the plant receives a night temperature of 60°F and a daytime temperature of 68°F to 70°F. Give it exactly 14 hours of darkness every day, from Oct. 1 until the Christmas blooming period. In some parts of the country, this will mean providing artificial darkness during the latter part of each day (such as moving the plant into a closet at a certain time) and providing supplemental light later on in the autumn, as the days grow shorter. Providing the extra light is simple, if you attach a 24-hour timer to an artificial light source. Adjust it every few days, as the days grow shorter. Admittedly, this is a bothersome procedure, especially when it is so much easier to buy a blooming plant from the florist for a few dollars, but some enthusiasts take up the challenge each year as a matter of pride, while others do it once as a learning experience.

Shrimp Plant

These make fine house plants. Give shrimp plant all the sun you can and plenty of water. A daily spraying with water of room temperature will help to keep it fresh. Cut back the plant each spring, to encourage bush growth. Root cuttings in sand or some other sterile medium, to form new plants. The shrimp plant will enjoy a summer outdoors.

DEALING WITH SPRING FROSTS

What can we do to prepare for spring frosts? How can we plant as early as possible, while still offering our plants a reasonable degree of protection against the unexpected? The answer is to use common sense, to understand the limitations of different plant species to frost, and to drag out every trick in the book.

Cold Frames and Hotbeds

The gardener's best ally in both spring and fall is the cold frame, cheaply and easily built, using old storm sashes and scrap lumber (Fig. 17-8). If you do not have one or several, now would be a good time to build one, using plans found in most any library or county agent's office. You can construct the frame (but not nail it together) in your basement right now, then set it up outdoors as soon as the ground is soft enough to dig. If you want to have a hotbed, where you can control temperatures precisely, then investigate the heating units advertised in many of the garden catalogs or see your local nursery center.

Plants started indoors can be transferred to the cold frame as soon as temperatures permit. If you keep them in flats, they can be hauled back inside quickly enough, if a really hard frost threatens. If the predicted low is no worse than 25°F or so, there is no need to bring the flats in. Simply bank up the sides of the frame with leaves or hay and cover the glass with old feed sacks, hay or other insulating material. Plants growing in a cold frame will make much faster progress than those growing in the house. The light is much better, for one thing (good light allows seedlings to grow sturdy and bushy, while insufficient light prompts "leggy" and weak stem growth), and the humidity is considerably higher. With the help of the cold frame, you can start plants earlier, and you can protect them from spring frost until it is safe to transplant them permanently in the garden.

Mulch and Soil Temperature

The wise use of mulch in spring can help your soil to warm up more quickly. If the afternoon temperature is above 40°F, winter mulch should be removed, until temperatures again begin to dip, around sundown. Then replace the mulch. Granted, this is an impractical activity in a large vegetable garden, but it should be done with perennial beds, asparagus and rhubarb patches, and other small areas. By the watchful removing and replacement of winter mulch, you can get your soil to warm up more quickly in spring, thus prompting the earlier production of perennials.

Cold Weather Crops in First

Many vegetable seedlings can handle some frost with no great problem. Included among the cold weather crops are peas, lettuce, beets,

Fig. 17-8. The good old cold frame is the gardener's best ally (photo by Jean Martin).

carrots, celeriac, chard, chives, corn salad, endive, garlic, horseradish, kale, kohlrabi, leeks, mustard, onion sets, parsnips, potatoes, radishes, shallots, spinach, and turnips. Especially if seeds are sown in the open, you should not have to wait until all danger of frost has passed for these crops.

Emergency Measures

If, after your seedlings have been transplanted to the open garden, an unusually late and hard frost is predicted, you should then be prepared with plant protectors, store-bought or homemade devices that can keep frost off your plants, if only for a night ot two. Cloches and hot caps are available commercially for this purpose, but you can save a great amount of money by making your own—starting right now.

Glass jars and bottles are most effective for protecting young plants and gallon jugs are perfect for larger individual plants. Wide-mouth jars can simply be inverted and placed over small seedlings. If you want to separate the bottoms from larger jars and jugs, here's how to do it. First, tie a strand of thick cord around the bottom of the jar or jug. Daub the cord with gasoline. Cap the gasoline and put it away. Set fire to the cord. When it has burned out, dip the jar or jug into a tub of ice water. The bottom should break off neatly, at the cord line. After you have covered a plant with a bottomless jug, keep the cap on during cold nights and take it off during the day to allow proper ventilation.

Less effective, but better than nothing, are milk cartons, cardboard boxes, inverted flower pots—nearly any container in an emergency. It will pay lasting dividends to begin collecting gallon jugs now. Barring accidents, they should last a lifetime.

For long rows of plants where individual covers would be impractical—bush beans, leaf lettuce, peas and spinach for instance—you might try lining hay bales between the rows and covering them with either storm sashes or other bales. Again, this is not practical on a large scale, but it has saved many plantings that would have fallen victim to late frosts. Commercial cloches are also available for garden rows—and they are not a bad investment, considering that they may be used year after year, as the need arises.

Still another trick to use in battling frost is to melt the ice crystals by sprinkling tender plants with the garden hose. This must be done before sunrise, but it is very effective.

Last, pay particular attention to those perennials and tender bulbs planted near to the house. The heat radiating from the basement wall often sends these plants into premature growth, and they are then most susceptible to late frost. Hardy bulbs—crocus, scilla, narcissus, hyacinths, and tulips—will likely need no protection, since nature has endowed them with a natural resistance to cold. Some of the more tender plantings should be covered with leaves or hay if a sharp drop in temperature is expected.

SAVING SEEDS

"If a garden is grown for increased self-sufficiency, shouldn't it provide its own seeds?" asks Douglas C. Miller, Bullkill Creek Community, Hersey, MI 49639, the author of a book, *Vegetable and Herb Seed Growing for the Gardener and Small Farmer.* Miller answers his rhetorical question by saying that "information on growing and saving one's own vegetable seeds should prove more valuable as seed prices rise each year. It is also possible that future disruptions in our economy due to strikes, energy shortages, civil unrest, and the like could temporarily reduce or cut off the supply of seeds, which come mainly from the West Coast."

He also stresses that gardening is the very heart of self-sufficiency, and should not be dependent upon the weather in one section of the country. Through a conscientious program of selecting, the gardener will develop varieties which are especially well-adapted to their own particular growing conditions. He might also have added that besides being a challenge, an education, a bit of an art, and an opportunity to work with neighbors, it gives one a tremendous feeling of satisfaction to take still another step toward independence.

Miller feels that literature on the subject is practically nonexistent and is of limited value to the gardener who cannot apply the large-scale techniques of the commercial seed grower. He draws upon the knowledge of plant breeders as well as seedsmen to come up with workable methods for the gardener or small farmer.

In his detailed and thorough little "kitchen table" book, he outlines exactly how to select, harvest, clean, treat, store and test seeds. They are organized into logical groupings: *Curcurbitaceae* (melon family)—cucumber, gherkin, muskmelon, watermelon, squash and pumpkin; *Solanaceae* (night shade family)—tomato, pepper, eggplant, and potato; *Leguminosae* (legumes)—pea, bean, lima bean, cowpea, and soybean; *Umbelliferae* (carrot family)—carrot, celery, celeriac, parsley, parsnip, anise, caraway, chervil, coriander, dill, and fennel; *Liliaceae* (onion family)—onion, onion sets, Welsh onion, chive, leek, shallot, and garlic. *Compositae* (goosefoot family)—beet, Swiss chard and spinach; *Graminae*—sweet corn and popcorn; *Cruciferae* (brassica root crops)—turnip, rutabaga, radish, and horseradish.

The book also covers such miscellaneous items as artichokes, asparagus, Jerusalem artichoke, New Zealand spinach, okra, rhubarb, and mushroom spawn. Here are some salient suggestions from the book.

Rotation

Since many plant diseases can be harbored in the soil and carried on the seed, rotation of crops on a minimum three-year cycle is desirable.

Beginning

Initiating a program of saving seeds, you should obtain open-pollinated varieties. Hybrids will revert back to the parent strains or undesirable combinations of them.

Start out simple. Don't count on cutting off all dependence on seed from professional sources in the near future. Begin with a few of the simpler vegetables.

Since most seeds remain viable for several years, it is not necessary to save seed from every variety every year. Plants which may cross with each other, such as beets and Swiss chard, can be scheduled to produce seed on different years.

Storing

All common garden seeds store best under cool, dry conditions. A good rule of thumb is that the sum of temperature (degrees Fahrenheit) and relative humidity should not exceed 100. For example, at 40°F, humidity should not exceed 60 percent or at 35°F humidity should not exceed 65 percent. Generally, basements and root cellars are too damp. An attic usually provides adequate seed storage in winter months where winters are cool, but gets far too hot in the summer. To avoid problems with humidity, seeds can be stored in airtight jars in a cool basement, cellar, refrigerator or freezer. Beans and peas, however, should not be stored in airtight containers.

isolation

The key to keeping a strain pure lies in keeping it isolated from other strains or varieties with which it is likely to cross. With vegetables such as peas and beans, which are almost completely self-pollinating, isolation is accomplished naturally. With vegetables which are pollinated to any extent by air currents or insects, isolation becomes a problem.

If neighboring gardeners are growing seed, you may find it to mutual advantage to coordinate your efforts to avoid some isolation problems. Grow the same varieties, or grow to seed on alternate years.

Caging

This involves isolating the plants which you want to cross by building a cage around them. Insect-pollinated varieties should be caged inside a mesh about as coarse as house window screening or coarse cheesecloth to exclude insects, yet should allow plenty of air circulation and light. Wind-pollinated varieties should be caged with a much tighter mesh—muslin, pillow casing, or an old sheet. They should be light colored and should not be installed until shortly before the flowers begin to open.

Introducing Flies

You must put insects into the cages of insect-pollinating varieties. Honeybees will soon die if kept away from their hives, but blue or green bottle flies, the type which gather on rotten meat, are the best and easiest to introduce into the cage.

Selection

To maintain or improve a variety, you must carry out a program of selecting for desirable traits as size, earliness, flavor, color, disease, drought and insect resistance, storability, hardiness, shape, thickness of flesh, etc. Rogue out any plants which don't conform to the rest of the crop. Look for such features as leaf shape and color, branching habits, bushing or vining, and general shape and appearance.

Hand-Pollinating

For gardeners who wish to save seeds from both pickling and slicing varieties of cucumbers, hand-pollination is in order (Fig. 17-9). The cucumber has both male and female flowers growing on the same plant. There are generally more male than female flowers. The female flowers are usually borne singly, while the males are generally in groups of five.

To hand-pollinate, trap shut the female flowers to be pollinated the day before they are to open. If you observe individual flowers from day to day, you will soon learn to tell when a flower is due to open. Simply clamp shut (trap) the petals of the flower to exclude any insects. The next morning, pick a male flower from a different plant, remove its petals to expose the pollen-covered anthers. Untrap the female flower. Carefully open the

469

petals and gently rub the anthers on the stigmas of the female. Once again trap the female flower to prevent further pollination by bees.

Despining

Carrot seed should be despined by rubbing seed between the palms of your hand, or for larger amounts in a threshing-despining box made of corrugated rubber floor mat. Scrub the paddle back and forth on the seeds, pour out seed, flow away the chaff, and pick out the sticks. You'll be amazed at how much seed comes from so few plants.

Fermenting

When your tomatoes are fully ripe, but not rotten, cut them open and scoop the seeds and pulp out into an open jar. Allow the material to ferment at room temperature for four to seven days, stirring a couple of times a day until the last day. The good seeds will sink to the bottom; bad seeds and pulp will float to the top and can be easily discarded. Fermentation not only separates seeds from pulp, but it kills seed-borne diseases. Wash seeds well in water and spread on paper or fine screen to dry. Store when thoroughly dry.

Hot Water Treating

Because several diseases, including black rot, are transmitted in the seed, all *Brassica* seeds should be hot water treated. Small amounts of seed should be wrapped in a piece of cloth and immersed in water held in a constant 122°F for 30 minutes.

Bagging Corn

Before the silk emerges, place small, white paper bags over the ears and fasten them with a rubber band. When tassels are mature (pollen can be

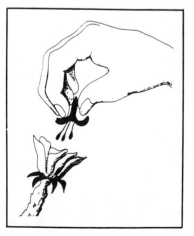

Fig. 17-9. When hand-pollinating cucumbers, gently rub the anters of the male flower, tip, on the stigma of the female flower, bottom.

blown or shaken off easily), gently cut off a tassel, and removing a bag from a different stalk, rub the tassel over the silk. Shake some more pollen into the bag and replace over the ear to prevent subsequent crossing. Slap the bag a few times to further pollinate the ear.

MUSHROOM GARDENING

Home-grown *mushrooms* are the epitome of good nutrition and good flavor, but they don't grow like peas and beans and barley grow (Fig. 17-10). Mushroom gardening requires a different set of rules and tools primarily because mushrooming plants, or *fungi,* have no chlorophyll and do not photosynthesize like green plants.

Consequently, fungi can be grown where other plants perish—from the darkest corner of the cellar to the abandoned chicken coop, the unused privy, the space under the stairs, or even in trays under your bed (Fig. 17-11). Each nook and cranny can house a little crop of mushrooms.

Equipment and Supplies

You'll need to acquire a few tools and supplies and do a little building to get started. Construct scrap lumber trays 10″ to 12″ deep, 2 × 3′ wide. Larger trays are unwieldy. If space is limited, make the trays so they can be stacked one on top of the other. Since moisture is held next to the wood for long periods, the boards have a tendency to warp, but if the trays are put together with screws rather than nails they will last through more crops. Next, try to find a long handled, five-pronged pitchfork to use when turning compost. You'll also need gypsum (purchase from a lumber yard), spawn, and peat.

Compost for Mushroom Cultivation

Since mushrooms cannot utilize the energy of the sun, you must provide them with an energy source—organic matter extracted from composted manure and straw. Composting is the process by which manure and straw are broken down into simpler chemicals as a result of bacterial and fungal activity. Therefore, a successful compost pile is the secret to mushroom raising. There must be enough moisture, warmth, and organic matter so that the microorganisms can thrive.

If possible, build the compost heap on a concrete floor under a roof. When it is placed outside on the soil, insects in the soil migrate to the heap and lay eggs. If this occurs late in the composting process, the eggs may remain viable and hatch, causing problems when the mushroom crop is developing. Rain should not be permitted to fall on the pile because it will wash essential nutrients from the compost, reducing its muchroom producing capacity.

Manure is the single most important ingredient in the compost pile. Use a "hot" manure, meaning one that is high in nitrogen. Horse manure is good; elephant manure is great. Other manures that can be used are chicken

Fig. 17-10. Mushrooms are flavorful and nutritional (photo by Mueller).

and turkey. If you're a bit adventurous, try whatever happens to be accumulating on your homestead—sheep, goat, rabbit, etc. Don't use cow pies because they don't contain enough of the all-important nitrogen.

If you haven't a source of manure on your lot, look around. Farms and horse stables are good sources of manure, but never use manure from veterinarian stables. It might have disinfectants mixed with it, and these chemicals inhibit the composting process. Also, avoid manure that has been mixed with wood shavings because it will be too acid to compost properly. While gathering manure, also gather several bales of straw. Thoroughly soak the straw until water begins to run off. Let the straw soak up water for at least a day and then mix it with dampened manure. Use about 1 part straw to 1 part manure. Sprinkle gypsum onto the pile as you build up the heap. About 20 pounds of gypsum is needed for each half ton of compost; that is enough compost to fill 60 square feet of trays and produce 100 to 150 pounds of mushrooms. That's a lot of mushrooms.

You can start with a much smaller quantity of compost, but if the compost pile is quite small, there is a greater surface to volume ratio. This will result in excessive water and heat loss. To circumvent this problem, keep a small compost pile covered with burlap and frequently dampen the burlap so the pile does not dry out. Turn the pile each week for five weeks, adding more gypsum if any area within the pile is black or slicky.

Whenever the compost is turned, add water if it appears dry but not so much that it runs off. The nutrients will be lost with the runoff.

As the manure and straw decompose, the material will begin to break down into little pieces, The mass will become chocolate brown in color. One week after the fifth and final turn, it is time to add spawn.

Spawning

Spawn is the substance used to start mushrooms. It is a pure culture of *dormant mycelia,* similar to roots, that is grown in laboratories under sterile

Fig. 17-11. A mushroom growing setup in the unexcavated portion of the basement. A walkway has been dug out between the rows of trays (photo by Mueller).

conditions and can be purchased from the suppliers listed below. Spawning means incorporating spawn into the compost. Several kinds of spawn are available, but order dry, flake spawn. This will arrive at your home in a cardboard cannister, looking somewhat like a mixture of peat and sand. Mix the spawn into the compost, using 1 quart of spawn for each 15 square feet of growing space.

Immediately put the spawned compost into the wooden trays you constructed, heaping it up slightly. Since full trays are too heavy to handle, it is wise to fill the trays after they are placed where the crop will be grown. After 24 hours firm the compost down into the trays, using a brick or piece of wood, so the compost is about 1½" to 2" below the top of the tray. If you can control the temperature in the mushroom growing area, increase the temperature to near 65°F at this point.

In two to three weeks the compost will become covered with a mass of white filaments known as *mycelium*. Throughout this period it is important that the compost remains damp but never dripping. This is best accomplished with light mist waterings at least twice daily.

Casing

After the mycelia cover the compost in a cottony web, there's one more step to take. Mushrooms will not emerge from the compost unless it is covered with a layer of casing. Peat is an excellent casing material because it holds water. Moisten the peat and then place a 1½" to 2" layer over the tray. Shortly after applying the casing, lower the temperature to 55° F to 60°F, if you can, and keep this temperature for the duration of the crop.

The moisture content of the casing is critical. Mushrooms need moisture to emerge, but if too much water is applied it will soak through the compost and damage the delicate mycelia. Several layers of newspaper will

473

help regulate the moisture. Keep the newspapers moist with light waterings twice daily. After 10 days, carefully remove the newspapers and water with a fine mist as before.

In a couple of days you can expect to see tiny pinheads that will develop into beautiful mushrooms in about one week.

Thereafter, mushrooms will appear in flushes every 10 to 12 days and will continue to produce for three to six months as long as disease and pests are controlled or until the energy within the compost is exhausted. Between flushes continue to water lightly twice each day, but don't get water on developing mushrooms as this will cause them to turn brown and deteriorate.

Picking

Mushrooms can be picked at various stages of development (Fig. 17-12). Small buttons are the most tender and are a delight eaten raw with dip or in salads. Larger, unopened mushrooms are used in basic mushroom cookery, and this is the stage at which most mushrooms are picked. Leave a few to mature into fully opened caps with light purple gills. The fully matured mushroom has a richer, deeper, more lush flavor and is excellent when used in sauces and soups. This stage is virtually impossible to purchase because they rapidly deteriorate after maturation.

Pick mushrooms by placing your hand over the cap with your fingers around the stem. Gently twist and the mushroom will separate from its mooring.

After picking a mushroom, be sure to remove and discard the residual "root" by cutting around the root mass with a paring knife. This is called trashing and is absolutely necessary if healthy, productive trays are to be maintained.

Temperature

The rate of mushroom development is temperature dependent. Mushrooms grow slower and the crop lasts longer if the temperature is kept between 55°F to 60°F, but the crop is produced faster and is of shorter duration if the temperature is raised to 65°F. Higher temperatures will usually cause increased problems with disease and insects, and the crop could be lost. If you are unable to control the temperature in the growing area, plan to raise mushrooms in the fall or spring, when the weather is mild. The crop can tolerate cool temperatures better than warm temperatures.

Pest Control

Conditions necessary for mushroom growth seem to encourage pests, including insect larvae and competing molds. With meticulous care, pests can be contained.

Fortunately, the heat produced during composting destroys most

474

destructive organisms. If the straw and manure are properly composted, stray seeds will have germinated and died, and molds and insect eggs will be killed resulting in an essentially pest free compost by the time it is put into the trays. The trick is to keep it pest free.

If the crop is in an outbuilding, screen the windows to exclude insects that might be attracted to the rich compost. If slugs discover the mushrooms, they will feast on the morsels, consuming vast quantities in a single binge. Since slugs are easy to see, they can be removed by hand, or if they get ahead of you, they can be controlled by submerging in the peat small vessels, filled to the brim with beer or brewers' yeast; the slugs will drink and drown.

Disease is most easily controlled if the crop is housed in different parts of the home or outbuildings. Place a few trays in a corner of the cellar, maybe a couple under the ping pong table, one in the washroom and so forth. Should disease strike, it will not spread rapidly throughout the crop. Finally, it is esential that the mushroom growing area is free of organic debris, stagnant water or other trash that might serve as breeding sites for mushroom-loving pests.

GROWING NUTS

With today's inflated prices, some nuts may well be worth more than a cent each when purchased at the supermarket. The homesteader or suburbanite who has available land is really passing up a good thing if he does not plan for nut trees to become a permanent part of the overall picture.

The monetary value of nut trees is really not the most important factor. Think about nuts as tiny beefsteaks, a very rich source of protein that falls from the not too distant sky and which may take the place, in part, of meat. Black walnuts, for instance, contain 27.6 percent protein, so their value as a diet addition is readily apparent. They are also high in vitamin C and contain vitamins A, B_1 and B_2. Almonds, containing vitamins B_1 and A, are one of the

Fig. 17-12. This tray of mushrooms is right at the peak of a flush and is ready to pick (photo by Mueller).

most nourishing foods and one of the richest nuts. The hickory is helpful in cases of low blood pressure, while pecans contain vitamins A and B_2. The real jackpot is peanuts which are a great food for growing children and adults alike, containing the pantothenic acid vitamins B_2 and B_1, as well as vitamin E in the oil.

Nut trees have another advantage. They can often be grown on land unsuitable for other food raising purposes.

Success in growing nut trees may be largely determined by careful selection of varieties which will grow and bear well in the zone in which you live. Where to place them is another factor to be carefully considered. Before buying and/or planting, give some thought to the size they will be when fully mature.

Nut trees vary in size and can be grown either as shade trees or as ornamentals. One of our largest native trees, the black walnut, reaches heights of up to 150'. The heartnut tree, a relative, grows little larger than an apple tree. Filberts, hazelnuts, and chinkapins grow smaller still. They may, in many instances, be little more than bushes. Also, these little ones are apt to bear much sooner.

As with other types of trees, nut trees should be planted with care. Whether planting bare-root or balled and burlapped stock, the first step is to dig a hole of sufficient size. If the nut tree has a long taproot, there can be no cheating. That taproot has to go straight down; don't try curling it around a little to save time and work. The tree won't like it.

As far as depth is concerned, plant the tree about the same depth it was growing in the nursery, or just slightly deeper (except the almond). You will be able to determine this by the soil line on the bark. Spread the roots carefully and cover with a few inches of good soil, packing firmly with your foot or a blunt stick.

Fill the hole with water to cover this and work the mud around the roots to fill all air pockets. Let the water settle, fill the rest of the hole, and repeat the process of packing, soaking, and puddling. When the hole is filled, leave a slight depression to catch rainfall. Almond trees should be planted high because they often settle a good deal after planting this may lead to crown or collar rot.

Care for your newly planted tree the first summer by preventing damage to the bark called "sun scald." Wrap the trunk of any trees that are 1″ or more thick at the base with burlap, heavy paper, or aluminum foil. You can even slit a length of old rubber hose down one side and use this as a wrapping, securing it at top and bottom, but not too tightly.

Nut trees, for the most part being deep rooted, make fine shade trees for lawns and many types of grass will grow well under them. Moreover, the nut, unlike fruit, is clean, odorless and does not attract flies. You can pick up nuts at a convenient time and their keeping qualities, compared to fruit, are excellent. Nuts vary in this respect.

When buying trees, biggest does not necessarily mean best. Often large trees are drastically set back when planted. Many times a smaller tree

476

will reestablish faster, and you'll end up with a nicer tree quicker. You may save enough by purchasing smaller trees to enable you to buy several more. Be sure, when purchasing, to buy from a reputable nursery—one that really takes the grafting seriously and offers good stock of varieties that will do well in your climate. You have to be the judge of this last criteria, however, for no matter how good the tree, you may not get a crop if it is unsuited to your area.

Black Walnuts and Pecans

Black walnuts are fine trees for the North, and pecans are fine for many southern areas. Walnuts will grow and do well in many southern sections and also bear, but pecans, while the trees will grow well in the North, seldom bear crops if, in fact, you get any crop at all. On the other hand, some hardy native pecan types will bear in the northern sections, while papershells will not. The smaller natives have more oil and more flavor than most of the larger papershells do.

All trees, including nut trees, are effective as dust catchers. They are one of nature's most effective dust traps. The hairy leaf surfaces clutch falling particles from the air and hold them, thereby keeping solid matter out of our atmosphere. When it rains, the particles are washed to the ground.

So effective are trees as dust catchers that one major city, Los Angeles, has to wash its trees periodically in a detergent solution. In another area, the dust count on a sheltered side of a planted section was 75 percent lower than a similar count on the windward side. Trees help keep our air clean.

Nevertheless, there is something you should know about trees. It is what happens when certain nut trees, such as the black walnut, have a substance called juglone washed from their leaves into the soil. This is believed to inhibit the growth of many plants within the area where the trees grow. Cultivated plants not compatible with black walnuts are apples, alfalfa, potatoes, tomatoes, blackberries, azaleas, rhododendrons, and heather. The butternut (*J. cinerea*) also seems to have this quality, though to a less extent. In southern areas, pecan trees may also inhibit the growth of some plants. Leaves, used as mulch, may also be toxic.

Besides these drawbacks, certain nut trees have qualities which are very beneficial to animals. Cattle like to shelter under large nut trees as they are less troubled there by flies and other insects. Black walnut leaves placed in the bed of a dog or cat (and changed from time to time) will aid greatly in keeping down fleas. Hogs fatten on beech mast and also on all varieties of acorns.

Hazelnuts furnish valuable cover and food for wildlife, and they can be beneficial in pastures and elsewhere against flies. Cows like to nibble on the leaves, which increase the butterfat in their milk, while the tannic acid also acts as a cleansing agent for their digestive systems.

"Aura" of the Oak

Many ancient beliefs concerning trees are being brought to light again today. Fields of energy that are apparently related to magnetic fields can be measured in the areas surrounding trees. Wilhelm deBoer, a master dowser of West Germany, claims that "this energy coming out of a large oak can temporarily increase the strength of a human aura or a person's vitality."

DeBoer tells a story about Bismarck, Germany's "Iron Chancellor" who would, on his physician's advice, put his arms around a tree for half-hour periods in order to recover from fatigue. Many people believe that trees, as well as other plants, will grow bigger and better if they are admired and appreciated. With nut trees this can be easy. You aren't going to dig them up and eat them as you do garden vegetables. Many will be growing in the same place for generations to come. Long ago in Greece there were groves, sacred to the gods, where people went to worship and give thanks to the trees.

If a storm comes up, do not seek shelter under a tree. Tall trees, especially, are believed to attract lightning. On the other hand, the olive, a small tree, is believed by many to be protective during storms.

Furniture, Paints, and Fertilizer

Entirely aside from their food value, nut trees have a lot going for them and their value as timber should not be ignored. The man who plants a grove of hardwood nut trees may be leaving his children something of far more value than stocks or bonds.

The usefulness of nut trees goes far beyond decoration or food production (Fig. 17-13). One of the finest veneers is milled from the black walnut; its nutshells are used by the oil industry as well as in nonslip finish paints. The same gravelike texture of ground up walnut shells makes them useful in the tread of snow tires. In some Midwestern states, walnut husks are chopped up in shredders for use as a natural fertilizer for vegetable gardens. The husks are high in soil nutrients and can be pulverized and spread on the ground in late fall to cover the garden for the winter. Following the spring thaw, the decomposed husks can then be tilled into the ground a few weeks before planting.

Pecan shells are also used as mulch and fertilizer for gardens. Hickory has long been favored for its strength and durability. Axe handles, sledge hammer handles and baseball bats are made of hickory. More uses for nut trees and their products are being discovered every day.

The care of nut trees is generally undemanding. Most are blight resistant and, with exceptions such as the pecan, most are also free from fungi and insect pests. You must keep injured branches pruned. You needn't worry too much about the squirrels either. Unless you have but one very small nut tree, there will be plenty of nuts for both you and the squirrels.

478

Fig. 17-13. Jewelry made of nut woods and nutshells. Earrings at upper left are made from black walnut shells; earrings at upper right are slices of butternut shells (photo by Louise Riotte).

GREEN MULCH SYSTEM

The homesteader with a cow and a calf or three goats and kids requires pastures and grain or root crops. He also needs hay to feed his ruminants during the winter while pastures are dormant. Hay is dried grass, legume, comfrey, or other nutritious plant material. It is dried so that it will not mold or decay while being stored. About three acres are required for this project depending on the length of your growing season, rainfall, soil quality, and crops. A good plan for northern climates is six, half-acre plots—one field in comfrey, one field in fodder beets or grain, two fields for pasture, and two for hay and corn. Dr. Myron T. Weiner tells about his green mulch system.

Equipment

Equipment consists of a two-wheel, 12-hp Gravely tractor with attachments, a flail mower, furrower, planter for corn and beets, manure spreader with a seat added, wagon, cart and cyclone seeder. Weiner built his barn into a hillside so he has road access to the loft. In the loft he installed a 48″ fan. His loft floor has spaces between the boards. He built with green lumber which left spaces when the boards dried. He has irrigation sprinklers set up in all of his fields.

Comfrey and Comfrey Hay

Some years ago Weiner purchased 100 comfrey roots which he planted in one of the six fields. Plant spacing is 3′ between rows and 3′ between plants. He also uses this field as a chicken yard. Three years later he lifted the comfrey roots and divided them into the 2,500 required to fill the half acre. The chickens fertilize the crop, keep it pretty much weed and insect free, and do not eat the growing comfrey. This is probably due to the water-filled silica hairs on the leaves. They will eat wilted comfrey or comfrey hay since the hairs disintegrate when the water content evaporates. Chickens will consume more comfrey if it is chopped than whole.

In cold climates, during the growing season, a half-acre of mature comfrey (over three years of age) will supply 12 tons of green fodder or 6 tons after wilting a day in the sun or 2 tons of hay (Fig. 17-14). This production requires a heavy application of manure and rainfall (or irrigation) and frequent cutting during the growing season, about every two weeks when the plants are a foot tall. He uses a flail mower and leaves the chopped fodder on the ground a day to wilt. He loads with a manure fork and wagon and moves the fodder to the barn loft (close the door and windows), and spreads the fodder on the floor to fan dry for 24 hours.

You can cut part of the field every day or every week. Weiner prefers doing it all at once. You can feed some fresh, however, Weiner prefers to save it for winter use since the best alfalfa hay is inferior to pasture.

Crop Rotation

The other five fields are rotated each year—two for pasture, one for fodder beets, and two for hay and corn. These five fields are planted to alfalfa, ladino clover, and rye with corn and fodder beets planted in rows separated by legumes and grass. Bess, Weiner's Jersey cow, is moved from one pasture to the other every three weeks. The field is mowed each time she is moved to the alternate pasture. The green mulch remains on the pasture for fertilizer along with Bess's meadow muffins.

New nutritious growth is ready for Bess when she returns three weeks later. All of Weiner's fields around the barn have gates to the barnyard. He leaves the barn door open all summer, Bess goes to the pasture after morning milking and returns for evening milking.

Fodder Beets

Weiner grows fodder beets and corn right in a hayfield by mowing the field and cutting rows with a furrower 4' apart (rows run north and south). He uses the same row placement every time he plants. He sets the planter for 6" spacing between seeds; however, beet seeds are really fruits containing several seeds so thinning is required. The legumes and grass are mowed when they begin to shade the fodder beets.

When the fodder beets are large enough to thin (Bess considers the thinnings a special treat), the mowed legumes provide a green mulch for the beets. Following thinning, the growth of the fodder beets fairly well keeps up with the legumes and grass. After the fodder beets show significant development—attaining a root size of 3"—he thins again so that the plants

480

stand about a foot apart. Sometimes another mowing is required in the middle of summer to prevent shading.

When Weiner started using this system of intercropping row crops with hay, he noticed an increase of wireworms and cutworms. When the field is used as pasture for Bess, he runs a family of White Chinese geese with her. They seem to keep the wireworms and cutworms under control.

Corn and Hay

Weiner plants corn 4' between rows and 6" between plants using the same technique, furrower followed by planter (Fig. 17-15). A rototiller could also be used. With a Troy-bilt, for example, remove the outer tines so that you will rototill a row 14" wide. Weiner keeps the legumes and grass mowed until the corn is a foot high. The mowed legume green mulches the corn.

About midsummer the alfalfa reaches early bloom. He mows between corn rows on a sunny morning. In the afternoon he uses a manure fork and cart to load and haul the wilted fodder to the barn. A night in the loft with the fan on takes care of drying.

You might consider an electric motor driven fan a "cop out" method. Weiner disagrees. Using traditional haying methods, much of the nutritious alfalfa leaf is left in the field. This is because of the rough handling required to field dry hay. When hay is brought to the barn while still green, every leaf comes with the stems. The leaf is where the high protein content is located.

In addition to high quality hay, Weiner's green mulch system also requires less fuel in the field. It takes considerably less energy to mow than to pull a plow or cultivating tools through the soil. If you have more cash than time, a vacuum pickup system can be used instead of a manure fork and cart for harvesting hay. It would cost about $1,500 and have its own motor and blower, thereby only requiring the Gravely to pull it. The cart would have to be quite narrow, or you would have to space the corn rows further apart.

Fodder Beet Storage

Harvesting fodder beets with a garden fork is a real muscle builder. A half acre of fertile soil can produce 25 tons of roots which have to be lifted and hauled. Of this quantity, 22½ tons are moisture content.

Fig. 17-14. A half-acre of comfrey will provide 2 tons of hay even in cold climates if it gets a heavy manuring and adequate water.

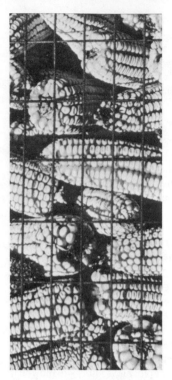

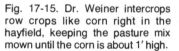

Fig. 17-15. Dr. Weiner intercrops row crops like corn right in the hayfield, keeping the pasture mix mown until the corn is about 1' high.

Storing fodder beets requires a clamp (as the English call it). A clamp is an insulated storage pit. Weiner boarded up a corner of his loft like a corn crib. At harvest time he layers chopped corn stover and fodder beets. He keeps the fodder beets at least 2' from the clamp's walls. The top of the clamp is insulated with 3' of chopped stover. The barn is insulated in winter with a foot of chopped stover on the loft floor.

Corn Harvest

Weiner harvests the ear corn by hand, and husks it in the loft where it drys in the crib. He feeds chopped ear corn with the cob, chopped fodder beets, alfalfa hay and comfrey hay to Bess from the loft by way of a chute to her trough. She has access to the barnyard at all times and usually goes out for a short time even on freezing days as long as the sun is shining. This is true even when the snow is 4' deep.

Corn Stover Harvest

Weiner runs the mower down the corn rows to chop the corn stover and let it field dry for a day or two. He then loads it on his wagon and dries it by fan if necessary. Chopped corn stover makes excellent deep litter bedding and insulation for the clamp and barn.

In the spring the barn deep litter bedding is heaped in the barnyard to compost with earthworms. A year later it is spread on the fodder beet field and two corn-hay fields.

A Circular System

We began this section with the goal of describing Weiner's method of making hay on a small place. The hay led to the pasture, which led to the corn, which led to fertilizing the soil, which led to Bess, which led to the barn and feed storage. You can't really separate one part of the system from the whole.

Every year Weiner has his soil tested at a laboratory specializing in working with organic farmers. He follows their recommendations which are generally to add specified quantities of seaweed and phosphate rock powder which he spreads with the compost. His fertilization program is primarily the green mulch system, pasturing and wood ashes from his meat smoker and Franklin stove added to the compost. He brings in no purchased feed other than mineralized salt and a little fertilizer, yet the organic matter content of his soil rises every year.

He attributes this to the deep rooted legumes and comfrey bringing up minerals from the subsoil; returning everything to the soil except the butter, cheese, cream, milk, and calf that Bess provides; taking only one cut a year of hay and leaving the other cuts as green mulch; alternating fields yearly between pasture and hay. Even the soured skim milk and whey are returned to the soil through the chickens and piglets. His operation is actually somewhat larger, encompassing 20 half-acre fields with goats, hogs, geese, ducks and chickens, however, it operates exactly as he has described.

Study Needed

It is apparent to Weiner that he could not purchase hay that has the quality of his "homegrown." He knows that his green mulch method improves his soil rather than depletes the soil. His equipment is tiny compared to standard haying equipment. It fits easily in his loft. It is practically repair free which is not true of very old standard equipment.

Even though Weiner has not done a fuel and labor analysis and comparison, he knows that his system and equipment requires less fuel and labor than traditional methods. Such a study is needed and should include an evaluation of crop nutrients, soil fertility, and livestock health and production. These qualities are inextricably tied to the value of the crops, which complicates this research.

A Problem

One of the problems encountered by returnees to organic methods in Vermont is that deer love unsprayed corn and avoid sprayed corn. The chemical people are going to have to come up with a product acceptable to the organic method—a taste or smell-actuated deterrent. In the meantime fences are not practical since deer have been known to jump 18' high ones. An 8' solid fence would work since they won't jump where they can't see. Weiner's solution is a fencerow of multiflora roses (illegal in Ohio and West Virginia) bordered by a two-strand electric fence.

He's also had success with a gaggle of goslings in a hay-corn field after the corn is over 2' tall. He supplies them with a water fount and a floorless dog house. The geese establish territorial rights and will keep any animal out of the field short of a bear, fox, or a weasel. They are a noisy bunch in the field, but they are good for hot smoking. The amount of hay and lower corn leaves they eat is insignificant.

The third solution to the deer-corn problem is making corn ensilage before the corn matures and becomes "deer candy." As you can imagine, any of these solutions becomes quite expensive to the large acreage corn farmer located in deer country returning to the organic fold. On the other hand, how can they feed sprayed corn to their cows knowing that deer won't eat it?

Advantages of Green Mulching

☐ It is less soil fitting even if you rototill the planting rows.

☐ It has better soil structure since most of the soil is not worked.

☐ There is less soil compaction since lighter equipment can be used.

☐ Crops can be planted during a wet spring since the tractor moves on established sod.

☐ Crops can be green mulch cultivated immediately after a rain.

☐ Legumes in the crop field supply the crop with fixated nitrogen as well as nitrogen and potassium from the green mulch.

☐ Soil organisms do not die or go dormant during cultivation since they are fed green mulch.

☐ Hay pastures are more productive since they become older rather than being plowed in a rotation.

☐ Green mulch protects crop roots from temperature extremes.

☐ Green mulch holds moisture after a rain.

☐ Green mulch and intercropping legumes prevents soil erosion.

☐ Less fuel and labor are required to green mulch cultivate rather than conventional cultivating.

MULCH GUARDS

Mulch around trees has a way of disappearing. Wind, rabbits, rain, and the mower all contribute to this. A very effective mulch guard that is aesthetically acceptable can be made from a discarded car tire (Fig. 17-16). Actually, you get two guards from one tire.

Cut the tire in half around the center of the tread, then turn each half inside out. This hides the worn tread and produces an attractive bell shape. You can paint it if you like. If the tree is small, pull the branches together

484

and slip the tire over it; if the tree is too large for this, cut the tire, place it around the trunk, and stake it in place.

We tried several ways of cutting the tires and found that a heavy, sharp hunting knife is best. It is impossible to cut down the tread as this causes the rubber to move in and bind the blade. Force the knife through once from the inside, then once the cut is started, cut from the outside. Cut toward yourself keeping the blade at an angle so the inner bead is cut first. The rubber will spread and cut easily.

Your mulch will last longer and compost well. If you hit the tire with your mower, there will be no damage. As a matter of fact, hitting the tire moves it slightly, flattens it, and permits very close mowing.

Here's a variation for trees that require heavier fertilization. Cut a tire in half as described, but do not turn it inside out. Put the tire in place like a trough around the tree and poke a few triangular or square-shaped holes in the bottom. The size of your knife will determine the hole size, but this is not critical. Fill the tire with manure and forget it. The tire will fill with rain eventually, and a nourishing slurry will form. This will seep through the bottom holes over a long period of time.

This use is especially good for evergreens (add coffee grounds) whose bottom branches cover the ground. The tire is hidden and needs no attention for years.

Fig. 17-16. Old tires make effective mulch guards.

SUN BOX LENGTHENS GARDENING SEASON

Everyone wants to start early and extend their garden season later, if at all possible. Unfortunately, nature doesn't always cooperate. Unless protected, many early plantings get off to a shaky start if they survive at all.

Most of the garden books recommend building a cold frame, but most gardeners don't have one. Why not, if they're so handy and necessary?

The simple answer is that the standard old fashioned cold frame shown in most every garden book is expensive and difficult to build, cumbersome to use, and very limited in its use. Most gardeners—especially new ones—are turned off the complicated drawings and formulas given, or by the cost of special wood and hardware when they go to buy the materials. The sun box, a triple-decker, portable cold frame is designed to help the backyard gardener start earlier and stay later (Fig. 17-17).

The sun box has all the capabilities of the traditional cold frame: protecting seedlings from frost in early spring, extending summer crops into fall, holding root vegetables over winter, and even storing harvested vegetables. Its unique design makes it both much more versatile and easier to construct than traditional models. For example, most garden books mention a simple cold frame and then go on to tell the reader to construct and fit a glass cover, complete with sash, cut sides at a difficult angle, attach hinges and handles, make a notched prop stick, ground stakes, and then how to preserve the wood, etc. To construct a sun box, you needn't concern yourself with any of these.

The sun box is simply an old wooden storm window; the frame is simply four pieces of 2″ × 4″ or 2″ × 6″ lumber (scrap, if you have it). Measure and cut the boards to fit the window; nail the frame together and you're all finished. Since the sides are all of equal height, no difficult angle saw cuts and expensive wide lumber are required.

You can get the slope needed to catch maximum sunlight by simply sloping your ground instead. To create a 15° slope, dig out 3″ of soil on the south side and pile it up on the north side. No hinges, handles or props are needed, either. Simply lay your storm window on the frame. Slide it downward for ventilation; hot air will escape through the opening at the top without drawing in any cold air to chill tender seedlings. Since your cover is supported by the frame, even when open, there's little chance of it falling and breaking (or when the toe of your boot unluckily nudges the cold frame prop stick or the wind blows the cover closed).

You now have an inexpensive, lightweight, easily constructed frame. Cut and assemble one or two more levels, and you have a portable double or triple-decker frame which is extremely versatile.

In spring or summer, move it right into the middle of your garden. You'll be able to start seedlings "on location" (no need for transplanting later) or hold over your favorite summer crops.

Stacking layers enables you to protect even your taller varieties. No more praying for warm weather to come before your plants start touching the top of the frame.

Fig. 17-17. The sun box is a portable cold frame (photo by Mel Bartholomew).

When not in use, it disassembles easily for convenient storage in the nooks and crannies of your garage or barn. To save even more space, hang the decks from nails high up on the walls.

Your sun box can be made even more versatile by substituting a screen cover for the top (an old window screen the same size works fine—again, no construction). Now you can start seedlings for a fall crop in mid or late summer using the screen for maximum ventilation. Replace screen with storm window as cooler weather approaches. Your screen top is also an excellent device for preventing airborne pest infestation without resorting to chemical insecticides.

You're bound to think of many handy uses for the sun box once you've built and used it for while. It makes an ideal nursery for flowering perennials in summer. Use one level with the glass cover as a substitute for black plastic mulch to warm up a portion of your asparagus or strawberry bed in the early spring. Staple wire screen to the bottom of the box, fill with 2" to 3" of sifted soil, and sow seeds to grow seedlings or plants that will be free of cutworms or other soil pests.

When starting seedlings in your sun box frame, space your plants the same distances in both directions, say 2" or 4" apart—no need for rows like in a conventional garden. Your plants will grow evenly all around, and you'll fit many more plants into the same space. With a sun box, you'll get the jump on nature this year and be a lot more successful.

Chapter 18

Vegetables and Herbs

Broccoli, cabbages, carrots, cauliflower, beets, turnips, spinach, kohlrabi, radishes, kale and Swiss chard, lettuce, endive, parsnips, squashes, milkweed, onions, beans, and tomatoes are covered in this chapter. Information on herbs like garlic, chamomile, sassafras, and persimmon is presented.

SECOND PLANTINGS WILL FILL THE CELLAR

In August, when tomatoes, beans, cabbages, and other "big" garden crops are filling our carrying baskets, refrigerators, freezers, and canning jars, it is somehow difficult to think of planting more vegetables. Depending on the fullness of the harvest, in fact, some of us might positively rail against the idea.

Still, we know that by the time the first autumn frosts threaten, we will be glad that we thought in August to make second plantings of lettuce, radishes, broccoli, cabbages, beets, parsnips, and other short-term growers. Some of these crops are especially welcomed in the fall because we have not tasted them fresh since the early spring plantings were harvested several months earlier. Others—in particular the root crops—are valued because they can be stored well into January and February, when supermarket prices are likely to be frightening.

Do, then, take a full day to devote to second plantings. Survey your garden now. Are there empty spaces where lettuce, radishes, peas, spinach, early beets, and onions have been harvested? Plan to use these right away for plantings of the longer-term second plantings—parsnips, cabbages, broccoli and cauliflower.

Then, look several weeks into the future. Will the bush beans have produced their limit by August 20th or so? Are the cabbages, sweet corn, eggplants and head lettuce nearly ready for harvest? Plan now to replace these, right after harvest, with some of the shorter-term second plantings: carrots, leaf lettuce, turnips, beets, radishes, Swiss chard, spinach, and various salad greens. Check the days-to-harvest data on your seed packets, and match up this to the number of frost-free days remaining in your locality. Remember that a few early frosts will do most root crops no harm, and in fact will improve their crisp texture and taste. Parsnips, in fact, need not be harvested at all until ready for use, even when the top several inches of topsoil are frozen solid.

Look over your seed supply now, and buy as many packets as you will need to complete your second plantings. It will be a good idea, also, to carry to the basement or cellar storage area enough soil and sand to store root crops for the winter (Fig. 18-1). If you live near a bog, gather up plenty of *sphagnum moss*, which is even better for root crop storage; it holds mois ture better and keeps the crops cleaner.

Before planting, till the soil well and replace the lost nutrients by incorporating plenty of well-advanced compost. If you are about to divide your earthworm beds, now is the perfect time to do so, since the spent bedding can be worked into the soil for second plantings. Don't plant root crops where root crops have just been harvested, since the phosphorus level is likely to be low in these areas. On the other hand, do plant leaf crops where peas have been harvested, since the nitrogen stored in the pea root nodules will stimulate fine top growth for lettuce, Swiss chard, cabbage, endive, and similar crops.

Many gardeners consider second plantings a tricky business, and some do not like the idea at all, reasoning that the natural climate patterns are all wrong for this activity. Seeds should germinate in cool spring weather, they say, and the plant should mature during the increasingly warm days of summer. Second plantings seem to defy this natural progression, being planted during the heat of summer and coming to maturity during autumn's cooling trend. You do take a chance in attempting this reversal.

Here are possibilities for August plantings:

Broccoli. (50 to 100 days.) Here is a plant that will sail through the first autumn frosts with no complaint. Broccoli will make fast and strong growth during August's warm days, and the development of its heads will be enhanced by the cool weather of late summer and early autumn. Mulch the plants well, after they have been established, and apply some compost tea after the heads have begun to form. The cabbageworm might be a problem, although it attacks the foliage and not the edible flower heads. Pick them off by hand, or, if the infestation is great, resort to rotenone.

Green Mountain is a particularly good variety for second plantings, since it thrives on cool nights. Other good short-season varieties are Spartan Early and Green Comet. All mature in 60 to 65 days.

Cabbage. (65 to 125 days.) This is perhaps the heaviest feeder of all popular garden vegetables. To do well as a second crop, cabbage needs a fairly heavy loam, rich in nutrient matter. It needs plenty of water, too, so a heavy mulch is essential, especially if the soil is sandy and does not hold

Fig. 18-1. You can bet that this root cellar will be filled by second, and even third plantings.

water well. Second plantings have a natural advantage over spring crops in that the cool weather of early autumn will prevent any seed heads from forming, as sometimes happens when heads ripen in the heat of midsummer. Root maggots might be a problem when planting in August, but they can be kept away from the young plants by placing tarpaper discs around the stems of the young plants at the soil surface.

After harvesting, cabbages may be kept in good condition for several weeks if the heads are pulled from the ground, keeping as much root as possible. Tie a paper bag around the head and hang it up in the cellar by the root. They may also be stored underground, in a pit or root barrel, covered with layers of soil and straw to protect them from freezing.

There are dozens of early cabbage varieties suitable for second plantings. Only a few (all of which mature in 65 days or less) are Wisconsin Copenhagen, Jersey Queen, Stonehead F1 Hybrid (55 days), Wisconsin Golden Acre, Resistant Golden Acre, Extra Early Jersey Queen, and Emerald Cross.

Carrots. (60 to 85 days.) Encourage carrots to make the fastest progress by giving them a rich and loose soil bed, and by supplying them with plenty of moisture through August and September. They can take a few light frosts, but should be harvested just when the first really hard frost is forecast.

Most varieties, even the long ones, mature in from 70 to 75 days, but you can harvest them anytime their size makes it worthwhile. If your soil is naturally heavy, do what you can to loosen it by the incorporation of compost, sand, and peat before planting, and then choose the half-long varieties.

490

Cauliflower. (50 to 120 days.) Few plants are more fun to grow than cauliflower. Like cabbage, though, it is a heavy feeder and will require your special attention to get a running start towards autumn harvest. Apply a heavy mulch as soon as the plants have become established, and never let the soil become dry. In second plantings, you cannot afford progress to be halted because of late summer drought. Be careful not to disturb the roots once the plant has become established, or else the heads are likely to become fuzzy and malformed. A lack of nitrogen can cause the plants to head prematurely.

When the heads are 3" or 4" in diameter, tie the outside leaves loosely over the head to produce white heads. Most important, however, is plenty of water and plenty of available nutrients. Supply both, and your chances of success in second plantings are great.

Choose any of the early varieties that mature in 70 days or fewer— Super Snowball, Improved Early Snowball, Snow King F1 Hybrid (50 days), Snowdrift, Early Purple Head, or a number of others.

Beets. (50 to 80 days.) Here is another heavy feeder requiring a nutrient-rich soil and plenty of moisture for a good fall crop. The danger of planting beets in August is that a spell of very hot weather might send them bolting to seed in mid-growth, making the roots woody and unfit to eat. Mulching, again, is important to keep the soil cool.

Beets are notorious consumers of potash. Therefore, if you have any wood ashes left, work them well into the soil before seeding the crop. Otherwise, apply potash rock.

Beets can be harvested just before the first hard frost. If an early frost kills off the top growth, the roots can be harvested and stored with no harm done. Otherwise, the tops make a fine boiled green.

Beets can be stored in barely moist sand at a temperature of 35°F to 40°F they will last well into January.

Nearly any variety is suitable for second plantings if you have enough frost-free days remaining for the variety you choose. Among the earlier varieties are Formanova (a cylinder-shaped beet), Early Wonder (53 days). Ruby Queen, Detroit Dark Red, Hybrid Pacemaker (55 days), and "Mono" King Explorer. Also think about Spring Red, which is said to be slow to bolt.

Turnips. (40 to 80 days.) Turnips, like most root crops, are best when grown quickly and eaten young. Hot weather will impede their development and harm their flavor. If all goes well, however, second plantings will come to maturity just as the cool days of autumn arrive, helping the plants along to extra crispness and full, tangy flavor.

Again, the idea is to spur quick growth by supplying plenty of nutrients. Work plenty of compost into the soil and be sure that it is fairly loose to allow quick development of the roots.

Among the earlier varieties are Purple Top White Globe (55 days), Purple Top Strap Leaf (46 days), Milan (40 days), and Tokio Cross (40 days). If it's luscious turnip greens you're after, try Shogoin or Foliage, both ready in about 30 days to use as foliage, or 70 days to use the roots.

Spinach. (30 to 50 days.) This crop needs plenty of water, nitrogen, and cool weather. A hot spell anywhere along the line can wipe out the crop, but spinach is so easy to grow that we are willing to take the chance.

Spinach will grow well in a wide variety of soils, although it is sensitive to acidity. Throw a few handfuls of lime on the soil before working it to give spinach the best chance for quick and tender growth.

Most varieties can be harvested six weeks after sowing. When thinning out young plants, cut every other one, to give the others room to spread out. Use the thinnings in salads.

Kohlrabi. (60 to 90 days.) Kohlrabi is another lover of cool weather and will do well in most soils, so long as ample nutrients and moisture are available. As with all these second crops, a heavy mulch is essential.

The mistake that most people make is in not harvesting kohlrabi early enough. The bulbs and roots should be picked before the plant comes to maturity, and while it is still tender. Use the roots and bulbs in salads, sliced, or boil them to use as a cooked vegetable. The crisp days of early October will give kohlrabi added crispness and zest. Two good varieties are Early White Vienna (60 days) and Purple Vienna (63 days).

Radishes. (22 to 30 days.) You probably harvested the last of your radishes in early June, if you are like most gardeners. How nice, then, to have another round in late September and throughout October. The only problem might be the heat, which can send radishes bolting to seed before the succulent roots have formed. Because radishes are so easy to sow, however, you can put some out every week for the next month, in odd places around the garden. If a hot spell gets one bunch, the others will likely escape it. Again, plenty of moisture and an adequate nutrient supply is essential for the quick development that brings succulent growth.

Most varieties mature in less than 30 days, so your choice of varieties is a wide one. For best results, choose the so-called "winter radishes," which have been developed especially for August planting. These include Round Black Spanish, New White Chinese, China Rose and China White. Although these take longer to mature—about 55 days—they can take some initial heat without bolting, and they will not be damaged by light frost.

Kale and Swiss Chard. (50 to 75 days.) The cultural requirements for both are similar, and both are grown for their large and tender leaves which can either be used young and raw, in salads, or cooked as a vegetable. The tender stems of chard may, in addition, be cooked and eaten like asparagus.

Both plants are easy to grow, requiring only an average soil and ample moisture. Leaves may be harvested as soon as they are large enough to bother with, and you may continue to harvest until after the first few light autumn frosts. Especially in the case of kale, the first few autumn frosts definitely improve the taste and quality of the leaves. A moderate weekly application of compost tea will encourage the quick growth you seek.

Lettuce. (50 to 90 days.) Leaf lettuce needs warm days and cool nights for optimum growth. As with the other succession crops listed here, ample moisture and nutrients are essential. Cos, loose-leaf, and butterhead varieties will all benefit from the cooler days of September and October, and in fact will probably do better than spring-planted crops, which often must face damaging heat when the plants are ready to head up. If you can grow plants in an area where the mid-afternoon sun is partially shaded by overhanging trees, so much the better.

Loose-leaf culture is by far the easiest. Butterhead, which forms a soft and loose head, is particularly suited to planting at this time of year—again, barring unusual hot spells during late August and early September. Cos, or Romaine, is a tall-growing type which provides beautiful salad greens. It is no more difficult to grow than the butterhead varieties.

The varieties are too numerous to list here, although you might think about the following: Black Seeded Simpson, Oakleaf, and Butter King (loose-leaf varieties); Buttercrunch, Summer Bibb, and Butter King (butterhead varieties); Paris White, Paris Island, Valmaine, and Sweet Midget (cos varieties).

Endive. (85 to 100 days.) The culture for endive, sometimes called *escarole,* is similar to that for lettuce, although its taste is far stronger. The problem with endive is that it does take a long time to mature—three months—although it may be harvested before maturity with no loss in quality. If you wish to blanch the heads, do so two weeks before harvesting, by pulling up and tying the outer leaves around the head, or simply set a large inverted flower pot over the head.

There is not much choice between varieties. You may have had success with both Green Curled and Full Heart Batavian, which are especially good for northern areas.

Parsnips. (90 to 150 days.) Here is a vegetable that not only tolerates autumn's hard freezes, but actually likes them. Parsnips aren't much good unless they have been exposed to hard frost. In fact, in most areas, they are left in the ground over winter, to be harvested and used as needed in the early spring.

Parsnips, which thrust fairly deeply into the ground, appreciate a loose and rich soil. In any case, they will grow slowly. Many gardeners plant radishes right along with parsnips. The radishes will come up first, and will be harvested just as the parsnips are making good progress. Parsnips planted by August 15 will offer the first harvests around Thanksgiving, and will continue to produce until the ground is simply too hard to dig them. Then, in spring, a new harvest begins. Hollow Crown is one of the better early varieties.

HYBRID VEGETABLES

Although organic gardeners have avoided the use of hybrid vegetables, there are important reasons why they should be the first to take advantage of their unique vigor and resistance to diseases and insects. The most common argument against hybrids is the high cost of seeds. Because they are produced by careful hand-hybridizing, the seeds of most modern hybrids do not come cheap.

Another drawback, for those who want to save their own seeds, is that they will not come true to variety the following year. Some of us save seeds because we need to economize; others do so for the satisfaction which comes from following an old pioneer custom.

Despite these small drawbacks, the tremendous benefits that come from growing hybrids far outweighs their high cost. R. Milton Carleton recalls the experiences of two neighbors who were discussing cucumbers. Carleton recommended that they plant a new hybrid called Gemini 7 because of its remarkable disease resistance and its tremendous production, nearly twice that of open-pollinated cucumbers. One man took his advice. His packet of Gemini 7 then cost 75 cents for about 30 seeds. His friend balked at paying that much for "just cucumbers." Instead he picked up a packet of Long Green at a nearby supermarket, about 200 seeds for 25 cents.

The Gemini 7 seedlings appeared three days before those of Long Green. Nine times out of 10, hybrids appear days ahead of open-pollinated varieties. This is due to a quality known as heterosis or hybrid vigor. Fruits on Gemini 7 were ready to pick two weeks earlier than those on Long Green and there were more than twice as many. The reason for the heavier early production was that Gemini 7 is what is known as a *gynoecious* hybrid. That is, it produces few or no male flowers. Since male flowers are produced first on open-pollinated varieties, there is a delay of several days before female flowers appear and are pollinated.

By August 1, Gemini 7 had produced four times the number of cucumbers of Long Green, partly because of earlier setting and partly because of more female flowers to produce fruits. By that time, Long Green had developed scab, mosaic, and anthracnose, which killed the vines shortly, so no more fruits were produced. Gemini 7, with mature fruits kept picked, went on producing until frost. Although the penny-wise grower of Long Green had saved 50 cents, he lost far more cucumbers than 50 cents would buy.

In the early days of hybrid vegetables, they did not come up to the flavor quality of old-time garden varieties. The first Golden Bantam hybrid corn, lacked the flavor of its parent, Golden Bantam, or Country Gentleman. Today, anyone who has ever eaten an ear of Silver Queen Hybrid would as soon eat field corn as one-time favorite Howling Mob, or even that darling of some fussy gardeners, Aunt Mary's.

Perhaps the most outstanding advances in modern vegetables has been in tomatoes. The beefmaster VFN mentioned above is a good example. This was bred by hybrid techniques from Beefsteak, a one-time favorite home garden tomato, and still widely listed in seed catalogs. Beefsteak was big with fruits weighing up to 2 pounds, but rough and ripening with green shoulders. The flavor was mild, but not great.

The biggest difference between Beefmaster and its parent is in those

494

initials, VFN. These stand for multiple resistance to verticillium wilt, fusarium wilt, and nematodes. Verticillum and fusarium are two of the most serious diseases of tomatoes, often cutting yields more than 50 percent. The organisms that cause them are universal. While nematodes do some damage in the North, they are devastating in the South. They form lumps or knots on roots that prevent free movement of water and food to the plant.

You will find varieties listed in the better catalogs which are resistant to many other diseases such as leaf spots, molds, and early blight. The variety Manalucie is not only resistant to a wide variety of ills, but is also resistant to the high heat of summer in southeastern United States.

In the past, yellows disease of cabbage caused widespread damage to that crop. Today, anyone who grows cabbage in a climate where the temperature stays above 85°F and 90°F day after day is asking for trouble, unless he plants varieties which are clearly identified as yellows resistant.

An interesting example of resistance is Kangold muskmelon developed by the Kansas Agricultural Experiment Station (AES). In addition to resisting powdery mildew, alternaria leaf spot and other diseases, it is highly resistant to attacks by cucumber beetles which transmit cucumber wilt.

A common experience in the past was to see an entire planting of cucumbers wiped out by various diseases. Today there are several hybrids similar to Gemini 7 which not only are highly resistant, but are also all-female and produce double the cucumbers of open-pollinated varieties. They include Cherokee 7, Hiyield, Meridian, Sweet Slice, and Explorer.

Organic gardeners who grow soybeans for their high protein content have trouble with downy mildew and with pod and stem blight. The Delaware AES has introduced Verde, a soybean resistant to these diseases.

Among snap beans, look for varieties rated as resistant to mosaic, anthracnose, and mildew. The winter squash variety Butternut has always been known for its freedom from squash borers. Now the variety Hercules combines that resistance with larger fruits and as an added bonus, resistance to mildew.

INDOOR VEGETABLE GROWING

Killing frosts won't ice your gardening for the year if you've done a little planning ahead. Fresh homegrown salads in January, even tomatoes in February are indeed possible, even in the far North.

Some of the goodies besides tomatoes you can enjoy indoors while the snow flies and cold rain drips are peppers and parsley, lettuce, chives, various herbs, watercress, and tiny carrots. You can have radishes, beets and Swiss chard, Chinese cabbage, spinach, garden cress, and even beans (Fig. 18-2).

The major limiting factors to your winter garden are your own time, energy, and dedication, and the amount of space you have available that's suitable for growing. You must be able to maintain a high humidity and fairly warm temperature and provide a good light source for 14 to 16 hours a day.

Fig. 18-2. You can grow vegetables inside during the winter.

The first steps toward a winter garden should take place in late summer and early fall. Round up plenty of clay pots and planter boxes. Fill a large tub full of pebbles to use in trays under the pots to keep wet in order to heighten humidity, and assemble the ingredients for mixing your own potting soil.

Get buckets of clean sand, a small bale of peat moss, large boxes of well-rotted compost from a hot pile, and soil from the best area of the garden. Sterilize the soil by putting small bucketsful in a leaky container and pouring boiling water over them.

Double check supplies of fertilizers such as bonemeal, fish emulsion, and liquid seaweed. They're hard to find in fall. You can set up a manure tea arrangement in the basement corner near the root cellar. Plants producing fruits and heavy foilage in the winter require just as much fertilizer as they would in the summer. In fact, some gardening books suggest that they require more because the plants may be subject to more stress than in the garden plot.

When planning your winter garden, you'll have to stick to dwarf or nonspreading vegetation. Obviously, you can't grow pumpkins in the bathroom or sunflowers in the bay window. Your crops won't come near to matching summer's quantity because of space limitations, but they should be of superb quality, if you're fussy and thoroughly attentive to their needs. Who cares if January's salad is a third the size of July's, anyway—if it's fresh and pure and your own harvest?

Large south windows, supplemented by grow-light lamps to give the equivalent of 16 hours of daylight are best for the highest quality results. You can raise fairly decent crops of parsley and chives by west window light alone.

The *pepper* is a perennial in its native state. It's only where winters freeze that it must be treated as an annual. You can either seed pots or boxes especially for indoors in fall, wait four months to harvest, and plant them outside again in spring; or you can reverse the process and bring plants in from the garden, over-winter them, harden them off as usual. When spring comes, set them out again. Either way gives a giant leap on the next outdoor season's produce.

Because peppers are tender, they must be carefully dug up, potted in deep pots, and pruned before there has been even a light frost. In a harsh climate, the plants should be given a cold frame-in-reverse treatment. Give them a week or two to get used to the pots before attempting to move them into the house. They should be safely acclimatized to the house before the building is heated. That will take adaptation on their part, too. If suddenly brought into a warm, too dry house, they will react to the shock by dropping their leaves and dying. This is generally true of all plants you may attempt to over-winter.

Make every effort to keep the humidity high around the peppers and other crop plants as well. Use pebble trays, mist sprays, pots of water on the stove, humidifiers, even recirculating waterfalls, if necessary.

All varieties of garden peppers—sweet green, yellow banana, and the green and red hots—will flower profusely and bear fruit during the winter months, if given enough light and humidity. The indoor peppers will be smaller, only one-half to one-third the size as when they're grown outdoors, but they can be harvested as soon as they're big enough to handle.

Since there are no insects in the house, you'll have to do the job of pollinating the flowers for them. Use a cotton swab or an artist's brush to hand-pollinate the fresh flowers.

Tomatoes will also need to be hand-pollinated. Also a perennial and a member of the same family as peppers *(solonaceae)*, the tomato can be a bright winter companion if you choose dwarf or cherry tomatoes, or determinate type garden tomatoes.

Tomatoes may be started for the winter. To do this you will have to allow the garden tomato plants you've selected to grow suckers grow long enough to get about ½" thick and to produce a bud. Then cut the suckers off the parent plant and root in a bed of clean sand. Transfer pots large enough to accommodate the roots when new growth is strong and healthy, and repot when needed.

The plants will require daylight conditions for 16 hours. They need to be fertilized every two weeks, but if you get too much leafy growth, prune them back to the point where the flowers are emerging. Don't forget to hand-pollinate the new flowers.

We've had particularly good luck with the cherry and patio varieties, especially the new Toyboy hybrid, since it was originally developed for container culture. The winter garden is where we can borrow ideas from our city friends who have learned to grow almost any vegetable in containers. When you put in the fall garden in July, seed some clay pots especially for the winter garden. Sink the pots right in the row, and two weeks before the first frosts are expected, prune the plants lightly and start "softening them off" for the house.

This method works well for *parsley, oregano, thyme,* the *mints, basil, winter savory,* and *rosemary.* (Fig. 18-3). *Parsley,* a biennial, can also be carefully dug from the garden and placed in a pot deep enough to handle its taproot. Trim the foliage severely, and let it adapt to the pot and to the house conditions. Later, when cutting it for use, trim the outer leaves, allowing the growth center leaves to develop outward before they're cut.

Use the same method for cutting *leaf lettuce* in the house. Late-sown lettuce plants may be lifted for the house, or lettuce can be directly seeded under the grow-lights. We favor the Buttercrunch and Oak Leaf varieties.

If you have a *watercress* bed, take cuttings in fall and root them in jars of water. Since the plant is a perennial, the cuttings can be planted in good potting soil when the roots are about ¼" long, and the pot placed on a pebble tray. This will give you a couple of crops during the winter. If you want just one crop, keep the cress in the jars, changing the water daily. Watercress can also be seeded even in the cold of winter, and if kept constantly moist, you'll have a crop in 50 days with enough left over to establish a bed outdoors in spring. We use a fiber-glassed wooden tray that's 6" deep.

Garden cress or pepper grass is the quickest and easiest salad green known. It's ready for harvest in two weeks and should be planted every week to maintain a continuous supply. Fertilize heavily and give plenty of soil moisture.

Chives may be brought indoors for the winter, but they need a "rest." Transplant a clump of garden chives into a 5" pot and sink the pot into the ground. After the first killing frost, mulch the pot or put it into the cold frame for about 90 days. Then bring the pot into a sunny location in the house and water it. There will be fresh chives for harvesting by January.

Shallot, a small onion of the multiplier type, lends its delicate flavor to French cooking. It may be grown indoors, treated like an onion, if planted in sandy soil and given ample moisture and fertilizer.

Beets grow well in the winter garden, especially the smaller and sweeter spring varieties. Thin the plants to 3" apart after they have their true leaves, and use the thinnings in salads. They're delicious. Fertilize heavily.

Swiss chard, a member of the beet family grown for its foliage, is a delight in the winter garden. It will stand repeated cuttings if fertilized well. It tolerates lower humidity than most other greens.

498

Any globe type *radish* will quickly pop up and be ready for eating in about three weeks. Thin to 1" apart.

Carrots are rewarding. Use the dwarf or short varieties and thin the seedlings to 1" apart. The tiny discards add variety to winter salads.

Spinach, like Swiss chard, is well adapted to winter culture. It thrives in cool temperatures of 50° to 65°F and demands heavy fertilization. It matures in 50-some days, but may be harvested whenever the leaves are large enough.

Chinese cabbage, which takes three months to maturity, can be individually planted in 3" pots. It is another cool weather plant, so it does well indoors. It's the basis for delightful stir-fry dinners in December, January, and February. Just add some sprouts, mushrooms, onions, various greens, and maybe a pepper or two.

There's one additional fillip to winter gardening that won't yield you much in the way of produce, but sure chases the winter blues—*miniature fruit trees.* Picking a fresh lime or lemon while the blizzard rages, or just simply drinking in the color of the bright, undyed oranges has rewards far beyond the vitamin C they'll add to the diet.

Order the miniature varieties from nurseries, pot in rich soil, water, fertilize, and mist frequently. There'll soon be beautifully fragrant citrus blossoms to hand-pollinate. The trees don't like drafts, and the humidity must be kept high. They will tolerate cool temperatures.

CUCUMBERS FOR THE SMALL GARDEN

If you have a small garden, have you neglected to grow cucumbers because of the space needed for the vines? A few posts, some heavy wire, and some heavy twine and you can grow cucumbers taking up no more area than a row of corn. This way wasted space such as the end of a garden can be put to use and help make some delicious salads.

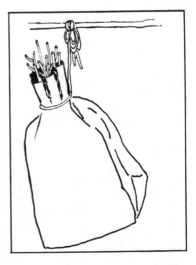

Fig. 18-3. Thyme is a common garden herb.

Site selection is important. A sunny area with no shade is best. Almost any soil is suitable for cucumbers. Especially good is soil high in organic matter. For a 50' row, four or five wheelbarrows full of manure or compost worked into the top few inches of soil is adequate. If your supply of organic matter is limited, a shovelful where each plant is to grow will be satisfactory.

Set the posts in the ground 8' or 9' apart down the row and standing at least 5' or 6' above the ground. Stretch a heavy wire between the post tops. Now you are ready for your plants or seeds.

When selecting your seeds, remember there are two types of slicing cucumbers. One type is the monoecious which covers most of the common varieties of cucumbers such as Straight Eights. This type has both the male and female flowers on a plant. The other type, genoecious, produces only the female blossoms on each plant, so the potential production is tremendous. For pollination other seeds are mixed in the package. Victory and Gemini are examples of this type of cucumbers.

For earlier production start your plants indoors approximately four weeks before you are ready to transplant. Keep the pots warm. Cucumbers need soil temperature of 65° to sprout properly. Once the seeds sprout, keep them in a warm sunny area. After the plants are well established with their second leaf thin them to two plants in each pot.

When your season is right, transplant outdoors 12" apart in the row under the wire. Cover the top edge of the peat pots to prevent excessive drying. When the plants are well established, thin them to only one plant in each pot.

After the plants are vining 2' or 3' long, tie a string to the wire above the plant long enough to reach the ground. Baling twine works best. Tie the string to the base of the plant and carefully wind the main stalk up the twine being very careful of the blossoms and developing cucumbers, leaving the top 6" or 8" loose so you do not damage the growing tip. Wind the plant every few days all summer. When the plant reaches the wire, let it hang down and grow back toward the ground. If you have it on hand, woven wire fencing works equally well or suitable ground beside an existing fence will also work.

When you cultivate your plants, remember that cucumbers are very shallow rooted so do not cultivate too deep. A good mulch would be preferable to cultivating at all.

Cucumbers are very heavy water users, so soak them weekly for best production and juicier cucumbers. When cucumber plants get dry and start suffering from stress, the cucumbers get bitter.

When picking, carefully cut each cucumber off with scissors to prevent plant damage. Pick often so that none of the cucumbers ripen or the plant will cease to produce. With this method you will discover that your cucumbers are clean, straight and easier to pick and take up very little space (Fig. 18-4).

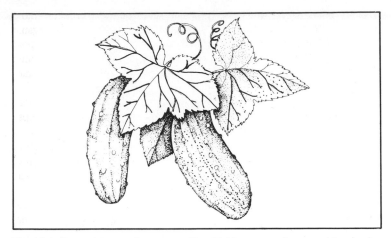

Fig. 18-4. Cucumbers can be grown without taking up much space (drawing by Fredda Burton).

SQUASH

If you are looking for a vegetable with a wide variety in types, *squash* is your baby (Fig. 18-5). You can grow squash all the way from half-dollar-sized patty pans to the whopper Hubbard or giant banana. Straight, smooth, warted, necked, striped, or plain are all in the realm of possibility in the squash and pumpkin family.

Even if your soil is rich, it cannot be too rich for this most greedy of feeders. The summer squash will do well on less nutrient-laden soil, but both summer and winter like plenty of fertilizer and plenty of moisture. Normally, do no more than dig in a couple of shovelfuls of manure where the squash hill is (which is, incidentally, to you beginning gardeners, simply a small area where several seeds are planted, usually in a circle, but not necessarily higher than the surrounding ground,) and plant the seed. If the soil is unusually heavy and/or wet, the seed can be soaked for half a day, for they will then germinate quickly instead of rotting.

After your squash is up, keep an eye out for the squash bug, a dull gray fellow who can suck the plants dry almost overnight, and the squash borer, who tunnels into the base of the plant with the same disastrous results. You can hand pick the squash bug, (wear gloves as they can cause blistering on sensitive skin), or dust with *pyrethum*, which is one of the few insecticides which will kill this toughie in short order. The borer can be controlled by dusting the base of the plants with *sevin*. Sevin dust should be kept off the leaves of all cucurbita plants, as this can cause burning of leaves in hot, sunny weather.

When the weather is settled and warm, and the squash is growing well and showing flower buds, *mulch*. This is most important to supply the second important factor in growing squash, *moisture*. Rich mulch like manure mixed barn litter is ideal for mulching, and spoiled alfalfa hay is good too. This should be applied rather thickly so it will settle down to about 6″ when rained upon or watered.

Squash will grow like Jack's beanstalk of storybook fame and will soon show the orange-yellow blossoms. You can tell which are the female and therefore the bearing blossoms by the minute squash under the blossom. The male blossoms have simply a stem and will drop off after blooming. Some people are very disturbed by the blossom drop, but this is a natural occurrence with all squash, cukes, gourds, and most other vining type crops. When you are at this stage, simply watch for the insects and water.

If, however, the blossoms all drop, try an application of a few tablespoonsful of superphosphate applied under the mulch. Phosphorus is normally the key element missing when plants repeatedly shed their blossoms, if other conditions are right.

Winter squash requires somewhat different handling. First, they need a much longer growing season. They also need a much larger area, due to their vining habit, although recently some compact bush varieties of winter squash have been developed. So winter varieties need more nutrients by far than summer ones.

A good plan is to dig down about 18″ and fill with manure, tamp down, fill to soil level or slightly above with soil, and plant the seeds. Be sure to keep the squash evenly watered if at all possible, as sometimes the flesh of

Fig. 18-5. There are many varieties of squash.

the winter varieties gets stringy if moisture supply is erratic or under-supplied. (This is another good reason for the mulch.)

If you are just starting gardening, the most easily grown winter squash is butternut. It is hardy, has very good resistance to insects, stores all winter, and is of excellent quality. If you want a "bragging size" squash or pumpkins, pinch all but one small squash off the vine. Choose a large variety like Hubbard, banana, Hungarian mammoth, or Big Max pumpkin and watch it grow.

Many people use a booster solution of manure water, commercial fertilizers or such, but if the soil is prepared with the growing requirements of the squash in mind, this will rarely be necessary. Harvest your crop when ready. For such summer squashes as patty pan, zucchini, golden crookneck and Mexican round, this means while small and delectable, with skin easily pierced with a thumbnail. For winters, when the rind is hard and the stem woody, carefully cut the squash loose with a couple of inches of stem left on the end for long storage. Cure a couple of days in a warm dry place. Then put the squashes in a cool dry one, and they will last well into spring.

MILKWEED

Sooner or later, no matter how much you mulch or how often you hoe, a few of those pesky weeds are bound to creep into the garden. Before you yank everything out that doesn't resemble a cabbage or a bean, take a second look at the invader. You may have the beginnings of a new taste treat right there at your "hoe-tip."

Long before man became civilized and domesticated, he lived off the land, eating whatever fruits and vegetables nature provided at the moment. Through the centuries, many of the "wild" foods which sprang up anywhere gave way to garden varieties which could be controlled and guaranteed to yield more. From time to time, some of the wildlings show up again, and it is definitely worth your while to give them a fighting chance.

Mountain folks call it "wild crafting", the gathering of wild edibles. Euell Gibbons just labeled it "reaping what we do not sow." Lots of folks have thought about going out for an afternoon of foraging for their dinner, but there is a garden to work first, chickens to be fed, and pump to be fixed, and somehow they never get around to that afternoon.

So there you stand, right there on your own property, and two or three of those wild "goodies" have had the nerve to drop in for a visit. The trick is to recognize which ones might be worth an introduction.

Nearly every child recognizes milkweed in the fall, with its silky fluff spilling out of dried and splitting pods. Identifying the luscious little plant in its infancy is sometimes quite a different story, but one well worth learning if you have ever tasted buttered milkweed flowers or pods.

Native to America, the common *milkweed (Asclepias syriaca)* flourishes in poor soil as well as finely tended garden loam. The young shoots have oppositely paired leaves ranging 4" to 9" long, less than half that wide. Each leaf is egg to oblong in shape, a dark green on top, a softer fuzzy gray-green on the underneath side. Clusters of fragrant white to lilac flowers droop from the 2′ to 5′ stalk, attracting a parade of butterflies. As the flowers are pollinated, minute green pods begin to appear, swelling as the plant dies, finally to turn brown and burst with their gift of parachuted seeds.

If you think that trespasser in the garden just might be milkweed, give it the "milk" test. Break off a leaf and watch for a sticky white sap to ooze forth, the milky liquor that gives the plant its name. Any further doubts as to the identity of the plant in question can be answered by checking a well-illustrated wild foods book such as Bradford Angier's *Field Guide to Wild Edible Plants* or the *Field Guide to Wild Herbs*, published by Rodale Press.

Lots of people recognize milkweed and pull it out anyway, for there are tales of cattle being poisoned by eating it, and more stories of the plant's horribly bitter taste. While there is some truth to these warnings, (ingestion of raw leaves can result in depression, weakness, spasms, high temperatures, and finally a comatose state ending in death), properly prepared milkweed is a delicious and colorful vegetable sure to whet anyone's appetite.

What parts are edible? The young shoots, up to 6″ in height, can be bundled and tied (like asparagus) for cooking. New leaves, picked from the top of the plant before it flowers, make wilted and cooked greens. The real delicacy of the milkweed fare is the unopened flower buds, tightly closed balls of pale green. Firm young pods, about 1″ in length, also cook up nicely. (Once the pods become tough and flexible, you might as well let them grow on to produce their seed, and start thinking about next year's crop.)

The sticky white sap is the culprit responsible for the bitter taste in raw milkweed. It permeates the entire plant and can only be removed in boiling water. The process is a simple one, taking longer to describe than to actually perform. Whether you are preparing young milkweed shoots, early leaves, unopened flowers, or tiny pods, the cooking procedure is the same.

Never let milkweed touch cold water. The cold somehow "sets" the bitterness in the plant, and no amount of cooking will get rid of it. Resist all temptation to wash the vegetable, and instead, fill the teakettle or a large pan with water and have it boiling before adding the milkweed. Let the vegetable boil for a full minute (you will notice a white scum form on the water's surface), then pour off the water and add more boiling liquid. After another minute, pour off the second water and go on to the third. By the fourth round of boiling water, the bitterness should be leached out. You can continue to cook the plant gently in the final water for ten minutes or so. Granted, you do lose some minerals and nutrients in the cooking waters, but even the hardiest of vegetable lovers would be hard-pressed to swallow the bitter taste. Add salt, pepper, or butter to your taste, and treat the family to a new vegetable delight.

During the cooking process, the dull green milkweed will transform into a bright green, reminiscent of early spring, making it a colorful vegetable to add to casseroles. Try lining a baking dish with cooked milkweed pods, pouring a can of cream soup (mushroom, celery, chicken) over it, sprinkle with cracker crumbs, and bake at 350° until the soup bubbles, usually about half an hour.

Milkweed can be preserved by canning (follow the same instructions as for green beans) or by freezing, though freezing can be a little risky if there is any of the bitter agent still in the vegetable.

If, after your first taste, you do decide that maybe that milkweed intruder is worth keeping around, keep in mind that the plant does extremely well in overworked, undernourished soil. Couple that with a root system that just won't quit (spreading out as much as 15'), and you may want to do your milkweed raising along the fencerow or the back corner of your property.

In addition to being edible, milkweed has a handful of other properties which have gained it some respect in times past. The stout stalk yields strong fibers once used by the Indians for cloth, while the fluffy down from the seeds has stuffed many a pillow as well as World War II life preservers. Dried milkweed pods have found their way into numerous crafts and natural weed arrangements. Surely any plant which hosts the lovely Monarch butterfly has its merits.

CHINESE CABBAGE

What do you do with *Chinese cabbage?* The first is that you plant it in July in most of the country. Monica Brandies was moving in July, so Chinese cabbage, sometimes called celery cabbage, was one of the few vegetables that was planted at its proper time (Fig. 18-6).

She just scattered seeds over a small area in her small, intensive garden. Germination was fast and astounding. She had hundreds of little cabbage-like plants to give away, transplant to any available bare spot of 10 square inches, or let grow in the original patch. She tried to thin, but it was hard with the garden in full production and no animals to help, to use up all the thinnings.

In late fall, when lettuce was all gone, she used the crowded, still unheaded Chinese cabbage instead. You can also use the outside leaves as needed. They are wonderful as lettuce. One or two leaves line a large salad bowl.

The taste is much milder than regular cabbage, and the texture and color is more lettuce-like than cabbage-like. Torn up in a tossed salad, you can hardly tell the difference.

In the refrigerator you can. Lettuce lasts only about a week. Chinese cabbage will last for months.

Use the center ribs of celery cabbage interchangeably in recipes. True, cut into raw strips, there is a difference in taste and an absence of strings. If you put out a plate of carrots and Chinese cabbage strips, chances are both will disappear. The latter are also good spread with dips, cream cheese, or peanut butter.

If your family balks at the strong flavor of cabbage, or if you just want a change, try Chinese cabbage rolls, hot or cold slaw, lightly steamed and

Fig. 18-6. Chinese cabbage is sometimes called celery cabbage.

buttered chunks, or shredded and stir fried with onions.

Long after the lettuce is gone, Monica Brandies is still using Chinese cabbage, first fresh from the frosty garden, and then from the refrigerator, cold room, or covered pit in the garden. True, cabbage and celery both store well, too, but for intensive storage as well as intensive growing, you can't beat the one vegetable that stands in for any of three.

Spring crops of Chinese cabbage are not recommended because it takes cool weather to form the big, tightly wrapped heads. When you harvest down to a vacancy in your midsummer garden, plant some Chinese cabbage. You won't eat much until winter, but when other fresh vegetables are few and far between, you can use Chinese cabbage in more ways than three of your favorites to make winter meals tastier and more nutritious.

CABBAGE

Although regarded by some as a plebeian among the brassicas, *cabbage* has quite a number of things going for it (Fig. 18-7). It's generally easy to grow. There's no tying of leaves, no having to snatch at the fleeting moment of perfection or risk ruination, and fussing about endlessly. Just some fairly good soil, sunlight and abundant moisture, and king cole will produce very nicely. Add to these attributes the ease of storing, and you have a vegetable with a larger number of pluses.

Cabbage is usually grown in the summer and early fall in the North and in the fall and winter in the South, because cabbage grows faster, tastes better and is less prone to insect attack when grown in cooler weather. Allow about six weeks for growing the cabbage seedlings. Try to keep your

506

planting medium on the lean side, with about half soil and half sand or perlite. Save the compost for the garden when you are setting the plants out.

In keeping with most of the cole crops, cabbage seedlings should be grown at fairly low temperatures, say 55° to 65°F, and with a high intensity light. If grown at too high temperatures or with a lack of good light, they will be spindly and weak. For fall and winter cabbages, the seed can be planted right in the garden, and the plants will be stronger and better for it.

You can greatly extend the cabbage cutting season. There are varieties which mature in as little as 58 days. Midseason (or main crop) cabbages will take from 70 to 80 days, and the really long season types can dawdle upwards of 110 days.

You can also select cabbages as to size at maturity. Some of the midgets are only 1½ to 2 pounds, and you can grow the mediums, which go to 4 or 5 pounds. The later season cabbages may hit 10 or more pounds.

When making your selections, don't overlook the Savory varieties. They have excellent flavor and are beautiful to behold in the garden, as are the red cabbages. Both the Savoy and red cabbages seem somewhat more resistant to the cabbage looper than "regular" cabbages, all things being equal.

Fig. 18-7. Danish Round type cabbage grown in New York state (photo by Jean Martin).

There are a few cabbage pests and diseases to watch out for, especially in those crops grown during the warmer months. The cabbage worm and looper, thanks to bacillus thuringiensis (Bio Dust, Dipel, Thuricide), are rather easily dispatched. If you have been troubled in the past with the "yellows" disease of cabbage, grow the yellow-resistant varieties such as Golden Acre, Early Jersey Wakefield (pointed heads and excellent quality), Gourmet, Prime Pac, and others. Aphids, mainly a warm weather pest, may be controlled by the old standby: a soap and water spray.

Some of the other insects which may attack are the harlequin bug (which seems to prefer over-wintered plants) and the fall army worm. The army worm can be done in as per loopers and cabbage worms with Bio Dust. Cutworm damage can be kept to a bare minimum by wrapping wet tissue around the stems of the plants or by putting a can (with the top and bottom cut out) around each plant. Cut worms seem to run in cycles—bad one year and nary a one the next.

The flavor of cabbages seems to be directly related to the temperature and water supply during the growing season. The really high quality heads are those which mature either before really hot weather or in the late fall or early winter during the really cool or cold temperatures. Many people claim not to like cabbage because it tastes too strong, but the degree of difference between your own homegrown and those commonly bought at the supermarket are unbelievable.

If you have trouble with cabbages splitting in the garden, you probably have very good soil and a very abundant supply of water. To retard splitting, give the cabbage (those which have either reached or are about to reach maturity) a quarter turn to break some of the roots, and they will be put on "hold" for a couple of weeks. You can also accomplish this by cutting close to the plant with a shovel that has a narrow sharp blade. At any rate, the cabbage is still good to eat, split or not split.

In general, most of the roundheaded cabbages will store well if they are fully mature. Incidentally, if you prefer the green cabbages for cooking, there are some types available which both store well and have a large degree of green leaves. (Stokes Seed Co. has a good selection of these types.) The pointed heads (Jersey King and Early Jersey Wakefield) are excellent for immediate use, but are poor storers. The flattened heads (Flat Dutch) are good for kraut, as they have mainly white inner leaves which is an appealing color for kraut, as do some of the larger ball heads.

Cabbage can be used in many ways, as it is a very versatile vegetable. It teams well with bacon, caraway seeds or dillweed and is good with butter, in various dishes, soups and don't forget, sauerkraut, which can add vitamins to your winter table.

If you do not like sauerkraut, cabbage heads are stored fairly simply, but it's best not to keep them in a root cellar under the house, unless very well isolated from the rest of the house. Even if all the cabbages keep perfectly, the odors given off are not aromatic. The firm, mature heads will keep well into spring in a cool, damp spot, if they are handled gently when cut and laid one by one, not touching. They may be stripped of their outer leaves and hung up by the roots and allowed to "paper over," which retards spoiling and cuts down evaporation from the head.

CAULIFLOWER

Another member of the many-faceted brassica family, cauliflower seems to be rated queen over the rest. Maybe this high rating is because of its unusual appearance, perhaps because of the almost magical growth of the large head from the small "button," or perhaps it's simply because the cauliflower has the reputation for being somewhat difficult to grow.

Like its cousins cabbage and broccoli, cauliflower needs a rich soil, cool weather, and adequate moisture. It will not stand weather below freezing as cabbage and broccoli will, if they have been acclimated to it gradually.

It will stand somewhat hotter weather when still quite small without detriment, though. Direct-seeded, summer-planted cauliflower in the garden will stand up under the fiercest heat, if given adequate water. Hot weather during heading will either make the crop fail or, at best, turn out heads of inferior quality. So you must time your crop to either mature before they very hot weather settles down to stay, or plan your fall crop to mature well ahead of very cold weather.

Almost any kind of cauliflower seed offered for home gardeners has the word "snowball" in it, except for the purple kinds, and most are well-suited for the organic garden. A few varieties are extra early, which means you can gain as much as two weeks on harvesting. If you are growing cauliflower plants inside, they should be started about six weeks before you expect to transplant them to the garden, which is normally a couple of weeks after cabbage due to their propensity toward freezing more easily. Two feet apart is about the right spacing.

If you grow a fall crop of transplants right in the garden, they will probably be ready in slightly less time, because of faster germination and growth due to warm temperatures. If you have grown the plants outside, be sure to check them as you transplant for "blind" plants, those which have had the center leaf bud eaten or fail to develop. Any plants with this defect should be discarded, as they will never form a head.

If you feel that the soil where you are growing your crop isn't rich enough, a half a shovelful of rotted manure or compost should do a world of good. A nitrogen-rich supplement, such as blood meal or cottonseed meal, is an excellent choice, too, for its slow release of needed nutrients.

While plants will need adequate moisture all through their growing season, they will need an extra amount when the head is forming. If moisture is not supplied by rainfall, irrigate the plants when the leaves are first tied up and then every few days until the head has fully formed.

When do you tie up the leaves? When the head is about as large as a half dollar, you can loosely tie the leaves over the "button" head or snap them over it. If you choose the latter, use the inner leaves as much as possible, as these larger leaves will supply food to the developing heads. The cauliflower may form a head in as little as six days or so, or it may take 2½ weeks in cool weather. Generally, the warmer and more moist the soil and air, the faster the heads form.

If you should have insect damage on the cauliflower leaves, try to get rid of the insects rapidly, as plants with severely damaged leaves will not make very large heads. The two most common pests are cabbage loopers and aphids. The loopers and other worms can be dispatched by *Bacillus thuringiensis* (Biodust, Thuricide, Dipel), and a soap spray will take care of the aphids, which usually occur in hot, dry weather anywhere.

Cutworms may be bad in the early spring. Either take cans with top and bottoms cut out and place around the newly planted cauliflower, or wrap several wraps of wet tissue around the stem, making sure that it will reach about 1" above and below the ground level. These two devices will foil the cutworms.

When the cauliflower heads are ready (and you can press through the leaves to see or untie one), harvest fairly soon, as the heads will lose quality rather rapidly, especially with a spring-planted crop. If the weather is quite warm, the heads will have a tendency to "rice out," or spread. Spreading will cause the flavor to deteriorate and sometimes will cause the heads to darken to a brownish color.

If you don't want to blanch, you can grow the purple varieties, but they should be cut soon after maximum head size is reached, too. The best way to preserve the quality of cauliflower is by freezing, as all varieties freeze well. The heads will keep a couple of weeks in a root cellar. Some gardeners like to keep them up to a month by placing in damp sand and keeping them in a cool place.

LETTUCE

Lettuce is easily grown from seed planted directly in the garden (Fig. 18-8). It will germinate in quite cold soil and stand quite snippy frosts, faring better in the cool temperatures than in the hot sunny days of summer. During the late summer when germination is difficult because of hot ground temperatures, soak the seed in a cup of water for a week or so and blot with a paper towel. Then plant, keeping it constantly moist. Dampen a paper towel and sprinkle the seeds in it. Roll it up and place it in the refrigerator. The seed will then germinate quickly, inspite of the heat.

There are several distinct types of lettuce. The leaf, or nonheading, type is the most easily grown, but the stem lettuce (also called *celtuce*) is easy, too. Incidentally, celtuce is grown for the stem rather than the leaves. The butterhead types have soft, small leaves which form a loose head of excellent quality, but this variety has a tendency to bolt to seed in hot weather, and doesn't need much heat to do so. The cabbagehead lettuces are the most commonly offered for sale in the supermarket and may weigh a couple of pounds or more. The last type is *cos* or *romaine*, and it grows tall,

Fig. 18-8. Lettuce is one of the first vegetables that can be planted in the garden.

somewhat like a head of Chinese cabbage, and has loosely headed, elongated leaves.

Rich soil which will retain moisture is good for lettuce, yet the soil should be well-drained. Lettuce likes neutral soil, and prefers a loam with plenty of humus, especially the cabbageheads. Additions to the soil should be along the nitrogen line, as lettuce is quite a heavy feeder. Blood, kelp, or cottonseed meals are all good as is well rotted compost.

When you purchase a packet of lettuce seed, you really get a bargain, as you are buying enough seed for plants to fill about 100' row. Keep in mind the time requirements of the various varieties to avoid disappointment. The leaf varieties will mature in as little as 40 days, but the cabbageheads need 90 days or more. Leaf lettuces, especially Oakleaf, will stand a lot of heat before turning bitter, especially if given ample water and shade during the hottest part of the day.

Lettuce seed should be planted ¼" deep, slightly deeper in the late summer, and thinned early. The excess small plants may be transplanted to another row, taking care to keep the tap roots straight. If you garden in an area where spring is long, you can probably plant three or four times to keep the lettuce supply coming all summer, especially if you use the heat-resistant varieties in the last two plantings.

Lettuce does have a few enemies. Cutworms will damage new plantings, especially those of the heading sorts, but a few wraps of wet tissue around the stem will deter this pest. Slugs and snails may be discouraged by sprinkling wood ashes or sharp sand around the plants. In very wet weather, lettuce rot can invade the lower leaves and then spread upward to the rest of

511

the head. If you live in a moist area or have had trouble with this rot, try hilling up the rows slightly to allow for good drainage and allowing an extra few inches between plants, especially the cabbageheads. Some of the larger of these should be spaced about 16″ to 18″ apart. This wide spacing will not only deter rot, but also the slugs.

Leaf lettuce may be used any time you feel that the leaves are large enough. They may be picked one at a time or the whole plant may be cut. Cos and heading types should be firm to the grasp for maximum harvest. Lettuce is usually best picked in the cool of the morning, washed, and put into the refrigerator in a plastic bag.

Vitamins abound in leaf lettuces and in the outer leaves of the heading types. Leaf varieties contain about 2,000 units of vitamin A, smaller amounts of the B vitamins, and most minerals in small amounts. The heading types have a small amount of the A and B vitamins, but about the same amount of minerals.

ONIONS

Probably no vegetable, with the possible exception of tomatoes, is used in so many recipes or eaten raw along with so many foods. *Onions* are rather unique in one respect. We lump them with the root crops, but their culture more closely resembles the leaf crops, as they need rich soil and lots of moisture but good drainage. Nutrients should be in the top 10″ or 12″ of soil as onions are rather shallow rooted.

With the addition of well-rotted manure or compost to the soil at planting time, you can kill the proverbial "two birds with one stone," because organic material will slowly release the needed nutrients. The soil will hold moisture as a result. If you lack the manure, try adding blood or cottonseed meal when you plant.

Onions may be grown from seed, sets, plants, or from top sets. Be sure the seed is *very* fresh, as onion seed deteriorates very rapidly, usually losing its vitality after a year. The sets and plants will make good large onions for drying, if they are not overly large to begin with. The plants shouldn't be larger than a thin pencil and the sets no larger than a dime.

The extra large sets or plants usually make "stiff necks"—a bulb which will not cure or keep well. You can use these extra biggies for green onions, but they are a disaster for long storage.

The top sets are normally shallots, the aristocrats of the allium family, and make a cluster of small onions similar to garlic. Either the top sets or a clove from the underground cluster may be planted, although the smaller top sets may not always mature the first year into the expected cluster unless conditions are excellent.

Spring is the usual onion planting time in the North, and fall and winter in the South. The onion foliage needs a fairly cool environment, but the bulb needs both warmer temperatures and longer daylight hours to mature.

Onions are among the few plants which are sensitive to light for bulb formation or blooming. Bermuda and Creole need about 12 hours of daylight to mature their bulbs, making them a popular variety for southern locations during the winter months. *Ebenezer*, a popular onion set variety, needs somewhat longer days. Red onions require the most light of all, needing 14 to 15 hours or so. Keep light requirements in mind when purchasing plants, sets, or seed to avoid disappointment.

When the onions are about 1' or so tall, take care not to let the soil dry out completely. If this happens the bulb, instead of being one, may form a split, often with a seed stalk coming from the center between the two bulbs. If you use extra fertilization, do so when the bulb is first beginning to form and keep that soil moist.

In southern climates, when hot weather settles in earnest and some of the tops of the plants begin to fall over, you can speed up the process by bending the rest down with the back of a rake or by stepping on them lightly. Usually in northerly latitudes, the onions will be drying by fall.

In either case, if possible, leave the onions in the ground until all the tops are dry. If the weather gets rainy, pull all the onions immediately to avoid regrowth and hang them in a covered location.

If there is no unexpected deluge, pull the onions and let them sun for half a day or so. Cull the splits and "stiff necks," and use them first as they don't store well. Braid remaining onion tops together if the bulbs are not too large and hang in a cool, dry place. Extra whoppers have the tendency to break loose from the tops and drop to the floor with a resounding "thud." The large onions are better stored in open-mesh bags. In either case, onions require cool, dry storage where temperatures stay above freezing.

BEETS

Consider the *beet*. Here are two vegetables in one. The tops, when used small, make a delicious green, and the root may be fixed a dozen different ways.

Beets, at least the common varieties, have many different seeds in the one brown corky-looking seed, so even though you swear you planted them evenly, they persist in coming up in bunches. Some of the vegetables that you thin must be thrown onto the compost pile, but you can leave the beets in place until they are a usable size for greens without detriment to the others growing nearby.

You can choose from many different varieties. The old standby is Detroit Dark Red, and the more modern Burpee's Golden. They are not difficult to grow and mature rather quickly. Two vital factors are humus-rich soil and plenty of moisture. A poor, dry soil will cause poor flavor and maybe a bit of string in the beet.

Like others of the root family, beets like a friable, loose soil with a pH tending toward the alkaline side. Potash is needed, but plenty of mature compost should take care of that, with perhaps a sprinkling of wood ashes. If you are growing a fall crop, probably no new fertilizer will be needed.

If you soak the seeds overnight, they will germinate more quickly and come up more evenly. Beet pests seem to be minimal, so probably you won't have to be concerned with protection from insects.

When the plants are large enough, you realize your first bonus—greens. They can be cooked in any way other greens can be, as with bacon bits, butter, vinegar, a-la-Chinese stir fried, and others. This is one time it will pay you to thin considerably. The more you thin, the more room is left for the developing roots.

Hill the remaining beets up somewhat to keep the tops of the roots from becoming rough and black looking, which doesn't hurt the flavor but is merely a question of looks. The roots will mature in about 50 to 80 days, depending upon variety chosen. This could be a factor in fall or in a crop which must mature before summer's heat, so choose accordingly, but whatever variety you do choose, you can enjoy two crops—greens and roots.

POTATOES

Potatoes are generally grown from pieces of the tuber having "eyes" or buds, but they also can be grown from seeds formed on fruits above the ground. Seeds are normally used for research and potato breeding work.

Flower production and seed formation occur only when the plants have ideal growing conditions, with especially cool temperatures. That happened this summer in many places and aroused the curiosity of gardeners who had not seen potato seeds before.

The potato fruit resembles a small tomato. Most seed balls contain from 100 to 300 mature seeds. The seeds resemble miniature tomato seeds without fuzz.

After storing for a few months, the seeds will germinate and grow readily. Each of the small seedling plants constitutes a potential new variety. Small tubers form and can be harvested within three to four months if growing temperatures are cool and light intensities are high.

BEANS

Beans come in many different colors, shapes, and sizes, bush or pole, and they are all delicious when picked at the proper time. In comparison with many other vegetables, they are fairly drought resistant, and freeze and can well. You can make old timey "leather britches", stringing them through with coarse thread and hanging to dry.

One of Judi Blucher's favorites is *Royal Burgundy Purple Pod,* which not only germinates well in cool soil, but turns an attractive green when cooked. It is touted for resistance to the bean beetle.

Another favorite is *Greensleeves* which outyielded all other varieties and was more resistant to aphids. The flat bean *Roma* is another good bean when eaten fresh and canned, but it seems to get rather mushy when frozen. *Topcrop* is a longtime favorite of Judi's, but its color is not first class when canned. Both *Kentucky Wonder* and *Old Dutch Half Runner* are favorites in the south, but again, neither is a real good freezer. *Pinto* is very good in flavor for a green snap bean when small, but doesn't freeze well. It also has a tendency to get rust and mildew easily if the weather is damp.

514

Of the yellows, *Brittle Wax* is a good variety. Judi believes yellow beans never taste as "beany" as the greens.

Culturally, beans are a snap and are simply planted in a furrow about 1½" deep, covered with soil, and tamped down lightly. Do not tamp heavily. The beans will have trouble emerging and simply snap their heads off in the process! You will then have a row of bare stems for your trouble.

Space the beans about 4" or 5" apart, especially the later plantings, as this cuts the need to water somewhat. If you feel that your planting may have trouble emerging, use soil and mix some sand, compost, or vermiculite with it and cover with that.

As far as insects are concerned, you can dust with that old standby, *rotenone*, which is nontoxic to warm blooded animals. With the larger spacing of the plants, you can hand pick the insects if you want, as they are more easily spotted. With the plants spaced out and not touching each other, the mildews and rusts do not spread so easily if the weather turns damp and rainy. If you get aphids in large numbers, you can usually kill them by using about two cups of Ivory soap jelly (made by grating the bar soap into water and boiling until melted) in a gallon of water, and spraying this upon the leaves, especially the undersides where they lurk.

Beans can be planted every 10 days or so for a continuous supply, at least in most locations. Sometimes it gets too hot and the beans will drop their blossoms instead of setting fruit. If you don't know which varieties do well in your locale, try your local extension agent if he is knowledgeable, or a local gardener.

As is true of so many vegetables, beans do mature rapidly under favorable weather influence (warm, damp, and sunny) and should be checked daily for best results. Most of the new varieties are stringless and fiberless when young, a far cry from the old "stringy bean" of yesteryear, with the exceptions being those normally planted for the dry bean, such as *pinto, kidney,* and *navy.*

TOMATOES

In a recent Gallup poll, *tomatoes* were found to be the vegetable most grown by gardeners. (Green beans were second.) This finding would seem to indicate an ease of cultivation and a sure harvest, but the tomato can be cranky, sulky, petulant and, at times, totally unpredictable. To better understand why the tomato grows and acts as it does and why it demands certain conditions to yield well, let's drop back into history and see where and how this curious fruit first originated.

History of the Tomato

The botanical group to which the tomato belongs (genus *Lycopersicon*) was believed to have been native to South America. In comparison to many other common garden vegetables, the tomato is a relative newcomer on the scene, as it was first described in European horticultural books in the late 1600s.

515

How did it get to Europe? Evidently (but this is just supposition), it meandered into the more northern countries of South America, into Mexico, from there to the Mediterranean region, and finally to northern Europe, conceivably through Spain. At this time, and for a long time thereafter, the tomato was grown as an ornamental curiosity. Although it seems ludicrous, the tomato was regarded as poisonous, perhaps because the family to which it belongs (*Solananceae*) contains some highly poisonous members, including Jimson weed and belladonna. This belief, no doubt, slowed its acceptance as a food. At one time, though, it was regarded as an aphrodisiac, as the name *pomme d'amour*—love apple—indicates.

Finally, in the middle of the 19th century, some brave soul discovered that the tomato had been slandered. Not only was it not poisonous, but it was very tasty and could be used in many ways. This early tomato, however, bore scant resemblance to our large, luscious beauties of today, as they were thin-walled, rough and irregular shaped, and sometimes had a few wrinkles thrown in for good measure.

A gentleman by the name of Livingston was one of the early pioneers in tomato culture. He worked about 20 years before developing a variety which he named Paragon. From this simple beginning, there are now more than 400 tomato varieties, with new ones being added every year. For a while, plant breeders got completely away from the wild cultivars, and so lost some of the natural immunity of the plant to various diseases. Soon breeders realized the worth of such charactersitics, though, and again went to the native species.

So what does their work have to do with your garden? A lot, for without the work of the plant geneticists, our tomatoes would not have the varying sizes, colors, disease resistance, crack-resistance, the qualities of setting fruit in excessively hot weather, sun scald resistance and a lot of other special traits. Our national favorite, the tomato, would be just that much more arduous to cultivate.

Selecting Varieties

The primary concern of most gardeners is the use to which they intend to put their tomatoes. So ask yourself a few questions. Is canning your goal, or do you simply want a goodly supply of slicing tomatoes to eat fresh? Maybe you need a good supply of tomato paste and sauce for Italian and Mexican foods. Do you use a lot of catsup? What other personal requirements do you have? What problems have you encountered in previous gardens? Do you have late frosts, a short growing season, disease troubles, nematodes or insects? Are the tomatoes to be caged, staked, sprawling, mulched, irrigated, or to rely on natural rain patterns?

After you have asked and answered these and any other questions you consider pertinent to your situation, *then* turn to the seed catalogs. Select a variety that will meet your needs and grow in your locale's environment.

Disease Problems

Lumpy, gnarled roots on nonlegume plants probably mean nematode damage. Select varieties marked "N" in the catalogs. Wilting plants usually mean verticillium and/or fusarium wilts. Use "V" and "F" marked seed.

Physiological Problems

These problems are usually caused by stress of some type, mostly that of weather. Blossom end rot, a rather common defect, is brought about by too tittle water followed by too much. Try keeping a fairly even supply of moisture available to the plants. A lack of calcium is thought to aggravate this situation, so correct the deficiency if necessary. (Apply ground limestone the fall before planting.)

Leaf roll is not caused by disease, but by too much moisture. Sometimes pruning too much foliage from the plants, especially when tying tomatoes to a single stake, cause this problem. The obvious solution is to leave more foliage on the plant.

Too little foliage can cause fruit scald, a type of tomato sunburn. The scalded place turns white or yellow and never does ripen properly. It may become dry and scaly, and you lose part of each tomato with this defect. Keep, especially in hot climates, sufficient foliage to shade fruits at least during the hottest part of the day. The only exception to this rule would be removing a large portion of the foliage to expedite ripening in late fall to avoid freeze damage.

"Zippers" and "catfacing" are generally caused by imperfect splitting of the blossom from very minute fruits. It will happen during the cooler, sometimes wet weather of early spring.

Abnormally small fruit can be caused by lack of moisture in the soil. It used to be thought that it was caused only by planting tomatoes too closely, but experiments have shown close spacing causes only fewer tomatoes, not smaller ones.

Quality of fruit will vary from site to site. A difference of as little as one mile can make a difference in the taste and flesh of a tomato. All factors which contribute to total tomato growth will influence its quality to some degree.

Blossom dropping can be caused by temperatures that are too cool or too hot. A prolonged August heat wave may cause drop, as will an early spring cold snap. If you have a problem with either, plant varieties which withstand such stress. If weather has not been abnormal, be sure your plants are receiving enough water and phosphorus, as a lack of either will cause the abscission layer to form—the death knell to tomatoes. The blossom then wilts slightly and drops.

Crack resistance has been bred into tomato varieties, so, if you have "gully washers" during your normal tomato ripening season, try to plant at least some which are resistant to splitting.

Length of growing season is an important factor to consider, too. If you have but a short season, consider determinate tomato types which mature most of their fruit at the same time, sometimes in as little as two weeks. Indeterminate varieties, on the other hand, keep growing and setting tomatoes and can produce fruit until frost, if not halted by disease or drought.

Direct sunlight is not necessary to ripen tomatoes. Leaf miners, which leave odd little "trails" in the leaves, rarely do any harm; they just look bad. Avoid walking among or picking tomatoes when wet with dew or rain to avoid spreading disease.

Staking Tomato Plants

Years of experience has taught Jesse (Jack) Sunderland, retired St. Albans, Vermont high school principal and grower of tomatoes for commercial markets, that there is a direct relationship between the care given tomato plants and the resulting yield. After much experimentation, he has perfected a unique system of staking tomatoes for his 700 to 800 plants (Fig. 18-9).

"It seems like considerable labor," he says, "but it pays off with a minimum of care during the growing season—good ripening, easy harvesting, and clean fruit. Practically no tomato ever touches the ground."

Jack uses one 6' stake for every two plants. With used baling twine, obtained at no cost, he runs the first string tightly from stake to stake about 10" to 12" above the ground from one end of the row to the other. On the return he strings the same twine in a half-hitch knot each side of the tomato stalk. This holds the plant up, but still gives it a couple of inches for movement and expansion.

As the plant grows and is suckered—about every 10 days—a second line is strung about 10" above the first. This time the string is woven from one side of a plant to the opposite side of the next, then around the stake and continued thus for the remainder of the row. The return twine catches the plant on the opposite side. This process is repeated every two weeks or so until the mature plant is supported with five to six rows of twine.

Long ago Jack was advised by an extension service agent to plant tomatoes in rows running north to south in order for the fruit to receive maximum sunlight. Plants should be at least 30" apart in rows 4½' apart.

After the ground has warmed thoroughly, he lays 18" strips of black plastic mulch on both sides close to each row of plants and generously beds them with early-cut swale (low grade hay). The hay and plastic smother practically all weed growth and help conserve soil moisture. The hay is eventually plowed into the ground to provide additional humus.

OKRA

Most seed catalogs treat *okra* most unkindly. It is usually delegated to the "good in soups and stews" category. Okra, member of the hibiscus family and, therefore, closely related to cotton, requires much the same cultural technique as cotton itself. It requires, most importantly, warm soil for germination. It can stand a lot of moisture and still germinate without rotting, but only if the soil has really warmed up.

There are six varieties of okra. Clemson Spineless is a popular, tall-growing okra, as are Emerald, Green Velvet, White Velvet and Red. Dwarf Green Pod is a much smaller growing variety, but it bears a crop somewhat sooner than the others. Red, incidentally, turns a dark green when cooked, and White Velvet is really a very pale green, but both are beautiful growing in the garden.

Planting okra is a simple task. Each packet of seed will plant about 15' of row, and the seed is scattered rather thickly in ½" furrows. (If the soil is quite dry, you might want to water the furrow for faster germination.) Cover and tamp down. In a few days your okra should emerge. There's not much advantage in early planting, as the seeds rot easily in cold soil. If by chance the plants do emerge, they will sit and shiver and probably turn a yellowish-green due to the cold.

The soil for okra should be moderately rich and well drained. Too heavy and poorly drained soil will result in root rot, a devastating disease in which the plant suddenly wilts. When you pull it up to see what happened, the root has turned into a slimy mass of nothing. About the only other real problem okra experiences is nematode damage. Rotate the crop if this problem has been noted. Stink bugs do occasional damage, but their sting only results in a somewhat deformed pod, and usually in no great numbers.

Fig. 18-9. Jack Sunderland shows how he stakes over 700 tomato plants each year (photo by Harriet Dworshak).

Watch your okra plants carefully after the first blooms appear, which can be in as little as 50 days after planting, for probably no vegetable matures in such a short time given the right conditions. The minute pod will be seen under the wilting blossom at the end of the day as the blossoms drop from the plants. (The blossoms are a beautiful cream color with a dark maroon throat.)

For true succulence, the okra pods should be no longer than 3", although some of the varieties grown especially for slicing are still quite good at 5" and 6"—if grown with plenty of moisture. The pods are easily snapped off from the plant. Place them gently into the picking container. Okra is a tender vegetable and should be so treated.

So what do you do with your harvest? In lieu of the seed catalog's suggestion, try slicing and tossing it lightly with cornmeal, then frying it until brown. Steam it with a minimum of water (to avoid the slimy aspect of the vegetable when overcooked in water). Okra gumbo, a combination of lightly fried okra and bacon diced and browned with onion, green pepper and tomatoes, is excellent with or without seafood or chicken pieces. Another unusual way of serving okra, is steamed okra with cider vinegar and freshly ground black pepper.

Even if you go on a short vacation and come back to okra with woody pods, don't throw them away. Allow them to dry, and shell out the seeds. Roast the seeds, then whiz them in a blender for a substitute for perk coffee—a tried and true substitute in the South during the Civil War when real coffee was unavailable. Naturally, you can dry okra slices or even the pods rather easily and add them to soup during the winter.

So do try okra. Other than picking it often to keep the blossoms coming and soaking it occasionally when rain fails, okra will keep on producing until fall. During blistering heat when other vegetables drop all their blossoms or simply wilt away, okra staunchly stands all summer and on into the fall. Besides, it has a good amount of all the important minerals, a fair amount of vitamin A and is low in calories, more good reasons for adding it to your vegetable favorites.

GREENS

It's spring and you can't wait for the taste of something fresh? How about greens? Do you like spinach, mustard, tendergreen, collards, chard, and turnip greens? If you opt for the mustard or turnip greens, you can have them on the table in 40 to 50 days, with minimal weather cooperation. With the exceptions of set-planted green onions and radishes, nothing will normally mature more rapidly.

As with all leafy crops, any greens will appreciate a rich soil and abundant moisture. In the spring, moisture will probably not be a problem. Lacking a ready plot, try using blood meal freely for fertilizer and mixing it with the soil.

After you have made your furrow (a wide one), generously sprinkle the seeds and cover them with about ¼" of soil. Plant chard slightly deeper.

Mustard greens, tendergreen, and turnip greens all usually leap out of the soil in about four days or less, if conditions are right. Spinach, chard, and collards are a bit more tardy and may take 10 days to two weeks to show.

All of these greens can stand some frost, so don't be afraid to plant a couple of weeks before the frost-free date, or even earlier than that if you are a gambler.

When the weather is still quite cool, the insects are usually at a minimum, something certainly not true later in the summer. If you should notice nibbles in the leaves, the cabbage looper has probably struck.

Bacillus thuringiensis, known under the brand names of Dipel, Bio Dust, and Thuricide, is an excellent biological dust or spray and will kill only leaf-eating plant pests. The worms soon turn yellow, a sickly gray, black, and then die.

If you planted the seeds thickly, you can use the baby greens in any number of ways when you thin. Try them stir-fried, steamed, with bacon bits or butter, chopped in a salad, or served with vinegar, or perhaps the "deep in Dixie" way, with "pot liquor" and white bacon bits.

When summer really arrives and your greens start to turn strong-tasting, pull them and either offer them to the various live-stock or put them in the compost pile. Leaving them past their prime in a hot, dry situation will probably call for attacks by various insects, which is something you can do without. After pulling, plant some warm weather varieties in their place.

SWEET PEPPERS

There are many diverse kinds, shapes, and hues of peppers (Fig. 18-10). In the North, selection may be somewhat limited by maturity dates so as to avoid the frustration of the plant being demolished by frost. Growing peppers successfully in cooler climates has been made easier in the last several years by the introduction of varieties which ripen in just over 60 days. Some of these varieties include Early Ace Hybrid, Peter Piper Hybrid, Merrimack Wonder, and Trueheart Pimento.

In southern regions or in areas with long growing seasons, just about any pepper will do well. The Yolo Wonder is fine because of its extra heavy foliage which protects the fruit from sunscald. Others which produce prolifically in warm regions are Sweet Banana, Sweet Cherry, Aconcagua (a cubanelle type) and, that old standard of perfection, California Wonder. Most of the time these peppers will produce a good crop in early summer, go into a semi-dormant state in the really hot weather of late July and August, and then produce again under the urgings of late summer and early fall rains.

Peppers require little in the way of nutrients, but excel in soil enriched with compost. Chemically-minded friends have bemoaned the fact that their peppers are producing all foliage and few peppers. They blame the weather, bad plants, seeds and whatever, when in reality all the plants need is a good shovel full of compost or well-rotted cow manure.

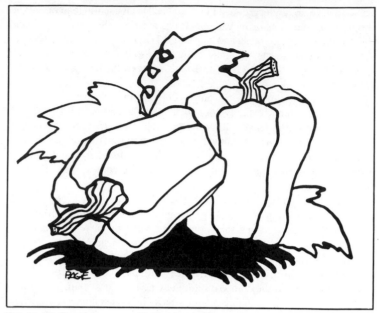

Fig. 18-10. There are many kinds of peppers.

If you have wanted to grown your own plants but have had trouble with germination, try these tricks. Soak the seeds at least 48 hours, and keep them in a warm place—above the water heater, on the water reservoir, on a wood burning cookstove, or other source of mild heat.

Use a seedling mix of somewhat more organic material than usual, adding peat moss or leaf mold up to about a third of the whole mixture. After planting the seeds about ¼" deep and soaking them thoroughly, cover the pots or flats with plastic wrap. Tape the wrap tightly or use a rubber band to secure it. Keep this cover in place until you see two or three plants emerging, and then remove immediately.

Peppers need some strong light during the seedling stage, but don't seem to be nearly as prone to "legginess" as eggplants and tomatoes. It sometimes seems as if they aren't growing at all, but suddenly they hit a period when they take off and make sturdy little plants.

If you live quite far north and have had no success with peppers due to the short growing season, try this. Start your peppers about one month earlier than usual, using the previously mentioned directions. Instead of planting the peppers in a little pot, however, use 5" or 6" clay pots and keep the little peppers inside until the weather is warm and settled. Dig about half a bucket of cow manure, other "cold" manure or compost into the site, and mix well with the soil.

This head start should give the plants the decided edge needed. Lacking the compost or manure, try to use the most sheltered and sandiest or lightest soil in the garden. All these ploys will speed up the date of harvest.

When ready to plant the smaller-sized, six- or eight-week old plants, use a spacing of about 18″ and protect the peppers from the eager cutworms by means of paper collars, cans, or cloches. If the peppers were not potted individually and have had their root systems disturbed, shade them from the sun for a few days. This protection is also a good idea if the plants were greenhouse grown, as they will be somewhat more tender than your own homegrown ones, and the foliage will sometimes sunburn badly if the weather is extra dry and sunny.

Peppers set the optimum amount of fruit with temperatures of 65° to 80°F. Temperatures too much higher or lower will cause many of the blossoms to drop or the plant to set small fruits and then drop them after a couple of weeks. Water the plants moderately and mulch with straw, dried grass clippings, or leaves mixed with other material which are less likely to pack.

Harvest the peppers when they are heavy and shiny, with a color characteristic of their variety. Bell peppers may be left to turn red on the plant, greatly increasing their vitamin C content. The taste change is very noticeable, gaining sweetness.

Any variety of sweet pepper can be used for freezing by simply chopping, slicing, or cutting in strips—no blanching needed. If you are fond of stuffed peppers, simply cut the top off the whole pepper, remove the seeds, and freeze. Peppers are also good pickled using many common pickling solutions and can also be easily dried for quick additions to winter meals.

GARLIC: THE WONDER HERB

One can hardly pronounce the word without "feeling" the aroma of this potent herb. A perennial of the lily family, garlic has been used for thousands of years for food and medicine (Fig. 18-11). Admittedly, the pungent odor is overcoming to most people, but fortunately the renewed interest in natural health care is encouraging many to sample its effects.

It is reputed to offer miraculous healing powers to sufferers of respiratory infections and ailments, as well as to those suffering from hypertension, worm infestations, intestinal putrefaction, flatulence, liver ailments, and skin disorders. Garlic stimulates digestion, aids in the absorption of vitamin B_1, and helps to alleviate both constipation and diarrhea. It is also an antiseptic of good quality. Its power seems to be very closely related to its "delightful" aroma (allyl disulfate). It has been said that this oil contains about one-tenth the strength of penicillin. Unlike penicillin and other drugs, it does not destroy the beneficial bacteria along with the harmful.

Garlic can be applied directly to the skin for various ailments such as athlete's foot, wounds, or abscesses. It can be mashed and held on the area with gauze and changed as it dries.

At the onset of cold symptoms, place a garlic clove in the mouth on both sides and leave for several hours; thereafter, renew with fresh garlic. If applied early, less than one day should be substantial treatment. This method is also helpful for toothaches.

One method of taking garlic internally (which lessens the resulting smell), is to take a drink of water, place the peeled, sliced garlic in the mouth, and drink enough water to wash it down. If one teaspoon of fresh lemon juice is added to the water, the odor seems to leave even more quickly. This method helps to reduce contact with the mouth and lessens the lingering odor. Also, if parsley is chewed after eating garlic, the chlorophyll will help to dispel the pungent odors. Garlic can be purchased in the form of "perles" and in compressed tablets.

You can use domestic garlic (*Allium sativum*), as well as the wild (*A. canadense*) and field garlic (*A. vineale*). The latter two you'll find in most fields, and the *A. sativum* is both easy to cultivate and helpful in repelling garden pests. Planted around the outside of your garden, it tends to discourage rabbits, mice, and moles. Plant it with carrots to discourage the

Fig. 18-11. Garlic is a perennial of the lily family.

carrot fly and with fruit trees to discourage borers. It's useful against aphids in your lettuce and roses and helps control blight in tomato and potato patches. Garlic can also be made into a spray for infestations of aphids and other insects.

CHAMOMILE

There always seems to be confusion when this name is mentioned or referred to by herbalists. Some think of only one plant when seeing *chamomile* or *camomile*; however, the name is used for a number of species in at least six genera. For the sake of simplification, this discussion will be limited to the two most important, *Anthemis nobilis* (Roman Chamomile) and *Matricaria chamomilla* (German Chamomile). Each of these is distinct and fairly easy to distinguish. Generally speaking, the plants are used interchangeably, with a few exceptions noted.

Description

A. nobilis is a low-growing perennial with creeping or trailing habits. The deeply divided leaves are alternate and about 1" to 2" in length, with somewhat hairy, gray-green segments which give it a feathery appearance. The terminal flower heads appear on erect stems. The center or receptacle is solid and conical with tiny chaffy scales appearing between the florets. The deep yellow color of the disk contrasts with the creamy white ray flowers which appear in later summer. Cultivated varieties have double flowers which are larger and whiter than the single flowered wild variety. The entire herb is strongly scented with an apple aroma. It occurs wild in western and southern Europe and is quite common in England, where it was probably first cultivated. It is also frequently found in the United States.

M. chamomilla is an annual herb which grows to be several feet in height. The leaves are also alternate, but not as deeply divided, and they appear to be coarser. As with *A. nobilis*, the flowers are daisylike, but are more numerous and smaller in size. They seem to appear in groups as compared to the solitary flowers of *A. nobilis*. The receptacle is more elongated than conical and is hollow and does not have the scales found on *A. nobilis*. It occurs throughout Europe and the United States. This species was known to the Greeks, and the name Chamomile was derived from the Greek words *Khamai* (on the ground) and *Melon* (apple).

Qualities and Uses

To make an infusion or tea, add 1 ounce of flower heads to a pint of boiling water and allow to steep covered for at least 10 minutes. This *tisane* is a very effective *nervine* and is especially soothing just before bedtime. It is also said to prevent nightmares. The high calcium content is probably responsible for the pain relieving and soothing effects received from drinking an infusion. In strong doses it acts as an *emetic*. The active principle in *A. nobilis* is anthemic acid, which is an aromatic bitter useful as a carminative and as a stomachic and tonic. When drunk cold after meals, it aids in reducing or preventing flatulence. Chamomile also stimulates digestive juices and is valuable in cases of poor digestion or during convalescence. *M. chamomilla* seems to be best for this use.

One of chamomile's earliest uses was for various childhood ailments including colic, digestive distress, and convulsions. Combined with catnip tea, it soothes and calms restless babies and reduces irritabilities and similar ailments during the teething period. As is suggested by its name (*Matrix*—Latin meaning "the womb"), *M. chamomilla* seems to benefit females. As an emmenagogue it promotes the menstrual flow in suppressed cases, and it also acts as an antispasmodic to relieve cramps. When taken after childbirth, it is said to cleanse and strengthen the uterus, as well as to relieve uterus pain during nursing.

To relieve tired muscle aches and pains, pour a strong infusion into a hot bath, climb in, and relax a while. This is especially beneficial if you are sipping a cup of tea. A somewhat weak infusion is soothing as an eye wash. It was also once used to treat scarlet fever and as a disinfecting mouthwash. Another use for the tea is as an insect repellent. The tea is sponged or poured on the body and allowed to dry. This seems to be very helpful for animals with fleas. For cases of inflammation, abscesses, psoriasis, eczema and similar skin conditions, moisten the dried heads with hot water and apply as a poultice.

Oil of chamomile acts as a stimulating massage for swollen or painful muscles or joints. It can also be warmed and used as eardrops. To prepare, take a pint of vegetable oil (preferably cold pressed) and add 2 ounces of dried leaves and/or flowers. Placing in a stainless steel or glass container, gently simmer for about an hour. Remove from heat and leave covered overnight. It is then ready to strain and use or bottle.

For medicinal purposes, *M. chamomilla* is now the only chamomile in the United States recognized as official. The French insist that it makes the most pleasant and efficacious tea. *Matricaria* flowers are used in Spain to flavor a sherry known as *Manzanilla* or "little apple." An extract of the flowers of *M. chamomilla* are also frequently used as a hair rinse to bring out delicate highlights in blonds. *A. nobilis* is also used, but does not seem to be as effective.

As a ground cover, *A. nobilis* is definitely a better choice, since it is low-growing and a perennial. The English utilize this plant well as an excellent ground cover on banks and other places not as suitable for grass planting. When walked upon or mowed, it releases its applelike essence.

In years past, *A. nobilis* was known as "the plant's physician." It seemed to help other plants prosper when planted among them. It was also said that a drooping plant would "perk up" whem chamomile was planted beside it.

M. chamomilla, according to the biodynamic method of gardening, is beneficial to cabbage and onions in moderate amounts, but in large quantities may be detrimental to wheat crops. When grown near mints, it seems to develop more essential oils, while reducing the oil content of the mints. As a spray, *M. chamomilla* is useful in eliminating problems damping off young seedlings. For this, dried flowers are soaked in cold water for several days, and the resulting mixture is sprayed gently upon the plants. In the compost heap, it is added just after construction. As the biodynamic gardeners say, it "guides the calcium formative forces in the breakdown of the raw materials."

Propagation

A. nobilis or the Roman chamomile can be propagated by seed (usually producing single-flowered plants) or by root division. If planting seeds, do so after the last frost in the spring, or sow early in flats and transplant later. Root division provides more consistent results. The runner should be cut in March, and planted in rows about 24″ apart with 18″ between plants. If a chamomile lawn is desired, the plants should be set about 6″ apart and watered regularly to establish them well. After the plants begin to fill in the spaces between them, they should be clipped to encourage growth. When about 4″ in height, they can be mowed with a lawn mower.

M. chamomilla or German Chamomile should be started from seed. The seeds should be fresh, as they lose much viability after the first year. Unlike many seeds, they need light for proper germination. They also may be started in flats and later transplanted or started outdoors after danger of frost is past.

SASSAFRAS

The *sassafras* (*Sassafras albidum*) is a small to medium size tree commonly found along roadways, in old fields, and woods. In the North it is usually of shrublike stature, but in the longer growing season of the South it has been known to attain heights of 80′-100′ with a trunk diameter as wide as 2′. This aromatic tree can be found from Maine to Florida and west to Texas and Michigan.

Sassafras can be easily distinguished by its unique leaf shapes, green twigs, and root beerish or cinnamon odor when broken or bruised. The sassafras tree has three different shaped leaves (Fig. 18-12) with all three often appearing on the same twig. Some of the leaves are smooth and some are lobed or indented. These lobed leaves are called "mitten-shaped," with some of the mittens having one thumb and some two. For the same reason, the sassafras tree is called the *mitten* tree.

The sassafras tree has a long history of medicinal, culinary, and other uses. Cut in the dead of winter, sassafras makes good fence posts. Sassafras poles used as roosts in the chicken house supposedly keep the chickens free from mites.

Sassafras tea is an ancient and once popular tonic. Brewed from the inner bark of the root dug in the spring or fall, sassafras tea supposedly thins the blood and prepares one for the long, hot days of summer. Actually, the entire root, except for the very outside bark, may be used for sassafras tea.

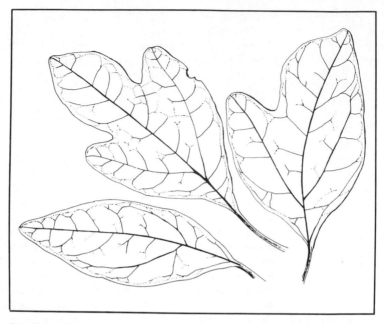

Fig. 18-12. The sassafras tree has three different shaped leaves (drawing by Fredda Burton).

It may be used fresh, or dried for later use. As an added bonus the young leaves of the sassafras are good chewing, right off the tree.

PERSIMMON

If visions of puckery mouths come to mind when persimmons are mentioned, then you probably haven't enjoyed the super-sweet ripe fruits. The common persimmon or sugar plum tree, as it is often called, is found growing wild from Connecticut to Iowa, Kansas, Florida and Texas (Fig. 18-13). They are usually found in fields and woods and often along roadsides. In Virginia, persimmons are rather small (less than 1" in diameter) but are plentiful. The tree is easily recognized with its gray to blackish bark which is deeply furrowed, forming rather square or rectangular patterns. Some say it resembles alligator hide. The maximum height is 130′ and the maximum width is 2½′. In this area, they are usually about half that size and are often more like a shrub. The leathery leaves are dark green above and paler beneath. These wavy leaves occur alternately along the stem. The fruit is green when immature, but later turns to shades of dull orange and even to reddish purple.

Although most think only of the fruit of the tree, the leaves make a tea similar in flavor to sassafras. This tea can be made with green leaves or with dried ones. The leaves have been found to be exceptionally high in vitamin C, thus the tea is especially good for wintertime. Also the seeds of the fruits can be roasted and ground for a coffeelike drink. As a member of the family *Ebenacea* (Ebony), the dark wood from *Diospyros virginiana* is valuable for making lathe projects, such as bowls. In years past, the wood was especially important in the making of shoe lasts.

If you wish to concentrate on the fruits, then do so. If you've ever tasted green persimmons, then you already know how astringent they are. The ripe fruit is as sweet as the unripe is sour. The fruit ripens at a time when most other fruits have been harvested and stored away for the winter. Depending upon the environment, the persimmons may ripen in late fall or sometimes not until later in the winter. Many insist that persimmons are not ready until the frosts have come. The frost does not ripen the fruit, but often comes when they are ripening. Sometimes persimmons may be ready a month before the first frost, and in other seasons they may not be ready until a month later. The warm sun is what encourages the fruit to ripen, so the frosts can actually delay the process.

When ripe, the berries are quite soft, mushy in fact. For this reason they are seldom found in market places. The large fruits of the Japanese persimmon *D. kaki* are sometimes available (tree stock can be purchased from various nurseries). Too often they have been picked early and never quite develop that delicious rich flavor of tree-ripened fruit. In translation, *Diospyros* means *"heavenly fruit"* and indeed it can be. Gathering persimmons is not really difficult. The easiest way is to spread an old blanket or sheet of plastic under the tree and gently shake. Since the fruits do not all ripen at once, take care not to disturb any green ones. After gathering from one tree, pick up your sheet and move to the next. Often you can find a group of trees within a small area. One thing though, sample the fruit of each tree before gathering. It seems as though not all trees bear the tastiest fruit. The persimmons that have already fallen are almost always dead-ripe and can be harvested too, unless they have star*t*ed to ferment.

Preserving

So now you've hauled home your fare and are wondering what to do with those buckets of sunkissed beauties. First, you need to sort out the

Fig. 18-13. Persimmon trees can be found growing wild from Connecticut to Texas (photo by Linda and Leith Campbell).

twigs and leaves and other foreign matter you collected along with the fruit. Also, reject any firm fruit; one slightly green persimmon will ruin your whole batch. You can set these out to ripen, if you have a sizable amount. Depending upon the quantity you have, there are lots of things to make with persimmons. If you like fruit leather, then you'll love persimmon leather. Separating the pulp from the seeds (usually two to eight flat ones) can be a problem. A Foley food mill seems to work pretty well. Some people suggest a potato ricer. After somehow getting the pump from the seeds and skins, you're ready to make the leather. As with apple or other leathers, the pulp is spread thinly on a cookie sheet (or something similar) and placed outside or in the oven to dry. After drying, it can be cut into small pieces and eaten as is or added to cereals, breads, etc. The fresh pulp can also be packed into small jars, sealed, and processed in a hot water bath for 30 minutes. It can be frozen, but will darken somewhat when thawed.

Index

A

A-frame	98
A-frame hog house	108
Agitator	274, 280
Agricultural, zone	60
Agriculture	62
Alcohol	225
Alimony	54
Alligator hide	528
Allyl disulfate	523
Almonds	475
Alpines	404
Aluminum paint	191
American Kennel Club	408
Anchor holes	204
Angle iron	246
Angora	404
Animal husbandry	64
Annunity	49
Antifreeze	224
Aphids	525
Appaloosa	387
Appeal of Abernathy	67
Appeal of Krechovitz	71
Aquifer	131
Arabians	383
Arkadelphia vs. Clark case	81
Arm	436
Arm block	341
Asbestos board	182
Ascorbic acid	418
Ash box	165
Asparagus	6
Australian cattle dog	409
Australian shepherd	408
Axe	24
Axe hanging	234
Axe mattock	24
Axes double-bit	235
single-bit	235
Azalea	461

B

Bacillus thuringiensis	510
Bagging corn	470
Baker's yeast	225

Balking	391
Barberry	378
Barkmann vs. Town of Hempstead case	70
Barn	12, 86
Basil	498
Baskets	368
Beans	254, 514
Bed	157
Bee yard	7
Beef, cutting	435
Beehive	306
Beets	460, 491, 498, 513
Belly or side meat	440
Berberis vulgaris	378
Bile sac	430
Bioshelter	103
Black locust	377
Black walnut	6, 477
Blackberries	146
Bluegill	137
Board feet	303
Board 'n' batten	20
Boiling water	136
Bone spavins	394
Border collie	408
Borough of Demarest vs. Heck case	78
Boston butt	440
Bow saw	24
Bowed tendons	395
Bowes vs. Inspector of Buildings case	68
Bramble fruits	6
Brassicas	443
Brazing	175
Bream	137
Brisket	432, 436
Broccoli	489
Buffalo berry	378
Buffer	445
Bumper jack baler	249
Bunsen burner	224
Butchering	423
Butternut	6, 411, 477

C

Cabbage	489, 506
Cabin	88
Cable	213
Cadet tractor	281
Caging	469
Caisson	131
Calcium	445
Capital	56
Carbon monoxide	225
Carp	137
Carp vs. Board of County Commissioners case	67
Carriage bolts	279
Carrots	417, 460, 490, 499
Casing	473
Cast iron	175
Catfacing	517
Catfish	137
Cattails	40
Cauliflower	491, 509
C-clamp	272
CDX plywood	123
Cellulose	226
Celtuce	510
Chain saw	120, 242
Chain saw mill	300
Chamomile	525
Chamomile uses	525
Channel iron	246
Chard	460
Chemical disinfection	136
Chemical fertilizers	450
Chices	498
Chick brooder	106
Chick waterer	107
Chickens	69
Chimney connector	168
Chimneys	169
Chinese cabbage	460, 499, 505
Chinkapins	476
Chrysanthemum	462
Chuck	436
Chudnov vs. Board of Appeals case	72
Chunk stove	171
Cistern	100, 132
Cleanout door	186
Cleaver	432
Cloches	466
Coal stove	166
Cold frames	465
Cold weather crops	465
Collards	520
Comfrey	6, 7, 412
Commercial, zone	60

Compact barn	86
Compositae	468
Compost	451
Compost bins	5
Compost privy	125
Computer	45
Concrete block wall	190
Cookstove	172
Corn	7, 258, 481
Cos	511
Cows	7
Cream separator	261
bowl nut	263
bowl nut tightener	264
bowl shell	263
central feed shaft	262
cream cover	265
discs	262
distributor	262
float	265
outlet	264
regulating cover	265
rubber ring	262
shutoff valve	266
skim milk cover	264
supply can	265
Creosote	170
Cress	460
Crop rotation	480
Crossbred	387, 409
Cruciferae	468
Cryptorchid	390
Cubed steak	438
Cucumbers	453, 499
Cull trees	308
Curcurbitaceae	468
Curing green wood	305
Cutting torch	365
Cutting wood	312
Cutworms	511
Cyclamen	462
Cydcnia Japonica	377

D

Dado groove	183
Dairy products	7
Damper	162
Dayton blowers	200
De Bendetti vs. River Vale Township case	70
Declining balance method	50
Decomposer	104
Deductions	48
Del Monte vs. Woodmansee case	71
Denim satchel	349

Depreciation	50	Firebox	161
Despining	470	Firewood	319
Diesel tractors	297	Flatulence	526
Diffusers	145	*Fleckles vs. Hille* case	71
Digging wells	129	Fleece	351
Diospyros	529	Flies	469
Disease	444	Flood irrigation	140
Dogs	82	Floodlight	335
Dormant mycelia	472	Fodder beets	480
Driftwood	304	Food for chickens	415
Drip irrigation	144	Footwear for infants	343
Drive gears	214	Foreshank	432
Driven well	135	Founder	394
Drop spindle	272	Front quarter	436
Dulcimers	300	Fruit and vegetable bin	124
		Fruit trees	499
E		Fungi	471
Earned income credit	53	Furrow irrigation	140
Easter lily	462		
Ebenacea	529	**G**	
Ebenezer	513	Garden cart	337
Eggplant	453	Garden cress	498
Elaeagnus angustifolia	378	Garden for goats	411
Emitters	145	Garden for rabbits	414
Endive	493	Garden sprinkler	143
English shepherd	409	Garden tray	327
Escarole	493	Garlic	523
Espalier	17	*Gaspari vs. Board of*	
Ethanol	224	*Adjustment* case	63
Euclid vs. Ambler		Gate and door latches	379
Realty case	59	Gearbox	208
Ex Parte Lusher case	75	Gelding	389
Ex Parte Matthews case	73	Gendermarie	64
		Geodesic dome	94
F		Gift plants	461
Fan assembly	211	Glass cutter	335
Farallones Institute	125	Glass jugs	331
Farm bookkeeping	44	*Gleditsia triacanthos*	377
Farmall tractor	282	Goals, reaching	42
Farmegg vs. Humboldt		setting	42
County case	62	Goat butchering	427
Farmers' alcohol	223	Goats	7, 73, 402
Farming, definition	60	Governor	212
small-scale	28	Grade horse	387
Fence and gate	378	*Graham vs. Kingwell* case	81
Fence, electric	369	*Graminae*	468
woven wire	372	Granary	13
Fence post preservation	372	Gravity water heater	187
Fermenting	470	Great Plains	217
Fertilizing	457	Green beans	411
Fidler vs. Zoning Board case	62	Green wood	164
Field capacity	148	Greenhouse	4
Fields	7	Green mulch system	479
Filberts	476	Green mulching advantages	484
Filtration	136	Greens	520
Fir	118	Ground beef	438
balsam	118		

Gutenberg 284

H

Ham 438
Hammers 231
    claw 231
    dry wall 233
    finishing 233
    handles 233
    machinist's 232
    rough framing 231
    sledge 232
    soft-faced 232
    tack 233
Hand-pollinating 469
Handi-cart 336
Handsaw sharpening 239
Harness 399
Harvesting equipment 253
Hauling wood 322
Hay 7, 481
Hay chopper 250
Hay feeder 309
Hazelnuts 476
Header 154
Heat absorbers 182
Heat indicator 178
Heat insulators 182
Heat reflectors 182
Heavy harness 384
Hedgerow 380
Hedges 374
Heller-Aller tower 206
Herbs 461
Hind quarter 435
Hold-down arm 341
Homestead, accounting 38
    functions 2
    location 1
    management 33
    site 2
    urban 14
Homestead hog hut 115
Honey locust 377
Horse, choosing a 388
Horses 76, 383
Horticulture 62
Hot horse 391
Hot water treating 470
Hot beds 465
Hybrid vegetables 493
Hydrangea 463
Hydraulic cylinder 247
Hydrocarbons 225
Hydrostatic traction drive 298

I

Indoor vegetable growing 495
Industrial, zone 60
Infrared lamps 192
Insect resistance 444
Internal Revenue Service 47
Investment credit 50
Iron plate 246
Isolation of vegetables 469

J

Jacket 343
James Washer 274
Japanese quince 377
Jerusalem artichoke 226
Jerusalem cherry 463
Jig 237
Jimson 422
John Olmstead vs. Robert
    Rich case 80
Jowl 441
Junkyard stove 171

K

Kale 412, 492
Kalite 198
Kelpie 409
Kerosene 269
Kindling 237
Kitchen 11
Kitchen appliances 229
Kohlrabi 418, 488, 492

L

LaManchas 404
Land clearing 23
Lanterns 368
Laundry appliances 230
Lawn and garden roller 336
Leaf lettuce 498
Leather 398
Lettuce 460, 510
Level, carpenter's 113
Life insurance 56
Light harness 384
Lighting ideas 230
Liliaceae 468
Livestock 6
Locoweed 422
Log carrier 362
Log splitter 246
Loin 440
Loopholes 54
Lumber 300
Lumberjacks 320

M

Maclura aurantiaca	377
Mallets	232
Management, controlling	37
coordinating	37
directing	37
organizing	37
planning	37
Mangels	412, 419
Manure	22
Manzanilla	526
Mare	389
Masonite	90
Masonry chimney	169
Matricaria flowers	526
Matthews vs. Scannell case	84
McNab	409
Meat, cutting	432
Mechanical drawing	325
Methane	88
Methanol	224
Milkweed	422, 503
Mini-barn	86
Mitten tree	527
Molasses	225
Monorchid	390
Morgans	383
Mortar	191
Muffler Mender	176
Mulch	465, 501
Mulch guards	484
Mushroom gardening	471
Mushrooms	460
Muskrats	40

N

Nail puller	119
Nematodes	446
Nervine	525
New Zealand spinach	456
Nextel	198
Nitrogen	406
Nitrogen dioxide	225
Norwegian Fjord pony	401
Nubian	403
Nut growing	475
Nylon rope	333

O

O'Connell vs. Jarvis case	85
Oil of chamomile	526
Okra	456, 518
Olympic wood range	304
Onions	512
Oregano	498
Organic gardening	442

Organic gardening mistakes	446
Ornamental pepper	463
Orthographic drawing	325
Osage orange	377
Outbuildings	12
Oxyacetylene cutting torch	246

P

Packaging meat	432
Pantothenic acid	227
Pantry	13
Parsley	498
Parsnips	493
Passive solar heating	20
Pea sheller	260
Peapods	420
Pecans	6, 477
Penicillin	523
People vs. Johnson case	66
People vs. McOmber case	80
Peppers	456, 460, 497
Persimmon	528
Pest control	474
Petros vs. Inspector of Buildings case	63
Pheasants	40
Phosphorus	406
Pictorial drawing	325
Pig manure	451
Piggery	65
Pikes peak roast	436
Pillows from raw wool	350
Pine	118
red	118
white	118
Pinion gears	215
Pipe cleaner	184
Planters	366
Planting straight rows	330
Plating parts	179
Pleasure horses	397
Plumb bob	210
Poinsettia	464
Polyurethane	286
Pond, small	137
Popular	118
Pork cutting	438
Potato hook	258
Potatoes	226, 514
Poultry	6
Power King tractor	282
Prefab chimney	169
Presser-foot	268
Przewalski's horse	402
Puli	408
Pulik	408

Pumpkin	411
Puppy	409
Pyrethum	501

Q

Quarter horses	383, 386
Quilting	355

R

Rabbit shelter	112
Rabbits	6
Radishes	460, 492, 498
Rain trap	135
Razor blade	280
Recycling baling twine	360
Recycling cans	365
Red beets	417
Residential, zone	60
Rhododendrons	477
Rhubarb	6
Rib	436
Riboflavin	227
Ric rac	346
Ridgling gelding	390
Ringbone	394
Robinia pseudocacia	378
Roller nose attachment	244
Romaine	511
Root cellar	13
Root crops	10, 417
Rosa multiflora	377
Rosemary	498
Rotary tiller	7
Rotenone	137
Round steaks	435
Rugosa roses	6
Rugs, braided	355
crocheted	354
hooked	354
rag	353
Rump roast	436
Russian olive	378
Rustoleum	198
Rutabagas	10, 417

S

Saanens	403
Saddle horse	385
Saddlebreds	383
Salt	186
Salvaging old buildings	117
Sassafras	527
Sausage	441
Saw teeth, filing	241
setting	240
Sawbuck	339

Sawhorse	338
Sawmill slabs	105
Scaffolding	209
Scoop from recycled cans	329
Seaweed	496
Seed planter	252
Seed sprouts	460
Selling firewood	323
Septic system	151
Septic tank	153
Shad	137
Shallots	460, 498
Shank	436
Sheep	404
Sheperdia argentea	378
Shetland sheep dog	408
Shingling hatchet	283
Shoulder	440
Shrimp plant	464
Simons vs. Fahnstock case	78
Singletree	427
Siphons	141
Sirloin steak	436
Sirloin tip	436
Skinning animals	425
Slab stringers	105
Slaughtering beef	428
Sledges	232
Smoke pipe	168
Smokehouse	304
Sock dolls	344
Socks uses	342
Soil sifter	330
Soil temperature	465
Solanaceae	468, 497
Solar collector	194
Solar-wind system	195
Soybeans	258, 411
Spanish bayonet	378
Spawning	472
Spiking sledge	232
Spinach	461, 492, 499
Spinning wheel	271, 358
Spitters	145
Splits	394
Splitting maul	321
Spreader bar	429
Spring frosts	465
Spring winterizing	138
Sprocket- nose chain bar	245
Squash	411, 501
State vs. Primeau case	68
State vs. Johnson case	76
Stile	374
Stock work	385
Storing seeds	468

536

Stout lever 213
Stove board 182
Stove painting 180
Stovepipe 167
Straight line method 50
Strawberries 6
Stud gun 232
Stump fence 380
Styrofoam 96
Sugar beets 419
Summertime gardening 455
Sun box 486
Sunflowers 147
Sweet corn 412
Sweet peppers 521
Swiss chard 492, 498
Synthetic blanket 356

T

Tailpipe 212
Taxes 47
T-bone steak 436
Thinning 455
Thiamine 227
Thrush 395
Thyme 498
Tillers, rotary 7
Tire feeder 332
Toggenburgs 404
Tomatoes 421, 460, 515
  history 515
  selecting varieties 516
Tower assembly 206
Tower raising 208
Toy train 326
Tractor care 284
Tractor tuneup 289
Tractors 282
Treadle sewing machine 267
Treadle wheel 269
Trenches 159
Triticale 10
Turnbuckles 212
Turnip greens 520
Turnips 491
T-wrench 312

U

Umbelliferae 468
Underwriters Laboratories 166
Union Pacific railroad 217

V

Varithane 281
Vegetables 258
Vent pipe 166
Visqueen 89
Vitamin C 528

W

Warming cabinet 178
Washboard 274
Washcloths 342
Washing machine,
  hand-operated 278
Water pumping windmill 202
Watercress 498
Watering 457
Wattage 274
Wedges 321
Weeping tile 157
Welding 175
Whiskey 225
Whorl 271
Wild cherry 422
Wind-powered heat pump 221
Windmill 100
Winship vs. Inspector case 71
Winter garden in the kitchen 458
Winter savory 498
Wolf trees 320
Wood sources 320
Woodlot 310
Woodshed 122
Woodstove operation 161
Woolite 351
Working stock dogs 407
Wyant vs. Figy case 81

Y

Yucca gloriosa 378

Z

Zippers 517
Zoning 59, 60
Zucchini 411

Country Wisdom:
The Art of Successful Homesteading

by The Editors of Countryside Magazine

Whether you're homesteading in a remote rural area, or a city-dweller looking for some back-to-basics hints for more economical, energy-efficient living, this fascinating guidebook is jam-packed with just the information you're looking for! From all the how-to's for organic gardening, tips on livestock raising; from info on butchering and wood-lot management to energy conservation and wood stove cookery. You'll find literally dozens of fascinating and practical ways to make *your* life simpler and more enjoyable!

Here's where you'll discover some great suggestions for starting your own herb garden, and making exciting country crafts. You'll also find lots of helpful advice on topics like fencing your property, irrigation, and building farm and garden implements.

There are loads of homesteading hints like how-to's for digging your own well or cistern, putting up fences, alternative energy solutions from home-made power to alcohol fuels, even advice on how to handle local zoning regulations. It's all here in this HUGE compendium of ways you can substitute ingenuity and resourcefulness for all the expensive ready-made gizmos and gadgets that complicate today's living . . . how you can live comfortably, happily, and healthily by becoming more *self sufficient!*